THINGS

CONTRIBUTORS
TO THIS VOLUME INCLUDE

E. ASHWORTH UNDERWOOD

B. W. BATHE

W. C. BRICE

R. A. BROWN

H. R. CALVERT

T. P. CAMERER CUSS

H. W. CATLING

FRANCIS CELORIA

J. A. CHALDECOTT

R. H. CLARK

G. R. CRONE

E. C. CURWEN

C. ST C. DAVISON

DAVID DIRINGER

SIR ARTHUR ELTON

ELLEN ETTLINGER

D. H. FOLLETT

R. J. FORBES

HENRI FRANKFORT

HELMUT GERNSHEIM

C. H. GIBBS-SMITH

K. R. GILBERT

F. GREENAWAY

VIVIEN GREENE

ORMEROD GREENWOOD

GEOFFREY GRIGSON

L. W. HANSON

D. B. HARDEN

AUDREY HENSHALL

T. I. ITKONEN

BARBARA JONES

ROBIN KENWARD

JAMES LAVER

HOPE LOVELL

H. J. R. MURRAY

W. T. O'DEA

F. W. PALMER

TSEWANG PEMBA

DOREEN PHILLIPS

DAVID PIPER

C. P. RANG

A. W. RUFFY

F. G. SKINNER

A. STOWERS

C. H. V. SUTHERLAND

GEOFFREY TAYLOR

REX WAILES

JOHN WARRACK

WILLIAM WATSON

G. F. WINGFIELD DIGBY

General Editors

GEOFFREY GRIGSON & CHARLES HARVARD GIBBS-SMITH

THINGS

A VOLUME OF

OBJECTS DEVISED BY MAN'S GENIUS

WHICH ARE THE MEASURE

OF HIS CIVILIZATION

HAWTHORN BOOKS, INC.

Publishers

NEW YORK

Published in the United States of America by Hawthorn Books,
Inc., 70 Fifth Avenue, New York City 11. All rights reserved
including the right to reproduce this book, or portions thereof, in
any form, except for the inclusion of brief quotations in a review.
Designed and produced by Rainbird, McLean Ltd, London. Printed
in Great Britain by Jarrold and Sons Ltd, Norwich, Norfolk;
color plates printed by Tillotsons (Bolton) Ltd; endpapers printed
by Van Leer of Amsterdam. Library of Congress Catalog
Number 56-10840
Second American Edition: October 1957

*T*HINGS IS A VOLUME FOR THE INQUISITIVE, *but not always for the solemn. The things from A to Z – Aeolian Harp and Aeroplane to Ziggurat and Zip-fastener – are very mixed, it will soon be discovered: some are useful, some are of no use; some are in use, some out of use. Some are little known, some are known to everyone. Some have emerged from recent history, some are as old (though not quite as old) as the hills.*

Before turning to the entries and the illustrations it might entertain the reader to set himself a few questions. Have we always used soap? His wife cooks with a pressure cooker: did such utensils exist before 1920? When did we, to take a medley of things, first use false teeth, fountain pens, water-closets, lawnmowers, violins, vacuum-cleaners, safety-pins, and thermos flasks? Origins are fascinating; but it is surprising what we are not told about the most familiar objects, instruments, or substances. So contributors have given a good many answers about things on which encyclopaedias are hesitant or vague – or silent.

When did men begin paying by cheque and carrying cheque-books? Who invented pneumatic tyres (easy to give the wrong answer)? What clothes did they wear in Bronze Age Europe? What pigments did they paint with in Altamira or Lascaux, twenty thousand years ago? When was it first possible to buy beef and pea soup, and anything else, in tins?

Some questions are trivially, some also fundamentally entertaining. Where and when was the wheel 'invented', and applied to traction or potting? Who were the first smelters of iron, the first blacksmiths? When and where was paper developed? Who gave us the alphabet? Who is it we have to thank for gun-powder, and what link is there between that deathly substance and the fact that the reader drives a motor-car? And what indeed was a pyramid?

On the whole the things described are familiar; they are often simple and basic elements of life, not belonging to the more secret land of the technician or the expert. And since Things has been planned as an entertainment, not as a textbook, and is concerned so much with origins, the reader can be promised an entry on the first explosive, but not the latest; on gunpowder, but not hydrogen bombs; or if he turns to Microscope, he will be offered more about Van Leeuwenhoek's simple microscopes of the seventeenth century than about the electron microscope of the twentieth. If the entry on House goes back to the palaeolithic shelter at Dolní Věstonice, it does not come forward to the United Nations slab in New York.

Much of this volume is set on a background of prehistory. Our ideas on the remote past often divide into the old trio, the Iron Age, the Bronze Age and the Stone Ages, as though these were divisions which cut across human societies all at the same time, like wire through a cheese; so a schematic plan is needed. I am specially grateful to Dr J. G. D. Clark, the most stimulating and the least vague of prehistorians, for his diagram of time-space relationships, reprinted from Prehistoric Europe (*Methuen & Co.*). *As a guide to which the reader may often want to refer, it is set plainly and firmly at the very beginning.*

GEOFFREY GRIGSON

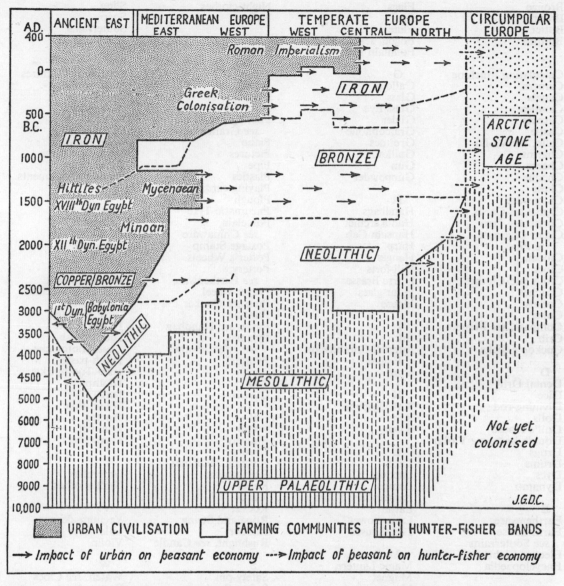

Time and space relationships of Europe and the Near East. (Upper Palaeolithic extends backward for more than double the number of years shown on the plan).

Things described in this volume

Bronze
Broom
Butter
Buttons

C
Calculating Machine
Camera
Canals
Candles
Carpets
Castle
Cello, *see* Violin
Charms
Cheese
Cheque
Chess
Chinaware
Christmas Cards
Christmas Tree
Cigar, Cigarette,
   see Pipe
Cinema
Clock
Cloth and Clothes
Coaches
Coffins
Coins
Compass, *see* Magnet
Crib
Cuckoo Clocks

D
Dental Drill
Dice
Divining-rod
Dolls
Doll's House
Double Bass, *see* Violin
Drugs
Drums
Dyes
Dynamo

E
Earthenware
Earth-house,
   see Souterrains
Electric Light
Encyclopaedia

F
False Teeth
Fetish
Fibula, *see* Safety-pin
Fields
Finger-prints
Firearms, *see* Gun
Fire-drill
Fire-engine
Fireworks
Fishing Tackle

Flags
Flail
Flute
Fogou, *see* Souterrain
Fountain Pen

G
Gallows
Glass
Glass Eye
Glider
Gramophone
Grottoes
Guillotine
Gun
Gunpowder

H
Handbags
Handkerchief
Hansom Cab
Harp
Henges
Hill-forts
Horse Brasses
Hour-glass
House

I
Ink
Internal-Combustion
   Engine
Iron

K
Kaleidoscope
Kilt
Kites

L
Lace
Lacquer
Lamps
Lantern, *see* Torch
Lathe
Lawnmower
Lighthouses

M
Magic Lantern
Magnet
Maps
Margarine
Matches
Maypole
Mazes
Microscopes
Mines
Motor-car
Musical Box

N
Newspapers

Night-clothes
Nylon

O
Organ

P
Paper
Passport
Pen
Phonograph,
   see Gramophone
Piano
Pictures
Pipe
Plastics
Playing-cards
Plough
Pneumatic Tyre
Porcelain,
   see Chinaware
Postage Stamp
Potter's Wheels
Pottery,
   see Earthenware
Prayer-wheel
Pressure Cooker
Printing
Purse, *see* Handbag
Pyjamas,
   see Night-clothes
Pyramid

Q
Querns

R
Radio
Railway
Razors
Reaping Machines
Refrigerator
Relics
Roads
Rocket
Rope and String
Rubber
Rushlight, *see* Candle

S
Safety-pin
Safety Razor
Sand-glass,
   see Hour-glass
Saw
Scythe, *see* Sickle
Sewing-machine
Sextant
Sickle
Silk
Skates
Skis
Sledges

Sling
Soap
Souterrains
Spectacles
Spindle
Spit
Statues, *see* Pictures
Steam-engines
Stereoscope
Stethoscope
Stone Tools
Strike-a-light,
   see Fire-drill
String, *see* Rope
Submarines
Surgical Instruments

T
Tapestries
Telegraph
Telephone
Telescope
Television
Thermometers
Thermos Flask
Threshing Machine
Tinder Box,
   see Fire-drill
Tinned Food
Tooth-brush,
   see Toothpicks
Tooth-paste,
   see Toothpicks
Toothpicks
Torch
Totem Pole
Tractor
Trumpet
Typewriters

U
Umbrellas
Underclothes

V
Vacuum-cleaner
Valentines
Violin

W
Watch, *see* Clock
Water-closet
Water-mills
Weights
Wells
Wheel
Wigs
Windmills
Wreaths

Z
Ziggurat
Zip-fasteners

Color Plates

The endpapers are of a cabinet, 150 years old, filled with miniature figures and objects in 'The Bears', Sumiswald, Switzerland.

Black and White Plates

BLACK AND WHITE PLATES (*continued*)

PAGE

PAGE

Text Figures

Publisher's Note

Because this book has been produced and manufactured in Great Britain for readers in that country as well as in America and elsewhere, certain spellings and uses of words are British. Where not otherwise indicated or obvious, it may be assumed that names, places, events and things are British or in Britain.

THINGS

'Soft floating witchery of sound'

The **AEOLIAN HARP** is a sound toy rather than a musical instrument. In brief, it is a rectangular sound-box with twelve strings tightened across two bridges. A lid, open on the longer sides, is fixed over the strings, which are tuned, a trifle slackly, in unison. The harp is then placed in a vertically opening window, the sash is lowered on top of it, and the current of air vibrates the strings, which produce 'sounds of magic and enchantment'.

Instruments of the kind are known among primitive peoples. The Aeolian harp as we have it was first described by the Jesuit man of science Athanasius Kircher in 1650 in his *Musurgia Universalis*. Kircher's wind harp was a pine-wood box, five palms long, two wide, one deep, with fifteen or more equal strings of gut. But the wind harp became popular only when it caught the fancy of English poets in the eighteenth century. A Scottish composer and violinist, James Oswald, settled in London in 1741, and was soon making Aeolian harps, and selling them in his music shop near the church of St Martin-in-the-Fields. His friends called him the inventor, claiming that the impulse came to him from Alexander Pope, who had noticed a passage in a Byzantine commentary on Homer suggesting that the wind could draw a harmony out of strings. But there can be no doubt that Oswald knew the account given by Athanasius Kircher. But he may be responsible for the name, harp of Aeolus, or Aeolian harp – the harp of the god of the winds.

Probably Oswald was acquainted with the Scottish poet James Thomson (1700–1748), and the Scottish novelist Tobias Smollett (1721–1771). Thomson owned an Aeolian harp and launched the toy in his poem *The Castle of Indolence*, published in 1748:

A certain music never known before,
Here lull'd the pensive melancholy mind;
Full easily obtain'd. Behoves no more,
But sidelong, to the gently waving wind,
To lay the well-tun'd instrument reclin'd;
From which, with airy flying fingers light,
Beyond each mortal touch the most refin'd,
The god of winds drew sounds of deep delight:
Whence, with just cause, the harp of Aeolus it hight.

Ah me! what hand can touch the string so fine?
Who up the lofty diapason roll
Such sweet, such sad, such solemn airs divine,
Then let them down again into the soul?
Now rising love they fann'd; now pleasing dole
They breath'd, in tender musings through the heart;
And now a graver sacred stain they stole,
As when seraphic hands an hymn impart,
Wild-warbling Nature all above the reach of Art!

The last line gives the clue to the rapid popularity of the new toy: it seemed to draw out nature's music, thus fitting the so-called Romantic era in which Nature was a goddess of all the arts. Tobias Smollett, in his novel *The Adventures of Ferdinand Count Fathom* (1753), imagines the new instrument being used in the seduction of Celinda, an innocent country girl – 'being properly applied to a stream of air', this 'twelve-stringed instrument ... contrived by a very ingenious musician', produces 'a wild irregular variety of harmonious sounds, that seem to be the effect of enchantment, and wonderfully dispose the mind for the most romantic situations'.

A long line of poets was intrigued and enchanted. Those in England alone who wrote poems about the Aeolian harp, or referred to it in their poems or other works, included William Collins, Christopher Smart, Gray, Mason, Macpherson, Bloomfield, Wordsworth, Coleridge, Scott, Moore, Shelley, Clare, Keats and Allingham. The toy became common also in France and Germany. It spread to Russia and to America (appealing to Thoreau, Emerson and Melville); it attracted not only poets and writers but musicians, such as Berlioz. Aeolian harps were regularly stocked by music shops through the nineteenth century. The classic poems in which this delightful, simple instrument plays are by Coleridge – *The Eolian Harp* (1795) and *Dejection, An Ode* (1802).

From ornithopters to jet planes

AEROPLANES derive, one might say, from a jealousy of birds, the idea of the aeroplane growing in the human mind from the study of the flight of birds. Thus many of the earlier conceptions of a flying machine took the form of the flapping-wing aeroplane known as ornithopters.

Ornithopters were suggested by Leonardo da Vinci and others, and have even been built, but they were never able to fly except in the form of small models powered by elastic or compressed air. After a number of adventurous and ingenious men had strapped wings to their arms and either killed or maimed themselves in their efforts to fly, it dawned on the more thoughtful inventors that the solution of aeroplane flight lay in keeping the wings rigidly outstretched and using some means of propelling the machine forward so that the air could act on the wings and sustain them. Yet no real progress in flying machines was made until the very end of the eighteenth century. The modern aeroplane derives, in fact, from the wonderful pioneer work of the Yorkshire baronet, Sir George Cayley (1773–1857), who first formulated the problem of heavier-than-air flight and defined the forces acting upon the wings. He made the first proper aeroplane known to man – a model fixed-wing glider – in 1804 and, luckily for his followers, published the results of his researches for all to read. Cayley also realized that one of the greatest difficulties facing the aircraft designer was the provision of a powerful but light-weight motor; and it was not until the end of the nineteenth century that this difficulty was to be overcome, a light enough full-sized engine depending upon the practical development of the petrol motor. Cayley, however, was confident that 'aerial navigation' would 'form a most prominent feature in the progress of civilization', and he wrote that 'an uninterrupted navigable ocean, that comes to the threshold of every man's door, ought not to be neglected as a source of human gratification and advantage'.

The ideas of both propeller and jet as a means of propulsion for aeroplanes were in the minds of many nineteenth-century inventors, but only the propeller proved feasible to begin with. It was in 1848 that a steam-driven propeller model designed by W. S. Henson and John Stringfellow was given its prophetic trials in Chard, Somerset. Although unsuccessful, it was the first completed model of modern conception and a milestone in aero-history.

In the second half of the nineteenth century the problems of flight were tackled more and more by trained scientific minds rather than by ingenious adventurers. Félix du Temple (1823–1890) and Alphonse Pénaud (1850–1880) in France, and F. H. Wenham (1824–1908) in England were typical of the practical experimenters, equipped to theorize as well, who laid the basis of aerodynamics, and designed machines which were prophetic in the ideas they embodied. Engineers, more concerned with automobiles than with aircraft, added their quota by improving upon N. A. Otto's four-stroke cycle internal-combustion engine of 1876; and the gliding pioneers, foremost among them Otto Lilienthal, the German, who died from a glider crash in 1896, demonstrated practical, man-carrying aircraft. By the turn of the century the situation was one in which the principal lines of development would soon be drawn together, with the certain outcome at last of a full-sized flying machine.

The race for victory was won by the two young American cycle-makers, Wilbur Wright (1867–1912) and Orville Wright (1871–1948). After evolving a successful glider between 1900 and 1902, they built and flew on 17 December 1903 at Kitty Hawk, North Carolina, the first powered aeroplane which could be sustained and controlled in the air, and which could land at a point as high as that from which it took off. By 1905 they had developed their aeroplane into a highly successful machine. By 1909 aeroplanes as we know them were evolving rapidly as a result of the initial inventions of Wilbur and Orville Wright combined with aeronautical developments in Europe.

Two distinct types emerged, the biplane and monoplane, and by 1910 the essentials of construction and control were standardized: for diving and climbing, the rear or forward elevator; for lateral stability and control, the wing-tip ailerons, which with the vertical rudder were also used to bank and turn the machine. In 1903 the Wrights had flown at thirty miles an hour; by 1905 they were able to stay aloft for more than thirty minutes. By 1914 the speed record for aeroplanes had risen to 126·7 miles an hour, and the record for duration to twenty-four hours twelve minutes. The highest altitude reached was 25,786 feet; and by the late nineteen-twenties air transport had taken its place as an essential and world-embracing means of travel.

When the jet-propelled aeroplane matured in the mid nineteen-forties the way was open to speeds and other performances undreamt of. The first practical jet aeroplane, propelled by a gas-turbine engine, flew in 1939. By 1944 there were operational jet fighters, and in 1952 – after intensive research and development the world over – the first regular jet airliner, the de Havilland *Comet*, went into service between London and Johannesburg. (See *Glider, Kite, Balloon, Rocket.*)

ILLUSTRATION: Plate 2 and page 74.

Alpha, beta, gamma, delta

THE ALPHABET is the substructure of our civilization; alphabetic writing, by means of a small number of symbols (generally between twenty and thirty) which stand for the various elementary sounds used in speech, is the last, the most highly developed, the most convenient and adaptable system of writing which the world has known. Now employed by civilized people over most of the earth, it was preceded by other systems, and even by various primitive devices of communication.

Prehistoric man probably did not think about true writing; neither did certain primitive people of more recent times. Upper Palaeolithic cave painting in France and Spain can hardly represent the beginnings of writing: they had to do with 'sympathetic magic' or ritual practices, it seems; and not with any desire to communicate ideas or record important events. The same may be said of the various geometric signs or conventional figures of men or animals, painted or engraved on rocks or stones, dating from the Palaeolithic ages to modern times and found the world over, from Central Asia to North and South America.

Nonetheless, as man rose from his barbaric state he felt a need to make some record to help his memory. Rude systems of conveying ideas are found everywhere, some belonging to ancient tradition, some in use today. Herodotus describes a 'letter' sent by the Scythians to the Persian king Darius. It consisted of a bird, a mouse, a frog and five arrows, and was supposed to mean 'Persians, can you fly like a bird, hide yourselves in the ground like a mouse, leap through swamps like a frog? If you cannot, then do not try to go to war with us – we shall overwhelm you with arrows.' Means of communication with the help of tangible objects are found amongst the Yebu and other tribes in Nigeria, amongst the Bangala people on the Upper Congo, the Lutze on the Tibetan-Chinese border, and the Cara tribes of Ecuador, and amongst primitive peoples in Eastern Turkestan, and in other parts of the world.

One of the commonest memory-aid devices is a knot tied in a handkerchief; the Catholic rosary is also a mnemonic counting device. Others which are widespread are the notched stick and the knotted cord. Notched sticks were employed in Italy, Russia, North America and elsewhere, and are still used in some remote parts of Yugoslavia, in Africa, China, Australia, etc. Notched sticks, or *tallies* were actually used by the Exchequer of England down to 1832, as receipts for money paid into the Treasury. In Australia and in ancient Scandinavia notched sticks conveyed important messages, convoking an assembly or promulgating war. Ancient China, Tibet, Japan, Bengal, Persia, Mexico and Peru all made use of knot devices, of which the best known kind is the *quipu* of the ancient Peruvians, a numerical recording contrivance of strings and knots, imparting information by variations of length, thickness, colour and position. The *wampum* of the North American Iroquois – consisting of belts or cords of coloured shell beads, and used to convey messages – and the North American Indian *calumet*, a sacred, decorated reed tobacco-pipe, employed to signify war or peace, were other memory-aid devices, a category which includes trade marks, heraldic signs, tattooing, potter's marks, mason's marks, property marks and symbols for magico-religious ceremonies.

A great step forward came when man began to draw a series of pictures so as to tell a connected story. Picture writings are found everywhere, though they can best be studied amongst some native tribes of North America.

All these primitive devices of communication are writing in embryo. None of them constitutes a complete system, such as we find in the ancient scripts of Mesopotamia, Egypt, Crete, the Indus valley, Asia Minor, China and of America before the conquest. These are known as 'ideographic', *i.e.* they employ characters to represent ideas or things. In fact, they are partly ideographic and partly phonetic (representative of the sounds of speech), the ingredients being combined in various ways. Such systems should rather be called 'analytic'. In these scripts a definite picture, selected by convention from the many which had been used for the particular thing, became the accepted symbol of its name.

On the whole, in embryo writing and in pure ideography there is no inevitable connection between the depicted symbol and the recorded speech. But in phonetic systems writing has become the graphic counterpart of speech, each element of writing corresponding to a specific element or sound element in the language. Generally there is no connection between the external form of the symbol and the sound it represents; and phonetic systems may be of two kinds – syllabic or alphabetic.

In the syllabic systems – these include the late cuneiform writing of the Assyrians, the scripts of ancient Byblos and Cyprus, the Japanese syllabic writings, and some modern syllabaries of North America, Western Africa and China – the single signs represent syllables, *i.e.* elementary sound-blocks (vowel, or consonant plus vowel) The script of the ancient Persian Empire and the Meroïtic script used at the ancient Meroë, north of Khartoum, were mixtures of syllabic and alphabetic symbols.

Of all systems it is the alphabet which has the most extensive, most intricate and most interesting history. It is now generally agreed that all alphabets derived from one original alphabet. In its broad lines, the story of this system from the end of the second millennium B.C. until now is not very difficult to trace, though its origin and many details of its development and of the origin of some individual alphabets are still uncertain. Various theories have been advanced from time to time since classical antiquity. At one period or another, by one scholar or another, the Egyptian, Mesopotamian, Cretan, Runic and other scripts have been considered the prototype. Probably the original alphabet was an indigenous, more or less original, invention of the North-west Semitic population of Syria and Palestine. It may be argued that this North Semitic alphabet arose in, or rather before, the middle of the second millennium B.C. The great achievement lay in the evolving of a purely alphabetic system, which denoted each sound by one sign only. No other people in the world has been able to create such a system, and the invention of the alphabet must be ranked among the supreme benefactions.

In the late second millennium and the early first millennium B.C., the original alphabet had developed from main branches, the Canaanite, the Aramaic, the South Semitic and the Greek. The main Canaanite scripts were early Hebrew – the original script of the Old Testament, the writing employed by the Hebrew kings and prophets – and Phoenician, including the Punic and neo-Punic forms. From the Aramaic branch sprang hundreds of scripts employed in Asia; they include Square Hebrew (parent of the modern Hebrew script), Arabic, Syriac, the Avesta alphabet, the Mongolian and Manchu alphabets, Brahmi (the parent alphabet of about 200 scripts now used in India, Ceylon, Siam, Burma, Indonesia and the Philippine Islands), the Armenian and Georgian alphabets, the Korean alphabet (which is the only native alphabet of the Far East), and many other scripts. The South Semitic alphabets were mainly confined to ancient Arabia, but one offshoot spread to Abyssinia and gave birth to the Ethiopic alphabet and its modern descendants.

That leaves the Greek alphabet, which came into being in the early first millennium B.C. Like the Semitic alphabets, the earliest Greek script was written from right to left, a style which was later superseded by the *boustrophedon* style (alternately from right to left and left to right); after 500 B.C. Greek writing invariably proceeded from left to right and from top to bottom. The Greeks transformed the purely consonantal Semitic script into a modern alphabet, and gave it symmetry and art. Through its direct and indirect descendants the Etruscan (the Etruscans were the famous predecessors of the Romans) and the Latin alphabets, on the one hand, and the Cyrillic (the ancestor of the Russian, Bulgarian, Serbian and other alphabets) on the other, the Greek alphabet has become the progenitor of all the European alphabets we use today; though the origin of some ancient alphabets of Europe (for example the Runes of the Teutonic tribes and the Ogham alphabet used by the Celtic population of the British Isles) is not absolutely clear. In the course of its long history the Greek alphabet had many other offshoots, such as the scripts used in ancient Asia Minor, the Coptic alphabet, in Egypt, and the Gothic alphabet, invented in the fourth century A.D. by the Gothic bishop Wulfila (also called Ulfilas).

Curiously the Latin alphabet fared poorly in the first five or six centuries of its existence. It arose in the seventh century B.C., developing from the Etruscan. A few letters were added and the single letters were externally transformed. To begin with, the Latin alphabet had only one style, the monumental script (which with insignificant changes we still employ in printed capitals); out of this there developed numerous varieties including the capital styles and the cursive hands. At the end of the eighth century A.D. the Caroline cursive minuscule hand developed, and became the main book-hand of Western Europe. In the late twelfth century there came into being the 'black letter' or 'Gothic' literary hand, which was employed in England until the sixteenth century.

In Italy, during the fifteenth century, two beautiful cursive minuscule hands were used, the Venetian minuscule (now known as *italics*) and the 'roman' type of letters. These were soon adopted in Western Europe, including England (in the sixteenth century) and are the styles now so widely used. (See also *Paper, Ink, Pen.*)

For protection and luck

AMULETS are smallish objects credited with inherent power to protect against disease, to ward off sudden dangers and to prevent evil influences threatening the person, the domestic animal or the house with which they are in contact. They were cherished with the utmost care and remained potent as long as their owner trusted them. Sometimes amulets were bequeathed in wills and we can assume that they served several generations. Their distribution is universal and they have been employed for such a long period that the original meaning of the word 'amulet' is a matter of controversy. Warfare and the plague created a great demand for them, and much light has of late been thrown on their psychological implications by a careful anthropological study of a Chinese epidemic. The following examples, relating to the British Isles, can be seen in the museums of London and Oxford. They represent but a fraction of the wealth of amulets.

The oldest amulets have been found in prehistoric graves; among them are shells, beads, white quartz stones, etc. Stone amulets have been preserved more frequently than others, but they are practically indestructible. Precious stones as well as rare metals were made into amulets; so also natural stones of striking shape or colour, prehistoric stone axes and flint arrowheads, fossils, *e.g.* belemnites, and minerals, *e.g.* iron pyrites. Often they were found in a field after a heavy storm had washed away the covering soil, the finder believing that they had fallen from the sky, taking them for 'thunderbolts' and crediting them because of their supposed celestial origin with supernatural virtues. The finder would carry the 'thunderbolt' on his person for luck, or give it to some ailing member of his family, or place it under the roof of his house to protect it against lightning; for it was assumed that lightning never strikes the same object a second time. Largish stones, with water-worn, natural holes, can still be seen fastened on the doors of cottages or stables; they are meant to protect the inmates and the cattle against fairies and witches. Protective signs on the door of a house are mentioned in the Bible (Exod. xii, 7; Ezek. xlv, 19); in England one can still find horseshoes or hares' feet attached to the door. Some stones, bearing a rough resemblance to parts of the human body – *e.g.* legs, feet, arms – were believed to cure diseases of those very parts, in accordance with the widespread notion that 'like cures like'.

It will be remembered that Charles Dickens's David Copperfield was born with a caul. As the fœtus lived surrounded by water, the caul was reputed to safeguard its owner against drowning; for this reason sailors used to pay astonishingly high prices for a child's caul, even as recently as during the submarine menace of the First World War. The animal and vegetable kingdoms likewise supplied amulets. The feet of a moorhen or wood-pigeon were carried against cramp and toothache; likewise the forefeet of a mole, which, however, had to be cut off the live mole. Cowrie shells are probably the most universal fertility amulet, on account of their resemblance to the female generative organ. Pieces of the unicorn's horn (in fact the tusk of the narwhal) were perhaps the most expensive amulets. Some of them were mounted in precious metals or elaborately carved. They were esteemed most powerful antidotes against poison. Sometimes the surface of the horn was scraped and the powder, mixed with water, taken internally as a medicine. The customary sign of an apothecary's shop in the seventeenth century was the figure of a unicorn. Its horn was so important a medicine that the Apothecaries' Society of London (founded in 1617) adopted two unicorns as the supporters of its coat of arms. Until 1741 the lists of drugs to be carried by every registered pharmacist in London included the unicorn's horn. The large roots of the Bryony (*Bryonia dioica*) were used as a substitute for the roots of the true Mandrake (*Mandragora officinarum*) and were supposed to possess similar magical powers. The belief in the magic virtues of the mandrake was based on its resemblance to human shape and on its poisonous effects. Its use originated in the East and was transmitted to Europe through various channels. Most mandrakes were, however, 'counterfited and made like little puppettes and so trymmed of crafty theves to mocke the poore people, and to rob them both of theyr wit and theyr money'. William Turner, who recognized this in 1551, was by no means the first to dispute the mandrake's powers. But the hoax was long-lived. Mandrake is still the most widespread country name for Bryony, and Bryony roots were obtainable from English herbalist shops as late as the nineteenth century. Strange tropical seeds, carried by the Gulf Stream and cast ashore in Scotland, were regarded with such awe that, for example, the seeds of the *Entada scandens* came to be used as amulets. Woody outgrowths, common on beech trees and ash trees, were often carried in the pocket as a cure for cramp, and potatoes likewise as a cure for rheumatism; but the potatoes had to be stolen, if the cure was to be effective.

Religious medals and pilgrims' tokens were looked upon as amulets, partly owing to their sacred symbols and inscriptions and partly because they stemmed from holy places, where medals and tokens were blessed. The frequent use of coins as amulets is evidenced by the fact that so many of them are pierced for suspension. The largest group among them are golden and silver 'Touchpieces' from the days when the touch of the Kings of England was believed to cure scrofula, 'the King's Evil'. Several such 'touchpieces' in the London Museum still have the white silk ribbon attached to them which the king placed round the patient's neck. The most fascinating one is the touchpiece in the British Museum with which, on the advice of an eminent physician of Lichfield, Samuel Johnson at the age of thirty months was touched by Queen Anne. In later years Queen Anne, crippled with gout, touched the sick with a lodestone, probably because she found this a less exacting procedure. A Danish gold medal was found in the pocket of James II at Faversham in 1688, when he was escaping to France and we are told that the King was most anxious to have the medal returned; he evidently put much trust in it.

A powerful house-amulet was the so-called 'Celestial Letter', a largish sheet of paper, headed by the well-known 'Sunday-Letter', said to have been written by Christ himself, which promised every protection to those who observe the Sunday rest and threatened dire consequences to the sabbath-breakers. The letter gave an account of Christ's cures and miracles, sometimes a woodcut representing His head, and the apocryphal correspondence between King Abgar and Christ as well as the apocryphal Epistle of Lentulus to the Senate of Rome.

For some objects which are commonly regarded as amulets but which are actually charms, see under *Charms*. Though happenings connected with amulets have rarely been recorded, we can easily imagine the moving details of their history. In these small objects, most of which were without any intrinsic value, mankind throughout the ages has sought comfort and protection against the manifold dangers of life. (See also *Charms, Horse Brasses*.)

Under the knife

ANAESTHETICS were used in a crude form in the Middle Ages, though it is very probable that some method of dulling pain was tried during prehistoric times. The operation of trepanning the skull was frequently performed during the Neolithic period, and there is evidence that it was done several times on the same individual. The juices of certain plants may well have been used on these occasions. The Egyptians are reputed to have used the fumes of Indian hemp, a theory which has been contested. In the classical period practically the only plant used to dull the pain of operations was the mandrake (*Mandragora officinarum*), which has associated with it many strange legends. In China the surgeon Hua T'o, of the third century A.D., used a wine called *ma-fei-san* for general anaesthesia. Apparently none of the means employed in ancient times was at all effective. All these drugs were given by mouth. The first attempt at the production of anaesthesia by inhalation is found in the use of the *spongia somnifera*, or soporific sponge, which is mentioned in a manuscript of the ninth century, in a recipe which contained opium, mandragora, cicuta and hyoscyamus. The drugs were supposed to be inhaled from the sponge held to the nostrils. Similar prescriptions for soporific sponges are found throughout the Middle Ages. In later centuries the difficulty in producing surgical anaesthesia was fully realized, and in 1832 the great French surgeon Velpeau stated that pain in operations could not be prevented. Hypnotism was tried in 1843 by James Braid and by John Elliotson independently. In 1846 James Esdaile in India carried out many surgical operations successfully under hypnosis. By the time his results were published, inhalation anaesthesia had become an established fact in Europe, and indeed in most of the civilized world.

The first suggestion that the gas nitrous oxide ('laughing gas') might be used to produce anaesthesia during surgical operations was due to Sir Humphry Davy in 1800. Henry Hill Hickman (1800–1830) carried out experiments on small animals between 1823 and 1827, using carbon dioxide as the inhalant. His method did not produce a true anaesthesia, but a state of 'suspended animation'. Two Americans between 1842 and 1845 extracted teeth under anaesthetics, Crawford W. Long using ether and Horace Wells making an independent use of nitrous oxide. But these were short operations of a special character. It was W. T. G. Morton, at the Massachusetts General Hospital in Boston, on 16 October 1846, who first used ether successfully in a major surgical operation. So Morton is regarded – though not unanimously – as the 'discoverer' of inhalation anaesthesia.

Morton's ether inhaler consisted of a glass globe about seven inches in diameter with two necks. The globe contained a sponge, and the ether was introduced on to the sponge through the uppermost neck. The mouthpiece, containing an inspiratory and an expiratory valve, passed through the neck at the side of the globe. The apparatus worked quite satisfactorily in Morton's hands. But he tried to patent it, whereupon the Boston surgeons used the sponge, saturated with ether, and disregarded the rest of the apparatus.

In England ether was introduced as a general anaesthetic on 21 December 1846, when Robert Liston at University College Hospital, London, carried out a classic operation. A year later, in November 1847, chloroform, which had been discovered in 1831, was first used as an anaesthetic for surgical purposes by Sir James Young Simpson of Edinburgh. It was found that chloroform produced a deeper degree of anaesthesia than ether, and induction was more rapid.

Both substances had posed problems of inhaling apparatus, which were tackled by John Snow (1813–1858), who in 1847 became the first professional anaesthetist. He devised the first ingenious inhalers both for chloroform and ether

which gave a predetermined concentration in the air the patient inspired.

Although chloroform is much less likely than

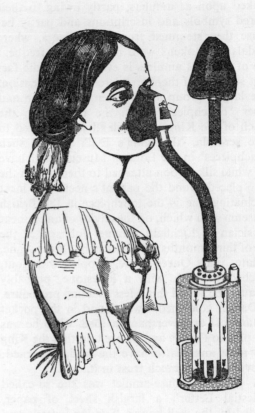

Fig. 1. Inhaling Chloroform from Snow's Inhaler.

ether to give undesirable after-effects – such as bronchitis – its margin of safety is rather small. In 1848 a girl died under chloroform at Newcastle. This was the first chloroform death, and there were others (in the Edinburgh School no special apparatus was used to administer chloroform. The liquid anaesthetic was simply poured on a towel held over the patient's face). The death caused a reaction, and a return in 1873 to the use of ether.

In 1862 nitrous oxide as a general anaesthetic in dental practice had been revived in the United States, and its use had become common in England by 1867. Anaesthesia was steadily refined. In 1864 an official committee in England had investigated the physiological properties of chloroform and had recommended the use of mixtures of chloroform and ether. Modern apparatus gives continuously any required percentage of either anaesthetic, or both, combined if necessary with oxygen. Administering nitrous oxide in combination with oxygen – much safer and more satisfactory than administering nitrous oxide alone – goes back to 1868.

Although various drugs and, especially, preparations of opium or its alkaloid, morphine, had been tried as local anaesthetics, no satisfactory results were achieved until Carl Koller proved in 1884 that cocaine produced excellent local anaesthesia for operations on the eye. This discovery arose out of work which Koller was doing with his friend Sigmund Freud on the use of cocaine in treating morphine addiction. Cocaine was soon given by subcutaneous injection or was injected into the nerve trunks. Cocaine was derived from the South American shrub *coca*, the dried leaves of which are chewed by Indians of the high Andes, and which was cultivated before the Spanish invasion. Thus like rubber (q.v.), and quinine, and the South American arrow poison curare (used to produce relaxation of the muscles so as to decrease the quantity of general anaesthetic required), the first local anaesthetic has been a gift of the New World cultures to the Old World and the world at large.

Peg-leg to prosthetics

An **ARTIFICIAL LIMB** is technically known as a 'prosthesis', and the craft of making and fitting artificial limbs and of training wearers in the use of them is known as 'prosthetics'.

Ancient as the use of wooden legs may be, prosthetics is not so old a craft. In literature perhaps the earliest reference to an artificial limb may be found in Herodotus, who tells how the Spartans captured Hegesistratus and condemned him to death, and how he amputated the foot he was chained by and so escaped. Hegesistratus made his way to a place thirty miles off, and fitted himself with a wooden foot. The oldest surviving artificial limb appears to be the metal leg now in the museum of the Royal College of Surgeons in London. It was found in a tomb at Capua, with other objects which suggested a date not later than 300 B.C.

Artificial hands, as well as mere wooden legs, were made – and with some ingenuity – in the late Middle Ages. There are several in existence dating from the fifteenth and sixteenth centuries. The most famous hand of all was unquestionably the one contrived in 1509 for Götz von Berlichingen (1480–1562), the Swabian knight so constantly at war with his neighbours, who is the subject of Goethe's play. He had lost his right hand five years before at the siege of Landshut. In his artificial hand all the finger-joints were movable and were held in position by flat springs. When the end joint of a finger was bent by the other hand or by pressing it against some object, the other joints of that finger were also bent, and all were locked by a ratchet mechanism. The flexed fingers could only be extended by pressing a button at the side of the hand. Götz von Berlichingen's artificial right hand was essentially designed for holding a sword; and at this period artificial left hands were as carefully designed for holding reins. Götz's hand was preserved at Nuremberg, where it was destroyed during the Second World War. Copies, though, exist.

Decidedly this celebrated hand was an instrument for battle, and it was the French wars of the sixteenth century which made Ambroise Paré (1510–1590) into the most important writer on artificial limbs in the early period of surgery. This greatest of military surgeons described a metal hand and forearm which superficially resembled the iron hand of Götz, though the thumb was fixed and the fingers all moved together. The fingers were kept extended by flat springs, and when one of them was bent to any position, all the others were similarly flexed and kept in position by catches which engaged on cogs. When a button on the hand was pressed, the fingers sprang open. Up to the time of Paré artificial hands were for forearm stumps only, but he illustrates a prosthesis for an upper arm stump, the socket for the stump being of iron. The elbow could be flexed to any degree, and was maintained in the desired position by a ratchet and pawl. When the pawl was released, the elbow was extended by a helical spring. For more peaceful occupations Paré also described a hand of moulded leather or 'papier collé' for those with a partial hand amputation; a short tube was fixed between the forefinger and thumb, and into this a pen could be stuck to enable the wearer to write.

Probably these hands and arms described by Paré were made for only a few favoured persons; for several centuries, until about 1800, the usual artificial arm consisted simply of a leather bucket with an attached hook. About 1818 Peter Baliff, a Berlin dentist, introduced the modern method of controlling the fingers of an artificial hand by the use of cords or a harness attached to the trunk and shoulders. In France the Comte de Beaufort devised an ingenious appliance about 1855. In one model a controlling cord passed from a button on the trousers round the back and through a loop at the rear of the shoulder on the sound side: it then returned over the shoulder on the affected side, passed round a pulley at the elbow of the artificial arm, and was attached to the hand. By various movements of his shoulder on the sound side, a trained person could produce excellent movements in an artificial hand, and by similar arrangements de Beaufort was able to control the thumb, and to effect the movement of individual fingers.

Bruegel the painter and Paré the surgeon were contemporaries. Bruegel's famous picture of *The Beggars*, now in the Louvre, shows the type of peg-leg used in the sixteenth century. Paré also described a kneeling peg-leg for amputations just below the knee. Much more elaborate was his artificial leg for operations above the knee. In this the knee joint and ankle joint were covered with overlapping metal plates, as in the armour of the period, while the knee was bent by means of a cord and locked in position by a spring, which

in turn was released by another cord. But for a long while the peg-leg was to remain the order of the day; artificial legs continued as simple as artificial arms, and it was not until the middle of the nineteenth century that a limb-maker named Potts invented the Anglesey limb, in which co-ordination of the movements of the knee joint and ankle joint was effected by cords.

With the inauguration of the antiseptic era by Lister in 1867 and its development into the aseptic era, amputations became more frequent, and many more artificial limbs were required. Prosthetics greatly advanced. Two world wars were a stimulus, much as the grim war casualties of the sixteenth century had been a stimulus to Paré. Artificial limbs improved in performance, comfort and appearance and lost their old clumsiness, strong light-weight materials such as aluminium and duralumin coming to the fore. However, attempts to make completely mechanical hands have not as yet been very satisfactory and problems still to be solved are the fitting of a knee-lock so that the wearer can climb stairs, the provision of a knee-brake for certain types of amputation, and introduction of artificial limbs which are not damaged by water.

ILLUSTRATION: Page 19.

The axe and the trees

The **AXE** is one of the most important and most ancient of the tools which man devised in his efforts to master his environment and improve his living. Prehistoric man needed an instrument with which he could fell trees, striking a violent cutting blow without hurt to himself. The requirements were a cutting blade on an axe-head relatively thick so as to bear the shock of the blow it delivers and heavy enough to reinforce the blow, a helve or handle which was parallel to the blade and long enough to multiply the power and to be used as a lever for extricating the axe-head when the force of the stroke had wedged it into the tree, and means of making the axe head immovable on the handle. Moreover the material for the blade had to be tough, and able to take – and maintain – a sharp edge.

The perfected axe had to await the invention of steel, but stone axes were vital in the Neolithic Revolution, which was the bridge in human history between savagery and civilization. In that phase men broke away from a nomadic existence to become food-growers rather than food-gatherers, animal husbandmen rather than hunters; and for their planned food economy open spaces were needed, first for the digging-stick, and then for the plough.

When the Neolithic Revolution spread to Europe, the areas suited to this kind of settlement were covered by deciduous forest, especially of oak, bounded on the south by the Mediterranean evergreens, on the north by the conifers of the sub-Arctic. The stone axe is a very special characteristic of neolithic man; with it he cleared a way in the forest to establish his plots. However, his soil husbandry was so poor that one tract of open ground fairly soon became exhausted, and fresh forest had to be cleared. So the farmer with his stone axe began that steady process which has nearly destroyed the deciduous forest zone of Europe to make room for hundreds of thousands of square miles of farmland and to make possible the fantastic increase in population that has followed the passing of the Old Stone Age. The care with which early men fashioned their axe-heads, the great trouble they took to get the best material, sometimes over great distances, shows how axes were esteemed. Indeed, amongst the Minoans the axe came to have a supernatural significance; and elsewhere axes are quite commonly found so carefully made and decorated so lavishly that they must be interpreted as purely ceremonial instruments vested with all the dignity of regalia.

The real history of the axe starts, not in Europe, but the Near East. It was in Mesopotamia, about 5000 B.C., that food-growing and the domestication of animals began for the Eurasian world. From here, over a period of some 2,500 years, the new way of life was slowly diffused through the areas geographically and climatically capable of a farming economy. With it went the

axe as a standard piece of essential equipment, the economic significance of which increased as it reached more and more thickly forested areas.

Neolithic axe-heads of a fine-grained stone, ground and polished, or of chipped and polished flint, show a strong similarity in cultures widely spread through time and space. The faces are practically flat, though the axe-head tends to thicken at the middle; the sides are either straight or slightly elliptical, and the cutting edge is usually rather short in relation to the length of axe-head. Such heads could be hafted by fitting the butt end into a slit cut in a wooden shaft. More common was the 'knee-shaft': a bough or sapling is cut off a little below the point where a branch grows out of it. The side branch is broken two or three inches from its base, and then split so that the axe-blade can be fitted into the cleft, where it is fastened tightly by binding. Axes of this kind are found with the earliest farming cultures yet known at such sites as Qalat Jarmo and Hassuna in Mesopotamia, which may be dated between 5000 and 4500 B.C. Not much later they are found with the earliest cultures of the Nile valley. By the fourth millennium B.C. they reached north-west Turkey – Troy, for example – and they have been found in occupation levels of this period in Crete, at Knossos, underneath the much later Palace of Minos. During the third millennium, axes spread across Europe, notably in the hands of the farmers of the Danubian culture, and they had reached Britain by about 2500 B.C. Flint mines were worked at Grime's Graves in Norfolk (other mines existed in France and Belgium) and a flourishing axe-making industry was carried on there to supply more than local requirements; axes of a fine-grained stone were made at Craig Lwyd in North Wales and at Great Langdale in Westmorland, and were distributed as far south as the Channel. Thus the development of the axe had brought with it the rise of the specialist craftsman, an economic event of the utmost significance. Modern tests on trees have proved, by the way, that stone axes were more efficient tools than one might fancy.

The advent of metallurgy revolutionized the axe. Stone or flint have to be worked laboriously to shape and impose severe limitations on design; but a material that can be hammered or, better still, cast to shape gives a tool which can cut better and be hafted more efficiently and tautly. By 4000 B.C. flat copper axes were being manufactured in Mesopotamia; they are rare objects, which shows the great value of such early metal artifacts. At first the new tools are essentially the old stone tools translated into metal, patterns which may persist a long while in some areas, both in copper and in bronze – as, for instance, in Cyprus, where they were used from c. 2500 to 1400 B.C. or even later. Metal and experience imposed their own modifications; the size of the cutting edge increases, and may become crescent-shaped, with very wide flanges, originating no doubt in the flanges caused by forging the cutting edge. Such axe-heads were manufactured in Ireland during the Early Bronze Age, and were traded to Britain.

With the metal axe-head shaft-holes were not adopted all at once. Egyptian smiths developed axe-heads with projecting lugs for tying the head to the handle. In Mesopotamia copper heads with shaft-holes must have been made as early as the end of the fourth millennium B.C., judging from clay models which have been discovered. Yet it is surprising that shaft-hole axes were not universally adopted until the coming of the full Iron Age. The shaft-hole axe spread from Mesopotamia to Syria and to Crete (by the second millennium B.C. it was used in Crete in the famous Minoan Double-Axe). Occasionally it appears with one immense improvement – a hole of elliptical section to prevent the handle twisting round in the socket under the strain of the blow. Yet elsewhere the shaft-hole axe was ignored, particularly in central and western Europe, where changes in design over a long period did little more than improve the fastening of axe-head to knee-shaft.

The use of iron, which began with the Hittites in the fifteenth century B.C., affected warfare to begin with, far more than industry, and the use of iron for manufacturing axes was very much secondary to its use for weapons; nor was its potentiality realized at first, for early iron axes are more or less slavish copies of bronze proto-types, much as bronze and copper axes had copied the stone axes (or in our time, much as early mechanical road vehicles copied the horse-drawn vehicle). Iron weapons and tools were in use in the Mediterranean by 1000 B.C., or soon after, though they did not spread north until about 650 B.C. (See also *Stone Tools*, *Bronze*, *Iron*, *Mines*.)

B

'Mighty barbarous music'?

BAGPIPES the English of our day think of as instruments peculiar to the Scots, though the fact is that the bagpipe was once widespread in and outside of Great Britain. It was English as much as Scottish, it was known to the Romans, its skirl has sounded at festivities across Europe. It is still to be found in Ireland, Northumberland and Scotland; and like so much which has passed away elsewhere, it has survived on the fringes of Europe.

A bagpipe is simply a bladder, inflated by mouth or by a bellows, into which one or more reed pipes have been inserted; the main pipe has finger-holes cut in it, and the others are known as 'drones', since they hold a fixed base note. The instrument, in fact, is a primitive hand-blown organ, the bag acting as windchest and maintaining a continuous supply of air to the pipes. The ancient history of the bagpipe is obscure. Some writers have maintained that the Greek word *sumphoneia* (which means literally an 'agreeing in sound') referred invariably to the bagpipe, which in modern Greek and Italian is called *tsampouna* and *zampogna*. Still, it is fairly certain that such an instrument did exist several hundred years before Christ. A terracotta figure of about 200 B.C. unearthed at Tarsus in Asia Minor shows (incompletely) on the player's chest a box-like contraption which was filled by a bellows; an older terracotta of the eighth century B.C. found at Susa depicts a similar instrument; and a bas-relief on an arch at Kermanshah in Persia and a carving on a monument at Nineveh date the bagpipe, or something much like it, earlier still. Moving into certainty, the Greeks did, in fact, know the bagpipe as *phusalis* (a 'bladder') and *askaulos*. The Romans knew it as the *tibia utricularis*. Suetonius the Roman historian says that Nero was an accomplished performer on the bagpipe (a coin of his bears a picture of a bagpipe), and this is confirmed by Dio Chrysostom, who wrote that Nero 'knew how to play the pipe with his mouth on the bag thrust under his arm'. Procopius records that bagpipes were used in the Roman army; and a bronze figure of a Roman soldier playing a bagpipe was found at Richborough, in Kent.

It was popular without any doubt through the Middle Ages and up to about 1600. The fourteenth, fifteenth and sixteenth centuries saw the high noon of its social success. It was taken up by the court and the church; it appears again and again in paintings and carvings of the period in the hands of celestial orchestras – yet all the time retaining a folk atmosphere. There were superstitions of its uncanny power over animals, the association of reed pipes and the skin of a goat carrying echoes of beliefs older than Christianity. Indeed the Devil himself is more than once seen in pictures slyly inflating the bagpipe; and it seems more natural to him than to the chubby angels clutching it under the white folds of their clothing. In Germany and in the Low Countries – witness Dürer's engraving (1514) of the bagpipe player, or paintings of Bruegel or Teniers – no jollities were complete without bagpipe or *dudelsack*; in France an elegant silk-clad *musette* was played by ladies of the court in their unconvincing efforts to imitate the pastoral idyll; in England royalty, nobility and clergy, as well as commons, took it to their heart on the wave of fashion; whilst in Scotland the first hints of the later fierce possessiveness seem to stir with a proclamation that piping was a royal prerogative on Sundays.

English medieval carvings in churches, on bosses, corbels, misericords and bench-ends, show merry playing of the pipes; and there are numerous references to its use (and abuse), fre-quently in connection with dancing bears and other animals. Chaucer's Miller was an expert and played to the pilgrims as they left for Canterbury:

A baggepype wel coude he blowe and sowne,
And ther-with-al he broughte us out of towne.

According to an early-fifteenth-century manuscript, such music was necessary on pilgrimage: 'I say to thee that it is right well done that Pylegremys have with them both singers and also pipers, that when one of them that goeth barefoote, striketh his too upon a stone, and hurteth hym sore and makyth hym to blede, it is well done that he and his fellow begyn then a Songe, or else take out of his bosom a Baggepipe for to drive away with soche myrthe the hurte of his felow.'

The English bagpipe was a quiet instrument: Spenser writes in his *Shepherd's Calendar* '... is thy bagpipe broke that sounds so sweet?', and Falstaff is once described (in *Henry IV, Part I*) as being 'as melancholy as the drone of a Lincolnshire bagpipe'. It should be noted, though, that Shakespeare's reference to 'woollen pipes' in *The Merchant of Venice* does not describe their tone or composition, but is intended for the Irish Uilleann or elbow pipes (also misrendered as 'Union' pipes). The Scots probably got their pipes from this Irish version in the course of the early colonizations of Scotland. English pipers still appear in paintings by Hogarth, but there is now no trace of bagpipes in the south of England, and even the gentle bellows-blown Northumbrian pipes are less known than the wild instrument from the other side of the Tweed.

From 1600 onwards the popularity of the bagpipe gradually declined; it was killed very largely by the development of music which could not accommodate its unremitting skirl. Yet serious music learnt from the characteristics of the bagpipe. Not only do we find the great composers using the drone bass as a 'truly rural' effect (as in the finale of Haydn's symphony *L'Ours* – here again appears the connection with animals), but, more importantly, the language of music has been enriched by the harmonic device known as the pedal, whereby a note is held for some time (usually in the bass) regardless of the passing harmony. It is in mountain districts now, especially in the Balkans, that the bagpipe holds its ancient popularity. It is not for a refined age; it has strength, it has an odd stirring beauty of its own, plucking at the feelings, as all will admit who have heard Scottish pipers playing *The Flowers of the Forest* or *Over the Sea to Skye*; but it gives, as Pepys put it, 'at best mighty barbarous music'.

ILLUSTRATION: Page 221.

Floating on the air

The **BALLOON** could easily have been invented a thousand or more years ago, had anyone drawn the right conclusion from watching burning debris rising from a camp fire. But the hint was not taken with any effect until the end of the eighteenth century, when two paper-makers, the brothers Joseph and Étienne Montgolfier of Annonay (near Lyons), made the first practical hot-air balloons.

Their stimulus had been the papers of Joseph Priestley on air, which he began publishing in 1774, and they had discovered that paper bags filled with hot air from the hearth would float up to the ceiling. In 1783 they constructed a large balloon, thirty-eight feet in diameter, of linen lined with paper, and made it soar at Annonay. In September 1783 they built a larger balloon at Paris, which they let up safely, on ropes, with a man standing in a gallery built around the neck. Next, to the wild acclaim of a huge audience, they sent up a balloon on a free flight from Versailles. Underneath dangled a basket containing a sheep, a cock and a duck, who landed safely. On 21 November 1783 two men, the Marquis d'Arlandes and Pilâtre de Rozier, made the first aerial voyage in history, when they flew in a *Montgolfière* across Paris from the garden of a house in the Bois de Boulogne, covering five-and-a-half miles before they came to earth. 'If we consider for a moment', wrote the scientist Tiberius Cavallo in the *History and Practice of Aerostation* in 1785, 'the sensation which these first aerial adventurers must have felt in their exalted Situation, we can hardly prevent an unusual sublime idea in ourselves.'

Without knowing how the Montgolfiers had raised their balloon – only having heard that a sphere had floated up from the ground – the French physicist J. A. C. Charles assumed that lifting power had been the light gas hydrogen, the 'inflammable air' described by Cavendish in 1766. So he went to work in Paris and designed the first hydrogen balloon. A small trial version left Paris on 27 August 1783, and landed fifteen miles away, near the village of Gonesse, where its silent and mysterious descent in a field caused a panic, the villagers puncturing it with their hay-forks and tying the envelope to a horse's tail.

By the time Charles saw the Montgolfier hot-air balloons in Paris he had already planned a full-sized hydrogen balloon, and on 1 December 1783, soon after the first aerial voyage, Charles and his companion Robert (one of two brothers who had constructed the balloon) made the first hydrogen balloon voyage from Paris. This was in every way more important than the Montgolfier ascent; Charles having designed a practical gas balloon with valve, net, basket, ballast and altimeter (a barometer). The voyage lasted two hours, during which the balloon journeyed twenty-seven miles to the village of Nesle. Serious ballooning had started with this prophetic vehicle. Reactions to this preliminary conquest of the sky varied. George Washington wrote to his French friend Duportail that the marvellous tales of the balloon led them to expect in America 'that our friends at Paris, in a little time, will come flying thro' the air, instead of ploughing the ocean to get to America'. Benjamin Franklin argued (much as we have argued about the atom bomb) that the balloon would make war impossible because of the threat of aerial invasion.

The hot-air balloon, which was inflated over a fire of wool and straw and carried another fire aloft in a brazier slung within the neck, was only short-lived, almost disappearing from the aeronautical scene after flourishing only for a year or two, but it had stimulated Charles and had inaugurated air travel. The gas balloon – the cheaper coal-gas was substituted for hydrogen in 1821 – immediately became the accepted type, and has remained in use for sport and for scientific investigation ever since. Even today ballooning is popular in Europe, but the number of aeronauts is steadily diminishing and balloon flights across the air lanes becoming increasingly dangerous.

The standard gas balloon has an envelope with an open neck at the bottom (so that the expanding gas can blow off harmlessly when the balloon rises); a net over the envelope from which the basket hangs; a valve in the crown of the envelope for venting gas; bags of sand ballast; a rope and anchor; and an assortment of instruments. This simple aircraft has seen a thousand adventures, and has been the means of lifting men so that they learnt to know the sky and its ways before they came to pilot heavier-than-air machines.

The English Channel was flown in 1785, by J-P. Blanchard and the American John Jeffries, after the first ascent in England the year before. The United States saw its first balloon ascent – by Blanchard again – in 1793, and balloons were pressed into the service of war in 1794, when Napoleon first used a balloon for military reconnaissance at Maubeuge. In 1849 balloons carried out the first air raid of history, when the Austrians sent pilotless *Montgolfières* to bomb Venice. The first live parachute descent from the air took place, when André Jacques Garnerin jumped from a balloon over Paris in 1797, and by the early years of the nineteenth century balloon ascents were common and popular fair-ground events. All sorts of ideas were thought up to make the sport entertaining: firework displays were given from the air – which incidentally caused the death of an early lady aeronaut in 1819 – showmen went up sitting on horses and even stags; ballet dancers rode the air in elegant poses; and adventurous gentlemen set off on long trips such as the famous journey of 480 miles from London to Weilburg in western Germany in 1836.

Scientists went up to observe the weather, and some of them fainted in the process and were killed; and in 1897 the greatest balloon adventure of all time took place, when the Swedish explorer Andrée and two companions set out from Spitzbergen to fly to the North Pole. The balloon disappeared and was never heard of again – until in 1930, by a fantastic chance and a severe arctic thaw, the whole expedition was found beneath the ice with records, photographs and equipment all in perfect condition.

Even as late as 1935 the balloon was winning its own triumphs, and two United States army officers (Stevens and Anderson) took their great helium-filled *Explorer II* up to the great height of 13·7 miles (72,395 feet), which remained for a long while the absolute height record for man-carrying aircraft.

The aesthetic delights of ballooning are no longer sufficiently exploited. In a balloon one can escape from the earth in smooth, silent flight; floating in the air, one has sensations and thoughts not possible to the pilots and passengers of the roaring powered aeroplane. Long ago, the English aeronaut C. C. Turner wrote these words of a flight on a cloudless and exquisite 31st of May over the English countryside: 'Fifteen hundred feet up and almost absolute silence, broken occasionally by the barking of a dog heard very faintly ... or by a voice hailing the balloon, and by an occasional friendly creak of the basket and rigging if I move ever so slightly. Then quite suddenly I am aware of something new. The balloon has come down a little, and I scatter a few handfuls of sand and await the certain result. But my attention is no longer on that, it is arrested by this new sound which I hear, surely the most wonderful and the sweetest sound heard by mortal ears. ... It is the combined singing of thousands of birds, of half the kinds which make the English spring so lovely. I do not hear one above the others; all are blended together in a wonderful harmony without change of pitch or tone, yet never wearying the ear ... their singing comes up from that ten-acre wood in one sweet volume of heavenly music.'

It was in the balloon that man first enjoyed suspension in the air and sky, a lesson completed by the glider. (See also *Aeroplane, Glider, Kite*.)

ILLUSTRATION: Page 67.

'These minor monuments'

BARROWS – the mounds built over the nameless dead which so stir the mind on the hills and plains of the British Isles and across Europe – are of various shapes and dates; and since Sir

Thomas Browne wondered at the way in which 'these minor monuments' were spared by 'Time, which antiquates antiquities', much ingenuity has been spent on recovering their secrets.

An embryo mound is the natural consequence of a burial, the body displacing so much earth. Barrows may have started in that way, though, as we know them, they are part of the ritual consequences of beliefs about the dead. The primitive mound becomes a protection *from* the dead, keeping them firmly in place lest they come as revenants.

The earliest English barrows are the 'long barrows' of the neolithic herdsmen, farmers and flint-miners who belonged to what is named the Windmill Hill culture, after a corral site in North Wiltshire. These were the men who introduced farming into England. Their barrows are long,

Fig. 2. Long Barrow.

huge, grass-grown mounds higher at one end than the other. The thicker, taller end covers the skeletons of the dead – or rather the skeletons and the skeletal remains, a necessary distinction, in view of the customary ritual which preceded the piling up of the barrow.

These early inhabitants of Britain, so it appears, made rectangular funerary enclosures, sometimes fenced with wood and devoid of gate or gateway. At one end they built a mortuary – a word which the dictionary defines as 'a chapel of rest, where bodies may be kept prior to interment'. This small mortuary was often constructed of turves, and here the family dead were stored until enough of them justified a barrow, which was then raised over the mortuary and its contents. So the bones have been found mix-muddled; those recently dead were included as well, bent and laid on their side, the bones not yet disarticulated.

When one of these barrows was investigated the egg-case of a snail was found inside a skull,

which must have been lying more or less in the open, in the mortuary, for a long time before the piling of the barrow. Long barrows of this kind range from Yorkshire and Lincolnshire to Dorset, and are most thickly grouped at the Wessex end of the transverse line of chalk upland on which these neolithic people of c. 2000–1750 B.C. kept their herds, cultivated their plots, and mined their black flint for tools. One of them in Wiltshire is 385 feet long.

Other neolithic peoples of Great Britain made long-barrows ('barrow' simply means 'mound', from the Old English *beorg*, hill or mound) of a different kind. They were still family tombs, but ones which could frequently be reopened (like the family vault in a modern cemetery), so that the funerary enclosure and the turf mortuary were not required. Inside there are stone-walled and stone-roofed passages or a combination of passages and chambers. The entrance has a funnel section with rounded ends, forming an external court or porch, on which ritual fires were lit.

Most of these megalithic long barrows are shorter than the unchambered long barrows – they may be a hundred to two hundred feet long. The entrance was blocked when the last of the dead had been enclosed. Inside there is fine dry walling between the massive stones which are set on edge to hold the roofing-slabs. When the mounds wore away with the wind and weather of time, an internal chamber was sometimes left like a huge table. This is the 'cromlech' or 'dolmen' of the older students of antiquity.

Investigation of these barrows, which are poor in content from a treasure-hunter's point of view, has revealed some curious things. The fifth metatarsal bone of the feet of some of the skeletons, for instance, has been shown to bend inwards, evidence that these neolithic people of Britain wore sandals.

Round barrows are more familiar. Broadly, these were introduced into Britain by new settlers who arrived c. 1900–1800 B.C. They are no longer family tombs, but single graves. Indeed, round barrows of earth or stones were to continue to be raised on top of the dead for two and a half thousand years, through the Bronze Age in the British Isles to the early Iron Age, the round barrow re-occuring in Romano-British times, and in the early period of the Anglo-Saxon invasions up to the mid-seventh century A.D. The Vikings also built round barrows.

In the long barrows and the chambered barrows, goods were scantily provided for the dead. When single burial succeeded burial by families, the goods increased, reaching at times to the point of treasure. Round barrows were first commonly raised by the so-called 'Beaker folk', invaders from the Continent who in Britain and their original homes from the Caucasus to Brittany fashioned characteristic beaker-like pots. It was these people – who made some use of bronze, though they were not fully involved in the great revolution of metallurgy – who were responsible for the foundation of the great stone temples of Avebury and Stonehenge. They buried their dead

Fig. 3. Round Barrow.

crouched in the curled position of sleep, leaving with them for their life in death or in the land of the dead not only one of their shapely beakers, but weapons, of flint and stone, and sometimes of the treasured bronze, necklaces, armlets, etc. Thus the grave goods from under a barrow at Winterslow in Wiltshire were found to include a beaker, two flint arrow-heads, a rectangular wrist-guard, worn above the hand which held the bow to protect the wrist from the recoil of the bowstring (for which modern archers wear a leather 'bracer'), and a bronze (largely copper) dagger.

Usually the dead person was deposited first in a shallow grave, over which the barrow was shaped. Sometimes he was contained in a stone box or cist. Heaping earth round a crouched, curled body laid on its side, one may remark, would naturally produce a more or less circular mound, from which the round barrow would derive.

The types of round barrow and the contents and the rites of burial vary through the Bronze

Age. 'Food Vessel' people in the northerly parts of Britain, new invaders who succeed the Beaker users who are also named from characteristic earthenware, put their dead in pits or stone chests covered by round barrows; sometimes, though, the barrows reveal oak coffins, made of split and hollowed trunks, which may even be in the shape of dugouts, and sometimes their dead were cremated. Round barrows in Wiltshire and Dorset also cover chieftains of the 'Wessex culture' (c. 1500 or 1450–1300 B.C.), who were buried with bronze daggers and objects of amber and gold, blue beads from Egypt, etc. One of the richest barrows opened was Bush Barrow, near Stonehenge, in Wiltshire. Here, in 1808, the excavators found the skeleton of a 'stout and tall' chieftain, whose grave-goods included a sceptre with a head of shale, a bronze axe, two bronze daggers (the handle of one was inlaid with gold) and gold ornaments including a patterned breast-plate. It seems that the fascinating variant called the 'disc-barrow', in which a small central round barrow is surrounded by a circular ditch and a circular bank, belongs to the Wessex culture; and there is ground for thinking that disc-barrows were reserved for women. Often disc-barrows and other variants of the round barrow occur together in groups.

By 1200 B.C., in the Middle Bronze Age, cremation became general; ashes were placed under urns, and the urns were covered with barrows, although 'urn-field' cemeteries without barrows were frequent, and were common by the Late Bronze Age. By meticulous excavation, it has been possible to reconstruct the ritual of barrow burials of the Bronze Age.

In the British Iron Age from c. 500 B.C., barrows were seldom raised, though in East Yorkshire, just above the Humber estuary, a Celtic people left groups of small barrows which date from the third century B.C. Ordinary folk were buried with a few goods including a joint of pork in an earthenware jar, chieftains were buried with their chariots, horses, harness and weapons.

In Roman Britain round barrows recurred, large and conical and ostentatious, though cemeteries were the rule, as they were in the Anglo-Saxon times which followed. In the early pagan period of the Anglo-Saxon settlement, chiefs were buried under small round barrows, several of which have been opened to reveal a wealth of goods for the chief's comfort in the next world. Notable are the ship burials of Snape and Sutton Hoo in Suffolk. Christianity brought the long tradition of barrow burial to an end in Europe.

ILLUSTRATION: Plate 15.

All kinds of basketry

BASKETS of prehistoric periods are rare, though a few specimens have been preserved in very dry soil, in the peat and mud covering lake dwellings and among grave goods; it has also been possible to reconstruct a number of basket patterns from impressions on prehistoric pottery.

Basketry belongs to the New World and the Old. In Europe basketwork creels or fish-traps go back to the Mesolithic period (and are still employed). Other basketwork certainly was made in the Neolithic and Early Bronze Ages. The materials have naturally varied according to region, papyrus reeds were used in Egypt, esparto grass in prehistoric Spain, willow rods in Rome, Iron Age Britain and Late Bronze Age Switzerland. In Scotland prehistoric and modern baskets have been made of hair-moss. In Sardinia baskets with patterns similar to Bronze Age figurines are made of asphodel. In the Isles of Scilly tamarisk has been the material for lobster-pots in lieu of withies. Whatever the material, basketry has been much more widely and variously used than it is among societies of the present day – in transport by land and sea, agriculture, household work, child-rearing, fishing, beekeeping, etc.

Over a wide area basketry has been employed as a means of transport for man as well as his goods. Wickerwork chariots and carts were fashioned in Greece and Rome. Not dissimilar to boats made by the Assyrians, coracles, which can still be seen in western Ireland, in Wales and on the Severn, and the curraghs of the Atlantic coasts of Ireland were originally skin-covered baskets. Being so light, so durable and so easily brought into convenient shapes, baskets are well suited to transporting food as well as stor-

ing it. On the Aran Islands and along the west coast of Ireland, side-creels or panniers of wickerwork slung on each side of a horse's back or a donkey's back are still a farmer's means of carriage, especially for heavy loads of turf for winter firing. Till a hundred years ago farmers in Devon and Cornwall still used their panniers (which they called dorsles), especially for carrying dung and other kinds of manure. The bottom was hinged, so that the dorsle emptied itself on the field. Wicker chairs and tables and bath-chairs of wickerwork are still familiar; even wickerwork cradles, which have a considerable antiquity. Medieval paintings often show that the Holy Child was supposed to have lain at Bethlehem in a plaited feeding-basket, not in the wooden trough of much later popular fancy. The ancient Greeks placed their infants in a winnowing-fan of basketwork, to ensure them a prosperous future, and William Hone recorded in his *Table-Book* (1827–1828) that in Perthshire, in Scotland, when a child was baptized privately, it was put upon a clean basket, having a cloth previously spread over it, with bread and cheese wrapped up into the cloth; the basket was then moved three times round the iron crook hanging over the fire, in order to prevent witches and evil spirits from harming the infant.

Wooden chip-baskets, made here and in other countries, illustrate the variety of materials. Swedish chip-baskets are especially fine. Thus a basket-maker at Hedared specializes in light basket-plates. The floor of his shed is covered with pieces of freshly cut fir-wood, about five feet long and four inches thick, which he splits into four lengths. With movements as rhythmical as those of a barber sharpening his razor, he trims the wooden splints before starting to pull off flat, long shavings. These are so thin that they curl up in the process; he then soaks them in a pail of water to make them even more pliable to suit the light basket-plates.

In Great Britain the earliest wickerwork yet found comes from the Iron Age lake-village at Glastonbury in Somerset, near Sedgemoor, which is still the centre of the English basket industry. It remains almost entirely a handcraft, though simple machines for peeling the rods are used by some of the Sedgemoor makers. (See also *Coffins*.)

PLATE 1

PLATE 2

W. S. Henson's design for an AERIAL STEAM CARRIAGE, 1843.

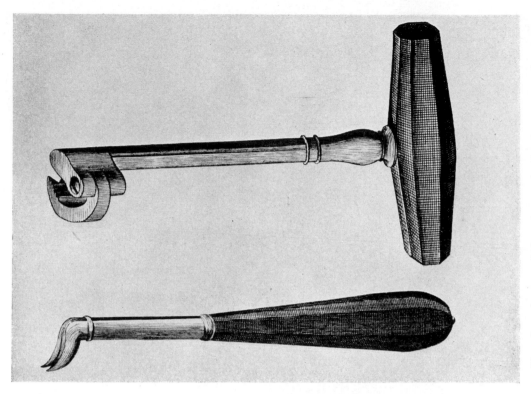

Dental punch, or goat's foot elevator, for drawing stumps and roots, and the English Key, for drawing teeth. Eighteenth century.

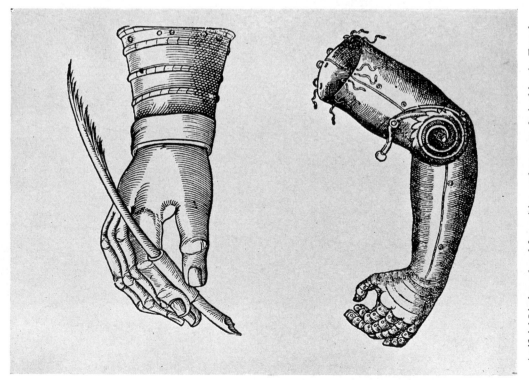

Artificial Limbs: a hand for writing and an arm, devised by the French surgeon Ambroise Paré (1510–1590).

Metal lamp on a stand – *Girl catching lice*, School of Gerard van Honthorst (1590–1656).

Hand lamp – *Young Man Walking*, School of Gerard van Honthorst (1590–1656).

Open fields of the Middle Ages, divided ridge by ridge. Whitchurch, Warwickshire.

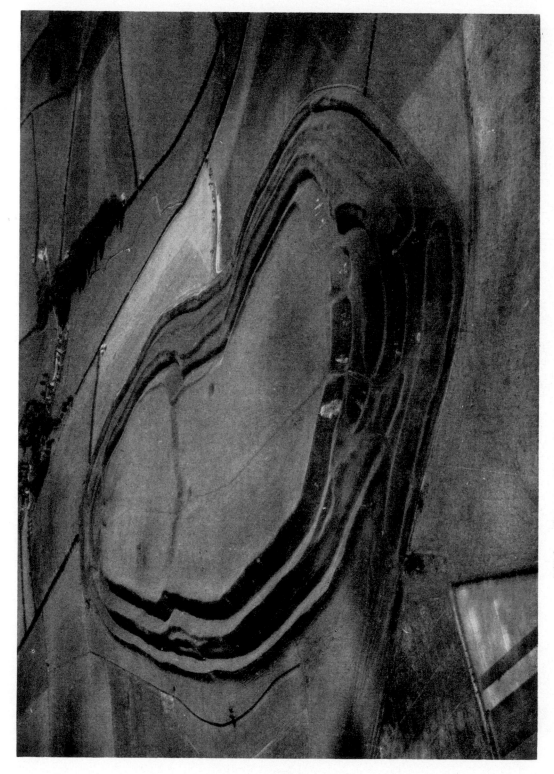

Hill-fort of Maiden Castle, Dorset, stormed by the Second Legion in A.D. 70.

Fire-engine on a sledge, from Böckler's *Theatrum machinarum novum* (1662).

Fire-engine with the first leather hoses, 1673, invented by Jan van der Heiden, General Fire Master of Amsterdam, who also drew and engraved the plate.

Roman Quern, from Sussex, fourth century A.D.

Rotary Quern, from Sussex, before 50 B.C.

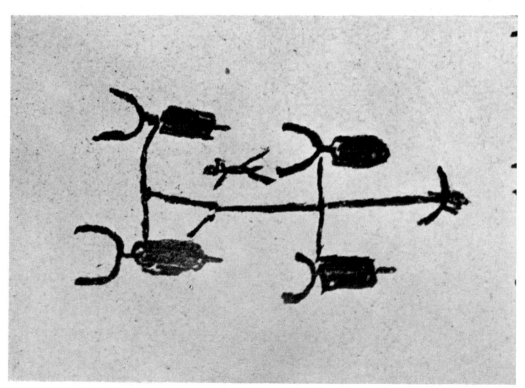

Bronze Age ploughs. Rock-engravings from Fontanalba, Italian Alps. (The originals measure 44×28 cm. and 29×19½ cm.)

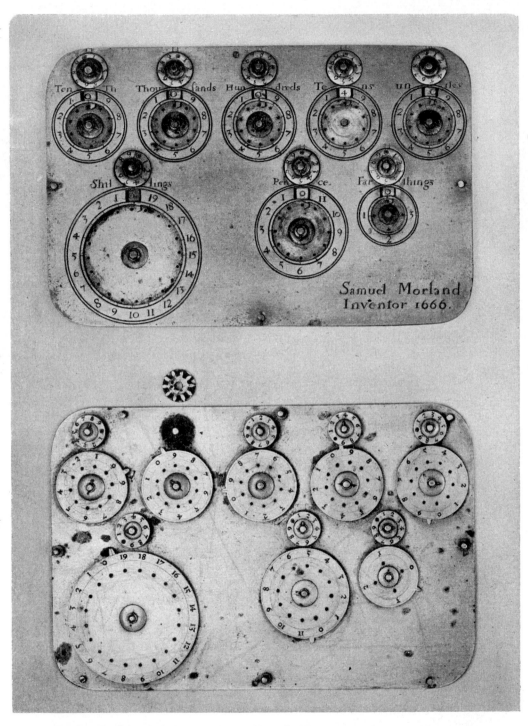

The first English calculating machine, 1666, devised by Sir Samuel Morland (1625–1695).

Copper smelting: a primitive method in nineteenth-century Japan (see *Bronze*).

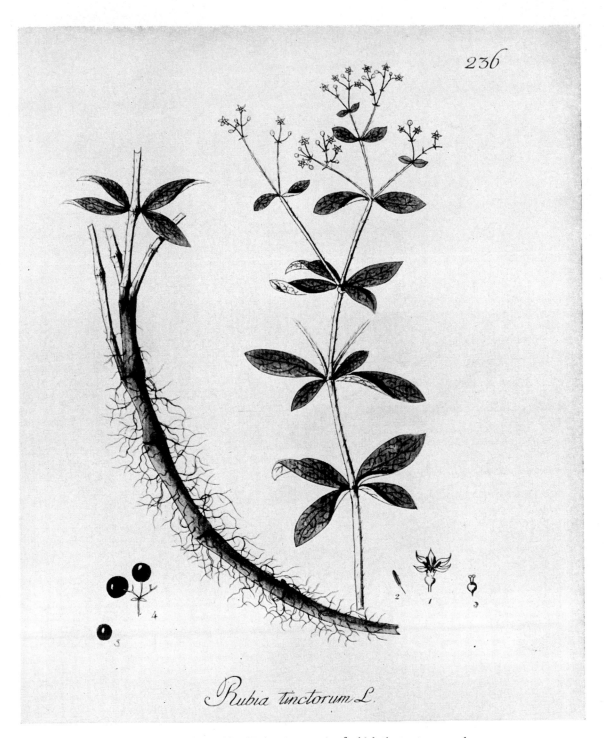

Rubia tinctorum L.

Dye plants. Madder (*Rubia tinctorum*), of which the root was used.

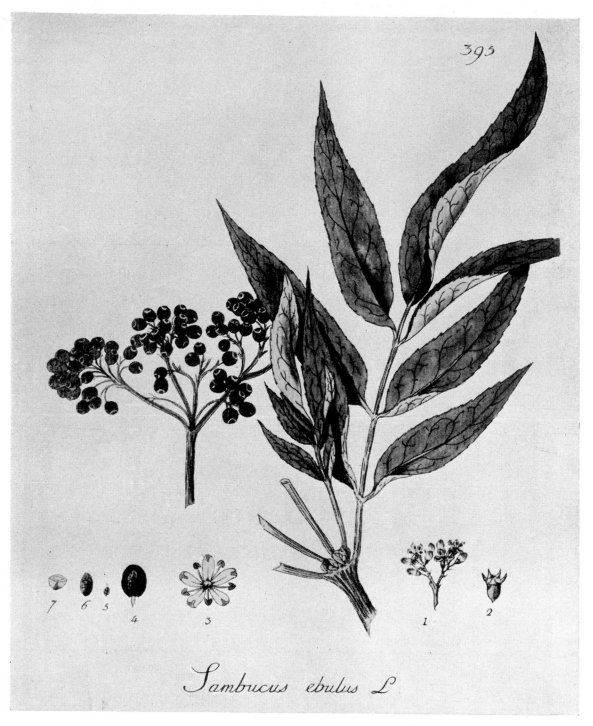

Sambucus ebulus L.

Dwarf Elder (*Sambucus ebulus*). A dye plant used by the neolithic inhabitants of Swiss lake-villages.

Camera obscura, forerunner of the camera. This is the tent camera obscura of the Abbé Nollet, 1733.

To secure a pleasing Portrait is everything.

Daguerreotypist, to cheerful Sitter — "The process will commence as soon as I lift up this slide. You will have the goodness to look fixedly at one object & call up a pleasant expression to your countenance."

Taking a daguerreotype, from Cuthbert Bede's *Photographic Pleasures*, 1855.

Jack in the Green, carving from thirteenth-century shrine of St Frideswide, Christ Church, Oxford.

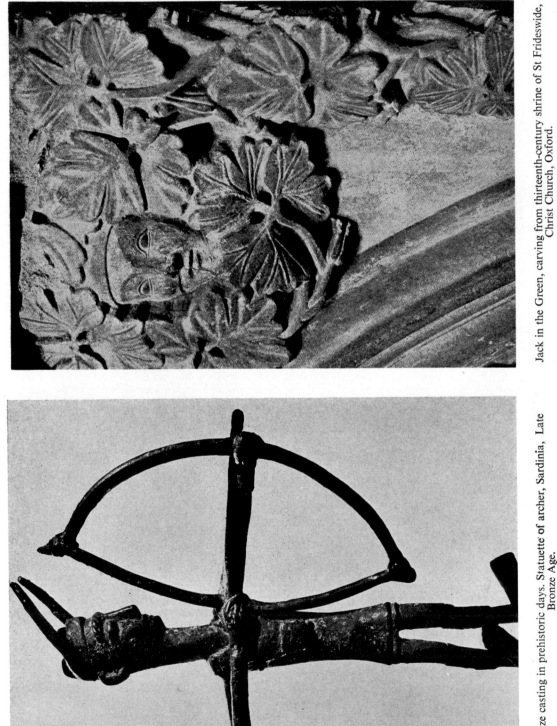

Bronze casting in prehistoric days. Statuette of archer, Sardinia, Late Bronze Age.

PLATE 3

ESKIMO KAYAK, watercolour ascribed to John White (*fl.*1590).

PLATE 4

KING OF DIAMONDS, from a French pack of playing cards, 16th century (enlarged).

Baths H. and C.

The **BATH** in the bathroom has had perhaps a more peculiar development than any other article of everyday use. We think of it as a receptacle for water used in a private house by one person at a time. Until recently mankind was not partial to bathing in this way, preferring the public bath; or no bath at all.

Of Greek bathing we know a good deal from excavation, literature and vase-painting. A private bath in the shape of a pottery bowl has been found at Phylakopi, the Mycenaean city excavated on Melos. Public baths of the Mycenaean era are known from Tiryns. Homer relates that when Hector returned from the battle-field he found a hot bath awaiting him, and that Ulysses and Diomedes bathed in the sea and then took to a hot bath. However, the Greeks enjoyed their hot baths generally at public bathing establishments, which were less elaborate than those built later at Rome in imperial days.

Under the Romans bathing spread far and wide. Thus the cult of bathing was developed highly in Roman Britain, where quite small communities had their baths. Baths which might have been used more or less privately have been found in isolated villas (*i.e.* farm or estate houses), but these belonged to wealthy persons.

Public bathing led to excesses; in consequence early Christians were against such ablution in any form, except as a religious rite. In the medieval monasteries of many orders, the hands and face were cleansed in a common wash-room, but the entire body was bathed only on Saturday evening, in preparation for Sunday. The Cistercians forbade bathing altogether, except at Christmas and Easter. But that was not typical of the Middle Ages, in which the upper classes attended a good deal to cleanliness. Hot bathing, public and private, returned to favour, largely as a result of the virtues of the hot springs at Aix-la-Chapelle and elsewhere. Jug and basin were kept in medieval sleeping-rooms; hands, faces, teeth were washed every morning, thus fulfilling the advice of the *Regimen Sanitatis Salernitanum*, the famous medieval guide to home medicine and hygiene:

C

Rise early in the morn, and straight remember
With water cold to wash your hands and eyes,
In gentle fashion stretching every member;
And to refresh your brain when as you rise
In heat, in cold, in July and December
Both comb your hair, and clean your teeth likewise

The *Regimen* was a little more guarded on baths

Wine, women, baths, by art or nature warm
Us'd or abus'd do men much good or harm –

but baths were taken every two or three weeks – not merely in the spring,

The spring is moist, of temper good and warm,
Then best it is to bathe, to sweate, and purge –

and a wooden tub was placed in the bedroom to be filled with hot water heated in pans over the fire.

In the sixteenth century the domestic and personal hygiene of the rich might have made some further advance. But this was the era of the Reformation, and nakedness was now religiously obnoxious; it was a state for witches at the Sabbath. Elizabeth I, it is true, had bathrooms installed in the royal apartments at Windsor; it was written that she did 'bathe herself once a month whether she require it or not'. But the public bath began to disappear, and nothing took its place; it was thought enough to change shirt and smock and wear fresh linen. People boasted they had never bathed. Louis XIV (1638–1715) in France bathed only once a year. The great ladies of his Court seldom washed their hands and faces more than once a week. At the end of the eighteenth century Marie Antoinette (1755–1793) did little better; and it was said that the lower classes in France never saw a bath tub from one year's end to the next.

Eighteenth-century England could hardly boast. Those who preached cleanliness were sometimes roughly handled in the press; and in 1769 the *Gentleman's Magazine* was stimulated to a mild but revelatory rejoinder. After pointing out that the ancients had bathed frequently, the journal added, apropos the mere changing of linen, 'Our shirts cannot answer the same purpose [as washing the body], however careful we may be to change them often. This is evident; for notwithstanding the frequent shifting of our linen, we still collect filth, which can only be removed by water and bathing.'

In the late eighteenth century there was a revival of sea-bathing in England, under medical stimulus. Dr Richard Russell, whose memory is still honoured in Brighton which he made popular, had advised sea-water for the cure of scrofula. Watering-places multiplied. All this was reflected later in personal hygiene, though in the first three or four decades of the nineteenth century, the pendulum sometimes made a ridiculous and extreme swing. Milk was not infrequently preferred to water. In France, the sister of Napoleon Buonaparte, the Princess Borghese, bathed in milk, and other ladies followed suit. In England Beau Brummel (1778–1840) frequently had a milk bath, and William Douglas, the notorious fourth Duke of Queensberry (1724–1810), had such a bath every day.

In the way of cleanliness there were difficulties which ought to prevent us from being too critical of our dirty ancestors. Some at least realized they were dirty – that they were members – to quote the phrase Thackeray invented in *Pendennis* in 1850, three years before Gladstone repealed the soap tax – of the 'Great Unwashed'. Baths had to be filled and emptied; and the favourite round wooden tub was not only inclined to leak – it soon stank. Water was not laid on; houses had no room easily convertible to a bathroom. Doctors, however, were on the side of soap and water, first by the shower, and then by the bath – or the bath-tub – which gradually changed, remaining to begin with only a portable bath, pleasantly enjoyed before the fire in the winter months. In the nineteenth century the wooden tub gave way to metal baths. These had to be light, easy to handle and easy to empty, factors limiting size, shape and depth of water; it is no easy job to empty an overfilled hip bath or tin tub, with its shallow water slopping from side to side.

The bath could not elongate, the luxuries of depth could not be indulged, until the bath became a fixture and until bathrooms began to appear in the eighties or nineties. Then at last man had no longer to bath in a crouched, contracted position, or else to sit in the tub with part of his legs outside and his feet on a bath-

mat. Many obstacles still had to be overcome. Efficient hot-water systems, and sewage systems, public and private, had to be developed. Builders had to be convinced that it was worth installing special bathrooms, landlords to be persuaded to carry out conversions. In the transitional period on either side of 1900 baths were frequently made of expensive materials such as marble, and great canopy constructions with many taps combined bath and shower-bath, before our simpler baths of enamelled iron or porcelain were developed.

Slowly tin tub and hip bath disappeared, slowly the mechanized bathroom and *the idea of the bath as a sine qua non* conquered after the First World War, though even in the twenties and early thirties it was still common for English and other hotels to charge extra for a hot bath in the one bathroom.

State housing in Great Britain meant baths for the working class, though superior persons forgetful of the bodily smell of their own bathless grandparents were apt to maintain that the working man's bath was useful only for storing the coal. The sting of this remark has long gone; and from top to bottom the modern public is more healthily bath-conscious than at any previous period in history. (See also *Soap, Water-Closet.*)

ILLUSTRATION: Page 178.

Clothes in the wave

BATHING COSTUMES involve an absurdity in dressing for a purpose which would reasonably demand the absence of dress. The Greeks and the Romans had no horror of the body, and would have thought it madness to put on clothes in order to go into the water. Medieval notions were different. The body became sinful through the Fall. The problem of bathing dress was therefore bound to arise sooner or later, when sea-bathing became popular.

This happened about the middle of the eighteenth century, and was due to a new belief in the medicinal benefits to be had from sea-water;

which led to the development of seaside resorts. At first the question of costume did not arise. The sexes were segregated, and they bathed naked, a situation illustrated by Thomas Rowlandson (1756–1827) in some of his caricatures. The practice was less startling than it might have been, because of the bathing-machine, in which bathers were drawn into the sea, an umbrella-like awning at the end of the bathing machine making it possible for them to descend into the health-giving waves without being seen.

For a time men continued to bathe without any clothes at all. Early in the nineteenth century, however, women began to shroud their forms in a species of flannel cloak which was tied around the necks and which hung down to their heels. This spread out on the surface of the ocean and provided effective concealment. At Brighton in 1824 John Constable painted in words a bathing-picture of the time in a letter to his friend, the clergyman John Fisher, not forgetting to mention the bathing-women to whose mercy the bathers committed themselves. Brighton, Constable wrote, was 'the receptacle of the fashion and off-scouring of London. The magnificence of the sea and its everlasting voice is drowned in the din and lost in the tumult of stage coaches, gigs, "flys" etc. – and the beach is only Piccadilly by the seaside. Ladies dressed and *undressed* – gentlemen in morning gowns and slippers on, or without them altogether about *knee deep* in the breakers – footmen – children – nursery maids, dogs, boys, fishermen – preventive service men (with hangers and pistols), rotten fish and those hideous amphibious animals the old bathing-women, whose language both in oaths and voice resembles men – all are mixed up together in endless and indecent confusion.'

Sea-bathing was losing, or had lost, its medical excuse. It was in part a parade. A lithograph of 1848 shows a new kind of women's bathing dress, almost exactly like a contemporaneous gown, with voluminous skirts, wide sleeves and (strangely enough) the fashionable off-the-shoulder décolletage. When wet it must have been extremely heavy and hampering. Men, on the other hand, when they did take to maritime concealment, adopted at first rather sensible small striped trunks.

By the middle seventies women's bathing cos-

tume had become stereotyped into a knee-length dress, shorter but very little simpler than an ordinary dress of the period, with no more décolletage, but with slightly shorter sleeves. It revealed underneath trousers which reached to mid-calf and were elaborately trimmed and braided. Again such costumes would have been clammy and extremely hampering to an energetic swimmer, but they were hardly expected to be immersed at all. A strange feature of the last quarter of the nineteenth century was the practice of wearing a corset under the bathing costume. It seemed impossible to dispense with the fashionable tight waist even in the water, and 'rustless' corsets were specially designed for the purpose. Human perversity could hardly go further.

Bathing costumes were no less a combination of the fashionable and the 'proper' in the early years of the present century. It was even thought necessary to wear stockings, either black or white. At this period it became the thing for professional beauties and musical-comedy actresses to have themselves photographed in bathing costumes, for the illustrated papers; they posed in front of the studio waves, in dresses which might have been the ordinary summer dresses of the day, though they were a little shorter.

We see, of course, a constant tendency to follow the fashion of the hour. In 1919, for instance, the over-tunic of the bathing dress was short and wide, as in the prevailing mode, and high-laced boots were worn. Bathing caps were now introduced, but they were not yet made of rubber and were obviously not meant to be wetted.

In 1920 the over-skirt showed the wide pannier effect of contemporary evening dresses, and in 1925 the shapelessness of the gowns of the period was hideously reflected in the tubular bathing costumes, which were still, by modern standards, extremely ample; in fact, in the nineteen-twenties the ridiculous position was reached that bathing costumes were almost more 'proper' than ordinary dresses.

It was not sea-bathing but sun-bathing and swimming in earnest which brought about the real revolution in clothes worn on the beach. In 1930 women adorned themselves in the first backless bathing costumes, although these had no less back than the evening dresses of the time. Then came the 'two-piece', not in the sense of the

Edwardian outfit of overlapping trousers and skirt, but in the sense of 'pants and brassiere' with a gap between. The gap between has continued to get wider and wider, until within recent years both pants and brassiere have shrunk to exiguous proportions. There has recently been a reaction against the 'bikini', but it continues to be worn at least in the South of France and in the more up-to-date resorts in England. It is frowned on by the Catholic authorities in Spain and Portugal, and even in Italy.

As for men, they have now reverted to the early Victorian trunks, after having been compelled for years (sometimes by law) to put up with the so-called 'University' costume, covering the torso. Some Scandinavian bathing establishments allow both sexes to bathe without any costume at all – probably because the old medieval tradition of the bath-house had continued in the North. It would seem to be the logical conclusion, at least for those who have perfect figures, but it is unlikely to be adopted in England or America in any foreseeable future.

ILLUSTRATION: Page 365.

Beds and bedclothes

BEDS and **BEDCLOTHES**, in one form or another, must always have been required. The human being spends about a third of his entire life in sleep. The body loses heat during sleep, and nights are chilly even in hot climates. Presumably the earliest bedclothes were animal pelts; and, after man had advanced to the pastoral stage, the whole fleeces of sheep.

The bare ground is uncomfortable to lie on. Rushes, reeds, small branches and springy plants such as heather and Lady's Bedstraw (*Galium verum*) added comfort to the night. Any modern camper knows that quite a comfortable bed can be made of heather or the fronds of bracken. The Virgin, according to a medieval legend of northern Europe, gave birth to Christ lying on a bed of bracken and Lady's Bedstraw. With the ad-

vance to farming and cereal crops, straw became an obvious material to lie on; from this it was only a step to enclose the straw in a bag and so to make the palliasse or straw mattress still used by troops. Vermin were a problem, however, and delayed the universality of permanent mattresses made of horsehair etc. In the Middle Ages and later the bedstraw in the bag was often straw or some other dry plant which could easily be emptied out, burnt and replaced. So with a double meaning, Chaucer in the fourteenth century exclaimed over the faithless young wife of the old husband 'O perilous fyr, that in the bedstraw bredeth'.

Modern 'divan-beds' obscure the distinction which long existed between bed and bedstead, the frame which upholds the bed.

Prehistoric bedsteads are visible in the neolithic village excavated from the sand at Skara Brae in the Orkneys. There in each of the houses or huts, which were some twenty by thirteen feet square, a bed-box of slabs of stone stands upon either side of the hearth, the bed on the right as one enters, always larger than the bed on the left. The archaeologist who excavated Skara Brae suggests that the right-hand bed was the man's, the left the woman's; and for shape he has compared them with the fixed plank beds used by the peasants of Norway. In Irish cottages a built-in wooden bed-box often stands in the living-room on one side of the hearth. In early times it was found desirable to raise the bed (i.e. the soft material in its bag) a few inches above the ground, partly, no doubt, in order to avoid the draughts which whistled through primitive door-fittings. In the Middle Ages beds were supported on a wooden framework with stout cords threaded diagonally across it. Over this was usually laid a plaited rush mat, and then the bed itself. By the fourteenth century at least feathers very commonly replaced the straw. Flocks of geese were kept on every common, so that there was little difficulty in obtaining the soft, fluffy, elastic down, which indeed retained its popularity until the invention of spring mattresses in our own day. The Wardrobe Accounts for Edward I of England in 1299–1300 mention '28 pieces of dimity to make a feather bed for the Queen and cushions for her couch. Two pieces of fustian, and 40 ells of dyed linen, to cover the said bed within and without and two pieces of silk cloth to cover the said cushions.'

Writing nearly a hundred years later, the Goodman of Paris, describing the preparation of a bridal bed, remarks: 'And note that if the bed be covered with cloth, there is needed a fur coverlet of half vair; but if it is covered with serge, embroidery, or counterpane of sendal, not so'. Vair was the fur of the grey squirrel; sendal or cendal a woven silk. Such luxuries were only for royal personages or great nobles; but the growing prosperity of the merchants in the late Middle Ages gradually brought them into more general use.

Bedding appears as an important item in household inventories and wills. Bed curtains, valances and counterpanes were often elaborately embroidered, and were so highly valued that they were handed down as heirlooms. Sheets were in general use, among the prosperous classes, from quite an early date, and so were pillow-cases, or pillow-beres as they were called in the fifteenth century. Both sheet and pillow-cases were made of homespun linen which varied in quality and fineness according to the means of the owner. Very coarse linen was known as 'towen', and poor people, who could not afford even that, had to be content with a material woven from hemp, which had the uncomfortable name of 'harden'.

The inventories say strangely little about blankets. A white or undyed woollen stuff known as 'blanket' (from the Old French blankete, meaning 'white cloth') was woven at Witney, an English centre of the blanket industry, five hundred years ago as it is today. It was used for clothing, especially for cloaks. The earliest references to blankets as bed-coverings occur in the fourteenth century. It is probable that fur rugs continued to be used.

The built-in box-bed, so frequently seen on the Continent, remained more popular there than in England. The four-poster with curtains enclosing the bed as a kind of tent was the usual English pattern until the end of the eighteenth century. Celia Fiennes describes in her Journal for the year 1696 a four-poster of this type which she saw at Windsor Castle: 'Green velvet strip'd down very thick with gold orrice lace of my hands breadth, and round the bottom three such orrices and gold fring all round it and gold tassells, so

was the cornish [cornice]; the inside was the same; at the head-piece was like curtains fringed round with gold and tyed back with gold strings and tassells as it were tyed back, and so hung down in the middle where was the Crown and Cypher embroyder'd.'

Beds have never been more grandiose than they were in the closing years of the seventeenth century. Modern beds make a very poor show beside them. The spring bed is now universal, and the feather bed now rests on top of us in the form of an eiderdown, properly made from the down which the eider of northern latitudes plucks from itself for its own nest. Sheets, too, are generally plain and the only decoration that remains is probably an 'old-fashioned patchwork quilt', or a gay coverlet. (See also *Night-clothes*.)

ILLUSTRATION: Page 125.

Hives and honey

BEEHIVES and beekeeping are of great antiquity, and the products of the bee were of an importance in earlier economies that we would hardly realize.

Prehistoric man was well acquainted with wild bees and honey, which one would infer even if there were not the direct evidence of a fascinating Late Palaeolithic (or Mesolithic?) drawing in red pigment in the Cave of the Spider, near Bicorp, in eastern Spain. Two honey-collectors hang by what appear to be creepers or possibly a ladder of creepers or rope. One carries a vessel slung over his back, the other, a woman, investigates the bees' nest with her right arm, while she holds a container for the comb in her left hand. A few bees are flying around; but she seems to be quietening the bees with smoke. In Ceylon the primitive Veddas collect honey in much the same way, going down over precipices on cane ladders, smoking the bees into quiescence and carrying down the comb in skin containers.

Probably the semi-domestication of bees was an element of that great neolithic revolution in the Near East which established and settled man as a farmer. Late in the Bronze Age which followed, bronze castings were already made by the *cire perdue* or wax-losing method, which involves coating a clay model with wax, on which the details are completed, and then coating the wax in turn with clay to form a mould; the interior wax is then melted and 'lost' through holes

Fig. 4. Collecting honey. Cave painting, Bicorp.

left in the outer covering of clay. If the wax (as archaeology infers) was beeswax, one may think that the bronze-smiths would hardly have relied upon a supply from wild bees alone.

Honey was of great importance in Sumerian and Egyptian culture; and bees were certainly kept by the Egyptians in the third millennium B.C. A relief on the fifth dynasty Temple of the Sun at Abusir shows hives in a row among trees and the preparation of the honey. Hittite beekeeping is evident from the Hittite law code of

c. 1500 B.C., which lays down a fine of five shekels of silver for stealing 'bees in a swarm'.

For the beekeeping of the Greeks and Romans there is plenty of evidence. Varro in the first century B.C. recommends willow hives, or hives of wood and of bark, or hives from hollow trees or the hollow stems of the Giant Fennel. Columella in *De re rustica* repeats him in the first century A.D., though he adds that the best hives, cool in summer and warm in winter, are made of cork. He was against pottery hives, as being too hot in summer and too cold in winter. Pottery hives pierced with a hole at the end are still used by Palestinian Arabs; and similar hives seem to have been used in the British Iron Age. When Casterley Camp, in Wiltshire, was excavated, brown jars were unearthed, drilled with holes, after the firing, at the end or the sides. The jars with the side holes may have been smokers, such as are still used in Greece, for example on Mount Hymettus. Iron Age end-holed jars are not uncommon. Fennel hives, as mentioned by Varro and Columella, are still made.

In some areas beekeeping may have begun actually in standing trees. In Polesye in Eastern Europe peasants in the last century kept their bees in hollow standing trunks. A later development would have been to cut sections from a hollow tree; finally building up vertical 'tree hives' in cylindrical shapes of bark, board or wickerwork. Some horizontally-laid pot hives may have originated in the wild bees' nest reached horizontally along a rock crevice.

The Skep (the word meaning no more than basket) developed from the woven willow hive mentioned by Varro and Columella. The older skeps are wickerwork, but straw skeps, however primitive by modern standards of agriculture, had the advantages of being light and easy to handle, easy to make, and relatively warm for the bees. Bruegel's strange and powerful pencil drawing of sixteenth-century beemasters in action shows the straw skeps and a long thatched protection which kept off the rain. The carefully protected beemasters are in the act of moving the hives to a better ground for another flower crop.

'My son, eat thou honey, because it is good', says Proverbs xxiv. 13, and men have wanted both honey and beeswax for a score of purposes.

Sweet, golden and pleasant smelling, honey was sacred; it was 'good' medicinally, and was recommended in the ancient civilizations by writers as various as the great Indian doctor Suśruta in the sixth century B.C. and Dioscorides in the first century A.D. It was, and is, an ingredient in several intoxicating drinks, from mead (*mádhu* is Sanskrit for 'honey') to the Scottish whisky liqueur, drambuie. It was essential in toothpastes; and it satisfied the sweet tooth of a world which had little knowledge of sugar. In the Greco-Roman world sugar from the East was certainly known in the first century of our era; the use of it increased in the Middle Ages, but did not spread widely in Europe till the eighteenth century, or very widely until the nineteenth century development of sugar from beet. So honey was supreme through thousands of years – for the living and the dead. It was used in embalming. The corpse of Alexander the Great was said to have been covered sweetly in honey. In Abyssinia living bodies have been rolled in honey in a neat form of execution, since the human honey-pillar was then exposed to ants.

As for the wax, uses for that were also innumerable from the preparation of mummies and making the surface of writing tablets to illumination by beeswax candles, still the proper illuminant of Christian altars.

Bees, beemasters and beehives are not unnaturally connected by many customs and beliefs. The bees are still told of their keeper's death. In some countries the hives are moved when he dies. In Brittany a black ribbon is tied to the hive. Breton hives are, or were, decorated with a red ribbon when the beemaster has a son or when the son marries. German skeps in Saxony were sometimes adorned with human faces to avert disease, theft and witchcraft. Bees, in fact, were creatures of wisdom and power. Man and bee were in partnership, an old state which scientific man has wished to change to domination of bee by man.

Thus the modern hive, of the age of closer biological observation and enquiry, has changed. One pioneer was John Gedde, who lived near Falkland, in Fifeshire (Scotland). In 1765 he placed a small straw ring or 'eke' under the hive to give the bees more room. That led eventually to separate spaces for the brood and for the

honey. Towards the end of the eighteenth century the blind François Huber, of Geneva, assisted by a faithful friend and servant, devised hinged frames, which made it possible to survey the interior economy of the bees' life. Old mysteries were now resolved, and a last blow was given to the ancient fallacy of 'spontaneous generation', according to which bees developed from dirt and carrion: 'Out of the strong came forth sweetness', said Samson, after he had slain the young lion that roared against him and had found, according to Judges xiv. 8, 14, 'a swarm of bees and honey in the carcase of the lion'.

In 1851 L.L.Langstroth in the United States discovered the bee-space, on which the modern movable frame hive depends. He observed that if a small space was left between the framed combs and the walls of the hive, the bees would leave it clear, not attempting to bridge the gap with wax. The movable frame meant that bee colonies could now be controlled to a new degree. It was one of the chief advances in the beemaster's ancient craft.

In 1915 it was discovered by K. von Frisch that bees distinguished between colours; since then the entrances to hives standing in a row have frequently been painted in different colours so that bees can find their own colony with greater ease and speed.

ILLUSTRATION: Page 270.

The evolving bicycle

BICYCLES go back to the hobby horse, patented by Baron Drais von Sauerbronn in 1818. This was a wooden backbone with two wheels, of which the rear wheel was fixed and the front carried a pivoted fork. Dennis Johnson, a coachmaker of Long Acre, introduced it into London in the same year and founded a school for tuition in riding 'pedestrian curricles'. The rider pushed himself along by a striding action in which each foot in turn gave a shove-off from the road surface; the pivoted front wheel enabled him both to maintain balance and change direction. He coasted down hills, but when he climbed uphill he heaved the machine, weighing about fifty pounds, on to his shoulder.

No driving mechanism was added until 1839, when Kirkpatrick Macmillan fitted cranks to drive the rear wheel by means of a to-and-fro motion of pedals. Treadles to drive the front wheel were a feature of the two-wheeled velocipede of 1850 – 'Straddle a saddle, then paddle and skedaddle'. The velocipede sold at £10 14s. which was well outside the reach of the skilled fitter receiving £89 per annum, to say nothing of the agricultural worker at £28 or the female domestic servant at £8 10s.

The original 'boneshaker' bicycles were made in 1865 by E. Michaux, of Paris. The front wheel, larger than the rear wheel, was driven by cranks mounted directly on its axle. Pierre Lallement, the designer, patented his invention in the United States in 1866. The wheels, of wood, had iron tyres. The wire-spoked wheel was first introduced by W. F. Reynolds and J. A. Mays in their 'Phantom' bicycle of 1869, in which the wires were held in tension between the hub and the wooden rim of a wheel, which was provided with a solid rubber tyre. In James Starley's 'Ariel' bicycle of 1870 there was provision for tightening the wire spokes, and weight was reduced by making wheels and frame entirely of iron. The front wheels were gradually enlarged to obtain increased speed without increasing pedalling speeds. Tubular frames were then introduced, and by 1884 a 'Rudge' ordinary bicycle for racing weighed only twenty-one-and-a-half pounds, although the front wheel had a diameter of fifty-eight inches (the diameter of the rear wheel was only sixteen-and-a-quarter inches). Saddles, in these 'penny-farthing' machines, were brought as near the steering column as possible. The result was that sudden braking or meeting an obstacle might easily tip the rider on to his head. So it is no wonder that the 'penny farthing' appealed mostly to the young and that there arose a demand for more sedate machines to serve the older portion of the cycling population, which grew apace in communities ill-served by public transport and unable to afford carriage and horses.

Cycles with a chain-drive through gearing (but still on the front wheel) and with rearward fixed saddles were the rule from 1878 for ten years or more. In these 'Kangaroo' cycles of 1878, with

Fig. 5. Kangaroo bicycle, 1878.

which, in 1884, a speed record of 100 road miles in seven hours seven minutes eleven seconds was put up, the front wheels were only three feet in diameter. The first rear chain-drive 'safety' bicycle was made in 1873–1874 by Harry Lawson, but was not produced commercially until 1879, when it was called the 'Bicyclette'. In 1888 the rubber pneumatic tyre was introduced by J. B. Dunlop.

Tricycles, for ladies and the elderly or staid, were introduced in 1876. The familiar but heavy 'drop-frame' design of bicycle for ladies goes back to 1884; although it was ten years or so before women began to appreciate the effectiveness of the design. A similar dropped frame had actually been introduced for the hobby horse in 1819, to make it suitable for women, but even male riders had been subjected to ridicule and women did not dare to venture out on these machines, which in any case weighed sixty-six pounds.

Variable-speed gears, to make hill-climbing easier, came in 1889. They were at first two-speed only, but in the early years of the twentieth century the three-speed gear was so improved that it found greater favour. The converse of the variable-speed gear was the free-wheel clutch to conserve the rider's energy when cycling downhill, a feature devised by Linley and Biggs in 1894. Few basic improvements have been made in the last half-century.

ILLUSTRATION: Page 74.

Swift, silent, deadly

The **BLOW-GUN** of South-east Asia and South America is a weapon specially suited to short-range silent hunting of birds and small game in close forest. It has also, though unexpectedly, been among the weapons of medieval Europe.

In Malaya forest tribes construct blow-guns of bamboo – sections of a slender bamboo inside a casing of a stouter bamboo the knots of which have been bored out. Light darts about nine inches long are fashioned from the midrib of palm fronds, scraped very thin and notched near the end so that the point breaks off in a wound. When the gun is loaded, a wad of fluffy fibres from the leaf base of palms is packed round the base of the dart to ensure a tight fit. Darts are treated with *ipoh* poison from the coagulated sap of the upas tree, *Antiaris toxicaria,* and they can be shot accurately up to 100 feet. Similar blow-guns are known in Japan, Celebes, Assam and in South India, where it is used for fishing. Possibly there is some relationship between such blow-guns and the early bamboo guns and firearms of China.

Shadow-play figures show that the blow-gun was employed as a weapon of war in ancient Java, as it is today in Borneo. The blow-pipe or *sumpitan* of the tribes of the interior of Borneo is a more finely finished weapon, made not of bamboo, but of the hard, straight-grained wood of the *jagang* tree. A section about eight feet long is adzed more or less to a cylinder, with a diameter of three or four inches. A platform is then erected about seven feet above the ground, and the piece of wood set upright, its lower end resting on the ground, and its upper end projecting through the platform. It is then firmly lashed. Next, the artisan, standing on the platform, begins boring a hole through the length of the beam with a straight iron rod about nine feet long, the end of which is sharpened to a chisel-edge. This cutting rod slides between firmly fixed forked twigs, the operator pounding and twisting it in the hole, while a helper washes out the chips with water. A very slight curvature is given to the bore, to counteract the bend due to the weight of the tube and the spear-blade, which is afterwards lashed

on in bayonet-fashion. The gun is trimmed down, the bore is smoothed and a small wooden sight fitted at the muzzle end. The darts are prepared and poisoned as in Malaya, except that they are padded at the base with small cylinders of pith, which have been shaved down to the diameter of the bore.

The tribes of Guiana and the Upper Orinoco make their blow-pipes from hollow canes and carry them sometimes in drilled palm-stems. In the Upper Amazon country, however, the pipe is made by splitting a length of palm-wood, grooving each half separately, and then fitting and binding them together. The bore, about $\frac{1}{4}$ inch in diameter, is polished by pulling through it strings coated with gum and sand. A mouthpiece of vegetable ivory is fitted to one end, and near it is fixed a small piece of bone to serve as a sight. The outside of the tube is coated with gum or wax.

Many more tribes of the Amazon country use the blow-gun now than in the sixteenth century, the weapon having spread along with the secret of preparing *curare,* the poison for the darts. This poison consists of a number of ingredients, of which the sap of the climber *Strychnos toxifera* is the most important. It is still only made by a few tribes, who barter it to their neighbours. Herdsmen in Ecuador drive their cattle with clay pellets shot from a blow-gun. A similar device was used as a toy in Mexico and by the Iroquois of North America.

The earliest known evidence of the use of the blow-gun in Europe is a French miniature of about 1475, which, among other methods of hunting, shows a boy aiming a blow-gun at a bird in a tree. This occurs as an illustration in a manuscript copy of Pietro de Crescenzi's *Opus ruralium commodorum* (*i.e.* Treatise on Rural Economy). Clearly this weapon could not have been inspired from the New World, and if it was not an independent invention, the idea, like that of the mariner's compass (see *Magnet*), may have been brought to Europe by Arab merchants. The trade cards of certain eighteenth-century English manufacturers of fishing tackle advertise 'trunks', which appear to have been a kind of blow-pipe for shooting darts or pellets. Children, it may be mentioned, have long made toy blow-pipes out of dry hollow stems of several umbellifers such as

Wild Angelica (*Angelica sylvestris*) and Hog-weed, known in Scotland as Ait-skeiters (*i.e.* 'oat-shooters', oats having been the ammunition) and Bear-skeiters.

In Italy the blow-gun was called *cerbottana*, in France *sarbacane*, in Germany *blasrohr*. Birds were hunted in the last century with blow-guns built up of joined sections. But the European blow-gun only survives now as the toy 'skeiter' and the pea-shooter. (See also *Gun, Gunpowder, Bow and Arrow*.)

ILLUSTRATION: Page 259.

The earliest boats

BOATS of many elaborate types can be made even without metal tools, and as ancient boats recovered from the mud of river estuaries make clear, boat-building is one of the oldest crafts.

Man had first to solve the problem of crossing rivers before tackling the open sea; his solution may be preserved in the widespread use today of rafts and floats of various kinds. One of these is the inflated animal skin, possibly suggested by the skin water-container still to be observed in eastern countries. In Mesopotamia, skin floats were part of military equipment as early as the ninth century B.C., if not earlier. On Assyrian stone reliefs soldiers are shown retreating hastily across a river, each one clasping in his left arm a balloon-like skin; he grips the opening between his teeth and leaves his right arm and his legs free for swimming. Similar floats have been anciently used in China, India and Europe, and are still used in the Near East and North Africa. Indeed, they survive in our own civilization in the water-wings of the swimming-lesson.

The raft may obviously have begun with the drifting log. Coastal aborigines in northern Australia still use logs as floats, instead of boats, swimming beside them. Evolutionary steps would now be sitting astride the log, and then binding several logs together into a floating platform. Rafts may also have the additional support of skin floats for greater buoyancy, a very ancient

device again portrayed in Assyrian reliefs and surviving in the *kelek* of Armenia and Iraq, which is admirable for shooting rapids. The *kelek* may be ten to fifty feet square and may embrace in its construction as many as a thousand sheep and goat skins.

It was on rafts of this kind that massive stone figures were floated to the palaces of Assyrian kings in Iraq; three thousand years later the same craft have been used to transport such figures on the first stage of their journey to European museums.

When there was no timber to hand, peoples in widely separated parts of the world who lived around marshy lakes used reed as a material for boats. Thus Egyptians of 3000 B.C. made canoes out of bundles of papyrus. The nature of the materials affected the design; the deck was solid up to the top of the gunwales, the high prow and stern were linked by a taut rope to keep the canoe in shape and a bipod mast was used, resembling a capital A. Craft that sail today on Lake Tsana, in Abyssinia, have preserved the form of these ancient boats. A similar reed canoe or *balsa* has developed independently through similar circumstances around Lake Titicaca, high up on the Peruvian and Bolivian altiplano.

Early man hunted animals for their skins, from which it is presumed that he made himself clothes. But man the tailor could, with these same skins, become man the sailor. The *pelota*, common in South America, consists simply of a dried skin with the corners tied so as to form a bowl-like craft. Such a vessel could have been made at a very early stage of cultural development, and would easily develop into the coracle (though the earliest date which can be ascribed to the coracle on present evidence is about 8000 B.C.; in the estuary of the river Ancholme in Lincolnshire a crouched burial was found inside what was described as a 'basket'. This may have been a coracle, though unfortunately the relics were destroyed in the Second World War.)

The coracle in one form or another has been recorded in every continent with the exception of Africa and Australia, and may have spread from a homeland in Central Asia. Beginning simply as a dried skin, like the South American *pelota*, it would be improved sooner or later by adding an internal frame, to brace the skin against softening and collapse. Different types of framework in different regional adaptations of the coracle today are to be regarded as independent efforts to overcome the same difficulty.

Oval coracles, such as the Welsh still use for salmon-fishing on the Teifi above Cardigan (though they make them now of tarred canvas instead of skins, and incorporate in them pieces of packing case and motor tyre), may have been ancestral to more elaborate forms of skin craft, including the Irish curragh, shiny with mackerel scales, and the Eskimo *umiak*. The curragh is probably a coracle adapted for sea travel, though its normal boat-shape may owe something to the Viking longboat built of planks. The *umiak* is an open boat. The Eskimo hunter's *kayak*, which John White portrayed so well in the sixteenth century, is almost covered in so that it cannot be swamped in high seas. Both craft are made of skin stretched over a wooden frame, but whereas the *umiak* is thought to derive from the coracle, the *kayak* is likely to descend from another form of great antiquity, the bark canoe.

Even before man had metal tools, or tough stone axes for felling trees to convert into dugouts, he could probably have stripped bark off the trees for boat-building. Australian aborigines have crude tools for detaching the bark they require for their canoes, which, with the canoes of the Fuegians, may represent the most ancient form of boat, long improved upon elsewhere. They consist each of a long strip of bark, the open ends stuffed with clay. In other bark forms the ends are gradually gathered up; bark boats culminating in birch-bark canoes of the North American Indian, in which the bark is kept in shape by a wooden framework.

The Kutenai Indians of British Columbia use a curious form of bark canoe. This has pointed ends, which are in line with the bottom of the boat. Exactly similar ends are found on Siberian canoes, on the same latitude, but on the opposite side of the north Pacific. In both regions the canoes are used for river travel, and are propelled by the double paddle.

It is from this form of bark canoe that the *kayak*, also used with a double paddle, may have derived. Skin was employed in a region without trees, and the transformation of a river canoe into a sea-going craft explains the top covering.

Dugouts one might expect to be a very primitive form; they are thought, in fact, to descend from the bark canoe. Such archaeological evidence as there is gives some comfort to this theory, since very ancient dugouts have been recovered with traces of carved 'frames', in apparent imitation of the wooden frame of the bark canoe. Neolithic dugouts unearthed in Great Britain had mostly been hollowed from oak, the favourite boat timber of modern times. A pine dugout, which must have dated back to mesolithic times between 7000 and 5000 B.C., was found in the last century near Perth in Scotland. Wooden paddles of the same period, implying boats, are known from Schleswig-Holstein and Denmark.

Dugouts, still used in Africa, Burma, New Zealand, Indonesia, Oceania and North America, are now a stage towards the plank boat. A fine group of 'missing links' in the evolutionary sequence of the plank boat has been studied on Lake Victoria, in East Africa. Some dugouts on the lake have one plank attached to the gunwales to increase the height of the sides. Others have more planks added to them, the original tree-trunk shrinking bit by bit into the familiar keel.

A problem that faced the builders of the first plank boats, and indeed those pioneers who first attached planks to the dugout, was how to keep the planks rigid against the stresses of the waves. The answer was to leave projections or 'cleats' in the solid wood when the planks were shaped. U-shaped frames could then be inserted across the width of the boat and lashed to the cleats, thus holding the planks in position. The plank boats which now replaced the dugout were either clinker-built or carvel-built. In the ancient clinker-built craft the overlapping planks were lashed to a framework subsequently inserted. Such boats were being made at the beginning of the Early Iron Age, about 500–400 B.C. The famous Viking ships of a later date were also clinker-built, a type of construction typical of northern waters. In the south, the plank descendants of the dugout were carvel-built – that is, the planks, instead of overlapping, were fixed flush to a frame. This was the method used by the Greeks and the Romans, and by the Phoenicians before them. Ancient carvel-built craft have been found in the north as well, notably two Late

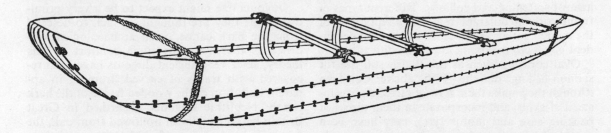

Fig. 6. Reconstructed boat of Iron Age, from North Ferriby, on the Humber.

Bronze Age boats from under the tidal mud at North Ferriby, in Yorkshire, on the Humber estuary west of Hull. The planks were skilfully sewn to each other with strong pliable lengths of yew.

Our modern ships show no basic change of construction. Metal plates have been substituted for wooden planks, engines for oars, paddles and sails; but we have done no more than develop logically step by step a constructional technique worked out thousands of years ago. (See also *Wheel.*)

ILLUSTRATION: Plate 3.

Roll to codex, and printed book

The **BOOK** as a thing that we see on our shelves does not go back beyond the fifteenth century A.D. But if by 'book' we mean a written literary production, then it goes back to ancient Mesopotamia, and we should have to credit the Sumerians with its invention.

The Sumerians conquered Mesopotamia before the middle of the fourth millennium B.C. They and the peoples of the surrounding regions in the Near East set down their considerable literature (epics, and magical, religious, historical, scientific, legal and economic texts) on clay tablets. If these can be called books, then the earliest preserved example of a book is an archaic cylinder found at Nippur and assigned to about 2400 B.C. Another tablet from the same

site, assigned to the early second millennium B.C. is the earliest example of a grammatical text; to this same period belongs a Nippur tablet containing the titles of sixty-two Sumerian literary productions – which might be called the earliest example of a book-catalogue.

As ancient Mesopotamia may be considered the cradle of the book in the connotation of literary product, so ancient Egypt may be considered the cradle of the book on perishable material, which is the direct ancestor of our book, as an intellectual instrument of wide circulation. Papyrus (see under *Paper*) was Egypt's contribution – the earliest preserved papyrus (without inscription) seeming to go back to the fourth millennium B.C. The earliest hieratic papyri to survive may be dated c. 2450 B.C. Some papyri attributed to c. 2000 B.C. are copies, more or less accurate, of treatises supposed to have been compiled before or about 2500 B.C.

The Egyptians had astronomical, mathematical and medical texts to record, as well as a rich literature of myths, tales, short stories, ballads and love-songs; and they used the roll form of book, the papyrus which they handed on to the Greeks and Romans, who continued the use of it themselves until the fourth century A.D. The roll simply consists of sheets glued together or sewn together by strings, fastened to a wooden rod, so that it can be rolled from one end to the other. The same kind of rod (called *omphalos* in Greek and *umbilicus* in Latin, the 'navel') we still use for rolled maps kept on shelves. Hebrew ritual Bible scrolls have two rods, at the beginning and the end of the roll.

To read a roll-book of this kind, one took the

rod in one's right hand, opened the roll with the left hand, and began with the first column. The columns stood at right angles to the long margins of the roll. The amount of text revealed between left hand and right hand was thus not greatly different to the double spread of a modern book, though the usual width of rolls for works of literature was ten inches; rather longer than the height of page in the ordinary modern octavo volume – to use a word enduring from this era of the roll-book, the Latin word *volvere*, to roll, giving *volumen*, which was the roll, and our 'volume'.

As one went forward, one rolled up with the left hand the portion already perused, and unrolled new columns with the right. Coming to the end at last, there was the tiresome business of re-rolling the book for the next reader, from right to left.

As for length, there are several Egyptian liturgical rolls of more than fifty feet; a few exceed even 100 feet. The Greenfield Papyrus in the British Museum is 123 feet long, and the great Harris papyrus in the same museum, 133 feet long. The length of Greek rolls varies from fourteen to thirty-five feet, though some appear to have been about fifty feet.

This was an inconvenient method for storage and still more for consultation – especially when using such a work as the Bible (Greek *biblia*, 'rolls', from *biblos*, the Greek word for papyrus). There was no easy way to refer to particular passages; finding a given section or particular phrase in the larger rolls might mean unrolling them to the end. Hence the codex form of book – the book with leaves to be turned over, in shape of the three-leaved wooden writing tablets (*codex*) from which it takes its name.

How early the codex form was employed it is impossible to say. It may go back to the first century B.C., and it was certainly in use among Christians from the early part of the second century A.D. If the codex was not actually a Christian invention, it was most promptly taken up by the early Christian community, and so brought into prominence. Papyrus was used, and did not go wholly out of use for some centuries, though succeeded by the more durable parchment or vellum.

From the third to the sixth centuries A.D.

papyrus roll and more rarely papyrus codex, vellum codex and (though very seldom) parchment roll or vellum roll, were all in use as forms of book.

By the fourth century papyrus roll was succeeded by parchment codex as the main form: the book had recognizably become the book we know, and was differently manufactured, with paper in place of the old expensive page materials and by means of the printing press. Thus before the European development in the fifteenth century of printing with movable type, the form and proportions of the book and the basic elements of our reading process had been established. Europe's first dated and signed printed volume is the psalter printed by Fust and Schöffer in 1457, a year or two years later than the completion of Gutenberg's forty-two-line Bible. By 1490 there were a hundred printers in Venice alone; by the end of the century 40,000 different books had been printed in Europe. England was then on the margin. The new book technique was slow in crossing the Channel. The first dated English-printed book, which Caxton issued from his press at Westminster, bears the date of 11 November 1477. (See also *Printing, Paper, Ink*.)

ILLUSTRATION: Page 115.

Bow and arrow

The **BOW AND ARROW** must have been one of man's earliest inventions, since the evidence for the combination of the two goes back 15,000 years to the Old Stone Age. The perishable wooden parts and the bow-strings of ancient bows are rarely found, surviving only in special circumstances, in a completely dry place, such as an Egyptian tomb, or in a very wet one, such as a swamp. But one can always infer the existence of bows from the flint arrowheads which survive in any conditions; the evidence for the bow's extreme antiquity, palaeolithic paintings in the caves of France and northern Spain appear to show arrows, while palaeolithic paintings in eastern Spain show bowmen in action.

The most ancient of man's weapons may have been the wooden spear, with its tip hardened in the fire. But in palaeolithic levels small triangular

Fig. 7. Hunting with bow and arrow, rock painting, Navazo, Albaracin.

points are found which were presumably hafted as arrowheads, since they are too small to have made effective spearheads. We may surmise that the point was inserted in a split shaft and bound tightly into place with animal sinews. At the lower end of these palaeolithic arrowheads there is a narrow tonguelike projection, or 'tang', which would have been no wider than the shaft of the arrow. In a bog at Stellmoor in north Germany about a hundred pinewood arrow shafts have been found, dating from the end of the Old Stone Age. Some of them had been thrown away as useless, since they retain the broken tang of the arrowhead inside the split shaft.

Arrow-making tools of this early date have also been found – flints with a sharp concave edge which have been termed 'spokeshaves', since they could have been used for smoothing the arrow shafts (or spear shafts, as well, it must be admitted), and pieces of grooved rock for rubbing the shafts to straighten them and smooth them.

In the Upper Palaeolithic art of the limestone caves, food animals are portrayed, and the careful workmanship of the artists is in direct contrast with disfiguring shafts scratched across many of the paintings, as though to 'kill' the animals by sympathetic magic (by the same principle, pins were stuck into a wax figure). Some of these shafts are painted on the walls, as if aimed at the animals, and feathers, or what appear to be feathers, at the end of them, in some cases, suggest that

they were arrows. In the rock-shelters of eastern Spain, paintings of a different style have been found, representing not single animals, but lively incidents, in several of which the hunters are indeed using bows – conclusive evidence of the bow's palaeolithic antiquity.

With the end of the Ice Age, about 8000 B.C. mesolithic cultures came into being in northern Europe, depending on the new conditions. The climate became gradually warmer, forest trees spread from the south into lands free of ice and snow, and forests took the place of tundra. This had its effect on the creatures which had been hunted by palaeolithic man. The reindeer which had given him meat and material (bone, horn, etc.) retreated north after its retreating vegetable food, and different beasts – e.g. deer, pig, wild oxen – moved into northern Europe, giving mesolithic man new targets for his arrows. The mesolithic peoples fished, gathered shell-fish on the coast and went fowling in the swamps which covered what is now the bed of the North Sea; but they were also forest huntsmen who have left evidence of their activities and their artillery. In their seasonal wanderings they would live for a few months on floors of bark and twigs: these habitation floors have been found in bogs and in damp ground on the coasts of the North Sea and the Baltic, and the dampness has preserved normally perishable parts of wood, bark and even fungi and leaves. From a bog at Holmegaard in Denmark mesolithic bows have been recovered, the most ancient bows we have, five feet long and made of elm wood. At each end a notch had been cut for the bow-string, and the centre had been shaped into a handgrip. At Holmegaard, too, an arrow was discovered with the flint point still bound in position. This arrowhead was trapezoid in shape, a form widespread in the ancient world. Tomb paintings show that it was used for hunting in Egypt. The business end was not a point, but a razor edge.

Another type of mesolithic arrow had a number of tiny flints or microliths inserted in slots at the end of the wooden shaft, which was pointed. These microliths, with a sharp cutting edge and rounded, blunted back, acted as tiny barbs; they would have caused the stricken animal to lose blood, so that it could be run down by the hunter. The barbs may also have been poisoned. At some mesolithic sites they have been found in groups in the ashes of fires, as if they had been thrown away with a lump of meat contaminated by the poison (possibly the arrow poison was derived from species of aconite, such as the deadly Monkshood familiar in gardens). In Denmark, too, curious blunt-headed arrows have been found, identical with arrows which Eskimos and other northern hunters use today to stun birds and small fur-bearing animals. Where furs were worn for clothing, it was important not to spoil the pelt.

The bow and arrow has spread over all the world (Australia excepted; Australian aborigines remained faithful to the spear), so that many different varieties have been evolved, down to the crossbow. The simple, one-piece 'self' bow was the type used in mesolithic Denmark, so that it has a respectable antiquity of some 10,000 years at the very least. The famous longbow used by the English in the Middle Ages was of this type, six feet from end to end, made of imported yew wood, and last used as a regular armament in war in the reign of Elizabeth I.

Another widespread type is the 'composite' bow, which originated probably in Central Asia. In this the bow-stave is made not of a single piece of wood, like the stave of the self bow, but from a strip of wood or horn built up with sinew. It is the weapon of peoples living in a treeless region. Thus the Eskimo bow-stave may be fundamentally a piece of driftwood; this is backed with a layer of sinew, which in turn is closely bound to the wood with more sinew, to provide the 'spring'. Composite bows are also used by tribes who live in wooded lands but have no tree, such as the yew, the elm or the wych-elm, with wood pliant enough for the stave. The composite bow was the weapon of the Near East in ancient historical times. Such a bow was found in Tutankhamen's tomb, dated to the fourteenth century B.C. In the first half of the last millennium B.C. the Assyrians stormed cities with long-range archers armed with the composite bow, recording these events in striking bas-reliefs. In Classical times it was the Parthians whose wheeling, mounted archers annihilated the legions of Crassus with composite bows.

On the self bows the notches for the bow-string may be seen on the *outside* of the curved stave. Composite bows are normally bent backwards, so that the notch will appear to be on the *inside* of the stave when the bow is unstrung. The extra power gained by this reversal is shown by the range, which is more than twice the three hundred yards of the English longbow. In ancient representations of archers the composite bow can always be distinguished by the double curve of the stave. The Greek bows described in detail by Homer must have been of the composite type – in fact, a Cupid's bow. The crossbow, an improved and more efficient form with trigger release and winding gear was used by the Romans and was described by Heron of Alexandria (between A.D. 62 and A.D. 150) in his *Belopoiica*, a treatise on engines of war. It was re-introduced early in the Middle Ages. The Chinese used the curious magazine crossbow in their war against Japan in 1894–1895. In England bow and arrow have left behind them the craft surnames of Bowyer and Fletcher (arrow-maker), and the fossil metaphor of 'drawing the longbow' for telling stories.

ILLUSTRATION: Plate 7.

Before the Iron Age

BRONZE today denotes a whole series of copper-tin alloys, each of which is made for some special tool, implement or purpose. The word is even used, quite wrongly, for alloys of copper and other metals than tin.

Historically, bronze is a most important metal. The Bronze Age of the archaeologists was the first phase of true metallurgy. Man had known metals well before he practised metallurgy. Certain metals, such as gold, silver, iron and copper, occur as such in nature. These native metals are often found in brooks or on the banks of rivers in the form of nuggets and pebbles, but sometimes very large pieces turn up. Boulders of native copper weighing several tons are known to occur along the banks of the North American lakes, and the Indians had chipped off pieces long before the advent of the white man.

However, prehistoric man (and this holds true for many primitive tribes even to the present day) did not practise metallurgy – that is, he did not know how to melt, cast and work such metals. He regarded these nuggets as coloured stones to be cut, ground and polished like precious stones, and he fashioned them into small amulets and beads which he treasured.

Then prehistoric man discovered an important fact – that the native metal liquefied with heat. He found that a stream of molten metal poured into a depression in sand or a cavity made in a stone would take its shape and retain it after cooling and solidifying. Having hit upon the true nature of metals, he could now melt them and cast them. About the same time he discovered another most important fact. If some of the precious stones which he had treasured for centuries, such as malachite and lapis lazuli, were heated with charcoal, they would yield a metal identical with the most common native metal. To put it in modern scientific terms, he discovered that some of these stones were copper compounds or copper ores, which when reduced with charcoal (*i.e.* carbon) would yield copper. These two discoveries made him a true metallurgist who began to make use of the basic properties of metals to shape instruments and tools, which were often better than the tools he had always shaped from wood, bone or horn. Man became master of a new technique which allowed him to create new shapes and forms of tools.

These discoveries took place somewhere about 3500 B.C. and probably in Eastern Persia and Afghanistan. Soon the art was brought to the Armenian and Caucasian mountain ranges, whence it spread to Egypt, Asia Minor and Europe. The production of copper from its coloured ores made the early smiths try the same process on other coloured stones, and thus they soon learnt to smelt the ores of lead, silver and antimony.

The art of alloying – that is mixing these metals in different proportions – arose from the two facts that it is difficult to cast copper in intricate moulds, and that pure copper is not very hard. How the new easily castable and much harder copper-tin alloy was first discovered we do not know. Probably it was obtained when tin ore or 'stream tin' was used to refine copper in a final smelting operation. Anyway, bronze became known shortly after the introduction of copper. Since the early smiths selected their ores by colour and form only, without any knowledge of chemical analysis, they made bronzes containing eight to twelve per cent of tin when aiming at an average of ten per cent. This bronze was eminently suitable for tools and weapons. Later on, special bronzes containing more tin were developed for the manufacture of mirrors of polished metal (twenty per cent), and for bells (thirty per cent).

However, tin ores were not readily available everywhere, and they were certainly much rarer than copper ores. In Egypt, where tin ores were completely absent and had therefore to be imported, bronze became common only by 2000 B.C. The inhabitants of ancient Mesopotamia were more fortunate in obtaining tin from the mountains to the north. Even so, the analysis of early Mesopotamian bronzes shows that before long these deposits could no longer satisfy the large demands; the percentages of tin had therefore to be reduced. For certain purposes 'bronzes' could be compounded by alloying copper with lead or antimony. For art objects, or for statues of the gods, such inferior bronzes were good enough and were substituted throughout the Near East.

For the manufacture of tools and weapons new sources of tin ores had to be found; and the early metallurgists started to look for them in foreign countries. The deposits of the Balkans, of Bohemia, of Brittany and northern Spain and finally those of Cornwall were discovered. As these remote regions were explored, the art of metallurgy was taught to the inhabitants of Central Europe, who soon became equally skilled, and transmitted the lore of the smith to the tribes of the West. By 2000 B.C. tin ores were also being smelted separately, so that instead of a trade in ore, bars of tin were produced and traded from hand to hand. This again allowed the smiths to compound their alloys more closely and to produce alloys of different tin content – a range of bronzes, in fact, for different specialized purposes.

As the craft of the smith became more complicated, specialists of different types arose, the miner extracting the precious ores, and the metallurgist making bars and cakes of crude metal, which were then traded to the great cities and centres of civilization. Each metal had its own form of ingot. Gold and silver were usually cast in rings or small bars; tin came in I-shape ingots, one on each side of a pack-animal. Copper and bronze were cast in round flat cakes in prehistoric western Europe, and in the form of double-axes in some parts of central Europe. In the eastern Mediterranean they took the shape of an ox-hide weighing some thirty kilograms (one talent); and it is well to remember that the Latin for 'money' (*pecunia*) is derived from 'cattle' (*pecus*). These bars of crude metal were, indeed, not only the raw material for smiths, but they also served as a primitive kind of money. Hence the currency units of the ancient civilizations were often weights of metals and other commodities as well. The primitive method of casting copper in round cakes prevailed in Japan till the nineteenth century. Water was sprinkled with a straw brush on the molten copper in the furnace. A crust was formed and hooked out, and then plunged into cold water.

In the big cities these bars were then processed by different specialists. Often the state or the city authorities bought ingots and kept them in a storehouse to be handed out to smiths for the manufacture of certain tools and weapons, for which they were paid per unit. Big centres of copper and bronze production like Cyprus could manage the market. We have cuneiform tablets telling us how the king of Cyprus delayed the delivery of large consignments of copper to Egypt, although he had already been paid. In fact, countries and states which possessed rich ores and a metallurgical industry now became a political force. One of the *Books of Maccabees* rightly reminds us of the conquest of Spain by the Romans because of its iron, tin, silver and copper ores; and Hannibal could never have invaded Italy without the mining industry of Cartagena in Spain. The Phoenicians and Carthaginians grew rich on the trade of metals, even when living in a country poor in ores. Earlier the Cretans, as Egyptian wall paintings show, had traded bronze ingots southward to Egypt.

By 2000 B.C. bronze had displaced the old stone and wooden tools in general, but not completely and not everywhere. For many things, such as

ploughshares or arrow-heads, stone remained a more appropriate material. Bronze was always rather an expensive alloy because of its tin content. The ancient smiths used to collect old and broken bronze tools and weapons and melt them down and recast them. By 1000 B.C. bronze was threatened by a new metal, iron, and partly displaced by this cheaper competitor. But the art of the Bronze Age smith in casting and alloying was never lost. Bronze had many virtues. When artillery and firearms were invented it still was the only metal at first from which cannons could be cast. Even to our day it is supreme for many purposes, such as engine bearings. Its value increased with the discovery of new metals which could be added to the copper-tin mix. Bronzes thus came to play a large part in modern coinage and in electrical machinery. (See also *Iron, Mines*.)

ILLUSTRATION: Pages 29, 34 and 311.

Before the vacuum cleaner

The **BROOM**, like paper, the clarinet reed and the pen, takes its name from the material from which it was made. In the same way *calamus* meant both a cane and the pen which was made from it; again, the Italian word for reed, *calamo*, and the word for magnet, *calamita*, recall that the primitive mariner's compass consisted of a magnetized needle inserted through a straw and floated on a basin of water.

Nowadays the flexible twigs of the wild broom (*Sarothamnus scoparius*) are no longer used for making either house brooms or besoms. For besoms twigs of birch or heather are now preferred. One of the last uses of broom branches for sweeping was in clearing the ice in the old Scottish sport of curling.

The manufacture of coarse brooms or besoms is one of the most thriving of the old English woodland crafts, for these besoms are required not only for sweeping roads and gardens and for use as fire-beaters, but also for brushing the slag from the surface of hot pig-iron fresh from the furnace. The foundries of the Midlands and South Wales make a steady demand for birch besoms for this last purpose, wire brushes not being so satisfactory. The principal places where the craft is still carried on are the open heathy wastes, the home of the 'broom Squires', near Hindhead (Surrey) and in Ashdown Forest (Kent), at Verwood in East Dorset and Redlynch in Wiltshire, at Baughurst and Tadley in Hampshire, at Hevingham near Norwich, and at Pickering in the North Riding of Yorkshire, where heather brooms are a speciality.

In making birch besoms, the twigs are cut in winter and seasoned for several months. They are then bound in bundles, a process which requires much skill and is crucial in determining the quality of the broom. Devices of many kinds are used for tightening the bundle while binding, and their variety illustrates the vigour of local traditions of craftsmanship. The Suffolk woodman simply tightens the binding strip by rolling and straining the bundle under his feet. In the New Forest the same method is used, but before binding and inserting the handle the twigs are boiled for about five minutes to make them moist and soft. In Hampshire and Durham the binder sits astride a 'horse', a sort of vice which grips the binding lap and tightens it at each turn with a foot treadle; in the Surrey workshops there is no treadle, and pressure on the 'saddle' gives the necessary tension. In Norfolk the binder sits astride a sloping plank and has a rope tied round his waist, which is given a turn round the bundle and then looped to a hook at the end of the plank; he slides up the plank on a sack, and the weight of his body strains the bundle tight. At Pickering in Yorkshire and Mansfield in Nottinghamshire, however, instead of straining the binding lap, a pincer vice operated with a pedal is used to compress the heather bundle, which is then fastened with the lap threaded through a large iron 'needle'.

For economy, the twig bundles in some workshops are now bound with imported cane, or even with wire, but these are never as satisfactory as the traditional materials – laps of ash wood split from a green bough, thin cleft stems of oak or sweet chestnut, the fibrous interior bark of lime, the core of brambles, or twisted hazel withies. Finally, the twigs are trimmed and a handle, sually of lime or hazel, inserted into them.

In Anglesey, until recently at least, a cheap type of broom was made from the reed (*Phragmites communis*), cut by a scythe in August and left in the open to dry and become crisp before being bound.

Though alder and birch will serve, the heads of the best modern domestic brooms are made of half-cylinders of turned blocks of beech, since this wood can be bored with the many holes necessary for taking the bristles without danger of splitting. There is an inner layer of beech, and a final veneer which may be made of any ornamental wood from pale horse chestnut to dark ebony, but the strength lies in the beech core. Nowadays these brooms are usually set with imported piassava fibre, which is cheaper than the fine twigs or spray of many kinds of willow which, stripped of their bark, were formerly used for this purpose.

The old-fashioned broom was associated with witches as the vehicle which they straddled when floating through the air, with the aid of 'flying ointment', to their unholy sabbats, and as the emblem which they wielded in their dances. This is certainly a recent association, since the earliest references to the flight of witches are in the sixteenth century, and at first their means of transport on these occasions was represented as sticks, not brooms. However, the broom was a powerful plant used by witches and against witches. Thus in the border ballad of *Broomfield Hill* the witchwoman tells the lady how to make her knight sleep more soundly in the flowering broom –

> But when ye gang to Broomfield Hills,
> Walk nine times round and round;
> Down below a bonny burn bank,
> Ye'll find your love sleeping sound.

> Ye'll pull the bloom frae off the broom,
> Strew't at his head and feet,
> And aye the thicker that ye do strew
> The sounder he will sleep.

Hazel wood is also a traditional material for the magic wand, and broom handles are often made of hazel, and witches' brooms were often specially described as being made of hazel. So for this reason as well the broom may have been considered a suitable witches' adjunct.

The broom was a common symbol in mumming plays and ceremonies. Varro, in a passage preserved by St Augustine, describes a rural custom of ancient Italy which took place on the birth of a child. In order to keep the wild Silvanus at bay, three spirits were invoked, Intercidona, Pilumnus and Deverra, represented by three men with the axe, pestle and broom. These symbolized the basic agricultural tasks of pruning the trees, pounding the corn, and sweeping the grain. In Yorkshire and Lancashire, the mummers on New Year's Eve enter the house with a broom, to 'sweep out the old year'. Molly, the man dressed as a woman who acts as chorus in the Berkshire and Oxfordshire Christmas mumming play, carries a broom, as does 'Bessie with a besom' of the Roxburghshire Christmas mummers. In these cases it is probably a sign of femininity, for the broomstick was the traditional symbol of women, as the pitchfork was of men; when placed outside the door it showed that the woman of the house was not in.

To hoist a broom to the top-mast head of a ship used to be a sign that it was to be sold. The origin of this custom is not recorded, though it has been compared with instances where the display of a bush or bough indicated an impending sale. Broom and brush were first mechanized as carpet-sweepers in the middle of the last century, the carpet-sweeper evolving into the vacuum cleaner (q.v.).

Butter's ups and downs

BUTTER is the fat of milk, separated by agitation. Nearly 2,000 years ago Pliny gave this account of how butter was made – and regarded – in his time:

Butter, also made from milk, is considered as a delicacy in foreign countries, and is one which distinguishes the rich from the lower classes. Though most comes from the cow and goat, the richest butter is made from ewes' milk. Whilst in winter the milk is first warmed, in summer the butter is extracted simply by agitation in long vessels. Air can get in though a small hole at the vessel's mouth which is otherwise bound up. A little vinegar [?] is added to turn it sour. The most coagulated part floats to the top;

it is removed, salt is added, and it is called 'oxygala'. The rest is boiled down in pots; the oily part that floats on the surface is butter. The more rank it is, the better is it liked. Old butter is mixed in with many medicines. By nature, it is astringent, emollient, repletive, and purgative.

Beside Pliny's account may be set a description of the sixteenth century from the English version (1577) of the *Whole Art of Husbandry* by Conrad Heresbatch:

Of Milke is made Butter ... much used of our old fathers, yea even of the very Patriarches (as the Scriptures witnesseth.) The commoditie thereof, besides many other, is the asswaging of hunger, and the preserving of strength: it is made in this sort. The milke, as soone as it is milked, is put out of the Paile into Bowles, or Pannes, the best are earthen Pannes, and those rather broad than deepe: this done, the second or the third day, the creame that swimmes aloft is fleeted off, and put into a vessell rather deepe than big, round and Cilinder fashion: although in some places they have other kinde of Charmes, low and flat, wherein with often beating and mouing up and downe, they so shake the milke, as they seur the thinnest part off from the thicke, which at the first gathers together in little crombles, and after with the continuance of the violent mouing, commeth to a whole wedge, or cake: thus it is taken out, and eyther eaten fresh, or barrelled with salt.

In Pliny's day, butter was made by churning whole milk. What he called 'oxygala' was a by-product resembling cheese. By the sixteenth century, dairy people were producing a butter much more like our own, by churning cream rather than milk. Heresbatch advised eating it fresh and no wonder, since butter made in his way very quickly becomes rancid and strong.

Pliny and Heresbatch both favoured souring the cream before making the butter; and it was in effect this sour-cream butter that all connoisseurs found so delicious in the days of farm butter before 1939. 'The churning of fresh cream', the Ministry of Agriculture advised in 1933, 'involves a greater loss of fat in the butter-milk ... Moreover, fresh-cream butter is rather flavourless, and does not possess that distinctive nutty flavour associated with butter from properly ripened cream.'

From 1939, the first year of the Second World War, butter was short; and since fresh-cream butter keeps better, that was the only kind permitted. After the war unsuspecting folk, who did not remember the taste of English farmhouse butter in the thirties, were startled by the strong flavour of the butter imported from Denmark.

Generally speaking, it seems that we shall now have a traditional butter no more. In 1914 in England there were two Co-operative butter factories at work. In 1954 factory butter is the rule, farm butter the exception. The Second World War brought an extra stimulus to factory production with the introduction of 'continuous butter-making' machinery, by which a high-fat cream can be converted into butter in a continuous stream. Continuous butter-makers give a rather flavourless product, and they are at work in Australia, Switzerland, Germany, Scandinavia and the U.S.A.

In India, more than half the butter-fat produced is turned into *ghee*. Ghee-making corresponds remarkably with the methods described above by Pliny. The milk is first converted into the yoghourt-like *dahí*; for which it is sterilized by boiling and then heated to separate the fat, which as *ghee*, has a very low water content.

Butter has varied in use and in status. It was less a universal article of diet at one time than a medicine. Reference to the medical uses of butter does not only appear in Pliny, but in suitable literature throughout the ages. Some people still use it for burns, bruises and the like. An Anglo-Saxon treatise written about A.D. 1000 advises pounding up yarrow with butter to apply to a swelling. In medieval and Tudor times, butter was usually made in spring and summer, a great deal being preserved by salting. 'May butter' was thought most nutritious, particularly for children. In 1584 the physician Thomas Cogan wrote:

It is to bee made chiefly in May, or in the heate of the yeare, by setting Butter new made without salt, so much as you list in a platter, open to the Sunne in faire weather for certain daies, untill it bee sufficiently clarified, and altered in colour, which wil be in twelve or fourteene daies, if it be faire Sunne shining.

In Cogan's day, butter was recommended for treating growing pains and for constipation. Sun treatment would certainly have made it very rancid and thus more purgative; but perhaps, too, it gave a sufficiently increased amount of vitamin D to enhance its reputation as a valuable food for children.

By the middle of the seventeenth century, butter was in disrepute, and Thomas Muffett could write in 1655 of butter as 'the chief food of the poorer sort'. In Georgian England, it went up a rung or two, since it was very widely used in the better cooking, as well as on slices of bread rather more generally than before. Mrs Beeton, the champion of Victorian gastronomy, is quite unequivocal about the butter *she* was prepared to tolerate:

A word of caution is necessary about *rancid* butter. Nobody eats it on bread, but it is sometimes used in cooking, in forms in which the acidity can be more or less disguised. So much the worse; it is almost poisonous, disguise it as you may.

It was the cattle plague of 1865–1867 which caused a shortage of butter, with a steep rise in price to one and twopence the pound, which now paved the way for the introduction of margarine. In the eighteen-nineties the public's worry was the fraudulent mixture of butter with margarine, which was now becoming popular.

By this time, most of the butter on sale in England was imported; the best of it came from Denmark, as it does today. (See also *Cheese, Margarine.*)

Buttoned up

BUTTONS, simple objects for use or for ornament with clothes or for the two combined, have a remote antiquity, but an interrupted career. One of the earliest sets must be the buttons unearthed in a grave of the third millennium B.C. at Ur of the Chaldees. The skeleton was discovered with a line of buttons down its breastbone from neck to waist. These fifteen Sumerian buttons were flattened, disc-shaped beads, one cm. in diameter, seven made of dark steatite and the rest of frit that had once been glazed. They lay in single file, almost touching one another; evidently they had served as buttons down the front of a garment which had otherwise disintegrated.

By 2000 B.C. buttons were being worn in Crete, made of some perishable material covered with thin gold foil. The foil is left and preserves two stitch holes. Similar button-casings of bronze have been found in Hungary dating to the Early Bronze Age. By the Middle Bronze Age they were fairly common in Europe. Going back in time to the third millennium B.C., the people of the Harappa culture and the great prehistoric cities of the Indus Valley were buttoning themselves with buttons of a very distinctive type. These were plano-convex discs, perforated on the flat face by two holes which converge to an inverted V; the holes, in fact, intercommunicate. Similar buttons are associated with the Beaker cultures of Europe, with peoples who arrived in Britain at the end of the neolithic period, somewhere about 1800 B.C. These V-buttons have been found at several sites in Britain, sometimes made of Whitby jet, decorated in low relief. They are known from lake sites in Italy and also from Malta, Sardinia, the Balearic Islands and Provence.

In Greece during the Late Bronze Age – the period of Mycenae – buttons are frequently found both in tombs and on settlement sites. It is uncertain what part they played in fastening the full, ankle-length, flounced and pleated skirts, and small, tight, short-sleeved jackets open at the breasts which, from frescoes, ivories and vase-paintings are known to have been the formal costume of the aristocratic ladies of Mycenae, and the other cities in Greece and elsewhere which shared that brilliant civilization. Though they are sometimes biconical, the normal shape for these buttons is either a flattened cone with the top cut off, or plano-convex. Others have a distinct shank that shades off imperceptibly into the body of the button. Between 1550 and 1400 B.C. they are normally made of terracotta, but later examples are often made of steatite, sometimes decorated with simple incised patterns.

All types are alike in being pierced by a single hole through the centre from top to bottom; they were evidently attached by threading a piece of stout cord, or a leather thong through this hole. The thong was knotted at the top to keep it in place; the lower part was then stitched to the garment. There is no means of deciding whether these buttons were used with button-holes or loops.

After the Mycenaean period a change in costume took place in Greece, and the sophisticated and extremely beautiful Mycenaean dresses were replaced by a simpler and more austere set of garments in which, for several hundred years, little or no use was made of buttons. The basic garment, worn with slight variation by both men and women, was the *chiton*, two types of which existed, the Doric and the Ionian. The Doric chiton was shaped like a blanket, folded in half and worn with the fold down one side of the body. The material was doubled at the shoulders, where, at either shoulder, the front and back folds were fastened together by pins which rested just in front of the shoulder-blade; the garment was gathered at the waist by a belt or girdle. In a second style of Doric chiton the material was shaped like a cylinder open at both ends; it was pinned at the shoulder in the same fashion. Pins, however, went out of use in Greece by the end of the seventh century B.C., and when the Ionian chiton replaced the Doric at Athens, buttons appeared in service again.

Herodotus has a strange story to account for this change, which he says took place at the time of a bitter war between Athens and Aegina; in a terrible battle between the two, all save one of the Athenians engaged were killed; as for this one survivor: 'When he came back to Athens, bringing word of the calamity, the wives of those who had been sent out on the expedition took it sorely to heart, that he alone should have survived the slaughter of all the rest; – they therefore crowded round the man, and struck him with the pins by which their dresses were fastened – each, as she struck, asking him where he had left her husband. And the man died in this way. The Athenians thought the deed of the women more horrible even than the fate of the troops; as however they did not know how else to punish them, they changed their dress and compelled them to wear the costume of the Ionians.'

The Ionic chiton was sewn up the side, opposite the fold, and across the top, leaving holes for arm and neck. Later, however, the top seam was replaced by buttons by which the dress was closed from the neck to the side seams. This was an improvement which must have made the garment much easier to take on and off and, incidentally, made matters very much easier for nursing mothers. The stuff was carefully pleated at a number of symmetrically chosen points, back and front, and then sewn into a pair of bands; the back and front bands were joined by buttons and loops.

Buttons were used by men on their chitons, but to a lesser degree. They sometimes used them also for securing armour. A black-figure amphora of the sixth century B.C. by the Attic painter Nikosthenes shows a soldier whose cuirass is fastened to its shoulder-straps by buttons, a detail repeated on some Etruscan bronze figurines of armed warriors. Buttons of the classical period in Greece were sometimes made of beautifully variegated glass, but more often they were small undecorated bone discs, with a single hole like their Mycenaean predecessors. The knot in securing the thong is often indicated on vase-paintings by a spot of dark paint in the centre of the button.

A long series of buttons, from the fifth century B.C. to the twelfth century A.D., has been found during excavations at the ancient city of Corinth. It is very noticeable that the button with single hole is much the most common type. A few with two holes appear in Roman contexts of the fourth century A.D., but the type does not persist. The very large number of buttons of the Byzantine period, many of which are very well made, lathe-turned, with a good deal of variation in form and decoration, all have the one hole, a type which persists to the present day in parts of south-east Europe – in Croatia, for example.

In Iron Age, Roman and Saxon Britain brooches were so widely used for the fastening of clothes that button are not conspicuous. In fact, even in the Middle Ages, though they were occasionally used for ornament, they do not seem to have made their way on to garments to any great extent before the fifteenth century. Buttons were doubtless tiresome things to manufacture in relation to their size and importance, they were not so necessary on loose-fitting clothes, and there were fairly satisfactory alternatives. From the seventeenth century the manufacture of buttons became one of the staple industries of Birmingham. Gradual adoption of modern European clothing through so much of the world has brought the button, now mass produced by machinery out of a variety of materials from wood and metal and horn and glass to rubber and plastic, to the peak of its unimportant importance. If the reader turns to count the number of buttons on his or her person at this moment, it will be realized that zip-fasteners and other contrivances are not killing the button. (See also *Cloth, Safety-pin, Zip-fastener.*)

C

Abacus to calculating machine

The **CALCULATING MACHINE** has a long history, especially if the abacus is included in the story. The word 'calculate', derived as it is from the Latin word *calculus*, meaning a pebble, indicates that from the earliest times the process required some external aid. The fingers have always been used for counting and adding; because we have ten of them, a decimal system of numeration was the natural outcome.

The abacus consists of beads sliding on wires; it is a primitive substitute for the cruder method of counting and adding on the fingers. Abacuses have been in use from very early times and are still handled with considerable dexterity by shopkeepers in China and Japan. In 1946, when the American troops with their latest office machinery occupied Japan, a competitive test of speed in calculating was held between an American using a high-speed electric machine and a Japanese using an abacus; the latter was found to be quicker.

The first calculating machine in the true sense of the word, that is a machine which embodies wheelwork, was invented by the great mathematician Blaise Pascal in 1642. Pascal was born at Clermont in France. His father, Etienne Pascal, was a judge and the family was wealthy. When Pascal was eight they moved to Paris, and he soon showed himself to be a human prodigy.

At the age of eleven, as a result of his own experimental investigations, he wrote a thesis on the production of sound by a tuning-fork. His father tried to discourage him from mathematical and physical studies, but when he was caught drawing mathematical figures on the bedroom floor instead of learning languages, his father realized his bent and allowed him to continue with mathematics.

When the Municipality of Paris withheld the interest on one of its loans Pascal's father was the ringleader of a faction which protested. A warrant for his arrest was issued, and he fled from Paris. Shortly after this there was a private performance before Cardinal Richelieu of a theatrical play in which Pascal's sister, Jacqueline, took a leading part. The Cardinal was so delighted with the piece that he had Jacqueline and her brother presented to him. Pascal, though only sixteen, was introduced as 'the famous mathematician'. Jacqueline handed a rhymed request for her father's pardon to Richelieu, who readily granted it. Etienne, returning to Paris, was graciously received and was appointed Steward of Rouen, where he was especially concerned with the collection of taxes. It was this train of events which impelled the nineteen-year-old Blaise Pascal to construct the first calculating machine, his intention being to lighten the labours of his father.

Pascal's is a stylus-operated adding machine and makes ingenious provision for carrying tens. Once the efficacy of the machine was realized other examples were constructed, and it is said that more than fifty were made either by Pascal himself or under his supervision. At least five of the originals are still in existence after a lapse of three hundred years.

The first English attempt to construct a calculating machine came some twenty years later from the diplomat and mathematician Sir Samuel Morland (1625–1695). He made a stylus-operated adding machine with no automatic carry from units to tens. Morland was educated at Winchester and Cambridge, and it is noteworthy that many of the pioneers in the development of the calculating machine were persons of wealth or leisure. Nowadays the contributions to progress in machine calculation are mostly made by organized teams of workers at universities or in government departments.

The next great step forward was made about 1671 by the philosopher and mathematician, Gottfried Leibnitz. Having heard of Pascal's machine, he devised one of his own. It was not only an adding machine but could be used for multiplication and division. The basis of the machine is the stepped drum, or stepped reckoner, sometimes called the Leibnitz wheel, which is amongst the most important inventions in the history of calculating machines. The first successful commercial calculating machine was introduced to the market in 1820 by Charles Xavier Thomas de Colmar, a native of Alsace-Lorraine. His Arithmometer was closely modelled on Leibnitz's machine. Many thousands were made, their manufacture being continued until about 1930. These Arithmometers were very reliable, and held the field unchallenged for fifty years.

There has been rapid development during the twentieth century and many new types have been introduced so that the desk calculating machine, capable of addition, subtraction, multiplication and division is a common feature of many banks and offices. Early in the nineteenth century, before calculating machines were more than a rare curiosity, Charles Babbage (1792–1871) visualized a more complete machine which would carry out a complicated computation from beginning to end and print the result. The machine would at the outset be instructed what to do, and would then operate without further human intervention. The control was to be exercised by holes punched in cards, just as the pattern woven by a Jacquard loom is controlled by perforated cards. Babbage worked for most of his life on the scheme, spending on it much of his private fortune as well as £17,000 which the government granted him for the work. No machine was finished, but his ideas were taken up by George and Edward Scheutz in Stockholm, who completed a machine in 1853; this Swedish machine was used to calculate and print actuarial tables for use in life-insurance calculations.

More recently it has been found that Babbage's far-seeing schemes for computation are applicable to the operation of the modern electronic calculators sometimes called 'electronic brains'. The first of these, the Eniac (named from the initial letters of Electronic Numerical Integrator and

Computer), was made during the Second World War for the wearisome calculations required to determine the flight of a projectile. This and the many other more recent electronic calculators operate by the transmission of electric pulses through circuits, so that their speed of operation, instead of being limited by the mechanical rotation of metal cogs, is able to approach the speed of travel of electricity. Thus the machine at Manchester University can perform 1,000 addition sums or 400 multiplications in a second, handling numbers of any size up to a billion. These machines can solve complicated problems which previously were considered too laborious to undertake: problems connected with the flight of aeroplanes at supersonic speed, the strength of bridges and the design of camera lenses. It has even been suggested that such a machine could solve the problem of the most efficient design of high-speed electronic computer, that is, it could suggest how its own design could be improved.

Since such machines have also been applied to the problem of playing a game of chess, it is little wonder that they have been likened to the human brain. It is quite true that a study of the way they can be made to function has provided ideas for the neurologist which have helped him in understanding the working of the brain.

ILLUSTRATION: Page 28.

Camera and Camera Obscura

The **CAMERA**, though few people are aware of its origin and antiquity, derives directly from the camera obscura. As its Latin name implies, this was first of all a dark vault or room, with a tiny hole in the wall or window-shutter through which the view outside was projected on to the opposite wall, or on to a white screen. Its invention is erroneously ascribed by various writers to Roger Bacon, Alberti, Leonardo da Vinci and Giambattista della Porta, but in fact it was described 250 years before Bacon by the Arabian scholar Hassan ibn Hassan, generally known as Alhazen (A.D. 965–1038). He stated that if the image of the sun during a partial eclipse passes through a small hole on to a plane surface opposite, it will appear crescent-shaped, but if the hole is large, it will take the shape of the hole. It is clear that Alhazen was aware of the significance of the relationship between size of aperture and sharpness of image (which in the photographic camera is regulated by a diaphragm).

For centuries the use of the camera obscura remained confined to the observation of solar eclipses (without harming the eyes by looking directly at the sun) as illustrated in a work of the Dutch physician and mathematician Gemma Frisius in 1545.

From this it was not a big step to the secret observation of what went on in the street; the fascination of seeing Nature in all its colours and in perfect perspective, as if painted on the white screen in the darkened room, led artists from the seventeenth century on to trace these camera obscura images of landscapes and portraits, and fill in the colour. This quick, easy and accurate means of making sketches was first pointed out by the Neapolitan scientist Porta in 1558, though it may have been known to Renaissance artists. (Leonardo da Vinci merely compares the camera with the eye, he does not mention in his notebooks its application to drawing.)

An important improvement in the camera obscura was the insertion of a convex lens in the hole, which permitted it to be made larger, resulting in much brighter and sharper pictures. This advance was due to Girolamo Cardano, a professor of mathematics in Milan, in 1550.

According to the laws of optics, the images received on the paper screen were upside down, and though Porta in a later greatly enlarged edition of his *Magiae naturalis*, or 'Natural Magic' (1588), revealed his 'carefully guarded secret' of how to make the images upright by means of a mirror, he had been anticipated in the publication by both Ignatio Danti (1573) and by G. B. Bennedetti (1585). Meanwhile another improvement had been introduced in 1568 by Daniel Barbaro – the use of a diaphragm to sharpen the image. Thus at the end of the sixteenth century the camera was a darkened room in a house, fitted with a lens and a diaphragm, and the landscape or portrait was reflected right way up on to the white screen by a mirror.

The first suggestion for a *portable* camera was

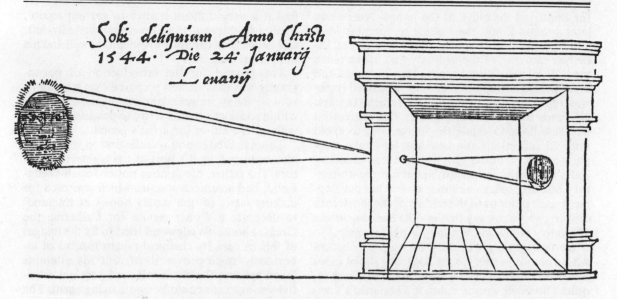

Fig. 8. Camera obscura, showing eclipse of the sun.

made by Friedrich Riesner, who, before 1580, recommended the construction of a light transportable wooden hut for the accurate delineation of topographical views. The German Jesuit scholar Athanasius Kircher illustrates this type, which he saw in use in Germany, in his *Ars Magna* (1646). It was carried like a sedan chair between poles, and the artist entered the little hut, made of lightweight but strong material, through a trapdoor in the floor.

When making a survey of Upper Austria in 1620, Johann Kepler the astronomer (in his capacity as Imperial Mathematician) used a little black tent, through the top of which projected a tube containing a convex lens, and a mirror to reflect the image down on to the drawing board. A hundred and thirteen years later Abbé Nollet submitted his re-invention of the tent camera to the Académie des Sciences in Paris.

The small portable box camera, which is the immediate parent of the photographic camera, dates from the middle of the seventeenth century. One of Kircher's pupils, Kaspar Schott, mentions in 1657 that a traveller in Spain reported having seen one small enough to be carried under the arm. Schott comments that it is not at all necessary for the camera to be so large that the

artist could get inside it; it is quite sufficient to look through an opening in the box, and to prove its practicability Schott had a little camera made consisting of two boxes, one slightly smaller to slide within the other, in order to adjust the focus – here, in other words, was the type of camera used in the early years of photography.

About this time tiny camera obscuras disguised as drinking goblets and books are mentioned as a novelty. In the former, the light-rays entered through a convex lens in the side of the stem of the goblet and were reflected by a small mirror fixed behind the lens on to the surface of the wine (which had to be white so that the image would show). This amusing magic goblet enabled a host unobtrusively to keep an eye on his guests. Probably with the same idea of keeping watch, a German schoolmaster disguised his camera obscura as a book. These were in a way the forerunners of the so-called 'detective' cameras which had a great vogue in the eighteen-nineties.

The reflex camera, nowadays so popular, was first mentioned by the German mathematician Sturm, in 1676. A mirror at 45° to the lens reflected the image right way up on to a piece of oiled paper stretched across the opening in the top of the camera, which was shaded by a hood for improved visibility of the image. Nine years later Johann Zahn, the leading representative of German monastic learning, illustrated several little box cameras, of the ordinary and of the reflex type. They were about nine inches in height and breadth and about two feet long. The oiled paper was replaced by a ground-glass screen (the first reference to the focusing glass). The camera lid had side flaps to shade the image, and to avoid internal reflections the box and lens tube were painted black inside. In size and construction, Zahn's cameras are prototypes of nineteenth-century box and reflex cameras: no further development took place until the middle of the nineteenth century, so we can say that *in 1685 the camera was absolutely ready and waiting for photography.*

In the eighteenth century the camera obscura was in common use. Count Algarotti stated in his *Essay on Painting* (1764) that an art academy required no other equipment than Leonardo's Treatise on Painting, casts of the finest Greek statues and a camera obscura. Among the well-known artists who made extensive use of the instrument were Crespi (Spagnolo of Bologna), and Canaletto and Bellotto, whose admirable rendering of perspective in their town views is always admired. The plates in Dr William Cheselden's famous *Osteographia, or the Anatomy of the Bones* (1733) were traced in the camera 'with more accuracy and less labour' than if drawn unaided.

For the convenience of travellers the camera was incorporated in sedan chairs and carriages, so that the tourist could make sketches whenever he came to a beauty spot without having to leave his conveyance. For portraiture, table models were made, the table-top being the drawing-board. In striving for increased portability, pocket cameras only six to eight inches long and two or three inches wide were made, and we even hear of one incorporated in the head of a walking-stick.

Edward Dodwell, who was sketching on the Acropolis in 1805, relates how the camera helped him to get rid of the mercenary Turkish Governor who constantly put difficulties in his way, in order to receive 'gifts'. One day the Turk, looking in the camera, was alarmed to behold some of his soldiers who happened to be passing, 'walking upon the paper'. Dodwell utilized his fear by telling him that 'if he did not leave me unmolested, I would put *him* into my box, and that he should

find it a very difficult matter to get out again'. Visibly frightened, the Governor hurriedly left, and henceforth carefully avoided Dodwell and his dangerous box.

The ground for the introduction of photography was thus so well prepared that it explains why so many independent attempts were made within so short a period to try to produce pictures without the aid of the artist's pencil.

Thomas Wedgwood was the first to whom this idea occurred, at the turn of the eighteenth century. His father, the famous potter Josiah Wedgwood, had a camera obscura which was used for making views of 'the stately homes of England' to decorate a dinner service for Catherine the Great. Thomas Wedgwood tried to fix the images of this camera by chemical means instead of laboriously tracing over them, but his attempts failed because the chemicals used were not sensitive enough, nor could he find a fixing agent. The first person to succeed in obtaining a permanent view in the camera by chemical means was Nicéphore Niepce (1765–1833) in France in 1826, and the same reasoning which had led Wedgwood and Niepce to photography brought success to the Englishman W. H. Fox Talbot in 1835 and to the Frenchman Louis Daguerre in 1837.

Early in the nineteenth century the room-type camera enjoyed a revival, and watching a busy street scene or a landscape with trees moving in the wind was an unending source of amusement, which may still be enjoyed in at least two surviving camera obscuras, one on the Castle Hill in Edinburgh, and the other on the Downs at Clifton, Bristol.

ILLUSTRATION: Pages 32 and 33.

Water roads from Egypt to Europe

CANALS, since man began to dig them early in history, have served a twofold purpose: they irrigated or drained his fields and they could provide cheap transport by water, which was particularly important in the days when roads were few and poor and vehicles had been little developed.

The early river-valley civilizations of Egypt and Mesopotamia and the Indus valley depended, like China, upon irrigation and drainage. Here one may look for the origin of canals. When these valleys were occupied by people driven towards the rivers by gradual climatic changes and desiccation, the newcomers had to face the enormous task of draining the swamps, felling the trees and clearing the scrub which covered the valley bottoms. The evolution of a system of dykes and canals was a communal task; it demanded co-operation and organization, and led to the formation of city-states, which were often amalgamated later on into larger kingdoms. Each city-state formed a drainage and irrigation unit, comparable to the 'polder' system of the Netherlands or the Fen district in England, north of Cambridge.

The great rivers rose every year; the canals which then conveyed the water to the fields were made by farmers working with simple tools such as hoes and baskets. Every Egyptian province had its 'water-house' for the inspection of dykes and canals, the regulation of the water supply and the apportionment among the farmers of the task of clearing out the silt and unblocking the channels after the yearly inundation. Similar state institutions are mentioned in ancient texts from Mesopotamia. Canals can still be traced by air photography, though the older systems have sometimes been destroyed by later Arabic works or effaced by the Mongol invaders, who turned much of Iraq into a waste land by destroying the canals, or filling them up. City rulers mention with great pride in the ancient texts the effort put into canal-building; and more than one war between such cities was waged because the enemy interfered with the local system of irrigation.

The building of such canals taught men the efficient handling of large quantities of earth and contributed materially to the skill of the architects who had to erect pyramids and great temple-mounds. This labour also found its repercussion in ancient mathematics, which abounds with sums for calculating the amount of earth to be moved in the construction of dykes and canals of various sections. These canals also served for the transport of goods, which went mostly by water in ancient Egypt or Mesopotamia.

Bolder enterprises were soon attempted. During the third and second millennia before Christ canals were built by which vessels on the Nile could circumvent the First and Second Cataracts on the borders of Nubia. An old branch of the Nile, the present Joseph's Canal, was canalized and extended to the desert depression west of the river called the Fayum; its fields were watered, and the Fayum became one of the richest provinces of Egypt. Also about 2200 B.C. a bold project was executed to obviate the transport of eastern goods across the desert between the Nile and the Red Sea. From the eastern branch of the Nile Delta near the town of Bubastis a canal was cut straight to the east through the valley of Tumilat (the Goshen where the tribes of Israel settled) up to the Bitter Lakes, and then south to the Red Sea near the site of the present Suez. However, shipping did not favour this early Suez canal; the shallows of the Gulf of Suez and the sudden gusts of wind were uncongenial to the Egyptians, who did not take readily to the sea. In the course of history this Suez canal was opened up again to traffic on several occasions. The Persian King Darius (c. 400 B.C.) tried to bring it back into favour, encouraging, as his monuments near Suez inform us, direct sea traffic between Egypt, India and Persia. But his efforts had little more effect than those of several Roman emperors who had the canal reopened for strategical reasons.

The Greeks and Romans were never important canal-builders. A few canals were cut to avoid dangerous and stormy capes such as those of the peninsula of Mount Athos. Several attempts were made to cut the now canalized Isthmus of Corinth, but even the Emperor Nero failed to manage the task, and ships crossed this neck of land on a 'diolkos' or bridge of rollers. In Italy Nero also attempted to connect the excellent harbour of Puteoli with Rome and the Tiber. This project of a canal 150 miles long was never finished, and the Romans continued to use the stormy harbour of Ostia at the mouth of the Tiber, which was constantly threatened by accumulations of silt. In the Low Countries several river-beds, such as the arms of the Rhine, were partly canalized.

Irrigation played only a small part in classical agriculture. Except for drainage canals in Boeotia in Greece, near the naval base of Ravenna in the delta of the Po, and possibly in the Fen district in Britain, few new agricultural canals were undertaken. In distant China some important shipping canals, forming part of the later Emperor's Canal, were created to regulate rivers and to provide for inland systems of communication between the northern and southern river valleys of China.

The great movement of reclaiming land or bringing wild tracts under cultivation which was set going about A.D. 1000 by monastic orders and city councils, led to a great revival of canal-building in northern France and the Low Countries. Soon the canals designed to drain the water from low tracts of land into the sea at ebb-tide came also to be used for shipping, and a system was devised of double lift-gates enclosing a pool. Ships could thus be conveyed from one level to another, and continuous transport was possible without unloading and reloading.

During the fourteenth century many of the prosperous republics and principalities of Italy were greatly concerned in improving shipping facilities, since boats were still by far the cheapest form of transport. Leonardo da Vinci and his contemporaries are known to have submitted plans for the regulation of rivers such as the Arno at Florence. Many of these plans for the rivers in the Po valley were realized. All around Milan engineers built a system of canals, the level of which was regulated by means of locks and *pavis* of locks. Leonardo da Vinci's contribution was to invent the modern form of hinged gate-doors for locks and the sliding small gate on these doors, which make it possible to equalize the level of the canal and the shipping pool inside the gates. These inventions soon spread to the rest of Europe.

The modern canal-system of Europe which links the great rivers began in fifteenth-century France, where the Seine, Loire, Rhône and Meuse were soon joined up for traffic. The greater part of England's elaborate canal system was devised late in the eighteenth century and early in the nineteenth century, in response to the development of industry. These canals were a factor in the rise of big sea-ports, including Liverpool and Hull, since industrial products could be cheaply transported by the canals to the good harbour sites, and the merchants had no longer to get their cargoes at the inland manufacturing towns. No sooner were the canals complete than the coming of the railway hit them severely, leaving many hundreds of miles of canal with lock, aqueduct and tunnel to sink into picturesque ruination.

ILLUSTRATION: Page 361.

Candles and rushlights

CANDLES one might think to be more ancient than lamps (q.v.), though in fact the notion of fat or wax melted and solidified around a wick is more complex than the early lamp, which simply consisted of a wick rising from a fuel reservoir. Moreover, they supplied a relatively good illumination, they were easily portable, and were not so messy in use or so offensive to the nose.

The Romans had both wax and tallow candles, and also knew the technique of the rushlight, which is a slender form of candle in which the wick is made of the prepared pith of rushes. They regarded candles as inferior to lamps (thus Martial writes in one of his poems of the first century A.D. 'I am sorry the footman has walked off with your lamp: you will have to do with a candle'), but this unusual state of affairs was probably because they possessed in olive oil an excellent and abundant lamp fuel. Candle and rushlight were popular in areas where wax or fat was easier to obtain than the better kinds of oil, and where normal temperatures were not high enough to soften candles to a troublesome degree.

The white candle of bleached wax is said to have been introduced to Byzantium in the fifth century A.D. The Anglo-Saxon chronicler Asser describes the time-keeping candles used by King Alfred (who reigned from 871 to 901 A.D.). These were made of beeswax and six of them, to burn twenty-four hours, weighed as much as seventy-two of the silver pennies of the time. This means that each candle weighed about two fifths of an ounce. A modern beeswax candle of this weight and with a wick of appropriate size does in fact burn for just about four hours.

Beeswax and tallow were the two older fuels

in the candle. For use in church the more expensive wax candles were obligatory, and well-to-do householders also preferred them; they smoked less, smelt less and did not require such frequent attention as candles made of tallow, which is simply the refined fat of animals. For banquets or festivities a good wax candle might be left for hours without disaster (though it would burn much better if trimmed), whereas a tallow candle could not be left for more than half an hour, by which time it might provide only a seventh of its original light.

The popularity of the tallow candle was a matter of economy: beeswax was a by-product of the production of honey, which in early centuries was the only material for sweetening purposes and for brewing such drinks as mead. Tallow, on the other hand, was a waste product, and tallow chandlers went round from house to house collecting surplus fat, which they often made there and then into candles for the household, without much refining. Craft guilds to regulate the profession of wax or tallow chandler were formed in both France and England in the Middle Ages.

Wax candles could not be moulded; they were made by hanging wicks of fibre from a cross bar and pouring melted beeswax down them at intervals until a wax wall of the required thickness had been built up around the wick. For large church candles of wax this process is repeated today in identical form, though the wicks are woven of cotton in a special way. Tallow candles were usually made by one of two processes: either the wicks were repeatedly dipped into a vat of melted tallow at intervals, thus building up the candle (so the expression *tallow dip* as well as the *tallow candle*), or the wick could be threaded through an iron mould and the tallow just poured in and round. The tallow shrank on cooling, and the candle could therefore be released from the mould.

Rushlights were simply tallow candles, usually with rather thin walls of tallow around the pith of rushes (which was also used for the thicker dips). In English country districts they were a usual cottage illumination well into the nineteenth century, and rushlight holders are common in the museum of bygones. Gilbert White in the *Natural History of Selborne* (1789) exactly describes the making of rushlights from the widely distributed rush *Juncus effusus*, which peels more easily than most other kinds. The rushes were cut in the summer or autumn and put in water, then peeled so as to leave one even rib of outer covering from top to bottom, which supported the pith. These wicks were left out on the grass to bleach and take the dew for several nights, and were then dried in the sun and dipped in scalding fat or grease. 'A good rush' of two feet four inches burned for three minutes short of an hour and gave a good clear light. White calculated that a poor family enjoyed four and a half hours of comfortable light for a farthing. Sixteen hundred rushes went to a pound and required six pounds of tallow, which the farm labourer might get from the scummings of his bacon pot. Nevertheless Gilbert White complained that the poor, who were 'the very worst economists', preferred to buy candles costing a halfpenny which would not last for more than two hours.

Other fuels which have been used and are still used include spermaceti and (in America) the waxy berries of the Bayberry, *Myrica carolinensis*, which give the green, sweet-smelling Christmastime candles. Modern candles are mostly made from paraffin wax, which is derived from mineral oil. The wicks are woven in such a way that they bend over into the flame and are completely consumed in the process. So they do not require that frequent snuffing, or clipping of the charred wick, which was necessary up to at least 1820. Paraffin wax is easy to mould, and the machines in use today are very similar to those developed in America in 1855 by Humiston and Stainforth. They cannot be speeded up, since candles need to be left in the moulds for about twenty minutes. (See also *Lamp, Torch*.)

ILLUSTRATION: Page 366.

Carpets from the East

CARPETS, though we know them as floor coverings, were hardly ever seen on floors in Europe till the seventeenth century.

Up to that time the floors were strewn with rushes and other plants (such as meadowsweet), whilst rush mats were used in the private apartments of the very wealthy and exalted. Rushes were a quite satisfactory form of floor covering, but as late as 1524 Erasmus wrote in a letter to Wolsey's physician complaining bitterly of the unhygienic condition of the floors, and attributed to it the fever which was so common a complaint at the time. He wrote, 'Again, almost all the floors are of clay and rushes from marshes, so carelessly renewed that the foundation sometimes remains for twenty years, harbouring there below . . .' and there follows a list of filth unnamable.

When carpets and rugs (the latter word simply implying a smaller size) first began to appear in Europe from the Near East they were used on tables, on cupboards, and were spread over boxes and chests. This is how they first appear in pictures and portraits, and they can be specially well studied in the interiors which the Dutch artists so loved to paint. Such floor carpets as were used were either particularly coarse ones, or were the prerogative of royalty, or at least of the highest aristocracy. In the later Middle Ages floor coverings (probably made of tapestry) were occasionally used, but only for important state receptions or beside the bed of someone of kingly rank. Carpets were also sometimes laid upon the floor in churches. The earliest carpets from the Orient arrived as rare and costly articles of commerce and it was the Italian city states, particularly Venice and Genoa, which commanded that trade. Italian and Flemish paintings of the fifteenth century show Oriental rugs used in religious pictures as objects of great price and rarity, and some of the oldest carpets we have are known to have once belonged to a church.

To use a good carpet as a covering for a table was in fact quite in keeping with Oriental tradition and feeling for the texture of a fabric which depends on a lush pile brilliantly dyed. For, although carpets were used as floor coverings in houses and mosques in Persia and Turkey, people there did not sit on high chairs, nor did they wear thick and heavy footgear indoors. They wore thin slippers or went barefoot, and they sat directly on the carpet, with legs crossed. Their proximity to the carpet was comparable to that of the Wes-

terner to his table, only the relationship was more direct and intimate. This explains the scheme and scale of design of Oriental carpets, which were not intended to be seen as pictures or like tapestries, although on special occasions they were hung on walls and used for general display.

The first carpets to come to Europe were from Turkey and not Persia, since all connection with Persia was blocked by the hostile Turkish Empire. From Anatolia and Egypt the Italian merchants imported the carpets and rugs which were greatly sought after in the sixteenth century. Cardinal Wolsey himself had great difficulty in obtaining a number of 'damascened rugs' from the Venetian Ambassador and used political pressure to gain them. Until well into the seventeenth century it is always Turkish carpets which are shown in pictures, and not till the second half of the century do Persian carpets begin to appear. The rare exceptions are those specially fine pieces brought by Persian embassies as presents from the Shah. Some of these are the finest sixteenth-century Persian carpets to survive, such as those presented to the Habsburgs and still in Vienna, to the Venetian Doge and Senate and now in St Mark's, and to the Royal House of Sweden.

The Turkish rugs attained an admirable standard, and some of the court carpets were excellent, but they never reached the artistic heights of the best Persian carpets of the Sefavid dynasty (1499–1736). These sixteenth-century Persian carpets were woven at the court; the designs were worked out by the best court painters; no money was spared in obtaining the very best materials, which entailed constant experiments with dyes; besides quantities of silk, the finest pickings from the fleeces of the best flocks of sheep were carefully graded, and the effects of climate and altitude on the flocks were studied. It is a combination of all these factors, together with skill in the weaving, which makes the best Persian carpets the incomparable works of art that they are. The carpet presented to the shrine at Ardabil in Persia in 1540 (now in the Victoria and Albert Museum, in London) is an extraordinary feat of abstract design in which religious concepts are expressed in pure patterns of colour and line. The rich and sumptuous beauty of the 'Chelsea' carpet depends not only on the pictorial motifs depicting the flowering of nature in forms of plant, animal and bird life, but especially on the quality of the wine-red ground, the deep luminous blue, and the whites, greens and yellows brought into play beside them. For the colours themselves depend on the texture of the pile, which is a wool fibre not soft and flaccid like modern wools, but stiff and resilient and imparting a special sheen to the dyes which have impregnated it.

If the court carpets set the highest standards of taste and lead the way with experiments in technique and material, the great bulk of Persian carpets were produced then, as later, for the market, if not for the immediate use of those who made them. At all times carpets were made by the villages and the tribes. Among the tribes, and especially the nomadic tribes (which formed a large part of the Persian population), the traditions of carpet weaving persisted in their simplest but most radical form. The camel- and saddle-bags and the tent hangings of the Turcoman tribes were a fundamental part of their life and rug-weaving was one of the mainsprings of their economy. As these fabrics were of prime utilitarian importance for them and were also prized on account of their quality, the Turcomans remained sound judges of their own work and exacted as high a standard as circumstances permitted. Skill in spinning, dyeing and weaving were high qualities looked for in the women. Turcoman rug patterns retain designs which go back at least to the fifteenth century, if not earlier.

The origins of carpets are lost in the years. If we define a carpet as a woven fabric with a knotted or looped pile, we can find traces of such fabrics as far back as eighteenth-dynasty Egypt. Monuments and textual descriptions can deceive one about the technical nature of a fabric, but it is certain that Babylon and Persia of the Achaemenid dynasty (c. 550–330 B.C.) had finely worked floor coverings, and Xenophon writes of thick yielding carpets on the floor. At Pazyryk in Siberia fragments of carpets have been excavated by Soviet archaeologists which can be dated to the late fifth or early fourth century B.C. These fragments which belonged to a chief's burial, were frozen in solid ice. A pile carpet has been found in Egypt which is attributed to the fourth

or fifth century A.D. A few scattered examples, such as those found by Sir Aurel Stein in Central Asia, testify to the persistence of the use of pile fabrics, and it is significant that whilst some of the early Egyptian fabrics are tied with a loop closely akin to the Persian knot, the fragments from Pazyryk have a single-warp knot which is characteristic of Spanish carpets of the fifteenth to sixteenth centuries. Spain belongs to the Arab world rather than to Europe in the history of carpets, and it is possible that rug-weaving there is in fact of Arab origin and much older than the Ottoman influence which is so apparent in the earliest Spanish rugs known to have survived.

It is in fact likely that pile fabrics are of the greatest antiquity and that each civilization in turn has developed special types to suit its culture and customs. Thus the Sefavid florescence of sixteenth and seventeenth-century Persia produced the last and possibly not even the most splendid carpet in this way. Meanwhile the nomad tribes of Asia continued to weave the simple but sterling rugs for the most practical purposes, as they appear to have done all down the centuries. The more settled tribes would tend to come directly under the influence of each succeeding culture and to reflect more vividly its peculiar style. This is what has happened in recent centuries, and during the last hundred years it has been the commercial civilizations of Europe and America which have had the strongest influence on them; the results have not been very happy.

ILLUSTRATION: Plate 12.

The lord's residence

The **CASTLE**, in the Middle Ages to which it properly belongs, was the private residence and fortress of its lord. That is the point to remember. Its residential character distinguishes the castle chiefly from the purely military forts of more modern times, and its private nature especially sets it apart from earlier fortifications, which, like the Anglo-Saxon *burghs* in England, were the fortifications of the community.

The origins of the castle lie with the origins of feudalism in far-off ninth-century France. The precocious centralization of the era of Charlemagne broke up and the fragments crystallized into petty feudal principalities under the double military threat of marauding Norsemen in one direction and the expanding empire of the Muslims in the other. Feudal society developed to cope with these circumstances; then and for a long time afterwards it was politically without a centre, it was based upon local lordship, and it was military in its upper levels. The symbol of the feudal lord and much of the reality of his power was the castle: it was both his personal dwelling and the stronghold in which he was secure from his enemies, both a firm base for aggressive military action and the centre and rallying point for the defence of his neighbourhood.

England then stood somewhat outside the main flow of European development, so the castle arrived late, and was unknown before the Normans introduced it. By their conquest they established in England an advanced feudal kingdom, purged of the worst elements of decentralization and private war, and they made castles the instruments of their policy. King and baron alike fortified their new conquests, and the path of the Norman conquerors in England, Wales, Scotland and subsequently in Ireland is marked by the castles which they raised. 'Castles he caused to be made, and poor men to be greatly oppressed,' says the Anglo-Saxon chronicle about William the Conqueror, and fifty years later the lament is echoed in the cry of the Peterborough annalist writing during the anarchy of Stephen's reign: 'They filled the land full of castles. They grievously oppressed the wretched men of the land with castle works.' From now on the history and development of the castle in the English kingdom differ in no essentials from its history and development elsewhere.

The first castles which the Normans built in this country were not the grandiose structures in stone which the word 'castle' brings to mind. With a few exceptions (these include the Conqueror's stone keeps at Colchester and the Tower of London), the early Norman castle was a simple but efficient stronghold of earthwork and timber. In its most usual form it consisted, first

and foremost, of a great earthen mound or motte, surrounded by a ditch; on the motte was the timber house of the lord inside the earthen rampart and the stockade which encircles its flat summit. At the foot of the mound lay the bailey, an enclosure containing the other timber buildings necessary to the lord's household and garrison, surrounded by its own rampart and stockade and its own ditch, which ran into the ditch of the mound. So the ground-plan of such a typical motte and bailey castle was not unlike a figure of eight, one segment enlarged to form the bailey.

The motte and bailey castle, quick and cheap to build, was exactly suited to the needs of the Norman conquerors. The great majority of English castles were founded in the first century after the Conquest and were originally of this type. But in time stronger and more permanent castles became both necessary and possible. The early stone castle was generally built piecemeal on the site of an existing stronghold, and was simply a translation of earth and timber into stone, a conversion which was most general in the second half of the twelfth century. The bailey was now surrounded by a stone wall, and it contained stone buildings, while the strong point of the castle and the lord's dwelling became the keep. The simplest form of keep was the shell, to be seen, for example, at Windsor; a ring wall round the summit of the mound, replacing the former stockade and containing the lord's residence. But the most characteristic product of late twelfth-century military architecture is the tower keep, at first and most commonly rectangular like Henry II's great keep at Dover and only later and more rarely cylindrical, as at Conisborough in Yorkshire.

The strength of the keep and bailey castle thus evolved was the strength of the keep; and its weakness was the weakness of the bailey. When in the course of the thirteenth century the defences of the bailey were improved, chiefly by the use of flanking towers to strengthen the wall, the keep as a self-sufficient ultimate stronghold within the castle became scarcely necessary. Such great new castles of the late thirteenth century as Conway and Caernarvon, raised by order of Edward I, have no keeps; they are simply fortified enclosures adapted to the site on which they

Continued on p. 83

Gliding. Otto Lilienthal makes one of his last flights, 1896.

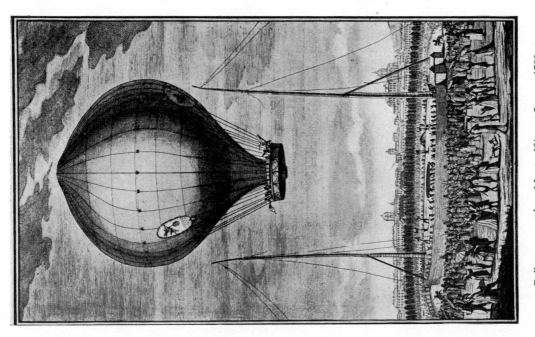

Balloon ascent in a Montgolfière at Lyons, 1789.

Cinema: Eadweard Muybridge's analysis of the movement of a racehorse, from his *Animal Locomotion*, 1887.

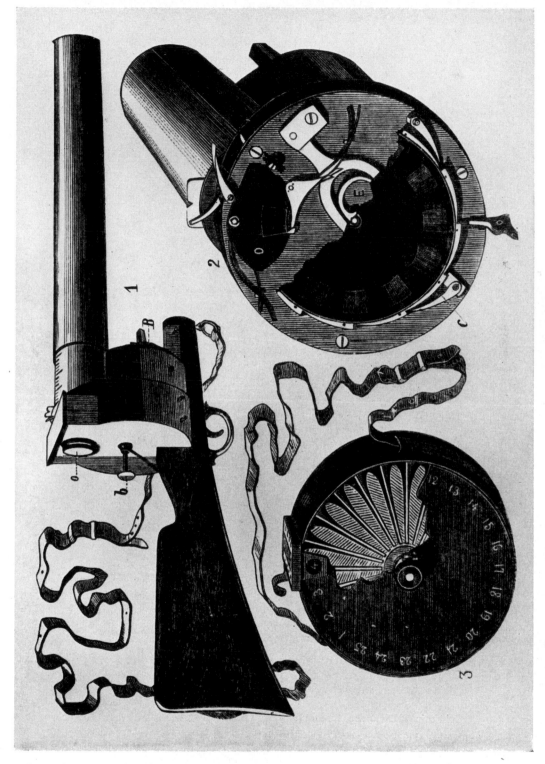

Photographic Gun, designed in 1882 by the cinematograph pioneer E. J. Marey. This took pictures at a rate of 12 per second.

Gold coin of Diocletian, Roman Emperor A.D. 284–305. Diameter 22 mm.

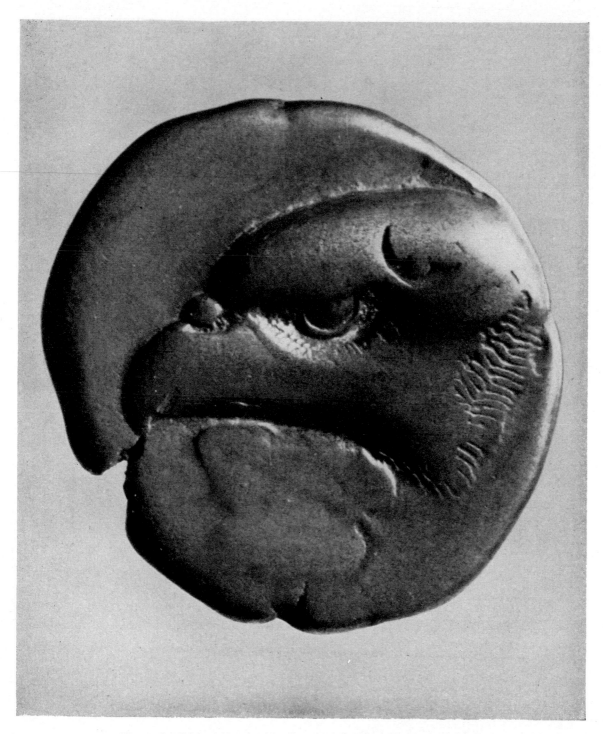

Silver coin of the Eleians, in the Peloponnese (c. 420 B.C.). Diameter 25 mm.

Harp player in Egypt, from a tomb of about 1900 B.C.

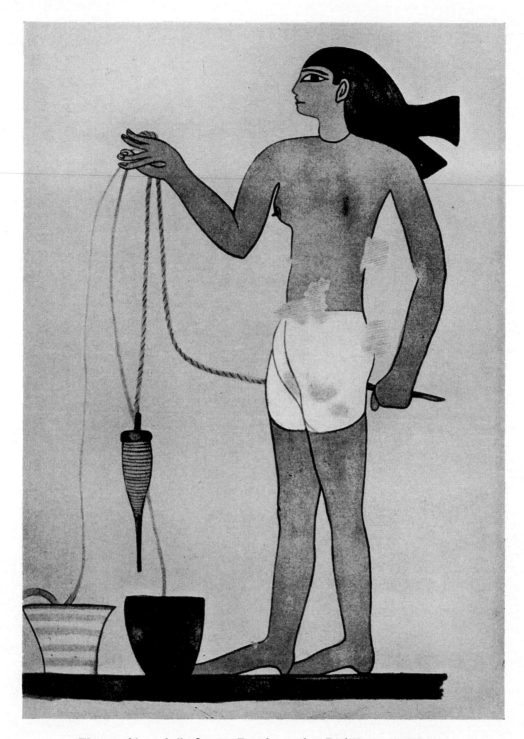

Woman with a spindle, from an Egyptian tomb at Beni Hasan, c. 1900 B.C.

Hobby Horse, or Dandy Horse, the foot-propelled forerunner of the bicycle, 1818.

The powered aeroplane flies for the first time, piloted by Orville Wright, at Kitty Hawk, N.C., 17 December 1903.

Rickett's steam car, 1859–1860.

Panhard and Levassor's petrol-driven motor-car, 1892

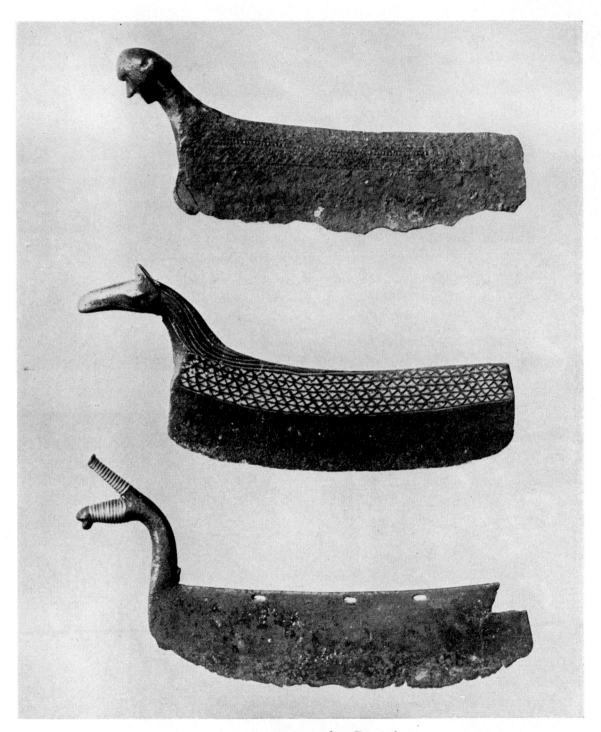

Early Bronze Age razors, from Denmark.

Bear 'totem pole', or house-post, from British Columbia.

A Venetian glass ewer, early seventeenth century.

Glass bottles from Egyptian tombs, sixth century B.C.

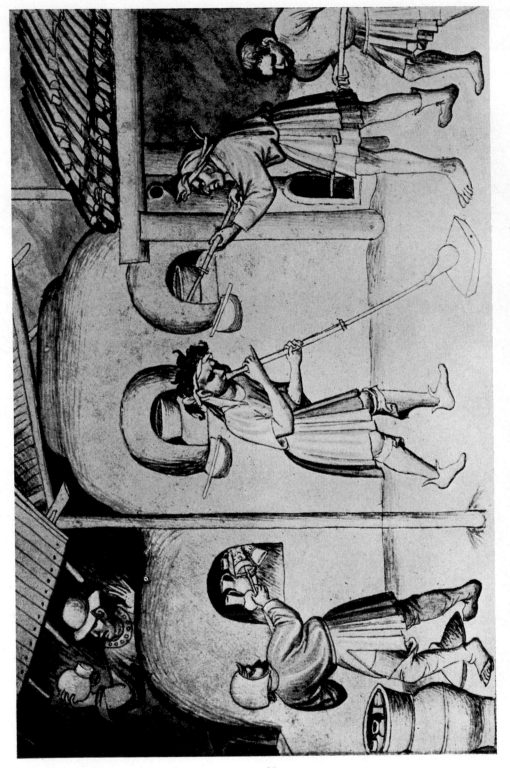

Medieval glasshouse, fourteenth century, from a French manuscript.

Electricity dynamos in Edison's power-station, Pearl Street, New York City, 1881.

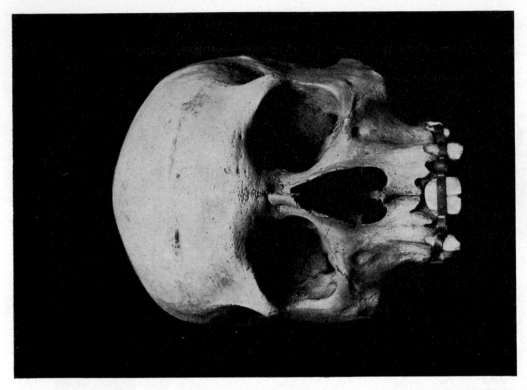

Etruscan false teeth in a skull.
Facsimile from the Wellcome Historical Medical Museum.

The fetish Mavungu, from Portuguese West Africa, seized by Portuguese troops in 1892.

stand, adequately defended by their towered walls and great gatehouses, safely containing within their circuit the residential quarters of hall, chambers and chapel, planned more spaciously than ever before. Even stronger were the 'concentric' castles of the period with their double ring of towered walls, like Beaumaris on the edge of the Menai Straits, again built by Edward I, or Caerphilly, raised by the Clare Earl of Hertford and Gloucester. Yet these great castles of the English in Wales, the finest to be found in all the land, are themselves somewhat exceptional in being built new in the late thirteenth century. The architectural history of the normal castle is one of continuous development from an early origin. More typical, therefore, of the fully developed English castle is the Tower of London; where the later additions of outer encircling towered walls have left the Conqueror's keep – the White Tower – now only the centre of a great Edwardian concentric castle; or Dover, where the bold circuit of towered walls, with the Constable's Gate, was added in Edwardian times to the earlier core of Henry II's keep and inner bailey.

From the fourteenth century, the military importance of the castle declined and amenities of the home were more emphasized than the strength of the defences. Such great castles as those at Windsor, Warwick and Kenilworth were transformed into palaces; and new castles, such as Kirby Muxloe, Wingfield, Maxstoke or Hurstmonceux were not so much castles proper as fortified manor-houses.

By the middle of the sixteenth century residence and fortress were separated. The normal residence of the great was now the more or less unfortified country mansion. It was the age of artillery, and the 'castles' of a shape intermediate between castle and fort. The forts which Henry VIII built along the south coast against the French at Sandown, Deal, Walmer, Pendennis etc., were designed more as gun platforms for the ordnance which was far enough developed by this time to make the fortifications of the medieval castle obsolete.

Through most of the medieval period, castles had been of the first importance. They dominated warfare both as strongholds for defence and as active military bases commanding the countryside. They were the residences of kings and magnates, and so were often the centres of wide estates and of local government and local affairs. They served frequently as prisons and as armouries (as indeed the Tower of London still does). They brought work, sometimes to thousands at a time, in their building and they gave security and prosperity to the towns which crouched under the walls and to the districts in which they stood.

'And now it is all gone – like an unsubstantial pageant faded,' wrote Froude of the passing of the Middle Ages. But there is nothing unsubstantial about the castle; it has remained throughout these islands, most of Europe and much of the Middle East, as the sturdiest relic of medievalism. (See also *Hill-fort*).

ILLUSTRATION: Plate 8 and page 315.

Pins in the clay image

CHARMS, unlike amulets (q.v.), were not only meant to avert evil, but also to cause severe injury to opponents. The time and manner of their production, often accompanied by ancient ritual and formal incantations, were of decisive importance for their efficacy. The purpose of a charm was well defined and often strictly limited; besides, the charm was expected to work in a relatively short period. There are, for instance, early Irish and Anglo-Saxon charms for the removal of a thorn from the foot, to ward off headaches, charms for ague, to staunch blood, to hasten childbirth, against snake-bite, for bewitched land, against thieves, to evoke love, etc. In many cases the material of the charm had ultimately to be destroyed in order to achieve its object; it was buried, burnt or put into running water. For this reason charms are less frequently preserved than amulets. However, many strange specimens can be seen in the Pitt Rivers Museum at Oxford; here are some of them, based upon the belief that the desired effect can be produced by its symbolic imitation:

1. Four short pieces of straw, cut at each side of a knot. These were used about 1895 by an old woman for curing warts. The straw was rubbed

E

over the wart nine times with incantations and was then buried. The straw would decay very quickly and the warts were supposed to vanish at the same time.

2. A rudely shaped clay figure, about a yard long, stuck over with pins and nails. In 1889 this was put on the doorstep of Major Grant's house in Glen Urquhart, Scotland. The workmen who found this death-charm broke it up in order to destroy its magical power, but Major Grant, who happened to come to his door at that moment, carefully collected the pieces and presented the 'Corp Creidh' to the Pitt Rivers Museum. In the Ashmolean Museum, at Oxford, there is a clay figure from Hawara, in Egypt, which represents a man and is tied to a scroll of papyrus, inscribed with incantations; the figure was buried for some magical purpose. The Scottish method of putting the death-charm in front of the door is a late form of the same idea; usually a death-charm was placed in a running stream in the belief that as it crumbled in the water the person it represented would waste away. The more that pins are stuck into such a figure, the more excruciating the agony suffered by the victim. When it was intended that the person should die a lingering death, care was taken that the pins should not touch the region of the heart; but when a speedy death was desired, the pins were stuck right into the heart. Reginald Scot, in his famous book *The Discoverie of Witchcraft* (1584), informs us that incantations were recited whilst the pins were being put into these images.

3. Less gruesome is a love charm, made about 1883 in Hereford: a small figure of a man in putty, lying on a piece of brown paper surrounded by withered rose-buds and lilies of the valley. It was found some fourteen years later in the attic of an inn named 'The Poplars', above the servants' rooms.

4. Imitative Magic is sometimes combined with Contagious Magic; according to the latter whatever is done to a material object will affect the person with whom the object was previously in contact. In the Pitt Rivers Museum there is a jug with a bearded face on its neck (a Bellarmine) which was found in 1904 in the bed of an old mill-stream course at Westminster. When its cork stopper was removed, curious objects were discovered inside: a small piece of cloth, formerly red, neatly cut into the shape of a heart, which was pierced with bent pins, and a small quantity of human hair as well as some finger-nail parings. It was obviously a malevolent charm, and it is believed to have been deposited by a maid-servant bearing a grudge against her mistress.

Written charms, such as the well-known 'Abracadabra' and the 'Sator' formula, consist often of ancient words, the meaning of which has been long forgotten at the time when the charms were made. Their outward appearance does not seem to have mattered at all; some are plain, others elaborate, as is borne out by two sixteenth-century magical rolls in the Bodleian Library at Oxford. They are of considerable length. The longer one covers twenty-four pieces of parchment stitched together. The shorter one is rather carelessly written in red ink; the other roll in most decorative letters in black and red. The red colour is reminiscent of charms written in blood. Both rolls contain Latin incantations, prayers, excerpts from the Gospels, magical symbols, crosses, pentacles, the various names of God and of spirits. The entire rolls may have been carried as amulets, but their special application remains uncertain. We know that one such magical roll was employed in a wager of battle in 1335 and yet another was burnt in 1466 in Cambridge.

Some two hundred and twenty years later Thomas Everard and John Wallis discussed in their correspondence a piece of old parchment with several 'odd' inscriptions. An old woman, Mrs Tucker, long under the suspicion of being a witch, was found dead with this particular parchment sewn up between two pieces of cloth on her breast. To the credit of Everard and Wallis it must be stated that both agreed not to infer that Mrs Tucker was a witch.

A delightful story is told of Sir John Holt (1642–1710), the Lord Chief Justice, who led a wild life as a youth, and on one occasion found himself near Oxford without any money. He procured a week's lodging by pretending to charm away an ague from which his landlady's daughter was suffering. He scribbled a few words of Greek on a scrap of parchment and, rolling it up, directed that it should be bound to the girl's wrist and left there till she was well. Many years after, an old woman was brought before him, charged with sorcery. The evidence showed that she professed to cure the fever-stricken by the application of a magic bit of parchment. Holt examined the fragment and found it to be the very piece with which he had worked his miraculous cure many years ago. His lordship confessed and the woman was acquitted; she was one of the last to be tried for witchcraft in England.

There is a written charm in the Pitt Rivers Museum prescribing as a cure for diseased cattle the piercing of an ox-heart with nine new pins, nine new needles and nine new nails; the heart had to be burnt at midnight while two curses from the psalms were recited. The curses indicate that the intention of the spell was to torture the person who had overlooked or bewitched the cattle. We have two fascinating descriptions of the writer of this charm, the 'wise man' John Wrightson, who flourished about 1830, at Stokesley in the North Riding of Yorkshire. Wrightson maintained that he owed his power to being a seventh son of a seventh daughter. The last sentence of his charm ran: 'Should this fail you need go to no one else as They will nor Can not Cure your Beast.' He stood in such high repute that he was at once resorted to in any case of sickness, distress, or loss of property. (See also *Amulets*.)

Cheese of all sorts

CHEESE has a pre-eminence amongst foods for its biological stability and its high nutritional value; and its importance is consistent with its long, though mainly unwritten history.

Most of the important nutrients of milk go into the cheese, which consists of the curds of clotted milk, from which the whey has been drained, decomposed by micro-organisms. Its stability is well exemplified by a good-quality Cheddar cheese, which can be very palatable after more than a year in a proper store; whereas liquid milk is not very nice after only a few days, even if it has been put in a refrigerator. Sour milk, which keeps better than fresh, cannot outlive the most short-lived kind of cheese. Furthermore, it is difficult for disease-producing bacteria to live in most cheeses; whilst milk, a first-class culture medium, has spread tuberculosis, scarlet fever, diphtheria, typhoid, dysentery, cholera and 'food poisoning'.

Nearly 3,000 years ago Homer told how Odysseus saw the giant Polyphemus making cheese from ewe's milk, which in France today is the only legal source of Roquefort. Cheeses have been made also from the milk of mares, camels and reindeer. Goat's-milk cheeses are not uncommon, but most kinds are made from cow's milk. An eighteenth-century recipe – *To make a* New-market *Cheese to cut at two Years old* – gives some of the essentials of cheese-making:

... take twenty quarts of new Milk warm from the Cow and colour it with Marigolds, when is done ... get ready ... a quart of fair Water, which must be kept stirring over the fire till 'tis scalding hot, then stir it well into the Milk and Runnet, as you do other Cheese; when 'tis come, lay Cheese-cloaths over it, and settle it with your Hands; ... as the Whey rises, take it away ... then put it in the Press, and press gently an hour; take it out again, and cut it in thin slices, ... and break it with your Hands as small as you can, and mix with it a good handful of Salt ... then press ...

Just as when making a junket for the table, the milk is clotted with rennet, a preparation of enzymes from the calf's stomach. The hot water warms the milk to a temperature suitable for the rennet to act and perhaps gives the curd some plasticity. Newmarket cheese may have been something between a Cheddar and the Dutch cheeses which can be bought today; only it would become pretty hard if kept for two years.

Rennet is not used for ordinary sour-milk cheese made at home: the protein is coagulated by acid produced by bacteria from the milk-sugar. This is so, too, for 'Gervais' and other commercial lactic cheeses. But most cheeses are made with both souring *and* rennet: the latter being used to clot the slightly acid milk. English cheeses are characteristically much more acid than Continental ones, and this fact may well be related with their history. Cheese-making is traditionally one of the duties of the farmer's wife in England. An eighteenth-century book on dairying is dedicated

to the excellent DAIRY-WOMEN of Great Britain

and asks

... how should a Man know anything of Cheese making?

Continental farm-workers, however, made the cheese themselves; having jobs to do elsewhere, they could not wait for it to become very acid, and so evolved cheeses very different from the English kinds. In other ways, too, English cheeses are more troublesome to make. Indeed, perhaps they are altogether unsuitable for factory production: the Danes, who, without a national cheese of their own, have imitated French, German, Swiss, Italian and Norwegian cheeses, have never gone in for English varieties. English cheeses suffer particularly under factory conditions, since they require so much individual attention and factory owners are interested primarily in high output, doing everything possible to speed the manufacturing processes. Factory Stilton, for example, is pricked with rods to allow more oxygen to enter the cheese, and this results in a more rapid growth of the blue-vein mould which is chiefly responsible for Stilton ripening. Some English microbiologists have commented recently that

The old type of unpricked Stilton, with its wide veining, ripens slowly ... The modern pricked type ripens more rapidly, but it often has a fine close veining, and has lost some of its subtle flavour and long keeping quality.

The discovery of cheese had been a consequence of the Eurasian domestication of milk-yielding animals, horses, oxen, sheep and goats; and cheese was familiar to the civilizations of the ancient world – to the Egyptians, and the Hittites, in Greece and Rome – as it is to pastoral nomads of Siberia and Central Asia. It may have come late across the Channel. In France, Germany and Denmark perforated pots of the late Bronze Age have been found which may be evidence of cheese-making, since they could have been used in draining off the whey. Early Iron Age pots of a similar kind have been excavated in Wiltshire and in Somerset. Classical writers have something to say of cheese in Europe. Both Strabo, in his *Geography*, compiled in the last century B.C., and Caesar in his *de bello Gallico* mention that the Gauls made cheese. Caesar observed that cheese was a staple food of the Germans, but Strabo also wrote of the Britons that

they were relatively simple and barbaric – 'so much so that on account of their inexperience some of them, although well supplied with milk, make no cheese'.

In the Middle Ages the English had only soft cheese, hard cheese, green cheese, and the herb-flavoured spermyse. 'Green' denotes freshly-made cheese which has not matured. William Langland in the fourteenth century describes the plight of Piers Plowman

'I have no peny,' quod Pers, 'poletes to bugge,
Nouther gees ne grys, bote twey grene cheeses,
And a fewe cruddes and craym, and therf cake,
And a lof of benes and bren i-bake for my children.'

It seems from Chaucer (and other medieval writers, too) that the traditional English repast

With breed and chese and good ale in a jubbe,
suffysinge right y-nogh as for a day

was well established in those times; and many varieties of cheese may have possessed their self-same characteristics for hundreds of years.

Improved transport in the eighteenth century led to cheeses from different districts becoming widely known for the first time. In England Stilton cheese was probably first made at the beginning of the eighteenth century. It was certainly sold at that time from a public-house at Stilton, in Huntingdonshire, even if the actual making was carried out in another village. Some writers say that the originator was Mrs Paulet of Wymondham, in the Melton district of Leicestershire; but there cannot be many well-established kinds of cheese with so clear an origin.

The beginning of the end of the great local cheeses of England came when in 1870 members of the Royal Agricultural Society were so concerned about the poor quality of English farm-made cheeses that they recommended the introduction of factory cheese-making in imitation of the Americans, who had set up cheese factories nearly twenty years earlier. Today over ninety per cent of English cheese is factory-made, and a number of great English cheeses, like those of Gloucestershire, have disappeared; but it is still possible to buy some strange varieties in the shops.

The largest cheese in the world, and many say one of the finest, is Swiss Emmentaler, which may weigh as much as 230 lb., by contrast with which French Brie is usually only about one centimetre thick. Mysost, the most popular Norwegian 'cheese', is made from curdless whey which is stewed down until it is a brown sticky mass; cream is stirred in and, when pressed, the finished food is salty and fudge-like. Perhaps the *pièce de résistance* of extant cheese curiosities is Japanese 'Roquefort', This concoction is made from soya flour instead of milk, the protein of which is dissolved in water, precipitated by calcium chloride in place of rennet, and ripened by means of a fungal mould quite different from that of the European blue cheeses.

Paying by cheque

A CHEQUE is defined by English law as 'a bill of exchange drawn on a banker, payable on demand'.

That gives the clue to the origin of cheques, but the cheque-book and its neatly designed and printed rectangles of paper have come late into our daily life, with the rise of modern banking and industry in the nineteenth century. Early in the Middle Ages, if not before, bills of exchange were in use in Italy, and spread soon to England. They were employed for foreign transactions, but they were payable to one person only and could not be transferred. At the end of the Middle Ages bills of exchange began to be passed from one holder to another through endorsement, and instruments also developed which were drawn in favour of 'bearer', the title on them passing by delivery alone, that is to say, without the need of further endorsement.

Cheques may have been used in Italian cities as early as the fifteenth century, the Dutch adopting them in the sixteenth century and London in the seventeenth. One of the earliest surviving English cheques is an order cheque in this form:

Mr Thomas ffowles
I desire you to pay unto Mr Samuel Howard or order upon receipt hereof the sum of nine pounds thirteene shillings and sixpence and place it to the account of
Yr servant
14th August 1675　　　　　　　Edmund Warcupp

Payable either to Samuel Howard himself or to his order, this cheque was addressed to 'Mr Thomas ffowles, Gouldsmith, at his shop betweene the two Temple gates, Fleetestreet'.

Hoare's Bank, the last of the great private banks in London, where it also developed from a goldsmith's business, can trace its cheques back to much the same time. The first one on record was drawn a year later:

Mr Hoare
pray pay to the bearer hereof Mr William Morgan fifty four pounds ten shillings & ten pence & take his receipt for the same
Your Loving friend
11 July 1676　　　　　　　Will Hale

54 : 10 : 10
for Mr Richard Hoare at
The golden bottle in Cheapside

A long time had still to pass before cheques were used as widely as they are by ourselves. First of all they had to become both safe and cheap; and it was some while before the word 'check' or 'cheque' even acquired its present meaning. Early in the eighteenth century 'check' meant the counterfoil of a bill or draft, which provided a *check* on a transaction; then – part for whole – it began to signify a draft or bill which had a counterfoil, narrowing, late in the eighteenth century and early in the nineteenth, to our particular usage. Thackeray's readers knew what he meant in *Vanity Fair*, published in 1849, when Mr Osborne, of the tallow trade and the City of London, talked of his 'cheque-book' and the way it revealed his generosity to Mr Sedley. Yet this is the first instance of 'cheque-book' in print known to the compilers of the *Oxford English Dictionary*.

Hoare's Bank were having cheques printed for their customers by 1763. The bank's printed cheques of 1810 had no watermark, no perforation between cheque and counterfoil and no number; Hoare's first numbered cheques date from 1860.

Even in Thackeray's heyday cheque and cheque-book had not triumphed; and for one reason in particular. As bills of exchange, order cheques (in England) were subject to an *ad valorem* duty; and it was not until 1853 that the duty was reduced to a uniform penny (increased to twopence in 1918). Only bearer cheques drawn within a limited number of miles from the place where the banker carried on his business had been exempt from duty altogether. But these were not very safe instruments; it was just as sensible to transmit bank notes as cheques drawn to bearer. And it was not till seven years later, in 1860, that a court judgement gave cheques in England the full status of negotiability.

Convenient, safe, cheap, negotiable, easily drawn for the exact sums required, and then returned as a receipt, cheques became a national currency for settling home transactions. A scrutiny not long ago revealed that of a million pounds paid into a London bank all but £7000 was in cheque form. In America, the word 'cheque' has fallen into disuse; 'check' is the common usage.

'That playe most royal'

CHESS is too well known to require a detailed description – enough to say that this greatest and most intellectually elegant of games of skill is played by two persons on a board of eight by eight 'squares', each player having sixteen 'men' – king, queen, two bishops, two knights, two rooks or castles and eight pawns, each type of man with its own powers of move and capture, the object of the game being to checkmate the adversary's king – to force him, that is to say, into a position from which he cannot move without capture. Chess was invented in India, and before Indian chronology was put on a sound basis, exaggerated ideas as to the age of chess were formed and these are still often repeated.

It is in Indian and Persian works of the first half of the seventh century A.D., that chess is first mentioned; and of these works the oldest is the *Karnamak*, a Persian romance in which the hero is said to have excelled all his contemporaries at chess (*chatrang*). This was written about A.D. 600. Somewhat later chess is mentioned by Bāna, in his Sanskrit *Harshacharita*, in which he describes the peace and good order of Northern India under Sriharsha (A.D. 612–647), in a pas-

sage full of puns: 'under this king only bees (*shatpada*) quarrel in collecting dews (dues), the only feet cut off are those in metre, only chess boards (*ashtapada*) teach the positions of the *chaturanga* (army or chess).' The ashtapada was a board of eight by eight squares which had reached India from Greece in the first millennium B.C., Greece and India having been in contact at least from the time of Alexander the Great.

The older Arab historians agree that chess was an Indian invention which reached Persia in the reign of Chosroes I (A.D. 531–579), and this is generally accepted as true. The invention of chess cannot be placed much earlier, for from A.D. 458 to 540 Northern India lay under the cruel domination of Hun hordes from Central Asia which 'shook Indian society to its roots and severed the chain of tradition'. The invention of chess is accordingly dated about A.D. 560. This leaves rather a brief period for the adoption of chess in Persia, a difficulty that can be met by the facts that Chosroes aided in the destruction of the Huns, and that his interest in Indian culture led to his sending envoys to India to obtain a copy of the Fables of Pilpay. Later Arab historians ascribed the inception of chess to an Indian sage they called Sissa b. Dahir, borrowing the name which belonged to the first Indian prince with whom the Arabs came in contact. In fact the story is mythical.

That the inventor's idea was to make a game of skill in which the operations of an Indian army could be illustrated is evident from the names which he gave to the game and its 'men'. The complete Indian army from at least the fourth century B.C. contained four kinds of troops, infantry, cavalry, chariots and elephants, the aggregate being called a *chaturanga*, 'composed of four elements'. In his game of *chaturanga*, the inventor added to these four elements the king and his minister or commanding officer; and he arranged his armies on the two opposite outer rows of the *ashtapada*, placing one army on the first and second and the other on the seventh and eighth rows; on the second and seventh rows he placed eight pawns, and on the first and eighth rows, starting from the corners of the board, he placed chariot, horse and elephant; on the two middle squares he placed king and minister, the two kings standing on the same file. He gave the king a move of one step in any direction, the minister one step diagonally; to the chariot he gave the move which the rook has in our modern chess, and to the horse the leap of the modern knight. The elephant leapt diagonally over one square to the square immediately beyond. The pawn took single steps forward on the file on which it stands, made captures on an adjacent square diagonally in advance, and was promoted to the rank of minister on reaching the end of the board. The aim of the game was either to checkmate the opponent's king or to deprive him of all his men. Stalemate, which has no analogy in actual warfare, he gave as a win to the stalemated king.

The Persians only made two changes in the Indian game. They translated the names of the men and they made stalemate a draw. The Arabs when they conquered Persia, in A.D. 638–651, made no alteration in the Persian rules. Pre-Islamic Persia knew the game for less than a hundred years, but this brief period had an effect of great importance upon chess, since it gained a fixity of arrangement, a method of play, and a nomenclature which have attended the game everywhere in its western career.

Islam absorbed chess quickly and the names of many chess players before 750 have been preserved. Wherever Islam penetrated, so did chess, as far west as Spain, as far south as Zanzibar, as far east as the Malay Islands and as far north as Turkestan. But lawyers maintained that playing chess was against tradition and the Koran. The matter was only settled for the Sunnite sect by ash-Shafi'i (d. 820), who was himself a chess-player skilled in blindfold play, on the ground that chess was not only a game but a training in military tactics (it is part of the modern training of Russian army officers); he held that chess was lawful provided it was played with conventional men, was not played for money or in public, and did not interfere with the performance of religious duties. The Shiite sect omits the first condition. These rules never troubled the caliphs, who played freely and patronized good players, watching what we should call 'championship contests'. Players were classified by their skill, and the names of the chess champions from 800 to 950 are known. Two of these, al-'Adli and as-Sūli wrote books on chess which are still quoted, and

al-Lajlāj, a pupil of as-Sūli, enunciated the principles of play.

Christians on the Spanish Marches were playing chess soon after A.D. 1000, and it was played in Italy not much later. By 1100 it was played in Bavaria, France and England, and by 1250 it had reached Iceland. English and French players adopted the eastern names when they did not understand the meaning, and translated them when they did. Thus in England the minister became a 'fers' (Arabic *firzān*, Persian *Ferzēn*, 'wise man', 'counsellor'), the elephant an 'alfin' (Arabic *al-fīl*, 'the elephant'), and the chariot a 'rook' (from the Persian *rukh*, for 'chariot'). Our 'checkmate' is from the Arabic *shāh māta*, 'the king is helpless', 'Chess', too, came into English in the Middle Ages and goes back through Arabic and Persian to the Sanskrit *chaturanga*. 'Pawn' comes from a medieval French word for a foot-soldier. The Italians made chess a model of the European state, the minister becoming a queen and the elephant an elder who was often carved as a bishop. When the Lombards acquired the reputation of being the best European chess-

Fig. 9. From Caxton's *Game and Play of Chess*, 1474.

players, these changes of name were adopted in France and England. Chess became immensely popular, first in royal and knightly circles, then in towns and finally and more sparsely with the commonalty. By 1250 the earlier prejudice of the Church against chess was weakening, since the game was patronized by kings, and the monastic orders were gladly accepting chess as an alleviation of the monotony of convent life. By 1300 chess had acquired a literature of its own, had become the theme of poems, sermons and moralities, and was influencing the plot of romances. Chess had also become a regular feature in the education of royal and noble children.

Despite the general popularity of chess, there were signs that players were a little disappointed with it: a game took too long. Giraldus Cambrensis towards the end of the twelfth century noted that English players were dropping chess and turning to the solution of chess problems in which fewer men were used and which had a prescribed length. On the other hand, in Italy, the Lombard players were strengthening the moving power of some of the men, and by 1300 had given queen, pawn and king, in this order and for their first move only, an additional power. These attempts culminated in the great reform of the fourteen-nineties which gave queen and bishop their modern moves, made the study of Opening Play both possible and necessary, and revivified chess altogether. These changes led to the great chess activity of the period 1550–1640 in Italy and Spain, during which the reform was completed by the addition of 'castling', the combined move of king and rook. The reformed game was then adopted in Europe generally.

ILLUSTRATION: Page 360.

Porcelain from China

CHINAWARE, or porcelain, next to printing, is the greatest of Chinese contributions to world civilization. Both in the East and the West it became the vehicle of a new expression and new enjoyment of the beautiful. In Europe the efforts to copy porcelain (in which Böttger of Dresden was successful in 1709) led to the invention of substitutes which in turn placed a more delicate crockery within everybody's reach, and at last banished the older vessels of wood, horn, metal and coarse earthenware.

The word 'porcelain' is said to be derived from the Italian *porcellana*, a cowrie shell, and in European usage it is reserved for a thin, hard ware, breaking with a conchoidal or shell-like fracture (not a granular one) and ringing musically when it is struck. The empirical Chinese, less precise in terminology, called it tz'ŭ, a word used also to denote other hard wares, made from somewhat similar ingredients, but lacking the translucency which caught the imagination of the West and was regarded as the indispensable characteristic of true porcelain. The recipe known to the Chinese as early as the eighth century A.D. and used regularly thereafter for the finest wares, is a combination of kaolin, or china clay, with petuntse, which is china stone. Kaolin is a white clay, chemically almost pure. Petuntse is china clay which contains equal proportions of felspar and quartz; it melts in the kiln at a temperature between 1350° and 1450° Centigrade, binding together the infusible clay particles. The glaze applied to porcelain consists of china stone, frequently softened by the addition of lime, and the firing of the glaze and the body is completed in one operation under the same fierce heat.

In the Middle Ages Chinese porcelain was known in the civilized centres of the Near East, although it had not yet penetrated to Europe. Fragments of fine white porcelain have been excavated on the site of Samarra, on the Tigris, a capital of the Abbasid rulers of Mesopotamia which was occupied between A.D. 836 and 883. Later caravans passing through Mongolia and Turkestan, as well as Chinese and Arab ships sailing round the coast of India, brought the ware to Persia and to Egypt. In Europe it began to be known from the sixteenth century when the Portuguese, to be followed later by the Dutch and the English, traded to the Far East round the Cape of Good Hope. Porcelain commanded so high a price that competition to discover the recipe was now inevitable. Moreover the manufacture of porcelain was a state monopoly in China, and the possibility of making it a state monopoly in Europe as well tempted European rulers. Venice, Ferrara, Florence, Rouen all tried to solve the puzzle, but in vain. After Böttger had re-invented porcelain in 1709, the royal factory established by Augustus the Strong of Saxony attempted to keep the secret to itself, but rivals soon sprang up at Vienna, Bayreuth, Berlin and elsewhere, and by the end of the eighteenth century the manufacture of true porcelain had spread over the Continent, although France as a result of French research continued for a long while to produce a soft-bodied pseudo-porcelain. Early in the century some English potters, bent on practical results at any price, had begun to use a paste consisting largely of ground oriental china, blended with lime and gum. A pamphlet issued in 1716 speaks of 'making china in England as good as ever was brought from India', claiming to describe a 'try'd and infallible method' – the grinding up of the real article. Pseudo-porcelains were made and the great English factories of Chelsea, Bow, Derby, Lowestoft and Worcester were all established about the middle of the century. Then in 1756 Cookworthy discovered china clay and china stone in Cornwall (where he noticed a church tower actually built of china stone).

In the methods of decorating porcelain, as in its manufacture, the primacy lay with China, and for long the decoration applied in Europe both to porcelain and to softer wares was influenced by Chinese designs or frankly copied from them. The rise of European porcelain coincided with the rococo trend which was most charmingly and spontaneously expressed in the fragile fantasy of porcelain figures and moulded vessels. By the eighteenth century the virtuosity of the Chinese potter enabled him to decorate his products with floral and figured designs which rivalled painting in delicacy of line and colour. The method (the one universally adopted in Europe), was to fix enamel colours on the surface of a finished, glazed pot by a second firing in a muffle kiln at a much lower temperature. The *famille verte* wares of the K'ang Hsi period (1662–1722) and the *famille rose* wares of the Ch'ien Lung period (1736–1795) appealed to an eighteenth-century Europe which did not appreciate the monochrome wares still made in China in imitation of earlier taste.

For many people it is these more or less green monochromes, characteristic of the Sung dynasty (960–1279), which are the greatest achievement of the potter's craft. The history of them begins early in the Christian era. Over a period of five or six centuries the Chinese made a near-porcelain, now given the generic title of Yüeh ware, at a number of kilns in central China. The glaze of this ware was grey-green, perhaps in imitation of jade, at all times the most highly prized material of Chinese crafts, and it was this that led on to the bluish-green and brownish-green celadon ware of the Sung period.

The white porcelain (of the kind excavated in Mesopotamia) was ancestor to Ting ware, a creamy-white glazed porcelain, often of astonishing thinness, decorated with moulded or carved designs. The Ju, pinkish-grey, and the Kuan, light greyish-blue and deliberately crackled, were other types produced at kilns under imperial patronage. Variegation of colour is found only on the Chün, with its lush mingling of purple and blue, and on tea-bowls decorated with the effects known as hare's fur and oil-spot, while colour pattern is almost entirely confined to spots and dappling of black and brown, and to the brown painted floral themes and relief scrolls of the Tzechow ware.

None of these types of porcelain were imitated in Europe. The earliest Chinese pottery which Europeans copied was the famous blue-and-white porcelain; this has been made continuously from the fourteenth century to the present day – until mid-nineteenth century at the imperial factory at Ching-tê-chên. The design was painted on the body of the pot before it was dipped in the glaze; pattern, glaze and body were then fired in a single kilning. This technique has not been reproduced in Europe, but from the seventeenth century onwards its effect was imitated on soft-bodied wares, at Delft, Lambeth and many other factories, and the tradition so founded continues to the present day in our domestic crockery.

When imports of Chinese porcelain were at their height, in the eighteenth century, it was not uncommon for English customers to place orders to their own specification through the agents of the East India Company. Thus 'armorial porcelain', bearing the crests of English families, was shipped from Hong Kong, and the Chinese factories strove to meet European requirements in shapes and design. This produced porcelain in European patterns with the most quaintly Chinese accent. When 'willow pattern' became popular in England after its invention about 1780 by Thomas Turner of the Caughley works, it was sometimes copied by the Chinese for the English trade.

ILLUSTRATION: Pages 128 and 129.

Stage coaches, snow and redbreasts

CHRISTMAS CARDS only began to appear in quantities in the eighteen-sixties. 'I hate those redbreasts', cried *Punch* in 1869; and it is startling to find that the cry is so old and was then so new. Not until 1877 did *The Times* pontifically declare them a great social evil, and it was following difficulties with the mail in 1879 that there came from the Post Office in 1880 the first insistent cry of 'Post Early'.

When we consider the antiquity of the Valentine (q.v.), which in its printed form is at least a hundred years older than the Christmas card, it is curious that no enterprising stationer should have thought of extending the notion of greetings; and that when Henry Cole had invented the Christmas card in 1843, it should have taken twenty years to popularize the idea. Cole's card, designed for him by T. C. Horsley, R.A., is in the form of a triptych, giving it a fashionably medieval flavour; the ornaments dividing the sections are derived from Dürer's Prayer Book of Maximilian. (This antique 'semi-Gothicism' recurs in another early Christmas card designed in 1848 by the artist William Maw Egley.) On the pioneer card the central section shows a jolly family eating and drinking (a point which brought Cole much criticism from the Temperance Movement), while the side panels show good works: clothing the naked and feeding the hungry. It was intended, not for Cole's personal use, but to be sold at his art shop in Old Bond Street, which had the object of raising public taste. For, as Horsley said of Cole: 'He devoted much time in getting artistic treatment applied to unconsidered trifles as well as the weightiest matters.'

Sir Henry Cole (1808–1882) was one of the most fascinating of the giant race of Victorian administrators of whom Chadwick, who equipped London with drains, is the best known. To some extent (and in fact a very large extent) Cole was responsible for the inception of the Public Record Office, the postal system and the Great Exhibition of 1851 with all the aftermath of its success: the development of the Museums' site in South Kensington, the system of Schools of Art, the Albert Hall, and the Royal College of Music. His particular concern was with industrial and applied art, which brought him at last, after many vicissitudes, to become first Director of the Victoria and Albert Museum which he had inaugurated.

In spite of his talent for publicity, Cole's Christmas card seemed abortive, until in the eighteensixties the idea was taken up by the tycoons of Victorian stationery: William Ward of Marcus Ward and Co., Belfast and London; Raphael Tuck, Thomas de la Rue, and Louis Prang of Boston, Mass. The suddenness of the conquest may be illustrated statistically. Jonathan King's English collection of cards issued between 1862 and 1894 contains 163,000 varieties, fills 700 volumes, and weighs between six and seven tons. The American Antiquarian Society's collection of Louis Prang's cards alone contains sixty-seven volumes, of which one small thin volume contains Valentines. The first trump card was played by William Ward when, in 1868, he saw the work of the young Kate Greenaway at an exhibition at the Dudley Gallery in London. Her first card (a Valentine) sold 25,000 copies in a few weeks. Her cards had nothing to do with Christmas. Indeed, so pagan and irrelevant was the general tone of the trade, that the Society for the Promotion of Christian Knowledge had to intervene and design its own *Christian* Christmas cards.

The reasons for the success of Christmas cards are easy to discover. In England before the Industrial Revolution, Christmas was still a traditional festival celebrated by families and neighbours within the village or town. As that Revolution proceeded, the Yule log, mummers and waits became picturesque survivals described by novelists and antiquaries, and all the festivities of Twelfth Night, the cake, the King and Queen, were gone and already forgotten. New symbols had to be invented or imported. Hence the Christmas tree from Germany, the children's party,

Santa Claus, and the Christmas card. The Christmas card went to friends and relations now scattered in the new towns, or overseas in California, Saskatchewan, New South Wales, Van Diemen's Land, New Zealand; or else it went to the Old Folks in the ancestral village to which no one proposed to return. The stage-coaches bowling along (now they had been superseded by the railway), the brigantines in full sail, the village churches with lights a-twinkle, the snowmen in the frosty yards, robin redbreasts in that Christmas snow which so seldom falls at Christmas, were emblems whose cosiness concealed both yearning and fear; a combination seen pre-eminently in the architect of the New Christmas, Charles Dickens himself. (See also *Valentines, Christmas Tree.*)

ILLUSTRATION: Page 368.

The Christmas tree

The **CHRISTMAS TREE** is a fairly modern symbol of rejoicing, although its main features – the evergreen foliage and the lighted candles – link it with ancient pre-Christian traditions.

It is hard now to grasp what darkness, cold and isolation meant in earlier days, when winter set in. The darkness of the shortening days as well as the fear of the winter certainly contributed to the names given to November, 'The Month of the Dead', 'the Month of Mourning'. Samhain Eve (Hallowe'en, 31 October) was particularly dangerous, because the dead were believed to return that night from the other world. Manifold attempts were made to welcome them to their old homes: green branches were put up, and fires were lit, for the dead love the warming fire. The Christian Church, in a struggle lasting many centuries, tried to wean the people from these pagan practices by sublimating the Samhain rites and transferring them to the more joyful feasts of midwinter: Christmas, the New Year, and Twelfth Night. It has thus become difficult to differentiate precisely between original Samhain rites and the customs practised at Christmas, on New Year's Eve and on Twelfth Night, and practically impossible to say whether a particular rite is a survival of the ancient welcoming of the dead or of practices supposed to avert evil spirits. They were confused a long time ago and have now been lost sight of.

A thorough investigation of the German origin of the Christmas tree and its gradual reception in other countries has recently been made by Mrs L. Weiser-Aall of Oslo. The first written evidence she has found dates from the beginning of the sixteenth century, when a decorated 'May tree' was put up at Christmas in the assembly rooms of various German guilds. By that time, the great cultural transformations which had begun in former centuries were more or less completed: until 1500, the old peasant culture and medieval religious notions prevailed; after 1517, Protestantism spread over Germany, and many new customs, fashions and habits were passed on from the new middle class, living in towns, to people living in the country.

During the second half of the sixteenth century the Protestant town-dwellers devised their own Christmas celebration. They adopted the Christmas tree of the Roman Catholic guilds, causing opposition among Protestant theologians, a fact to which we owe the first reference, in 1642, to a Christmas tree in a private house. Liselotte von der Pfalz, the famous letter-writer, remembered having seen in her childhood, about 1660, a box tree, the branches of which supported candles. During the seventeenth and eighteenth centuries the custom spread from town to town, from the courts of the German princes to high officials and to the wealthy middle class. Shortly after 1822 German merchants introduced the Christmas tree to Norway and England, notably first to Manchester. Mrs Weiser-Aall has found that clergymen, civil servants, teachers and emigrants returning from the United States, also helped to spread the custom, as well as sailors who had seen some Christmas trees in Germany. Prince Albert's Christmas tree at Windsor (1841) and many descriptions and illustrations in journals and books gave further popularity to the custom.

In many Protestant countries the distribution of gifts among the children was postponed in the nineteenth century from St Nicolas's Day (6 December) to 24 December – and in course of time St Nicolas, the patron saint of schoolboys, became Father Christmas. Only small gifts were usual in the nineteenth century, and they were often fastened to the Christmas tree itself: dried plums, raisins, nuts, apples, gingerbread in the shapes of Adam and Eve or animals. The apples as well as the figures of Adam and Eve are reminiscent of the medieval Paradise plays and of the legend that the apple-tree of Paradise was, by Christ's birth, relieved of its curse and was allowed again to bear fruit (A. Spamer, *Deutsche Volkskunde*). In the countryside the farmers were for a long time too thrifty to make presents, but eventually the custom of present-giving conquered the countryside together with the Christmas tree, which the children were often allowed to 'plunder'; it usually remained in the house until Epiphany.

In Germany the children were never allowed to see the tree before the candles were lit on Christmas Eve; only sometimes the older children are allowed to help with the decoration of the tree, from which long chains of silver and gold tinsel or coloured balls reflecting the candlelight are suspended. Nowadays the decorations are often less colourful: silver lametta, 'angels' hair', and silver balls allude to the glittering of hoar-frost and icicles. In Bavaria, small Christmas trees are taken to the churchyard and are put on the graves of the recently departed. In England, as well as on the Continent, we are now witnessing the unfortunate change-over from wax candles to coloured electric bulbs. Here and elsewhere, for example in London and New York, we may also notice the 'Christmas Tree for all' in churches or on public squares. Soviet Russia has its public Christmas trees with Grandfather Frost and the Snow Maiden, as well as domestic Christmas trees. Since 1950, Norway every year has sent some of her finest fir trees as presents to English and Scottish towns. In Great Britain the now widespread popularity of the Christmas tree among all classes means also an extensive trade in young conifers, in particular the Norway Spruce, much of which is supplied from the new state forests.

Mrs Weiser-Aall has shown in a convincing manner that true symbols such as the evergreen tree and the lights never die out. Their interpretations may vary in the course of time, but the fundamental experience remains the same. Sometimes the Christmas tree is interpreted as a Christian symbol. The 'Christmas Tree for all', which has been adopted by many countries, is now understood as a symbol of unity and concord among nations, religions and classes.

ILLUSTRATION: Plate 14.

Moving pictures

The **CINEMA**, or cinematography, depends on the principle of the persistence of vision, a phenomenon mentioned by Lucretius about 65 B.C., by which we often attribute to an object which moves very rapidly before our eyes, a size and a shape it does not possess. Or the object may be seen in more than one place at once, if it moves fast enough. All this is due to the fact that the retina retains images for a fraction of a second ($\frac{1}{10}$ to $\frac{1}{20}$ of a second, according to the brightness and colour of the object seen). Early in the nineteenth century a keen interest in optics led to the invention of many amusing toys which depended on these peculiarities, and which, like the earlier magic lantern (q.v.), were steps in the evolution of the cinema.

The first was the thaumatrope, invented by Dr Fitton about 1826, though generally attributed to Dr Parris, who made it for sale. This is simply a cardboard disc painted with a bird, for example, on one side and a cage on the other; when twirled round rapidly by means of a cord fixed to the sides of the disc, the bird appears to be *in* the cage, because both sides of the disc are seen at once.

A more elaborate application of the principle was the phenakistoscope of the Belgian scientist Joseph Plateau, and the stroboscope of Simon Stampfer of Vienna, independently invented by them in 1832. In these a number of drawings of different phases of a movement were arranged round the edge of a cardboard disc and viewed through another disc with a number of slots corresponding to the number of pictures. On making the discs revolve rapidly, the observer gains a momentary view of each picture in the series as each slot arrives opposite the respective image. Owing to the persistence of vision, all the pictures blend on the retina, giving a lifelike impression of a figure in motion. Another instrument for the production of animated pictures was devised by the mathematician W. G. Horner in 1833 (and named zoetrope in 1867); in this a similar series of drawings is arranged round the inside of a revolving slotted drum.

The first person to project animated effects on a screen, by painting figures round a glass disc and illuminating them by a magic lantern, was Franz von Uchatius, an Austrian officer, about 1850. His apparatus was put on the market by a Viennese optician in 1853, and soon after a showman named Ludwig Döbler gave public performances with it all over Europe – the first person to earn his living by moving pictures.

Fourteen years later an English amateur photographer, Alfred Pollock, suggested taking on a circular rotating plate a series of fifty instantaneous photographs of a walking man, and arranging the positive prints around a phenakistoscope or stroboscope disc, remarking that if revolved and viewed through a slotted disc 'the image might walk at the same pace as the subject had done'.

Professor Janssen, the French astronomer, constructed such a camera for photographing the transit of Venus in 1874, and he foresaw the possibility of recording rapidly with his 'revolver' camera (in which 48 photographs were taken in succession) the movements of animals and birds, provided that faster plates were invented. His suggestion did not pass unheeded, for after the introduction of gelatine plates (which were twenty times faster than wet collodion) in 1880, the physiologist Dr E. J. Marey of Paris adapted Janssen's camera for recording birds in flight. In 1882 he devised a photographic gun which was aimed at the flying bird like an ordinary rifle, the pictures being taken round the edge of a circular glass plate at the rate of twelve per second. As these photographs were extremely small, Marey copied the different images in wax, and their animated effect was exceedingly realistic when viewed in the zoetrope.

Five years later he devised a camera to take photographs of moving animals and human beings on a roll of sensitive paper, which in 1889 he replaced by transparent celluloid film. The camera had two spools, one containing the paper (or film), which was unrolled in a series of intermittent movements, coming to rest at the moment of exposure; on the other spool the exposed film was rolled up again. The film was kept tight by a compressor, and the feed motion was effected by a cam. The exposure of one thousandth of a second was made by two slotted discs rotating in opposite directions. The whole mechanism was put in motion by turning a crank, and the moment the subject (animal or human) began to run the operator pressed a trigger to start the film. Photographs were taken as long as pressure was maintained on the trigger. This camera, which Marey called the 'chronophotographe', enabled him to secure a much longer and more rapid series of pictures than had ever been possible before. As many as sixty exposures a second could be made.

Marey was stimulated to animated photography by the pioneer work of Eadweard Muybridge (1830–1904), an Englishman, bred as Edward Muggeridge, who settled in America and in 1878 and 1879 had taken an extensive series of trotting and galloping horses on the private racecourse of Governor Stanford of California. Muybridge used a battery of twelve to twenty-four cameras in a row to record the movement; the horse itself making the exposures by breaking threads stretched across the track from the camera shutters. His photographs showed that the conventional 'rocking-horse' attitude in which galloping horses were represented was inaccurate; but to counter the scepticism aroused by the curious attitudes which are too rapid for the eye to perceive in nature, he devised a projection instrument, the zoopraxiscope, in which the photographs were arranged round the edge of a glass disc.

Muybridge demonstrated the zoopraxiscope to audiences in Paris, London, Berlin and New York in 1881 and 1882. Everywhere people flocked to see this animated projection of horses trotting, galloping and jumping over hurdles, deer leaping along, birds flying, athletes wrestling and turning somersaults, just as if it were all happening in real life. It was a sensation no one wanted to miss, and we may well regard these demonstrations as the first cinema shows. Between 1884 and 1885 Muybridge greatly extended the series of his animated photographs with the encouragement of the University of Pennsylvania, increasing the battery of cameras up to thirty-six for a still closer analysis of movement. He obtained more detailed pictures owing to the much faster gelatine plate which had meanwhile been introduced.

For the purpose of commercial shows the projection of photographs on a glass disc proved a cul-de-sac, for the number of pictures which could be placed on a disc was very limited; the most that was ever achieved, by a spiral arrangement, was 300, in Leo Kamm's Kammatograph (1898). His tiny photographs were taken and projected by the same camera, the performance of the movie lasting exactly forty seconds.

Inspired by Muybridge, a host of experimenters now took up animated photography; but as a battery of cameras was both expensive and impracticable, like Marey, they tried to secure similar results with a single camera and from one point of view. Complete success in the reproduction of motion was not possible until improvements in the manufacture of celluloid provided a long, thin strip of sensitized material upon which any desired number of photographs could be taken in rapid succession. This was placed on the market in the autumn of 1889.

Pre-eminent among the early experimenters and inventors of cinematographic apparatus using celluloid roll film were Marey and his assistant George Demeny, the brothers Auguste and Louis Lumière in France, J. A. R. Rudge, William Friese-Greene and Mortimer Evans, Louis le Prince, Robert W. Paul and Birt Acres in England, and Thomas Edison in America.

As with so many inventions, there is some dispute about the credit for the invention of cinematography, and national feelings run rather high in these matters. Both Friese-Greene and Marey had perfected their cine-cameras using celluloid film by 1889, while the first perfected projector, the 'cinematographe', was introduced by the brothers Lumière in 1895 when they gave the first public performances in France (and indeed anywhere). On 20 February 1896 followed the earliest public 'cinematographe' show in Britain, at the Polytechnic Institution in Regent Street. The same night R. W. Paul gave a semi-private show at the Finsbury Technical College with his 'theatrographe' (later called 'animatographe'). A fortnight later the Lumière show (of fourteen short films) moved to the Empire Music Hall in Leicester Square, where it proved such a draw that the neighbouring Alhambra Music Hall, wanting a similar show, invited R. W. Paul to exhibit his moving pictures there.

During the next few years several London variety theatres added a moving picture show (usually news-reels) to their programmes. Motion pictures also became profitable attractions at restaurants, tea-places and fair-grounds. The Balham Empire, in London, deserves mention as the first 'picture palace', dating from 1907.

Most of the early films were news-reels, humorous 'shorts', and travel items, averaging 75 to 150 feet. Many small firms, apparently, were in the habit of faking topical events in those days, for the Warwick Trading Co., then the largest film company in the world, explained that their news-reels from all parts of the world were taken 'on the spot, and not on Hampstead Heath or in somebody's back garden'. They sent their Bioscope men to the Boer War – the first war to be covered by cinematography.

The most ambitious attempt at a film drama before 1900 was due to the same enterprising firm. *Joan of Arc* was a film 800 feet long, and 'A grand spectacular cinematograph production in twelve scenes, with about 500 persons, all superbly costumed'.

ILLUSTRATION: Pages 68 and 69.

Clocks and watches

The **CLOCK,** *i.e.* the mechanical clock, was a medieval invention. The ancient world had measured time, none too accurately, by the sundial and the water-clock. Both these were devices known to the Babylonians in the second millennium B.C., and both were improved by the Greeks.

When and where the first machine clock was made is still a matter for investigation and disagreement. A conservative date is the early fourteenth century, and the place was probably northern Italy or southern Germany. Much was certainly involved in the development of the clock – the cloudy north (sundials had been well enough for the cloudless weather of Mesopotamia, Egypt, Greece and the Mediterranean), the daily time-table of monks, and what one might call man's invasion of the night as he found for himself better illuminants.

By 1350 clocks had reached some degree of perfection in the primitive stage of the craft. Most, if not all, of the early clocks were large; and were set up in church towers, where they guided monks in the performance of their office. They were made of iron, by members of blacksmith's guilds; and were driven by the suspension of weights, mainsprings not being introduced till late in the fifteenth century. Smaller clocks may have existed in the early period, but none has been discovered. It has been argued that the earliest clocks may have been constructed in wood, and so failed to survive.

A mechanical clock, by definition, is not merely a series of tooth-wheels: it must – and this is the distinction – have a controlling device, an 'escapement', which regulates the speed of the wheels and so the speed with which the hands traverse the dial. For more than 400 years the primitive 'verge escapement' performed this duty; though the improved anchor form, introduced in England in 1671, became general soon after in long case or 'grandfather' clocks.

The controlling escapement must itself be controlled, which was effected till 1657 by the foliot, the weighted cross-bar of the early turret clocks. As an alternative to the cross-bar a balance wheel was used in the smaller domestic clocks. In 1657 Christiaan Huygens, the Dutch physicist and mathematician, made both forms obsolete by introducing the pendulum to control the escapement speed. Huygens's pendulum and William Clement's anchor escapement of 1671, between them, made accurate timekeeping possible at last. The pendulum has a natural and regular motion under the attraction of gravity, and since the time of vibration of a pendulum varies as the square root of its length, regulation is easily effected by increasing the length or decreasing it.

Other improvements and inventions were to follow, but the principles of timekeeping had now been settled. A step had been taken towards our organized world of mensuration.

Up to the introduction of the pendulum, domestic or chamber clocks were cased in metal – at first iron, then engraved and gilded brass. Since the earliest chamber clocks were driven by weight, they had to hang on the wall. After the medieval development of the mainspring, clocks could be smaller and made to stand on the table, as shown in Holbein's picture of the merchant Georg Gisze. Elaborate casing now began; and a great many such table clocks were made by German craftsmen in Augsburg and Nuremberg during the seventeenth century.

One may say broadly that from the sixteenth century each country developed its own national styles. Thus England's distinctive wall clock was the type now known as the lantern clock, cased in brass with a silvered chapter or hour ring, and surmounted by a large bell. These lantern clocks enjoyed a long vogue of more than a hundred years from about 1610. The Fromanteels, a Dutch family of clockmakers, brought the pendulum over to England about 1660, three years after it had been introduced by Huygens. The grandfather clock was now developed, the cabinet-maker joining his craft to that of the clock-maker. Fine wooden cases were also made for the mantel or table clock, and design reached its perfection in England between 1675 and 1720.

The craftsmanship devoted to the movement, the hands and the dials by the clockmaker and to the case by his cabinet-maker were exquisite, particularly in the early years.

A watch, in all its essentials, is a clock made small and portable; and it descends from the table clocks which followed when the mainspring was introduced as an alternative to the suspended weight. By 1510, or thereabouts, Peter Henlein of Nuremberg was making clocks so small that they could be 'carried on the bosom or in the purse'. The small portable clocks of this period were contained in a drum-shaped case about two inches in diameter. The first watches may have been similar, with a ring attached to the case to take a neck-cord or chain. Such watches were certainly made around 1575, but records of Henlein's time prove that another type – the spherical or musk-ball watch – was specially associated with him.

The musk-ball or musk-apple, or pomander, was a pierced ball filled with herbs and scent against infection or against stench, and was attached to the lady's girdle. Made in imitation of the musk-ball, Henlein's watches were pierced to emit the sound of the bell, since they struck the hour.

Watches were unmistakably worn as ornaments by 1600, in cases of brass, gilded and chased and bejewelled with pearls and garnished with coloured enamels. Between 1600 and 1650 the shapes became fanciful – stars, crosses, skulls, buds, etc. If the cases were usually of silver or of gilt brass, often now they were cut from rock crystal, agate, or some other ornamental stone.

After the middle of the seventeenth century watch-cases were usually circular and rather thick, and they were rounded at the circumference – in which we see the forerunner of the pocket watch; the watch, in fact, was housed in the breeches pocket until the evolution of man's dress produced the waistcoat.

Watches so far had been poor timekeepers: Huygens once more came to the rescue; and in 1675 made known his use of the hairspring, a spiral spring coupled to the arbor (i.e. axis) of the balance wheel, as controller of the escapement. This was as important to the watch as the pendulum had been to the clock: it made for more precision and placed watchmaking on a scientific basis. Watches could now be provided with a minute hand. Previously an hour hand had sufficed, and the dial had been calibrated only into hours and quarters.

If the balance spring opened the way to exact timekeeping, it also set watchmakers a great many technical problems. First an improved escapement had to be evolved to take full advantage of the timekeeping properties of the balance spring. Ultimately Thomas Mudge devised the lever escapement in 1759, which in principle is the escapement used today. Improvement was driven forward by one matter of urgency: mariners needed an accurate timekeeper 'to find the longitude'; and that meant counteracting the

effects which heat and cold have on the balance spring. The solution came before the end of the eighteenth century, and was the cumulative work of several men; balance wheels were contrived of two metals with different expansions. Ordinary watches benefited from this work of perfecting the marine chronometer, and by 1800 a good watch might be expected to keep time to within one minute in twenty-four hours. From the early nineteenth century the watch has remained fundamentally the same machine, improved in many details, particularly in being all of a piece, without the need of a key for winding and handsetting.

Many of the adjuncts of the modern wrist watch (strapped there as the one place where the watch is at once easily and quickly read and also conveniently out of the way) are simply old ideas perfected and brought down to wristwatch size. These include the automatic or selfwinding mechanism, the calendar and the alarm. (See also *Cuckoo Clock, Hour-glass.*)

ILLUSTRATION: Page 273.

Cloth and clothes in Europe

CLOTH and the making of cloth developed in the neolithic economies of man out of the simpler and more primitive basketry and matting. But since ancient cloth survives only in exceptional circumstances – usually constant dampness and constant temperature are the best preservatives – it is rash to generalize about prehistoric cloth and clothing in western Europe.

The earliest surviving cloth of western Europe comes from the neolithic lake dwellings of Switzerland, c. 2000 B.C., and all of it is made of linen thread. Vegetable fibres seem to have been used extensively in the Early Bronze Age in England, and that flax was known and grown in Holland and Britain at that time is proved by the occasional impressions of flax seed found on pottery. Flax was grown and linen was made in Egypt before 3000 B.C. Nettles yield a good fibre, and were certainly used to weave a linen like cloth in Denmark from the Late Bronze Age until the nineteenth century A.D. (there is evidence for the direct cultivation of nettles in historic times in Norway and Denmark). A shift from vegetable to animal fibres was inevitable with the rise of mixed farming. In Mesopotamia sheep were raised for wool some five thousand years ago, and from the Bronze Age wool was undoubtedly the commonest material for cloth in northern Europe.

In Britain two examples of wool cloth are known from the Early Bronze Age, and later on it seems to have ousted the vegetable fibres. For minor items of dress horsehair was occasionally used. It is curious, since one naturally thinks of pelts as the first clothing, that there is no direct evidence of the use of animal skins in this way in northern and western Europe until the Early Iron Age, when they become predominant.

All the early cloths are worked in a plain (tabby) weave. They have firm and elaborate selvedges on three or four of their edges. The reason was partly economy of thread and partly the method of preparing the warp for a vertical loom. Some of the Danish Bronze Age cloths are quite large, and two people must have worked at the loom side by side.

Other techniques used to make garments include a type of twined work which originates in basketry. It was laborious and employed only for vegetable fibres in the Neolithic and Bronze Ages. Parallel hanks made the foundation and were held together by widely spaced transverse pairs of twisted threads. A form of netting, known in Scandinavia as 'sprang', was also suitable for smaller garments.

The pieces of neolithic linen from the Swiss lakes (described by E. Vogt, *Geflechte und Gewebe der Steinzeit*, Basle, 1937) are now black and carbonized so that the colouring is lost. However, there are indications that at least two colours were employed in a piece, and probably more. One intricate brocaded design has been reconstructed, and consists of borders of chequered and dotted patterns, the centre containing two elongated triangles with a panel of stripes similar to the border between. Stripes in other cloths are formed by introducing a secondary weft thread which floats across the face of the cloth, held down only by every fourth warp thread. The beginning and finishing selvedges are often most elaborate, making a thick rep effect; sometimes

they have extra threads inserted to form plaited fringes.

Most of these neolithic cloths are too fragmentary to suggest a reconstruction of the garments they formed, but one piece of twined work, in which tufts of fibres were inserted while it was being made, is twenty inches long and may be part of a cape, possibly similar to the Maori feathered cloaks.

We know more about Bronze Age woollens, owing to spectacular discoveries in Denmark of clothed bodies in oak coffins made of split and hollowed trunks. Seven of them are sufficiently preserved to give a fairly complete picture of the dress worn between 1400 and 1200 B.C. All the cloth was made from brown wool of poor quality (Broholm and Hald, *Costume of the Bronze Age in Denmark*, Copenhagen, 1940). The women wore 'jumpers' made from one piece. There was a slit for the head; and deep horizontal cuts into the cloth about halfway up the sides enabled the upper half to fold over horizontally, so as to form the shoulders and the elbow-length sleeves, while the lower part was joined in a vertical seam at the back. The jumper on the woman found at Skrydstrup was embroidered, the neck outlined with concentric lines of twisted threads, the upper side of the sleeve decorated with a series of raised ribs.

The other main garment seems to have been the curious 'corded skirt', which perhaps was not so unsuitable for the pleasanter climatic conditions of Bronze Age Europe. This skirt consisted of a narrow woven band at the top, from which there hang a series of thick cords ending in loops caught in place by a pair of twisted threads. The garment went twice round the body, the top band extending beyond the skirt to enable it to be tied in front. The skirt rested on the hips and reached down almost to the knees.

The Skrydstrup woman had remarkable long fair locks which were arranged under a net of horsehair. More substantial caps worked in 'sprang' were found in two graves. The belts were most carefully made, in rep weave (in one case with an effect of vertical zigzags due to spinning the threads in different directions) and the belt ends had been finished with elaborate tassels. The belts were used to support an ornamental bronze belt-plate at the front of the waist or to suspend a comb or knife. Footwear was common to both sexes; a small cloth round the foot and ankle served as protection from the leather shoe, which was made in one piece and held in place by thongs across the instep.

The men's clothes consisted of a cloak, gown, cap and belt. The cloak was a large oval piece of cloth; one such cloak had a sewn-in pile, and was worn hanging straight from the shoulders to the calf, with the edge against the neck turned back. The shorter under-garment or gown worn by men was wrapped round the body under the armpits, and was secured at the waist with a belt of leather or wool and over the shoulder by a strap. Men wore both plain caps of cloth and more intricate caps with thick sewn-in piles. There is some indication that these fashions may not have been peculiar to Denmark. For instance a belt of horsehair was found at Armoy, in Co. Antrim, Ireland, which seems to be a copy of the woollen ones already described; it had thick tasselled ends and a zigzag pattern, which had been made by using a herringbone weave.

The use of twill weaves and simple variants appear in the Late Bronze Age and become common in the Iron Age. The first cloth with a recognizable check pattern also appears in the Late Bronze Age, known from a cloak found at Gerumsberg, in Sweden, woven with narrow stripes of two shades of brown in an irregular herringbone weave. A cloth of similar date found in a salt-mine near Salzburg has a brocaded check pattern of green and brown on buff. The Iron Age saw much refinement in weaving, not only in the variety of pattern and use of colour, but in the regularity and fineness of some of the products: thus a beautiful diamond twill has been discovered at Balmaclellan in Kirkcudbrightshire, Scotland, of the second century A.D.

For a picture of Iron Age clothing one has to turn to scattered finds from the bogs of Scandinavia and northern Germany. There was a marked change in fashion beginning at the end of the Late Bronze Age, partly because the climate was now more severe and partly because of classical influences seeping northwards from the Mediterranean. One feature already mentioned was the extensive use of animal skins for clothes. In contrast with Bronze Age cloaks of wool, hide cloaks were now worn, made of many pieces

shaped to a yoke, either symmetrical with a centre opening or asymmetrical with a side opening leaving the right arm free. The cloak was fastened at the throat either by thongs or by a button and loop. Some oblong cloths which have been found may also have been worn as cloaks. Under the cloaks men wore tunics and trousers. The tunics were made of cloth; they reached below the waist, where they were held by a belt, and they had wide transverse slits for the head. Across the sleeves and shoulders they were unnecessarily wide, so that they were worn gathered on the forearm. Some had long sleeves and tight-fitting bodies, others were wide in the bodies with short sleeves. The trousers are only represented so far by leather examples. At the upper edge there are straps for taking a belt, the legs are either long with a flap over the instep and inside the shoe-lacing, or short, coming just below the knee. Leather skull caps were also worn, and one is known with thongs which tied under the chin. Footwear had hardly changed since the Bronze Age.

Only one skirt is known from the Early Iron Age, long and full, made of a boldly checked twill. A thong was slotted through to draw the skirt up at the waist. This skirt of about 400 B.C. was found in a peat bog at Huldremose in Jutland; above and over the skirt the woman wore a skin cloak. Another garment seems to have been similar to the classical *peplos*, sometimes woven as a cylinder and sometimes a normal open cloth. For this no sewing was required, the cloth was fastened together at the shoulders, generally with brooches, the rest of the top edge hanging down to form armholes. A cord drew the waist into folds. Quite large rectangular pieces of cloth seem to have been worn at the shoulders and the neck.

Greater 'skin-comfort' in clothing first came to Europe with silk from China, and with cotton, which was anciently woven in India, Egypt and China (and also in the New World before the arrival of Europeans). Until late historic times cotton fabrics were introduced only as articles of trade, climate limiting the cultivation of the cotton plant to the warmer areas. (See also *Spindle, Silk, Nylon*.)

ILLUSTRATION: Pages 170 and 171

The 'cart of Kocs'

COACHES spread through Europe in the six-teenth century, the word for them in English and in most languages going back to the *kocsi*, or in full the *kocsi szeker* or 'cart of Kocs', which is a small town of northern Hungary between Buda-pest and Vienna.

Rumbling round a corner out of fairyland, gilded and glittering in a procession to Westmin-ster Abbey or the Houses of Parliament, a coach, or a 'state chariot', now seems to us an archaic and cumbrous vehicle. But the coach began a re-volution in transport. Four-wheeled, weather-proof, more sumptuously equipped, lighter and more comfortable, since the body was suspended on leather straps, the new vehicle looked forward over the centuries to the railway coach, the limou-sine with what we still call fine 'coach work', and the motor-coach. For a long while awkward and heavy vehicles of one kind and another, and even covered vehicles, had been in use; but these had carried goods rather than passengers, generally speaking, the passengers being chiefly women. The coach began an era of enclosed travel for men as well as women; and before the coach long journeys and short journeys were made to a far greater extent upon horseback, in all weathers.

Coaches reached England early in the Tudor period. The Elizabethan chronicler Stow main-tained that the first English coach was built in 1555 for Henry Manners, second Earl of Rutland, but there is evidence for the coach on English roads some twenty years at least before that time. In England and in other countries moralists were upset by the new vehicles: they were luxurious and they were effeminate; and at first they were indeed the perquisite of privilege and wealth. Queen Elizabeth had her coach – and her Dutch coachman – and before 1600 coaches were a fa-miliar sight in London, the satirist of *Pleasant Quippes for Upstart New-fangled Gentlewomen* (1595) writing of wantons who dashed in coaches 'from house to house, from street to street':

> As poorer truls must ride in cartes,
> So coaches are for prouder hearts.

It was these vehicles of fashion which began the endemic traffic problems of London and other great cities, blocked streets, becoming still more of a nuisance in London in the first twenty years of the seventeenth century, when coaches for hire were added to private coaches. Attempts were made to ease matters by more than one royal pro-clamation, such as Charles I's *Proclamation for the Restraint of the Multitude and Promiscuous Uses of Coaches about London and Westminster* (1635). In 1634 Sir Sanders Duncombe had intro-duced the sedan-chair from France in hopes of easing the congestion. The introduction of coaches and then of sedans also inaugurated the decline of the use of the Thames as London's water high-way. Though roads were poorly surfaced and quagmires were axle-deep in the winter, by the sixteen-thirties the English countryside was being linked with stage-coaches, which the railway was to drive out three centuries later.

The coach was quickly improved in the seven-teenth century. The body was hung by its straps from C-shaped steel springs instead of pillars, glass windows and complete doors were added. The tendency was to lighten vehicles, as roads im-proved in the eighteenth century, and the private coach reached its apogee in the travelling chariot, which lasted into the nineteenth century. Stand-ing to the stage-coach as the private car stands to the modern bus and motor-coach, the travelling chariot seated two persons inside, and two ser-vants on a seat outside and behind. It was equip-ped with a box for swords and pistols, and a large trunk-like cupboard over the front wheels for the luggage. There was no box seat and no coachman, the horses being ridden by postillions. For short journeys the owner used his own horses. For long journeys post horses were hired at each stage, at intervals of about ten to fourteen miles. The tra-velling chariot was the vehicle used by young Eng-lishmen for the grand tour of the Continent, which completed their education.

The more archaic and more luxurious state chariot was used by the nobility and country gentlemen (if they could afford so splendid a ve-hicle) for ceremonial occasions – openings of par-liament, levees, coronations, royal weddings, etc. The body was hung high on C-springs two or three feet from the ground; four folding steps were provided on each side. The interior, design-ed to seat two passengers, was upholstered in padded silk brocade with lace trimmings. There was a platform behind for two footmen; and a box seat in front for the coachman, covered with a most elaborate hammercloth trimmed with velvet and silk and embellished with a large silver-plated or brass coat-of-arms. These state chariots were drawn by two big horses, usually Cleveland Bays. The Carriage Museum at Maidstone has a magnificent example with the body painted yellow and the inside upholstered in white satin brocade, which belonged to the Dukes of Buccleuch. The state coach of the English sovereigns, built in 1761 to the design of the architect Sir William Chambers at a cost of £7,562 4s. 3½d., is of the same pattern, though designed to hold four persons instead of two.

The hackney coach plied in London until ousted by the cab (French *cabriolet de place*), which was introduced from Paris in 1820, and which in turn gave way to the taximeter cab, taxicab or taxi, with the development of the motor-car.

Road accidents did not begin with the motor-car. Driving coaches was a matter which required skill and control. Thus Cromwell involved himself in difficulties with his coach by taking the reins himself in Hyde Park in 1654. The incident was described by the Dutch Ambassador writing home to his government.

His Highness was accompanied by his Secretary, Thurloe, and some few of his gentlemen and servants, went to take the air in Hyde Park, when he caused some dishes of meat to be brought when he had his dinner and afterwards had a mind to drive the coach himself. Having put only the secretary into it, he whipped up those six grey horses, which the Count of Oldenburgh had presented unto his Highness, who drove pretty handsomely for some time, but at last, provoking these horses too much with the whip, they grew unruly and ran so fast that the postilions could not hold them in, whereby His Highness was flung out of the coach upon the pole, the secretary's ankle was hurt leaping out and he keeps his chamber.

Better road surfaces in the early nineteenth century allowed speeding on the roads, especially between stage coaches. Racing, drunkenness, and overloading led to many fatalities which could also be blamed on the narrowness of roads inherited from the past. (See also *Hansom Cab, Motor-car, Road, Wheel*.)

ILLUSTRATION: Plate 11.

Box of the dead

COFFINS have to fulfil the obvious purpose of protecting the corpse against weather, soil, wild animals and body snatchers; but the deeper meaning of the coffin in ancient times was to prevent the dead from returning and haunting the survivors. Evidence of this purpose is provided by extremely heavy stone lids for coffins as well as by stone heaps piled on ancient burials. The English word 'coffin' is derived from the Greek *kophinos*, meaning 'basket'. Wicker-work coffins were used in Sumeria and Egypt; and the Ute Indians covered their dead with a large carrying basket. 'Around 1926 a contracted human skeleton was found in an oval basket in the clay of the Ancholme estuary' in the North of England (J. D. G. Clark, *Prehistoric Europe*, 1952).

One of the oldest forms of the coffin, originating in the Stone Age, but frequently found in the Bronze Age, is the 'tree of the dead'. A tree, very often an oak (which was a sacred tree), was split in two, the lower part was hollowed out like a trough to hold the corpse, the upper part served as a cover. This special form has been explained by two ancient beliefs:

1. Men were supposed to have grown out of trees.
2. The 'tree of the dead' is very much like a dug-out, and it may therefore have been considered appropriate for the last journey of the dead 'across the water'.

Such coffins found in Denmark show the amazing preservative properties of the tannic acid contained in the oak, which has preserved for a thousand years the cloth tunics and hoods of the men, the jackets and fringed skirts of their women. Where tree-trunk coffins are still in use, as for instance in a Yugoslav village, rationalistic explanations are offered. According to a recent statement by Professor M. Gavazzi of Zagreb, Yugoslav villagers explain that they use trunk coffins to preserve their dead from bears, which would find it impossible to open the slippery round covers.

A further reason for the use of coffins may have been the protection of the earth itself against death-pollution. To understand the fear of death-pollution as well as of the 'revenant' (the spirit who leaves the grave to haunt the survivors), we should remember that the newly dead were believed to be in an intermediary state between life and death, still possessing a certain awareness of what happened to their bodies. Every contact with the dead was therefore believed to be highly dangerous. In Cormac's Glossary (c. A.D. 900) we are told that a wand of aspen, which served for measuring bodies and graves, was always kept in the cemeteries of the heathens, and that it was a horror to everyone to take the fearful thing in his hand. An analogous idea has been met with in an Oxfordshire village, where the corpse was always measured with a string and never with a rule. The rule, after having been in contact with the corpse, might have polluted the next object which had to be measured, whereas the string could easily be destroyed. In Wexford (Ireland) the corner pieces cut off the lid and bottom of coffins were only used to make crosses which were usually hung on old trees.

Very often the feet of the dead were fettered, but even greater precautions were taken with suicides and witches. Sometimes their heads were cut off and placed between the legs, in order to 'loose the spirit'. A medieval stone coffin with such a mutilated corpse has been found in Yorkshire. Another method was to drive a stake through the body.

To prevent the return of the dead the coffin was carried out of the house with the feet towards the door. In Sweden old farmhouses may have two doors opening in opposite directions, one of them, usually the north door, would only be opened to carry the coffin out of the house. If the dead man should return he would find this door well barred. Similar precautions recorded in England are to take the coffin to the cemetery either across a running water or by a roundabout way which the dead would not remember. In the graveyard at Seagoe in Ireland the coffin was carried three times around the old church and was made to touch the four corners of the church at each round, whilst the bell was rung.

In order to prevent the pollution of the earth, the coffins were put down on their way to the graveyard on special 'resting stones'. In Ireland quite a good number of such resting stones still exist; for instance a large flagstone serves this purpose at the entrance of Layd graveyard. In Brittany the same idea was depicted in the thirteenth-century church of St Léhon in an old stained-glass window of the translation of the shrine of St Magloire. Unfortunately the window was destroyed by bomb blast during the Second World War; but a faint photograph, displayed in the church, shows the carriers sitting down to a hearty meal, whilst the saint's shrine rests safely on the solid branch of an apple tree.

As for the shape, the gabled coffins of continental Europe are said to owe their form to the pentagram, the points of which would coincide with the five corners of the coffin, the pentagram being an ancient symbol of life through death. The English coffin woods are oak and also elm, which has the property of enduring in damp soil. In olden times Swedish country people when still hale and hearty often made their own simple coffins from pinewood. The coffin was usually painted black; for children white or possibly blue. Black coffins are no longer in use, but white ones are still made; though the Swedes now prefer polished oak wood. The great botanist Linnaeus had a big elm tree cut down three years before his death from which his coffin was to be made. (See also *Barrow, Wreaths*.)

ILLUSTRATION: Page 124.

Coinage from the earliest days

COINS have been made in Europe and the Near East for about 2,500 years: in China their history is equally long. They have almost always been made of metal: sometimes, in a crisis, people have had to use leather or card, and sometimes they have preferred materials like porcelain or glass; but gold, silver, copper, brass and bronze were most often used in the past. Russia experimented with platinum at one time. Now nickel, aluminium and hard-wearing alloys have replaced silver, and gold is hardly ever coined: only bronze remains of the older choice. Coins have been round in shape at nearly all times, for convenience, and for centuries they have had designs stamped on each side. The early Romans manufactured their coins in the temple of Juno Moneta, and hence come the words 'money' and 'mint'.

Groups of people living together in primitive conditions without a system of money have always had to buy and sell by exchanging things. A man with corn to spare exchanged his surplus for (say) a cow which his neighbour had to spare. Difficulties would arise when the miller wanted to sell flour worth only half a cow to the butcher, for the butcher might not have a customer available for the other half. What each of them needed was something that each valued equally and wanted equally. Many different things have been used in this way: bars of salt, lengths of cloth, and other such things are used even today in some backward parts of the world. But long ago people realized that metal is a much better thing to be exchanged from hand to hand. Metal does not melt or rot or go bad: it is needed to make things of every variety, from jewellery to arms and cooking-pots; and it is just scarce enough to make everyone glad to have it. Gold was placed first, for its durability and appearance. Silver is a good second. And, of the base metals, fine red copper makes an obvious third, as it is fairly easy to work.

The earliest western coins were made in Asia Minor about 700 B.C., either by merchants of the Kingdom of Lydia or by Greeks of the coastland – the Greeks themselves were uncertain which story was correct. At first the coins were simple lumps of metal very roughly marked, and of varying weight. In trade this meant that each lump had to be weighed out – an inconvenient waste of time – and it was quickly realized that if the lumps were made to a given weight in a given district, and marked with a mark that stood for that district, there would be no need to weigh them time after time. The distinctive mark also served as a guarantee that the coin was of good metal and so full value. This was a simple and clever idea, and all the coins of today, with their portraits and badges and pictures and inscriptions, owe their existence to it. Every coin now tells us where it was made and (usually) what it is worth, and so everybody, in his own country, is willing to put the same value on the coinage.

The actual making of early coins was quite simply done. An engraver had to hollow out the designs on pieces of specially hardened iron. One of these dies was set firmly in a metal block, like an anvil, standing on the floor. When blanks for the coins themselves, of the right weight and shape, had been prepared, these were placed, one by one, on the anvil die: a workman held the other die firmly above the blank in a long pair of tongs, and another workman brought down a heavy hammer on the whole 'sandwich' (die, coin-blank, die). Under the sudden pressure the coin-blank took the impressions from the engraved dies on either side of it. Any metalsmith's hut containing a small furnace would suffice for the operation provided that an engraver could be found; and, with constant variations and improvements, coins of all lands were minted in this way down to the sixteenth century.

As soon as designs, or 'types' (to use the technical phrase), appeared on the early Greek coins, one city after another took up the idea. For some time their designs were simple badges – a sea-turtle for the island of Aegina, an owl (sacred to Pallas Athene) for Athens, a winged horse for Corinth. But the Greeks quickly elaborated their coins, making them among the loveliest the world has seen. Their favourite metal was silver, fairly evenly distributed in the Greek world; and fine, large coins of this lovely metal were minted in many cities. The 'heads', or obverses, showed some form of city-badge – often the head of a city's patron god or goddess, like Athene's head at Athens, or that of the local spirit of a river or a fountain, as at Syracuse, where the fountain-nymph Arethusa was pictured. On the reverses were types which symbolized aspects of a city's national life or commercial activity – a bunch of grapes or an ear of barley or fish for cities rich in vineyards or arable land or fisheries. By the middle of the fourth century B.C. an immense variety of types had been used, some simpler, some more ornate: the men who designed the best coins became famous, and even signed with their names the dies which they engraved. This work was seldom much more than an inch in diameter, but it possessed all the grandeur and simplicity and technical mastery which only the greatest artists can combine. The Greeks took a pride in their fine coins, which, by showing that their cities were go-ahead and inventive, were therefore good for trade. And everything depended on brisk trade: cities were small, by modern standards, and small cities quickly get left behind, or simply starve, when international competition is keen.

They could not stand up to Alexander the Great: his kingdom absorbed most of the free Greek cities, and his coins pushed theirs out. Previous coins had shown a city-badge. Alexander's showed a royal badge – the half-divine portrait of Alexander himself, the natural symbol of the vast empire he built up from Macedonia, its centre, to India: Alexander *was* Macedonia. From that time kings put their heads on coinage as a matter of course.

Greek coinage was 'struck', that is, hammered between dies: early Roman coins were differently made. Italy had no gold and scarcely any silver, though she was fairly rich in the metals which form bronze. But bronze is not a precious metal like gold and silver: it took a deal of bronze to be worth anything, and they coined it by the pound, for that is what Rome's first pieces weighed. Hence the £ (from *Libra*=pound) of our £ *s.d.* These great coins, too large to strike, had to be cast from moulds, just as Chinese coinage was cast for many centuries until quite recent times. Later on, Rome captured sources of silver and began to strike silver *denarii* (the *d.* of our £ *s.d.*, for the English penny used to be of silver) with types which were seldom beautiful but nearly always interesting, since they glorified the legend and myth of Rome's earliest history.

The Roman Republic was collapsing when Julius Caesar was killed in 44 B.C.: Augustus, his adopted son, transformed it into an empire within twenty years. Like Alexander, he now put his head on the coinage, which henceforth bears a magnificent series of imperial portraits (in gold, silver, brass and copper) for over four hundred years. Brass and copper coins of the Empire were quite large and enabled die-engravers to make really fine designs, and the coins themselves were excellently struck by the mint-workmen who hammered the coins out. The engravers probably used sculptured portrait-busts of the emperors as models for their superbly realistic and strong coin-portraits. Combined with the types on the backs of the coins (which generally said what the emperor was trying to do for the welfare of his subjects), these portraits must have suggested

the force of imperial personality very vividly from end to end of an enormous empire which had no radio or newspapers to spread official news. From Britain to Arabia the imperial coins of Rome acted as an imperial gazette: unlike those of Greece, their types were changed very frequently in order to spread the latest news – of a battle won, a victory celebrated, a building erected, or an era of peace and plenty begun (compare the varied postage stamps of many countries, such as the U.S.S.R.).

A thousand years of Greek and Roman coinage had developed all the essentials of later coinages. The use of gold, silver and the baser metals: the technique of engraving dies and of hammering the blanks between the dies; the appearance of royal or imperial portraits, together with other designs serving as national badges or symbols – all these were standard features in coinage for a further thousand years. And there was one other feature contributed by Rome. Christianity, after being for a long time tolerated by Rome, was officially adopted by many of the later emperors: Constantine the Great protected the new faith. Many coins of the late empire are of a more or less Christian character or feeling. When the imperial control of Europe collapsed in the fifth century, and barbarian invaders took over, they adopted much of this Christian symbolism on their coins; coinage of the Byzantine empire of the East, which survived until Constantinople fell to the Turks in 1453, showed not only the portraits of the Byzantine emperors, but often a portrait of Christ himself as 'King of kings'.

In medieval Europe, therefore, as one kingdom after another was carved out and stabilized, coinages developed in an essentially Christian and yet also a Roman tradition. Venice with its lozenge-shaped badge of the Christ; Charlemagne with his type of a church surmounted by the inscription 'Christiana Religio'; today's portrait coinage of Elizabeth II of England, described, in Latin, as 'Defender of the Faith' – all come from the same ancient origins. Three main changes have occurred. First, the invention of coining-machinery in the sixteenth century revolutionized the minting of money, which is now done in huge quantities by immense power presses. Dies are seldom now engraved by hand:

instead, they are modelled in relief, and machines then engrave them automatically. Secondly, many countries have lost the old habit of varying their coin-types for the sake of seeking designs which are both new and good: Eire was an exception when she brought out her coins showing horses, salmon, chickens and pigs – symbols of her agricultural fertility. Thirdly, precious metals like gold and silver have become too valuable and too expensive to use as money. Great Britain, for example, no longer mints gold and silver. Instead of gold pounds the Government uses pound notes, which promise that the citizen will be paid twenty shillings if he prefers it so; but these 'silver' shillings – of cupro-nickel and not of silver at all – are worth only a fraction of the actual value written on them. In other words, modern coins are tokens, which everyone is content to accept at a value more than they are worth simply because they have enough trust in the governments which mint them.

ILLUSTRATION: Pages 70 and 71.

The Ox and the Ass and the Star

The **CRIB** and its cult – how could it be otherwise? – can be traced back to Bethlehem, where, according to Origen (who died about A.D. 254) devout Christians knelt in the Cave of the Nativity in remembrance of Christ's birth. The Emperor Constantine erected a basilica over the cave, to which pilgrims came as early as the fourth century.

From Bethlehem the cult of the crib spread to Rome; and there in A.D. 360 Pope Liberius built for the Feast of Christ's Birth a special church, which from the seventh century onwards was called Maria ad Praesepem (Mary by the Crib). The church is now called Santa Maria Maggiore, and its treasures include five small, narrow wooden boards set in crystal and silver which are held to be relics of the original crib (but see *Basket*) as well as the oldest Italian Christmas crib, carved by Arnolfo di Cambio (who lived c. 1232– c. 1310). The crib as it developed owed much to the growth of legends of the Nativity outside the

accepted books of the New Testament, notably the additions of the ox and the ass which were added to the scene of the Nativity by inference from a text in the Old Testament, and the story of the Three Kings elaborated from the brief account in St Matthew's Gospel which says only that 'wise men from the east', neither named nor numbered, were led by the star to where the young Child was, where they fell down and worshipped him and offered their treasures, and gave him gold, frankincense and myrrh.

Cribs and the cult of cribs are associated, moreover, with St Francis of Assisi. The story, as told by Professor Giulia Sorvillo, is that St Francis in Rome in 1223, old and worn out by fasting, determined to go back to his poor dwelling at Greccio in Umbria at Christmas-time, to realize a cherished plan of a life-like representation of the Nativity; there his friend Giovanni Velita helped St Francis to build a stable, in which they set wooden figures of the Holy Family, the shepherds and some animals. St Francis then sang the words 'and they laid him in a manger', and knelt down, whereupon a child appeared in his arms surrounded by a brilliant light.

Ever since cribs have been seen at Christmas-time in every Italian church and home. At the beginning of December the preparations begin; a grotto is built in one corner of the living room. Shepherds are seen bringing lambs, fish, and baskets with fruit; animals crowd outside the grotto, only the ox and ass are allowed inside. In the background a small stream glistens under a bridge. Snow-covered farms, hamlets, country inns and windmills are seen in the distance. The only light comes from small lanterns carried by men and women hastening to the grotto. The Christmas Crib remains on view from Christmas Eve until Epiphany.

Since the end of the fifteenth century Naples has been famous for its cribs and Professor Sorvillo describes the picturesque eighteenth-century crib in St Martin's Museum, in which an astonishing variety of figures appear in oriental robes and contemporary Neapolitan costumes: courtiers, tradesmen, peasants, soldiers, mothers and children, walking or riding on horses, donkeys, camels and even elephants. Fires are depicted inside the inns, where people are resting, eating, drinking. Professor Sorvillo observes that some of the finest wooden, clay, or china figures in Neapolitan cribs were made by humble craftsmen who lived in the poorest and oldest quarters of the city.

Something is known of customs connected with cribs in other countries or preceding them (see L. Kretzenbacher's *Weihnachtskrippen in Steiermark*, 1953). In the tenth century the nuns in the Nonnberg in Salzburg used to rock to sleep a wooden figure of the new-born Saviour; at Christmas they sang him a lullaby. Farmers' wives and townswomen in Austria also wished to rock their Christmas 'Kindel' to sleep and took their own figures of wood or wax to the church for a 'Singandacht'. This custom was continued in the homes, and some of the old Christmas lullabies are still among the most popular of carols – for example 'Auf dem Berge da wehet der Wind ...' Realistic Christmas plays in the church of Reichersberg in Upper Austria are mentioned in 1162, and a little later we hear of similar plays in France and Spain. Cribs for the 'Play of the Three Magi' were put up, either in the porch or behind the altar. In 1252 an 'eternal light' was presented to the crib at St Martin's at Füssen in Bavaria, though we do not know what the crib looked like. A crib from the middle of the fifteenth century, with clay figures and the Three Wise Men from the East presenting their offerings, is preserved at Carden on the Moselle.

Austria remains a great centre for cribs, though the earliest extant Austrian crib dates only from 1525; this is at St Nicholas in der Hinterlobming and it suggests that the carver took his inspiration from Gothic paintings and carved triptych altars. The Virgin Mary, whose forehead is covered with a white veil, wears a dark blue coat, while St Joseph's coat is brown with a yellow lining. Behind him kneels the ox, pushing his head forward towards the Child. The fat donkey has one long ear standing up stiffly and the other pointing downwards. On the left is a crowd of angels; their wings are painted blue, red and white. The foremost angel lifts up the linen on which the infant is resting. Through an open door one sees St Mary and St Joseph on their way to Bethlehem. Two shepherds, one fast asleep, the other wide awake, and a colourful crowing cock complete the scene.

The Counter-Reformation, in the middle of the sixteenth century, brought about a vigorous revival of religious customs. In the Jesuit church in Prague a Christmas crib was put up in 1562, and many cribs followed in other Jesuit churches, Franciscan monasteries, convents of all kinds, and princely palaces. The middle class soon copied the court, and the crib was conquered by the Baroque with all its splendour. In Styria remarkable cribs at Admont and St Lambrecht, date from the middle of the eighteenth century. The figures of the Admont crib were carved by Joseph Thaddäus Stammel and painted by Anton Pottschnik. The shepherds with their sheep seem to be rushing towards the Infant, which is lying in a plaited basket in front of the Virgin Mary. The Three Wise Men from the East quietly pay their homage. Above the grotto is a mountainside where half-naked shepherds guard their sheep. In the background are the palaces of Jerusalem and the Temple. The crib at St Lambrecht comprises 134 human figures and innumerable animals and buildings. On Christmas Eve, when the monks are singing in the choir and the inhabitants of St Lambrecht and the farmers from the surrounding villages are coming to the church, the Infant is placed in the crib. All figures can be moved about, and seventeen different scenes are presented between Christmas and Candlemas Day.

In England, where Christmas customs are now particularly emphasized, cribs have become a great deal more common in recent years in Anglican churches, though carving, colouring and arrangement often leave much to be desired.

ILLUSTRATION: Pages 178 and 220.

Cuckoo, cuckoo, cuckoo ...

CUCKOO CLOCKS, imitating the best known of all bird notes, were first made in the Black Forest about 1740, and were invented probably by Franz Anton Ketterer (1676–1750). They spread rapidly through Europe.

From the beginning the cuckoo has appeared out of its little door, bowing and opening its beak and wings as the hour is called; and it has been suggested, picturesquely though feasibly, that Ketterer took his cue from the medieval tower clock of one of the churches in Villingen. When this clock struck the hour, there was music and the Three Kings appeared from a door on one side, travelled round and bowed before statues of the Madonna and Child, continued their traverse and disappeared through a second door. The cuckoo notes are produced by a pair of organ pipes actuated by bellows.

In the Black Forest clockmaking had started as a home craft in the middle of the seventeenth century. It was an offshoot or development of the woodcarving to which the families turned when work on the farm was halted by the winter. Till late in the eighteenth century these craftsmen made clocks of every kind almost entirely of wood. Even in 1870 wood was still being used for the movement frames.

Yet the first cuckoo clocks were plain uncarved affairs, fitted with a plain wooden front, rectangular, and with an arched top. This front was the clock face with painted hour numerals, and flower patterns in each corner. The cuckoo had his door in the arch.

About 1845 cuckoo clocks (and other Black Forest clocks) took on a new form: they were transformed into picture-frame clocks, the carved or moulded frame enclosing an oil painting, usually on metal, with a smallish dial which was enamelled in white. The paintings, done by local artists, were scraps of sentimental romanticism, landscapes, figures in naturalistic settings, and occasionally episodes of legend or folklore. When the Black Forest makers took to carving the cuckoo clock, they gave it a Victorian Gothic sentimentalism, which was as dear to the Germans as to the English; towards the end of the century the cuckoo's call sounded through carved oak leaves or vine leaves, and a gable on top gave the case a farmhouse effect. The central emblem surmounting the clock in the middle was sometimes a deer's head; sometimes the carver took to hunting emblems – horn, pouch, guns, hares and pheasants.

The cuckoo also was given a companion, another bird, the quail, which is more often heard than seen, as it skulks in the grass or corn and cries out *wet my lips*. The quail came out of a twin door, and called the quarters, the cuckoo

still announcing the hours. Still more elaborate cuckoo clocks incorporated a musical box which was set playing after the 'striking' of the hours. (See also *Clock*.)

D

The dentist's armoury

The **DENTAL DRILL** and other implements of the dentist's craft have their history, ancient and modern; the priority, as one would expect, going to the implements of extraction.

Forceps (simply the Latin word for 'pincers') have probably been used to draw the teeth since ancient times; they were described by the Indian physician Suśruta, who flourished in the sixth century B.C. An instrument of lead, designed for the extraction of teeth, was placed in the temple of Apollo at Delphi. It was probably a copy in lead of an iron instrument which was then in use. The Arabian writer Albucasis or Abulcasis (tenth century A.D.) gave diagrams of the forceps he recommended. But none of these early instruments have survived, and it is uncertain whether the ancients were really skilled in the extraction of teeth. Thus the Greek 'Father of Medicine', Hippocrates, assumed that only loose teeth could be drawn. For practical purposes our knowledge of the exact form and efficiency of dental instruments begins in the mid-sixteenth century; and besides forceps, one may consider pelicans, elevators and dental keys.

A pelican is an instrument for levering a tooth out of its socket. The operator forces the lever downwards in the case of a lower tooth (or upwards in the case of an upper tooth), the adjoining tooth being used as a fulcrum. In its simplest form a pelican is no more than a straight lever (the shaft), enlarged at the end into a 'bolster' which is shaped so as to rest securely against the part chosen as a fulcrum. To a point about the middle of the shaft there is hinged a straight shank, the end of which is curved to form a claw. When the shank is placed parallel to the shaft, the claw curves over the upper surface of the bolster. In use, the bolster is placed against the affected tooth – or preferably an adjoining tooth – and the claw is adjusted over the tooth and kept in place by a finger of the left hand. The right hand then applied pressure to

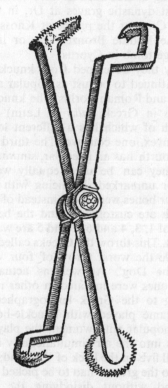

Fig. 10. Double-ended pelican.

the shaft, and the tooth is – or luckily *was* – levered out, often with considerable damage to the tissues or to the other teeth. The pelican was first mentioned in the second half of the fourteenth century. Various types of pelican continued to be used until at least the second decade of the nineteenth century.

Dental elevators, which are often used for drawing stumps and individual roots, were described by Arabian surgeons in the tenth century.

An elevator consists of a short metal shaft with a pointed end; and the whole is mounted in a handle. The top part of the shaft may be curved or grooved for particular purposes. The elevator acts on the principle of the lever. During the nineteenth century some authorities advocated the elevator for the extraction of teeth as well as stumps.

The dental key, common until at least 1860, consists of a metal shaft about four inches long, with a transverse handle at one end. To the opposite end a claw is hinged, so that it moves in a plane at right angles to the axis of the shaft. In many keys there is a projection from the shaft on the side opposite to the attachment of the claw; this projection is known as the heel or, once more, as the bolster. The shaft was held horizontally, with the bolster against the gum below the tooth to be removed, and the claw hooked over the tooth. The handle was then turned forcibly, so that the tooth was drawn by the upward and lateral pull. The dental key probably originated in England at some time after 1730, and it was first described in medical literature in 1742. On the continent of Europe it was frequently known as 'the English key'.

Dental forceps have undergone many changes in form during the course of their evolution. It is doubtful whether those which are illustrated in the manuscripts of Albucasis could have been very effective. From the middle of the sixteenth century onwards the surgeon or tooth-drawer used several forceps, each designed to extract a different group of teeth, and he had special forceps for roots. From the sixteenth to the early nineteenth century the particular kind of forceps was often designated by a name descriptive of the shape of the blades, such as crow's bill or parrot's bill. Shaping the blades to grip each particular type of tooth began early, and was carried to its logical end by the work of Cyrus Fay and the dental pioneer Sir John Tomes, independently, in the middle of the nineteenth century.

In using forceps the operator extracts the tooth in a lateral direction, since in this way the roots are most easily detached from their sockets. Nevertheless, it has been held in the past that the most satisfactory method was to extract the tooth in a perpendicular direction, for which various ingenious, though often clumsy, contrivances have been designed. None of these have been very successful.

An early form of the drill which prepares the tooth for filling is described by Pierre Fauchard (1678–1761), who is regarded as the Father of Dentistry, and whose great work *Le Chirurgien dentiste* was published in 1728. He explains the method of loosening decayed tissue by means of a drill which was twisted to right and left alternately by means of the fingers. He also described the use of the jeweller's bow-drill, but this was in the manufacture of artificial teeth. At a later date the bow-drill was employed by others in the treatment of cavities, but it was not a success. The Archimedean drill was also used. In 1829 James Nasmyth, later famous for his development of the steam-hammer, invented a flexible shaft, consisting of a closely coiled spiral wire, for driving small drills. Such a shaft, enclosed in a flexible cable, was soon used in dental work. In fact, it was re-invented by others more than once. By 1860 several types of hand drill with short flexible cables and shafts were in use. By 1870 the rotating shaft and flexible cable had been extended in length and driven by a foot engine. About 1908 electric power was applied, and this led to the construction of the highly efficient and more merciful dental unit of the present day. (See also *False Teeth, Toothpick*.)

ILLUSTRATION: Page 19.

Dice and knuckle-bones

DICE (which, it may be remarked, is the plural of 'die') are playthings peculiarly well adapted for the satisfaction of man's gambling desires; and they have an uninterrupted history of 5,000 years, whether in the hands of Sumerian courtiers, young Athenians of fashion, Roman emperors and their intimates, English servicemen off duty, Americans shooting craps, or children playing ludo.

These six-sided cubes, with the sides marked with dots from one to six so arranged that the sum of the numbers on any two opposite sides is always seven, are normally made of wood, bone

or ivory, or a modern ivory substitute; but dice are also known in bronze, lead, amber, crystal, terracotta, and various kinds of stone. Sumerian dice of 3000 B.C. have been found in Mesopotamia. They were also used in dynastic Egypt, and in fact they appear sooner or later in most parts of the ancient world. Exactly how they were played, one cannot tell. Dice nowadays are played as a game on their own, or as an adjunct to other games. In ancient times they may have been used with gaming boards such as have been found in the earliest dynastic graves at Ur, in tombs in Egypt, in Crete at the palace at Knossos at the end of the Middle Bronze Age, or in a Late Bronze Age tomb in Cyprus.

Possibly they developed from knuckle-bones, which continued to be just as popular as dice in the Greek and Roman worlds. The knuckle-bone (*astragalos* in Greek, *talus* in Latin) has four faces, each of which has a different look. One face is convex, one concave. The third is nearly flat, the fourth has an irregular, sinuous profile, so that they can be used equally well either marked or unmarked. In dicing with knuckle-bones, four bones were used (instead of the three dice which are customary), and the best throw was a set of 1, 3, 4 and 6 (2 and 5 are wanting on the bones). This throw the Greeks called 'Aphrodite', while the worst throw of four ones was called 'The Dog'. As well as actual bones, knuckle-bones were imitated in other materials. According to the Greek lexicographer Pollux, another game played with knuckle-bones was specially popular with women; the player threw five bones into the air simultaneously and tried to catch all five on the back of the hand; any that dropped to the ground had to be picked up in the same hand without dislodging the knuckle-bones already caught.

If the account in literary sources is to be relied on, dice have always figured large in the expenditure of men's spare time, to say nothing of money that may or may not have been spare. Homer tells us how Patroclus as a boy killed his friend, the son of Amphidamas, in a fury over a quarrel at dice, in consequence of which he was sent to be brought up with Achilles; though, according to one ancient theory, dice were only invented at the siege of Troy, when the hero Palamedes taught his compatriot Achaeans to play as they sat by their tents and their ships waiting for something to happen (dice have always belonged to the boredom of war). Herodotus, on the other hand, maintained that dice and other games as well were invented by the Lydians in a time of famine, so that they played games one day and fed the next. Dice were extremely popular in Classical Greece, so much so that dicing terms passed into everyday speech, especially in the phrase 'Triple Six', the most coveted throw of all. There is a terracotta model gaming board of about 550 B.C. in the Copenhagen Museum on which lay three dice originally, all with the 6 uppermost, to remind us of the words that Aeschylus, in the *Agamemnon*, puts into the mouth of the Watchman on the palace roof at Mycenae when he sees the beacon fires heralding the return of his master from the Sack of Troy, 'I'll count my master's fortune fallen fair now that my beacon watch has thrown a triple six.' The Greek comic poets Antiphanes, Euboulus, Alexis and Amphis are all known to have written plays called *The Dicers*, none of which have survived. On the road between Athens and Eleusis there was a shrine of Athena Skiras which became so associated with dicers who made it, so to say, their private chapel, that the word for a gambling house came to be a '*skirapheion*'. A very popular subject with vase painters was one depicting two heroes of the Trojan war, usually Achilles and Ajax, seated ready for the battle, gaming board between them on their knees, intent on the fall of the dice. At least one vase of this kind has the ancient equivalent of subtitles painted on the background – 'A three for Achilles – Ajax has a four'. Even theological observations were sometimes expressed in gaminghouse idiom, for a fragment of a lost play of Sophocles preserves the sentiment 'The dice of Zeus always fall well.' Perhaps his dice were loaded, as some Greek dice certainly were. This cheat's device, whereby extra weight is concentrated on one side of the cube so that the highest value will almost always fall uppermost, seems to be nearly as old as the game itself. Ancient dice treated in this fashion have been found; in the *Problems* ascribed to Aristotle there is a reference to *astragaloi memolibdomenoi* or 'leaded dice'.

Finds in Italy show that the Etruscans were much given to dice; it was perhaps from them that the Romans inherited an affection for dicing which became so excessive that strenuous and probably unsuccessful efforts were made to control it by law. Dicing, indeed, was made illegal except during the religious festival of the Saturnalia. Dice are often found in Roman tombs, as if the dead would want to shoot craps in the afterlife. Sometimes also dice appear carved on the façade of a tomb, where they are taken as symbols of the uncertainty and vicissitudes of human life. Many Roman emperors took a keen pleasure in the game, some to the extent of setting aside a special dicing room in the Imperial Palace. Even the staid Augustus wrote to a friend on one occasion describing a game in which he had taken part, and mentioned the special names given to the different throws. The scholar-emperor Claudius went so far as to write a treatise on dice, which was pilloried after his death in the *Apocolocyntosis* – or 'Pumpkinification', a skit on the deification of the dead Emperor. After the Olympians have refused to have him as one of themselves, Claudius is escorted to the underworld where he is tried and convicted for his alleged offences. When a variety of possible punishments has been considered, it is eventually decided that he shall spend eternity playing dice from a dice-box with no bottom, and pass his time grovelling on the ground after the fallen dice. Dice-making was apparently a fairly lucrative occupation, and there exists a tombstone of a certain Lucilius Victorinus whose profession is given as a 'maker of dice for play'.

Dicing did not remain the prerogative of the civilized Mediterranean, but spread into Northwest Europe, where dice are frequently found in Iron Age sites. Tacitus in his account of Germany records that the tribesmen were so addicted to dicing that when they had lost every possession at play, they would finally stake their own liberty; if they lost, they became the slaves of their successful opponents. In Britain, too, dice were well known; bone dice and a bone dice-box have been excavated at the Iron Age lake village at Glastonbury, in Somerset.

Turning eastward, there is reference to dicing in the Indian saga of the *Rig-Veda*, and the game was common enough in ancient India for a 'Superintendent of the Dicing' to have existed in the Vedic period; treatises were also composed on the game, which preserve the pet names given to the throws, and there were public gaming houses for dice. In America before the arrival of Columbus the Aztecs gambled in a game which they called 'patolli', using four kidney-beans instead of dice or knuckle-bones.

There is little sign that the popularity of dice and dicing is abating. In 5,000 years we have advanced from dice to – dice, even if they are now used for crap shooting or for that remarkable variant, Poker Dice.

ILLUSTRATION: Page 364.

The forked hazel twig

The DIVINING-ROD, still used by the dowser to discover water, was first described in 1556 in Georg Agricola's mining treatise *De re metallica.*

This German scientist described the rod as an instrument for finding metals, but made no mention of the search for water. The value of the method, he says, is a subject of contention between miners: the forked twig is usually cut from a hazel bush, although some diviners use different kinds of twigs for different metals, hazel twigs to find veins of silver, ash for copper, pitch pine for lead and especially tin, and rods made of iron and steel for gold. The clenched fingers point upwards, and the junction of the twig is raised, the twig beginning to twist when the holder stands over a vein. Such at least is the contention; but after examining all the claims made for their art by the diviners, Agricola rejects it as a serious method of prospecting. He points out that the twisting motion of the hazel twig is suspiciously unlike the result of direct attraction by amber or loadstone, and considers it is brought about by dexterous manipulation of the pliable bough. He concludes that this practice is a survival among superstitious miners of the belief of the ancients in the power of magic wands to change substance.

Possibly the divining-rod was suggested by the common belief that metallic ores attracted certain trees, which drooped over their lurking place; and it seems that the lore of the divining-

rod was of German origin and was spread by German miners from the Harz Mountains and elsewhere. Thus the rod was introduced to England in the sixteenth century when German miners were brought over to various mining districts.

In the early days various woods were used besides those mentioned by Agricola – among them the apple, the willow, the pomegranate, which was preferred in Sicily, and the mistletoe, all trees to which magic power was ascribed. Hazel, the favourite, was another powerful tree, a tree of knowledge and fertility and a proper substance for all effective wands and rods, able to keep away snakes, elves, fairies, witches, wizards, etc. The forked hazel stick is still the favourite divining-rod of modern dowsers, though some will work with any wood – even with wire.

The efficacy of the rod was explained sometimes on the principle of 'sympathy' or 'attraction and repulsion', on the analogy of gravity and magnetism, and sometimes by demoniac influence acting through the rod or the operator. Consequently, to avoid suspicion of sorcery or dealings with the Evil One, the diviner often baptized his rod by laying it in the bed with a newly christened child, by whose name it was subsequently addressed, with the addition of pious formulae. But the aroma of witchcraft was not easily dispelled in the seventeenth century, and two of the most famous of the early diviners, the Baron de Beausoleil and his wife, who operated in many parts of both Europe and America, were indicted on a charge of sorcery, and ended their lives in prison. The Baroness de Beausoleil was the first diviner to claim the power of discovering water as well as metals by the use of the rod, and in her book of 1632, *Véritable déclaration ... des riches et inestimables trésors nouvellement découverts dans le royaume de France* she describes how she divined the waters of Château-Thierry.

However, an episode in the autobiography of the Spanish mystic St Teresa suggests that water-divining may have been practised in the previous century. Teresa in 1568 was offered the site for a convent to which there was only one objection – there was no water supply; happily, a Friar Antonio came up with a twig in his hand, stopped at a certain spot, and appeared to be making the sign of the cross; but Teresa says, 'Really, I cannot be sure if it were the sign he made, at any rate he made some movement with the twig and then he said, "Dig just here"; they dug, and lo! a plentiful fount of water gushed forth, excellent for drinking, copious for washing, and it never ran dry.'

When the divining-rod began to be used for detecting water as well as minerals, it spread rapidly. It was a frequent matter of contention between churchmen, some approving of it, others, like the Jesuit priest and mathematician Kaspar Schott (1608–1666), denouncing it as an instrument controlled by the devil. Schott, however, later withdrew his strictures, and he and the scientist Athanasius Kircher (c. 1601–1680) were the first to suggest that the movement of the rod is due to unconscious muscular action.

In 1692 the instrument was put to a new use, that of detecting criminals. In that year a peasant of Dauphiny named Jacques Aymar gained great notoriety by apprehending a murderer, who later confessed, with the aid of the divining-rod. Aymar was later discredited by failing some rigorous experiments devised by the Prince de Condé, and after 1701, when the Inquisition issued a decree against the employment of the divining-rod in criminal prosecution, it was rarely used for this purpose.

In the late eighteenth century another peasant of Dauphiny, Barthélemy Bleton, acquired fame as a 'hydroscope'. Pierre Thouvenal, a physician to Louis XVI, became interested in his achievements, and in 1781 published an involved essay comparing the phenomena of the divining-rod with those of magnetism and electricity. In 1782 Bleton underwent a series of tests in Paris, which did not prove entirely to his credit. At this time the theory of 'animal magnetism' and 'terrestrial magnetism' were widely accepted as an explanation of divining. But when Bleton and others failed their tests, this hypothesis was abandoned. Instead, most serious investigators in the last century held the view that the motions of the divining-rod, like those of 'table turning' and the 'magic pendulum' were due to involuntary movements on the part of the performer.

The Glasgow geologist, J. W. Gregory, put forward this same view in 1927, adding that the diviner, by no means necessarily a charlatan, is guided by his experience and observation of soil, topography, vegetation and other surface signs; and more recently professional African diviners (who do not use a rod) have been seen at work in Nigeria, where they display a remarkable gift for finding underground water. Even so, there are well authenticated cases where the movement of the rod seems to have been too violent and powerful to be explained by simple movement of the hands.

ILLUSTRATION: Page 312.

Dolls in Egypt, Greece and Rome

DOLLS, historically and prehistorically, are puzzling objects. One is faced at once with the problem of what was and what was not a doll.

From palaeolithic times men have fashioned human figurines in all kinds of material for magical and religious purposes. Possibly the doll originated with such ancient figures as the Venus of Wellendorf, the woman of Lespugue, or the serpentine statuette from Savignano, palaeolithic sculptures whose shape and curves and details suggest the practice of sympathetic magic to ensure fertility. This may explain why the dolls of antiquity commonly represented, not children or infants in arms, but adult females. Possibly such figures were given to female children as talismans or charms, a symbolization of what was hoped for when they grew up; and possibly, a child's nature being what it is, talisman or charm was converted into a well-loved plaything.

Yet dolls must long have retained something of their magical significance. In Classical Greece girls on the eve of their marriage dedicated their dolls at the shrines of one of the goddesses peculiarly associated with women, notably Artemis or Aphrodite. At Rome this same dedication was made to the Lares and Penates. Some charming lines in the Greek anthology remind us vividly of this practice:

Maiden, to thee before her marriage Timarete gives,
Her pap, her tambourine, her favourite ball,
And as is meet, Oh! Artemis, the maiden brings
Her childhood toys, her dolls and all.

In some cases it seems that owning a doll symbolized virginity. In the tomb of a Vestal Virgin at Tivoli, belonging to the third century A.D. (her name was Cossinia) there was found a charming bone doll, about a foot long, with necklace, bracelets and anklets of gold. The doll lay close to the dead virgin's shoulder.

Dolls are often depicted on tombstones of unmarried girls of the classical period in Greece. One stone of the fifth century B.C. shows the girl holding her doll, while a young slave-girl carries another toy, or duck, for her mistress. Sometimes not only dolls, but dolls' furniture was dedicated to the goddess. Such a set, made of lead, including tables, a chair, candelabra, dishes and kitchen things, has been found at Terracina.

Figures with limbs that can be moved up and down are found in Egypt, belonging to the third millennium B.C. Whether these are playthings or cult figures such as we know to have been carried in certain religious festivals, it is hard to determine. A doll or figure of the time of Amenenhat I in the Twelfth Dynasty had real hair. The doll itself was cut of dark brown wood, a series of holes were bored in the head, and the hair was then inserted and kept in place by little pegs. The hollow eye sockets had once been inlaid, looking forward to the modern refinement – or barbarity – of the doll whose eyes open and shut. An ivory doll or figure of the same period has ears pierced with tiny bronze earrings. Dolls were very common in Egypt – of wood, ivory, limestone, terracotta, rags, even bronze.

Perhaps the earliest dolls to appear in Europe were the curious little painted terracotta figures found in Mycenaean tombs and settlements in Greece, Rhodes, Cyprus and elsewhere from about 1300 B.C. The limbs do not move, the representation is sketchy, if vital, and they are far too small to have been cuddled, but they frequently occur in tombs where children have been buried. In the same grave are terracotta bulls, horses and pieces of furniture.

After the Mycenaean period in Greece, dolls became very abundant, and before long show that mass production was busy. An amusing series made in Boeotia in the Early Iron Age show women with giraffe necks, voluminous embroidered bell-skirts and queer little articulated legs poking out beneath them. By the archaic period,

dolls are widely spread through the Greek world, limbs articulated with wire. By Xenophon's time dolls with a hole in the head were common. A string passed through the hole and was connected to the limbs, turning the doll into a marionette. Xenophon mentioned a travelling salesman who kept himself by selling puppet-dolls of this kind.

Dolls were no less common in Roman Italy than in Greece. A doll of the Antonine period in the second century A.D. achieves perfection in design and workmanship. She is about twelve inches tall, carved out of dark oak, well modelled, with limbs carefully articulated at the shoulders and the hips, and again at the elbows and the knees, by beautifully adjusted tenons and mortices. This doll came out of the sarcophagus of a young girl of about fourteen.

It is not much of a step from the wooden dolls of Egypt in the third millennium B.C. to the wooden 'Dutch dolls' of the Victorian era. But it is a far stride from the Dutch doll to the ultra unrefined realism of the plastic doll of the nineteen-fifties walking, talking, eating, drinking, with nylon hair which can be washed, and a face like a child film star.

Baby house and doll's house

The **DOLL'S HOUSE** originated in South Germany or possibly in the Low Countries. In England it was known as the Baby House, from the use of the word *baby* for doll or image. After 1830 this name gave way to Doll's House, except with conservative writers for children such as C. M. Yonge and Sarah Tytler.

The earliest recorded example of a doll's house was commissioned by the Duke Albrecht of Bavaria in 1558 (according to Dr Karl Gröber, the historian of doll's houses). This was destroyed by fire in the eighteenth century; and the oldest houses now in existence date from the early seventeenth century. These are extremely elaborate and were clearly intended, not as playthings for children, but as an interest and occupation for adults who shared a common human delight in

Continued on p. 131

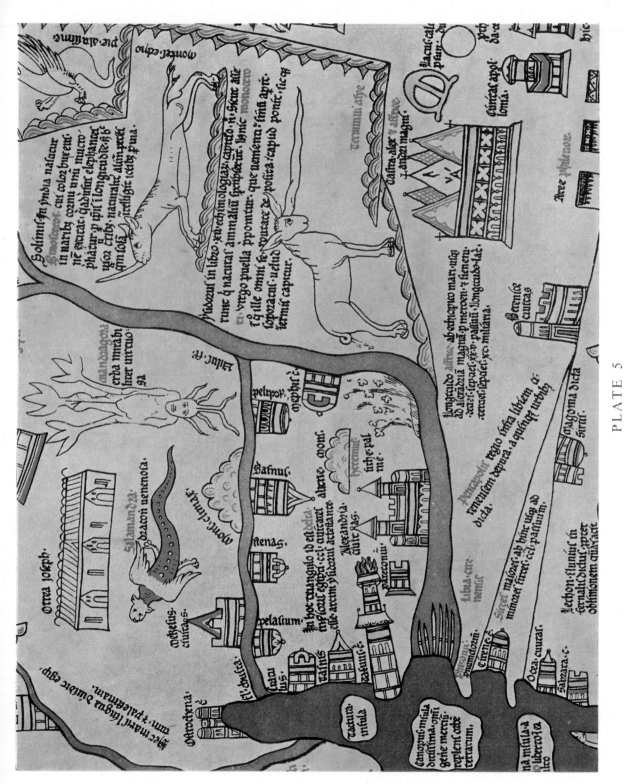

PLATE 5

THE NILE DELTA, detail from the Mappa Mundi, c.1280, in Hereford Cathedral.

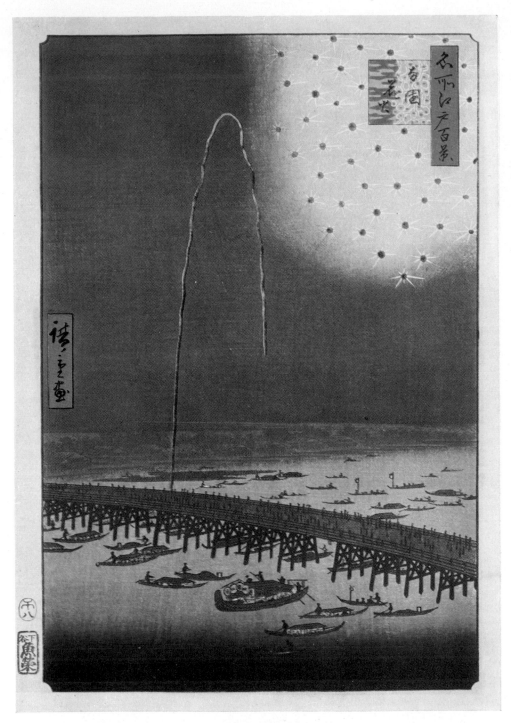

PLATE 6

FIREWORKS AT RIŌGOKU, 1858, colour print by Ando Hiroshige (1797–1858).

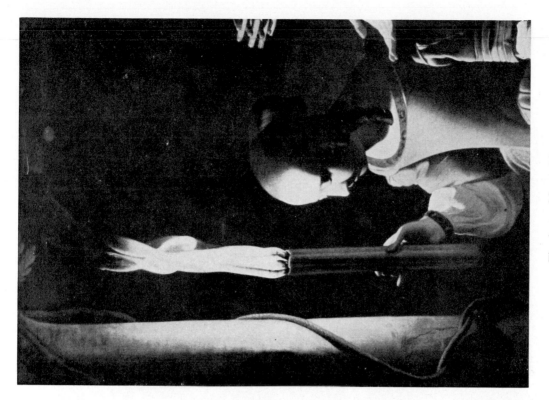

Flambeau of four wicks.
Detail from *Saint Sebastian* by Georges de Latour (1593–1652).

Girl with stylus and codex, the leaved writing tablet from which our
book evolved. Pompeii first century A.D.

Electric Light. Edison lamps in a New York drawing-room in the eighties.

Electric Light. Edison's incandescent lamps light up a New York art gallery, 1882.

Lacquered wooden mask of a Bodhisattva, from Japan: Fugiwara period (A.D. 986–1159).

Lacquered cover of a Japanese writing-box by Shibara Zeshin (1807–1891).

Gallows, detail from the *Triumph of Death*, by Pieter Bruegel (c. 1525–1569).

Traitres regardez et tremblez elle ne perdra son
activité que quand vous aurés tous perdu la vie

Guillotine, engraving by J. B. M. Louvion (1740–1804).

Mazes. Prehistoric maze patterns, Trethevy, Cornwall.

Mazes. The 'Troy town', St Agnes, Isles of Scilly.

Mazes. Labyrinth for the Parc d'Enghein designed and engraved by Romeyne de Hooghe (1645–1708).

Mazes. A double maze of yew at Hatfield House, Herts, laid out in 1841.

Oak coffin: tree-trunk coffin of the Bronze Age from the Storehoj barrow, Egtved, Denmark.

Bed of stone slabs, near the hearth, in a neolithic house at Skara Brae, Orkney.

Spectacles held in place by a metal band around the head, from an eighteenth-century watercolour.

WE THREE LOGGER-HEADS BE.

Wigs. 'We Three Loggerheads Be'. Watercolour by Thomas Rowlandson (1756–1827).

Porcelain bowl, Ming dynasty, c. 1500.

China: Porcellaneous stoneware bowl. Sung dynasty, A.D. 960–1279.

Replica of Sir Isaac Newton's telescope, 1668.

Umbrellas on Ohashi Bridge,
colour print by Ando Hiroshige (1797–1859).

PLATE 7

BOW AND ARROW—The Martyrdom of St Sebastian, detail from predella of *Madonna and Child Enthroned*, by Carlo Crivelli (*c*.1430–after 1493).

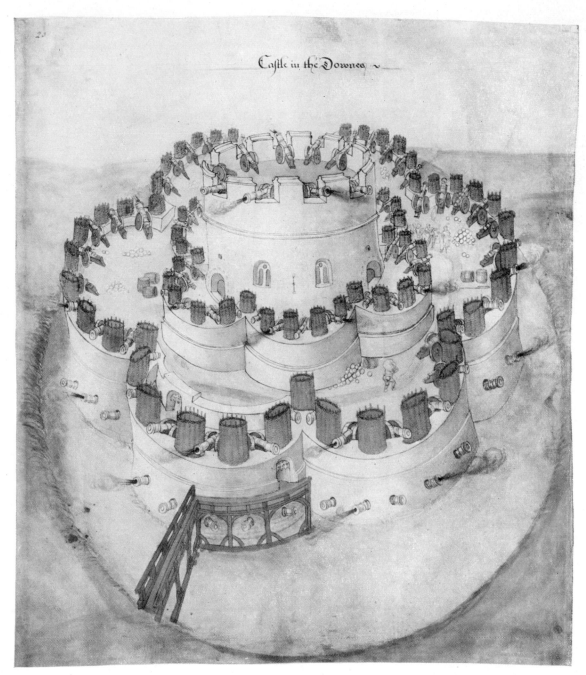

Castle in the Downes

PLATE 8
TUDOR FORT, SANDOWN, KENT. Watercolour *c.*1535 (see *Castle*).

miniatures and models. The Dutch houses were made to look like cabinets on stands, the doors were richly inlaid with ivory, tortoiseshell or amber, or were decorated with marquetry work. The interior often appears to have been furnished as a replica of the owner's home, and it sometimes included stables and wine cellars, or a music-room with an organ, a picture-gallery hung with original paintings, a library or a chapel.

As a toy for children the baby house seems to have developed directly from the single-roomed toy kitchens exported from South Germany after 1650 and hence commonly called 'Nuremberg Kitchens'. These were designed to educate the small girl in housewifery and they contained a complete *batterie de cuisine* in copper, pewter and turned wood. By the end of the century, kitchens of this kind and also single rooms representing butcher's shops, linen-draper's shops, etc., were being made in England.

English baby houses were at first designed by architects, who commissioned the furniture and fittings from regular craftsmen, the cabinet-makers, the tinsmiths, silversmiths, and so on. These houses too had stands to begin with, but they were invariably given 'real' façades with tiled roofs, glazed windows and panelled front doors. The Westbrook Baby House, c. 1705, made of polished unpainted oak and filled with its original furniture, is the finest surviving example, as well as being one of the two earliest houses *recorded* as having been made for a child. The other is the much simpler structure, c. 1700, given by Queen Anne to her godchild Ann Sharp. Like the Westbrook house, this royal house still belongs to the descendants of its first owner. It has lost its front, if it ever had one, but it contains splendid furniture in walnut and lacquer as well as the original dolls and some very early miniature silver.

From 1720 to 1790 was the golden age of the English baby houses. In this period they were often extremely large (five feet long or more, and too heavy for a stand); their elaborate façades were topped by balusters and urns, they had sometimes a double flight of stairs to the front door, or a garden frontage of gravel and grass. The interiors may have pedimented doorways, marbled chimney-pieces surmounted by swags of carved flowers, chairback panelling and other

G

delicately detailed work. These houses and their furniture were usually made by the estate carpenter; this was true of the superb Nostell Priory Baby House of 1740, the carpenter working to a design by the architect of Nostell, who was James Paine. Other fine English houses are at Uppark, at Wythenshawe, in the museums at Bethnal Green and Kensington Palace, in London, and in private hands. One such with a spiral staircase traditionally by Chippendale had furniture in the Chinese taste repeating in miniature the Chinese-style furniture he had executed for the mansion of the owner.

The late Georgian and Regency baby house was often a much plainer structure, without a stand, but smaller, and with iron handles at the side. Often there is no staircase, and the architectural details are less elaborate. Clockwork jacks in the kitchen are the height of ingenuity, but these now give way to an oven of cast iron (sometimes an oven of the Kitchener model, patented in 1795). Houses of such design continued till about 1840, the fireplaces plain, the interior often much simplified in every way, even to the loss of connecting doors or landings. Mass production had already begun, though the Victorian doll's house preserved the good proportions (so, too, the earlier Victorian houses and streets and villas of London, etc., remained seemly for a while). From the mid-century the doll's house is of thinner construction and sometimes has a low stand. The front almost always opens in one piece like a door, the façade of the bigger houses being handsome in a heavy manner remotely derived from Palladian architecture. Interior details, though, are coarse and clumsy; the staircase, if any, is mean and steep. In the late fifties and at least to the eighteen-eighties much furniture was imported from Germany, and this is enchanting, especially the series with marble tops. After the seventies doll's house architecture and design progressively deteriorated, now that the doll's house was established as a universal toy, much as the design of the urban dwelling-house deteriorated. The gabled villa appeared at the turn of the century, and since then the very few fine houses made in England have been – as in the earliest examples – specially designed for the pleasure of an adult; of these the best known are Sir Neville Wilkinson's 'Palace', the house presented by the people of Kent to the Duke of Kent on his marriage in 1934, the house made by the villagers of Burford to commemorate the Festival of Britain in 1951, and above all the doll's house given by the English nation to Queen Mary in 1920 as a token of affection.

ILLUSTRATION: Pages 212 and 213.

Materia medica

DRUGS from plants, or rather plants as drugs, are so widely familiar to primitive peoples that they must also have been known in prehistoric times, associated, no doubt, as in the early historic periods and in contemporary folklore, with magic and the supernatural.

Widespread in space and time are beliefs that the gods are herbalists, that kings delight in medicine and that the virtues of plants have been supernaturally revealed to men, and that medicinal plants were to be gathered with precise ritual. Such beliefs go back to ancient Greece, for example, and Egypt, and continue in many countries; the Irish have a story that the fairies were thrown out of Heaven, God throwing down plants after them, with orders that they should be good and useful. Welsh knowledge of drugs begins, by tradition, with the fairy woman Nelferch, who emerged from a lake in the Black Mountains, married a human husband, and taught her son, the first of the hereditary line of the Doctors of Myddvai, all the healing properties of herbs.

The ancient civilizations of the Mediterranean and the Near East have left much information about their knowledge of drugs. The Assyrians and Babylonians had some 250 drugs, the Egyptians in their materia medica used upwards of 700 different substances, beer, wine, aloes, cassia and caraway figuring among their vegetable remedies. Among their animal remedies were the excreta of human beings and certain animals, putrid meat and lizard's blood, among their mineral drugs, it appears, vermilion, lead and iron.

Greek medicine was helped by a long list of drugs. The Hippocratic physicians used them for specific diseases and divided them for internal use into narcotics, emetics, purgatives, and soporifics, the narcotics probably including opium and the purgatives such drastic remedies as colocynth. But they laid great emphasis on diet, and used drugs much less than the later physicians of Greece and Rome. About the first century B.C. the rhizotomist or herb-gatherer Krateuas, physician to King Mithridates, compiled a herbal illustrated with drawings of the individual species of plant. Neither herbal nor drawings survive, though a century later the Greek army doctor Pedanius Dioscorides compiled his famous *De materia medica*, which was illustrated (though we have no contemporary manuscript) with figures based on those of Krateuas.

For 1500 years this admirable, sober work was a basic authority on drugs, influencing the materia medica of the herbalists and physicians throughout Europe in the sixteenth and seventeenth centuries.

Drug plants thus have a long continuity. Autumn Crocus or Naked Ladies (*Colchicum autumnale*), which gives Tinctura Colchici, still essential for the relief of gout and still included in the British Pharmacopoeia, was known for the same virtue to the Alexandrian physician Paulus Aegineta, in the seventh century A.D. Dioscorides five centuries before had described *kolchikon* as a deadly poisonous plant (which it is); and an allied species of Colchicum was also familiar to Assyrian doctors.

Knowledge of the soporific qualities of mandrake (*Mandragora officinarum*) likewise descended from the Greeks, who called it *mandragoras*, going back beyond them to the Assyrians, who named it *nam-tar-gir*, 'male plague-god plant'. It is mentioned by all the classical writers from Hippocrates onwards, and may have been used as an anaesthetic before operations. Shakespeare was speaking to the book when he talked of poppy and mandragora and 'all the drowsy syrups of the world'. Pythagoras (c. 582–c. 507 B.C.) is supposed to have pointed out the resemblance of forked roots of the mandrake to the human figure, which has been the cause of so much magical and legendary practice.

Dioscorides also described a species of orchid, saying that the women of Thessaly gave the tubers in goat's milk, the young firm tuber for exciting sexual appetite, the wrinkled tuber of the previous season (they are found in pairs on the plant) for restraining it. Orchid species in consequence provided the western world with aphrodisiac medicines until a late period. A hundred and fifty years ago salep from dried tubers of orchid was still looked upon as a wholesome and strengthening food.

Bechion, included by Dioscorides as a plant to be smoked against a dry cough, was equated with coltsfoot, which goes into modern cough sweets. Coltsfoot leaf, Tussilaginis Folium, is still included in the British Pharmaceutical Codex (1949 edition) as an ingredient in herbal tobacco for coughs.

Houseleek, much used even now as a cottage remedy in England, and grown on lean-to roofs over the back door, has a dossier of more than 2000 years. The Greek botanist Theophrastus (c. 372–287 B.C.) wrote that houseleek (*aizon*, everliving) grew 'on top of earthy walls, and particularly on roof tiles, when there is enough sandy earth.' Dioscorides remarked that 'some plant it on the tiles above their houses.' Here is a case of a drug plant inseparably entwined with magic. English country people make a soothing ointment of the juicy leaves, but it was also planted on the roof to avert lightning. Thus the Romans called it both *diopetes*, the plant 'fallen from Zeus' and *Iovis caulis*, 'Jupiter's plant', given by the god to protect houses from his own thunderbolts. The Irish still realize that it protects the house from fire and name it *luibh an toiteán*, 'fire herb'. It was, and occasionally continues to be, grown on clay ridges above thatch, a fact noted in 1661 by the English naturalist John Ray when travelling through Lincolnshire.

Houseleek, too, was one of the many medicinal plants of the Old World taken to the New World by settlers in the seventeenth century, John Josselyn in his *New-England's Rarities* (1672) observing that 'Houseleek prospereth notably'.

It is to northern folk medicine and not to classical sources that we owe one powerful and respectable drug, the derivative of the Foxglove (*Digitalis purpurea*). By clinical investigations summed up in his *Account of the Foxglove* (1785), William Withering showed that digitalis acted upon the heart and was a good diuretic. Long

before the poisonous Foxglove had been employed in the countryside as a purge, a vomit, and against colds, scrofula and dropsy. It was associated by the English, the Irish and the Welsh with fairies (an Irish name is *lus na mban sídhe* 'plant of the fairy women', a Welsh name *bysedd ellyllon*, 'elves' fingers'), and the juice of Foxglove was rubbed as a test on supposed changelings; the plant was also used in Ireland to recover changelings.

The great Hellenistic physician Galen (A.D. 129–200), doctor to the gladiators' school at Pergamum, mentioned in his writings drugs and mixtures of drugs, some of which persisted for centuries. Among them was the *hiera picra*, supposed to have been discovered about 50 B.C. The composition varied, but a main component was aloes, together with Indian bark, mastic and saffron, Galen's formula including also cinnamon and spikenard. This formula was not dropped from the London Pharmacopoeia until 1788.

After Greek culture died away in the West, it was preserved by the Arabs, who had captured Alexandria in A.D. 642. From the beginning of the eighth century the Arabs concerned themselves much with science and medicine. The works of the Greek medical authors were translated into Arabic, and in this form or in Latin translations from the Arabic they continued to influence medical practice for eight centuries. Many drugs, such as camphor, rhubarb, tamarinds, senna and manna, were handed on to us directly from Arab sources. The Arabian physicians were addicted to the giving of mixtures of many drugs – to that polypharmacy which persisted in medicine until recently (the 'diasatyrion' included in the seventeenth-century Pharmacopoeia of the College of Physicians in London included orchid tubers, bitter almonds, dates, pine nuts, Indian nuts, pistachio nuts, peppers, ambergris, galingale, clover, musk, barley sugar, cinnamon, saffron, nutmeg, mace, grains of Paradise, ash-keys, Malaga wine, borax, benzoine, wood of aloes, cardamons, nettle seed, avens root, and the belly and loins of 'scinks').

The Arabs also used precious metals and stones. Thus Avicenna (980–1037) probably introduced the practice of covering pills with gold or silver; and mercury in the form of corrosive sublimate, though correctly regarded as a deadly poison, was employed externally for skin conditions. Arab drugs were not all of them rational. Avenzoar (c. 1090–1162) was probably the first to describe the supposed benefits of the bezoar. According to him, it comes from the eye of a stag: stags eat serpents, and immediately run to a stream and stand in it, a liquid then exuding from their eyes and congealing into bezoars. All other authors say that the bezoar stone is a concretion which is formed in the bowel of the Persian wild goat. In fact, it probably consists of a deposit of lime phosphate around a nucleus of hair. So-called 'genuine' bezoars were highly regarded throughout Europe for the treatment of poisoning, skin diseases, and even leprosy, well into the eighteenth century. Ambroise Paré, the French surgeon of the sixteenth century, advised that they were ineffective, but even his authority did not prevail against them.

In the sixteenth century, the herbal of Dioscorides was eagerly and seriously studied, attempts were made to identify and investigate his drug plants, and doctors broke with magical practices which had grown up in the post-classical world. More and more essential oils were distilled from plants. Paracelsus (c. 1493–1541) was exhorting his followers to abandon the use of worthless mixtures of plant juices, and to employ the metals mercury and antimony as staple drugs for many purposes. He also advocated extracts and tinctures as being more likely than infusions and syrups to contain the active principles of a plant. The approach of Paracelsus was essentially chemical, and in the following century there arose a protracted controversy between those who advocated chemical remedies and those who adhered to the plant remedies of Galen.

This was the battle between the Galenists and the Helmontians, or followers of the Flemish physician and chemist J. B. van Helmont (1577–1644). The decision lay ultimately with the Helmontians. In London the College of Physicians had decided some years previously that 'chymical' remedies must have their official sanction, and in 1618 they were included in the first pharmacopoeia printed by authority of the College.

The eighteenth century was a period of consolidation in the production of drugs rather than of new remedies. Physic gardens had already been long established at most of the large universities. The second half of the eighteenth century saw, however, the great discoveries in inorganic chemistry made by Black, Scheele, Priestley, Cavendish and Lavoisier, which were crowned in the early nineteenth century by the discoveries of John Dalton, Dumas and Berzelius. All this led to the rise of organic chemistry and the work of Wöhler, Liebig and Chevreul, and the eventual synthesis of new organic substances of importance in pharmacology.

A critical date in the history of drugs is 1806, when the German apothecary Sertürner discovered morphine, the first organic alkali – an alkaloid – obtained from a plant. From at least the fifteenth century chemists had sought for the active principles in plants, and Robert Boyle and others had worked on opium without success. Sertürner's long series of investigations, the publication of which was not completed until 1816, finally established the chemical nature of the active principle and opened the way to the discovery of many new alkaloids, all of which could be used for the production of different salts.

One may mention the alkaloid emetine, isolated from the ipecacuanha of the New World in 1817 by the French chemist Pelletier and the physiologist Magendie, strychnine which Pelletier and Caventou isolated from nuxvomica in 1818, and atropine isolated from belladonna (Deadly Nightshade) in 1833.

In 1820 Caventou and Pelletier at last showed that cinchona or Jesuit's bark, which the Spaniards had brought from Peru as a specific for malaria or ague, contains at least two alkaloids, to one of which they gave the familiar name of quinine. Even now the alkaloids of cinchona have not been completely unravelled.

ILLUSTRATION: Pages 268 and 269.

A noise like thunder

DRUMS are among the most primitive and ancient and widespread of musical instruments, powerfully resonant and offering pleasurable, stimulating, or terrifying possibilities of rhythmical pattern. Uses of the drum and types of drum differ, but from primitive drums to the timpani of a modern orchestra the refinements are slighter than those which have changed modern wind and string instruments.

From first to last the best of drums has been the kettledrum, which is a bowl, not a cylinder, covered with skin. Plutarch describes the Parthians advancing into battle beating upon such drums to frighten the enemy, and there are many other classical references to the use of the instrument in religion and war, mostly in the East. It was, in fact, from the East that the kettledrums originally came, and it is there, and in Africa, that they are still used in greatest variety and with most subtle skill.

Usually the kettledrums went in pairs, one high in pitch and one low; in war the smaller drums were carried at the waist of the player and the larger ones were slung over a horse or camel. They first appeared in England towards the end of the thirteenth century, in a small form then known as 'nakers' (from the Arabic *naqqára*, an instrument which persists unchanged in the Near East). Probably the Crusades were responsible for this early introduction – the description by a knight of Louis IX's Crusade, 'Lor il fit sonner les tabours que l'on appelle nacaircs', shows that in name and nature they were unfamiliar. Horns and trumpets had been the musical adjuncts of European warfare; but now the use of kettledrums spread quickly and widely: Edward I's band included in 1304 one Janino le Nakerer, and later that century Chaucer wrote in the *Knight's Tale* of

> Pypes, trompes, nakers, and clariounes,
> That in the batail blewe bloody sownes.

Two centuries later the term 'kettledrum' appears to have been current; Shakespeare could make the King in *Hamlet* cry,

> ... let the kettle to the trumpet speak,
> The trumpet to the cannoneer without,
> The cannons to the heavens, and the heavens to earth,
> 'Now the King drinks to Hamlet!' ...

The large cavalry drums spread through Europe in the fifteenth century, arriving by way of Hungary in the course of one of the wars against the Turks. Henry VIII sent to Vienna for a pair, and like other European monarchs retained a royal monopoly in them; Elizabeth I used to have her dinner enlivened by a band including kettledrums, which, so Hertzer's *Itinerarium* informs us, 'made the hall ring for half an hour together'.

By now the timpani (as they are generally called in their orchestral forms) were thought of more seriously by musicians, and they were being made with more care. Arbeau tells us in his famous *Orchésographie* of 1589 that such a drum was 'made of a half sphere of copper mouthed with a strong parchment about $2\frac{1}{2}$ feet across', and that it gave 'a noise like thunder'. By the seventeenth century they were established in the orchestra, though two centuries had still to go by before all their possibilities were grasped by the serious composer. Beethoven emancipated them to a great extent, but his use of timpani was still limited. By now these timpani could be tuned by handles at the rim for tightening or loosening the parchment; and this made them still more superior to other drums: they were no longer devices for making organized noise, but real instruments of music, on which even melodies were possible. The first known instance of a drum melody occurs in Graupner's *Dido* of 1707, but melody is contrary to the nature of a drum, and instances of it are rare, and even then freakish. Instantaneous tuning by a pedal was introduced; and by the end of the nineteenth century three kettledrums made up the normal complement for an orchestra, though Berlioz demanded four for his *Symphonie Fantastique* and no less than sixteen for his *Requiem*, writing for drums with unprecedented imagination and understanding. The greatest modern masters are Stravinsky and Bartók – Stravinsky by reason of his genius for elaborate and exciting rhythm, Bartók for his deep practical understanding of the nature and technique of all percussion instruments. A few solo works exist for timpani – there is a concerto by the composer-drummer Pieranzovini, and a brilliantly constructed sonata by the contemporary Welsh composer Daniel Jones – but the best use of timpani is certainly in orchestras and bands. A notable modern example is in the section of Bliss's war symphony *Morning Heroes* where a narrator declaims Wilfred Owen's

'Spring Offensive' over an accompaniment composed only of growling drums, in which, at the furthest point of their development and sophistication, the kettledrums have come back to their first European home – which was the field of battle.

Five other drums are more or less regular members of the modern orchestra: the side-drum, which is double-headed, and has lengths of gut, called snares, stretched below the skin, giving the characteristic military burr when the drum is struck; the bass drum, very large, giving a deep boom of no particular pitch; the tenor drum, mid-way between these two in size and noise; the tambourine (another very ancient instrument), which is in fact a small, shallow, single-headed drum, though little metal plates are let into the frame, jingling at the slightest provocation; and the tabor, rare in the orchestra but familiar in folk music in the company of a pipe, which has a long barrel and a narrow head, generally with a single snare across it.

Jazz depends upon drums for its basic pulse, and the jazz drummer is often a considerable virtuoso, surrounding himself with instruments of every size and sound, and working elaborate solo 'breaks' upon them from time to time. Yet it is still in Africa that drums are best understood. There technique of drums is developed almost to the point of articulate language. Not only can the bush telegraph speak lightning messages across hill and forest, valley and river, but a skilled native drummer can inflame his hearers to varying emotions in a way that, for all its resources, is denied to a symphony orchestra. The secret lies deeper than anthropology has yet penetrated; a musician can only state baldly that the African drum rhythms which have been collected and written down show a range and technique that defy expressive notation, and make even Stravinsky seem like a child tapping a toy.

ILLUSTRATION: Plate 1.

For a peacock world

DYES and the art of dyeing are amongst the oldest of the discoveries by which man has made life agreeable as well as merely bearable. We know from cave paintings that colour was significant in the life of palaeolithic man. Very early on after the invention of weaving, man must have discovered how some vegetable juices would stain, and how some, applied under special conditions, would give a fabric a colour which was not easily removed by water or by exposure to air and light. Such a contrived, more or less permanent, colouring of a material, done by altering its own qualities rather than by applied pigments, we call dyeing.

The earliest surviving dyed materials are Egyptian: a fragment of matting from pre-dynastic times and some blue-dyed linen from the Middle Kingdom (c. 2000 B.C.). Tomb paintings of the Old Kingdom (c. 3000 B.C.) also show red, yellow and green materials. Chemical tests prove that Egyptian blue dye was due to indigotin, the substance responsible for the blue colour given by indigo and woad.

Woad, from the tall biennial crucifer *Isatis tinctoria*, was one of the best known of all dyes and one of the most widely used, for its own blue and as a foundation for other tints. The use of it spread probably from Assyria into the Mediterranean and the west, though it came late to Northern Europe in the Iron Age. At the moment there is only literary evidence, from Caesar and Pliny, for the use of woad by the British (as a body paint rather than a dye). The archaeological evidence for woad in Britain (where it is not an indigenous plant) goes back only to Anglo-Saxon times, though the place name Glastonbury may be derived from the old Celtic for woad. However, the preparation of woad from green leaf to dye is a complex process, demanding a degree of civilization. The prehistoric peoples of Europe probably used dyes of simpler preparation, yellows from weld or Dyer's Rocket (*Reseda luteola*) for example, or purples from the purple berries of the dwarf elder (*Sambucus ebulus*). Traces of both these plants, but not of woad, have been recovered in the excavation of neolithic lake dwellings in Switzerland.

From the earliest times until the nineteenth century the repertory of dyes was limited. Vegetable dyes included, as well as indigo and woad and weld, madder (which gives red), archil or orchil (a purple dye from lichen), and yellows from safflower and saffron, though it was weld which gave some of the most brilliant of all yellows. Weld, woad and madder were the staples of the craft. Thus Chaucer in the fourteenth century, in one of his minor poems, talks of the innocent life before the coming of industry and litesteres or dyers.

> No mader, welde or wood [woad] no litestere
> He knew; the flees was of his former hewe.

The ancients also knew the animal dyes Tyrian purple (from a species of mollusc), and kermes (a red from the dried bodies of female lice).

They also knew the supremely important art of mordanting, that is of treating a fabric with a metallic compound, which enables the dye to 'take'. Without this their colour range would have been limited to the inadequate results obtainable by direct dyeing.

The most celebrated of the ancient dyes is Tyrian purple. The legend goes that Hercules' sheep-dog was biting at a shell-fish when his master noticed that the dog's jaws were becoming stained bright red. He immediately ordered a robe to be dyed with the stain. (Actually the colour takes some time to develop.) This dye was used by the Minoans in Crete as early as 1600 B.C. The great Phoenician city of Tyre became the chief centre of the Mediterranean purple trade, which survived until the rise of Islam. The best purple obtainable from these shell-fish is not a brilliant colour by modern standards, but because of its uniqueness and its permanence it inevitably became associated with wealth, power and authority. Kermes was also known from early times, and there was some competition between kermes and Tyrian purple, since it gives a very good red.

The Romans knew indigo (from the Asiatic plant *Indigofera tinctoria*) but as a pigment. Their blue dye was obtained from woad. It was known to the Greeks (indigo is from the Greek *indikos*, 'Indian'). One of the oldest recorded chemical tests, quoted by Pliny (first century A.D.) is that for indigo which, when thrown on to a hot plate, gives 'a violet vapour and a smell of seaweed'. In a document surviving from the same period (the Stockholm Papyrus) there are to be found dyeing recipes which were in use in Alexandria certainly at the beginning of the Christian era and probably hundreds of years before. Careful controls and tests for getting the best results are described and several recipes explain how to obtain different shades from a particular dye by varying the mordant, using, say, alum in one case and copperas (ferrous sulphate) in another.

In the Dark Ages the art of dyeing declined. Madder cultivation, for example, died out in the West for some time, though it gradually revived under Charlemagne. There was an even more general revival of dye practice following the Crusades. The staple dye, however, continued to be woad, which maintained its dominant position until the Portuguese explorers and navigators of the fifteenth century opened up new sea-routes to India. From then on indigo began, bit by bit, to compete with woad, although only in the face of bitter resistance from the established dyers with their stake in the protection of the woad industry. Many were the statutory prohibitions and restrictions placed on indigo, but gradually it won a foothold. At first it was used only to strengthen the woad vat. Then it replaced woad entirely when it was found to be much the more potent dye. A notable stage in the career of indigo was its adoption for the new British navy uniform in 1745. The cultivation and preparation of woad continued in Lincolnshire until the nineteen-thirties, when the last two mills in Lincolnshire – and in the world – were abandoned. These horse-mills crushed the young leaves before they were moulded into balls, dried, powdered, wetted, and fermented to liberate the dye; the fermentation was one of the smelliest and most repulsive processes in old-world industry.

The maritime expansion of the sixteenth century brought into general use other vegetable dyes which had previously been used only in a small way, and also introduced one new dye of animal origin. The Venetians had imported brazilwood or sapan wood from India as early as the twelfth century, but it only became widely used after the fifteenth. Other brazilwoods were found in the newly discovered South America, extracts of which give a bright red colour with an aluminous mordant, but it is not much employed now. Logwood, on the other hand, still finds a use for giving purples on animal fibres and a black on cotton. It was discovered by the Spaniards in Mexico, to the great benefit of their own cloth trade. Their English contemporaries resisted its use, to their own disadvantage, until it was freed from statutory restrictions in the seventeenth century.

The new animal dye, brought to Europe by the Spanish, was cochineal, obtained from a bug-like scale insect which thrives on cactus. It had been used by the Aztecs, and supplied by way of tribute, long before the arrival of the Spanish invaders. The Spanish continued to demand tribute of cochineal, and were thus able to import large quantities of it into Europe, where it displaced kermes as a red dye. It was itself replaced by the aniline dyes of the nineteenth century. ('Aniline' is from *anil*, an older name for indigo, ultimately from the Sanskrit *nila*, which means 'dark blue'.)

A large part of the great chemical industry of today owes its origin to the accidental discovery in 1856 of the first synthetic dyestuff, mauve, by W. H. Perkin (1838–1907). The distinguished German chemist A. W. von Hofmann (1818–1892) had been brought to England (at the suggestion of the Prince Consort) to teach at the new College of Chemistry. Perkin was acting as his assistant in attempts to synthesize quinine. One of many abortive efforts produced a black residue from which alcohol extracted a violet substance capable of dyeing animal fibres. Perkin saw and seized his opportunity and set up a small factory at Greenford, Middlesex. It prospered as it deserved.

Other workers soon added new dyes. Hofmann made magenta in 1858. In the same year Peter Griess, working in a brewery at Burton-on-Trent, discovered the important diazo reaction, a general method of chemical synthesis which has been the means of producing a vast range of colouring matters, starting with Griess's own aniline yellow in 1859. In 1868, for the first time, a naturally occurring dyestuff was reproduced synthetically, and in appropriately dramatic circumstances. Caro, Graebe and Liebermann in Germany and Perkin in England arrived independently at the synthesis of alizarin, the dyestuff of madder. Perkin's patent application reached the British Patent Office one day behind that of his rivals. The priority meant little to the French madder industry for whoever was entitled to the credit, it meant ruin.

Synthetic indigo followed in 1880. From that time on thousands of dyestuffs have been produced, surpassing in variety and brilliance anything known to the ancient world or even to the modern world before the mid-nineteenth century. This is not to say that there are no unsolved problems. The new artificial fibres involve their own difficulties. When cellulose acetate came into prominence after the First World War it was resistant to dyeing by the methods hitherto practised. Ultimately a new method of dyeing was evolved, in which insoluble substances are applied in a dispensed state, to be deposited in the fibre. Dyes of this type are now used for the newer synthetic fibres, including nylon.

Into the manufacture of dyes go so great a variety of reagents and intermediates that it has grown into a system of general chemical production. The commercial association of many firms has led to the formation of huge combines. Whatever may be the morality of such organizations, it must be admitted that their research resources promise a colourful future. In the recently discovered Phthalocyanine pigments we have the fastest colours yet made. The new fluorescent 'white dyes' which are incorporated in modern washing powder give a brilliance to today's laundered linen that was a physical impossibility in the past. The modern dyemaster may seem a less romantic figure than the Phoenician shell-gatherer, but it is he who has possessed us of a peacock world.

ILLUSTRATION: Pages 30 and 31.

Dynamo-electric machine

A **DYNAMO** is a machine for converting mechanical energy, such as that of steam power, water power, or the power of an oil engine, into electrical energy which can be transmitted over wires to the locations at which it is to be used. If the demand comes from a large number of users requiring power in relatively moderate quantities at various times of day and night, then it is much more economical to generate the power at a central station in bulk. It even becomes economical to combine many central stations into an inter-connected system, or 'grid', so that at the very slack hours most stations can be closed down almost entirely and the load can be supplied by one or more stations working at nearly full pressure. The advantage of electricity is that as much power as may be required at any time can be made available in a form that may be transmitted easily to wherever the demand may be.

The first dynamo – that is, a rotating machine for converting mechanical energy into electrical energy – was purely a laboratory device made in London in 1831 by the remarkable scientist Michael Faraday (1791–1867). He rotated a copper disc between the poles of a large iron magnet, and showed that a small electric current could be registered as an indication that the manual work of turning the disc had resulted in the generation of electric power. Later in the same year Pixii, in Germany, made a more convincing demonstration, using copper coils instead of a copper disc. There was, however, no practical demand for mechanically generated electric currents until, in 1844, Woolrich of Birmingham built a big, clumsy machine of coils and permanent magnets that was used to supply current, when driven by a steam engine, to the plating vats of Messrs Prime and Company. In 1858 a much bigger machine, on roughly the same principle, was driven by a three horse-power steam engine to supply current to an arc lamp at the South Foreland lighthouse. The machine had sixty compound horseshoe magnets and one hundred and sixty coils mounted on two wheels, each nine feet in diameter. The arc-lit lighthouse shone out with the unprecedented strength of 1,500 candles.

By this time generators had been greatly improved. The permanent magnets of earlier dynamos had been replaced by electro-magnets. The principles of self-excitation, by which a machine burgeoned automatically instead of requiring an auxiliary supply to its electro-magnets, had been discovered, and arc lamps, if not for lighthouses, provided a ready-made load. Each arc-lamp installation had its own little generating station, for there were no public electricity supplies. In Paris the Avenue de l'Opéra, in London the Embankment and later in New York City the areas between Madison and Union Squares,

all had their arc-lamp installations. It was Thomas Alva Edison (1847–1931) in New York City, who had the brilliant idea of building a central electric power-station to give a public supply for his newly perfected carbon filament electric lamps. His power-station at Pearl Street was an engineering *tour de force* with dynamos of as much as 15 horse-power driven by high-speed steam engines of advanced design. In this station, opened in 1881, two or more machines could be connected if the load increased beyond a certain capacity. The word 'dynamo', from the Greek *dunamis*, power, energy, appeared late in these developments. In 1867 the German electrical engineer Ernst Werner von Siemens called a dynamo of his invention the 'dynamo-electric machine'. The use of the shortened name 'dynamo' was recommended by an English professor in 1882.

Many power stations today are operated by water power, which takes the maximum advantage of the bounty of nature. If water is allowed to drop from a height it can be made to do work in turning a dynamo machine. The water can be stored at a height by means of a retaining dam, and can be led to the machines as required. The storage reservoir can be filled in the wet season and drawn upon as required throughout the year. Civil engineering schemes for water impounding are expensive, but in the main they provide power much more cheaply than by other methods. The difficulty is that the source of power is often very far away from the centre at which it may be consumed. A highly industrialized area (such as most of England) may be so ill provided with water-power supplies that alternatives have to be sought. In Britain there is abundant coal. Coal can be used to provide steam under pressure; and the steam can be made to drive the dynamo machines. At first this was done by means of reciprocating steam engines in which the steam was led into a cylinder to push a piston forward, and then exhausted as the piston came back. The backwards and forwards motions had to be converted mechanically into a rotary motion to turn the dynamo, and it was not difficult to believe that if the steam could be made to turn a wheel directly it might be more efficient.

The steam turbine was first introduced by Sir

Charles Parsons in 1884. The steam expanded through a series of blades arranged round the periphery of a wheel, and in doing so turned the rotor, and the dynamo on the same shaft, at the prodigious speed of 18,000 revolutions per minute. It was not at first as efficient as the ordinary reciprocating steam-engine drive, but by 1892 it had achieved parity, and by 1900 it was well ahead. The bigger the size the greater the efficiency, although problems were introduced by the exeedingly high peripheral speeds. Nevertheless a set of 1,000 kilowatts capacity was built by 1899; and of 25,000 kilowatts by 1912. In 1931 a set rated at 165,000 kilowatts was built in the U.S.A., but something of the order of 60,000 kilowatts has been found to be the most useful and economical size for the larger electric networks.

The dynamo to be driven by these great prime-movers has been developed to a very high pitch of efficiency. To begin with, most dynamos generated direct currents. When a copper conductor is rotated in a magnetic field, a current is induced in it. When it passes a north magnetic pole the current induced is in the opposite direction to when it passes a south magnetic pole. Electro-magnets around the circumference of a dynamo machine are alternately north and south. The copper conductor consists of a coil embedded in iron so that it may experience the greatest magnetic effects. The ends of the coils were originally led to a device known as a commutator, which reversed the current collection each time the coil changed from a north to a south magnetic field. The result was that the current collected was always in the same direction and was known as direct or continuous current.

In later days it was found that many machines had to be combined together in one system and that the centre of load was often far away from the place of generation. In these circumstances alternating currents were desirable, as it is very easy with them to reduce losses by transferring upwards into higher voltages for transmission and then transforming down again into lower voltages for consumption. The design of dynamos altered accordingly, and in the latter years of the nineteenth century a still greater change took place. For lighting by incandescent lamps it did not matter much whether the supply was continuous or alternating, and at first the lamp load was almost the entire demand on a power station. Gradually the electric motor load became more important, until today it is the mainstay of industry and may outweigh all other demands put together. For technical reasons the three-phase alternating current motor has great advantages in large industrial units. Three-phase means, in effect, that the coils of three generators are inter-woven around the periphery of a single machine and are then inter-connected electrically. The complication in design that this entails cannot be explained simply, but as early as 1901 the first three-phase turbo-alternator set of 150 kilowatts was built by Sir Charles Parsons for the Ackton Hall Colliery in Yorkshire.

The modern turbo-alternator may run at 1,500 or 3,000 revolutions per minute, and the peripheral stresses in a rotor of large diameter are far higher than those in the tiny 18,000-revolutions-per-minute machine built by Parsons in 1884. The extreme edge of the rotor may be travelling at very nearly the speed of sound. To reduce friction losses the whole electrical machine may be enclosed in a gas-tight housing and cooled by a flow of hydrogen gas. The voltage of generation may be as high as 33,000 volts, which may then be stepped up to 132,000 volts, or even 275,000 volts for transmission to the consumption area, where it may be stepped down again, by stages, to the 400 volts three-phase or 230 volts single-phase used in factories and homes. There are many intricate engineering problems in the design and production of these machines that make them one of the most beautiful examples of engineering skill. The fact that plugging in to an electric circuit or turning on an electric lamp is accepted as commonplace is perhaps the finest tribute to their success. The bottle-shaped little dynamos on pedal cycles, powered by the turning of the back or front wheel, so cheap and so efficient, are an example of how this much-perfected invention of Faraday has been taken for granted – how few people know, or care to know, how they work. (See also *Lamp*.)

ILLUSTRATION: Page 81.

E

Clay into earthenware

EARTHENWARE emerges from what is probably man's earliest utilization of applied chemistry, involving the discovery that a substance which is plastic and friable undergoes a remarkable change with intense heat, becoming completely non-plastic and resistant to water.

Clay consists of alumina, silica and water. The water mechanically present gives clay its plasticity, and can be driven off by exposure in a dry atmosphere. But wet the clay, and it will take up water and become plastic again. The water present chemically can only be driven off by strong heat; and in this process the unalterable change takes place. The clay becomes a pot. It comes out of the fire with the shape it was given when pliable and soft. Yet it has become fixed and hard; brittleness is the only drawback.

When and how did man discover that with the aid of fire he could construct artificial fossils in this way, in any shape he liked, at little cost and without much labour? He may have observed that water stood on surface clay after rainfall, and so may have lined his baskets with clay to waterproof them. Suppose such baskets to have been burnt accidentally: the basketry disappears, but the clay waterproofing survives in the same shape, transmuted and toughened, with qualities in many ways superior to those of the original basket. That is one possibility; and it is generally held that the manufacture of pots developed 10,000 or more years ago. Mesolithic pottery has been found in Kenya and the Sudan.

However, there may have been pottery, so to say, before pots, or earthenware before utensil. Recent excavations at the palaeolithic site of Dolní Věstonice in Czechoslovakia suggest that the property of fired clay was discovered much earlier, but first applied to small clay figures and pellets. A rough low hut, more or less circular (see also *House*), was excavated containing what the investigators interpreted as a crude kiln, in which the figures and pellets were baked. Thus the manufacture of earthenware would be taken back to some 25,000 years before our time, or to some 15,000 years before the mesolithic date ascribed to the invention of pottery – the production, that is, of vessels.

Pottery has been found in Mesopotamia on the earliest sites yet excavated, and was in use there by 5000 B.C. But there are still some difficulties about regarding it as an exclusively neolithic invention. There existed well-developed neolithic cultures – for instance, in Cyprus and Palestine – which had no pottery; more puzzling still, in north-west Europe, there was pre-neolithic pottery: men of the mesolithic Ertebølle culture, in north Germany and Denmark, who lived an unsavoury existence on top of their own kitchen middens, also possessed pottery at or before 5000 B.C. This does not fit; and it seems so curious a freak that some archaeologists are driven to suggest that in some extraordinary and still more freakish way the craft of making pottery must have been diffused to Ertebølle man from the archaeologically respectable centres of the first appearance of pottery in Mesopotamia.

Whatever the true story, a consideration of the process or separate processes, each one of which must be efficiently performed to produce a good pot, will show what a remarkable and complex technique had been developed. When a suitable clay has been found, it must first be washed and cleaned. Then it has to be kneaded carefully to get rid of every air bubble and reduce it to an even texture. Next, while it is damp and plastic, the potter must work his clay to the desired shape.

Nothing more can now be done until the pot has dried to the 'leather-hard' state, which takes about twenty-four hours in a fairly dry atmosphere. The pot can then be handled, its surface trimmed and smoothed out, and perhaps decorated with patterns lightly incised.

Much primitive pottery is polished or burnished at this stage with a pebble or a piece of bone, to make the pot more waterproof by closing the pores of the clay and to give a better appearance, since polishing and burnishing persist after the pot is fired. Ancient potters now painted the 'leather-hard' pot, which was set aside for two or three days to dry completely, for if an excessive amount of water is driven off in the kiln, the pot is likely to crack and warp.

At last the pot is fired; and of all the processes, this is the most tricky and unpredictable. When, as they were in the earliest days, pots and combustibles are heaped together, the results will be erratic; pot surfaces will be a patchwork of reds, browns and blacks.

Furnaces were built with devices for producing higher temperatures by a forced draught; at first pots and combustibles inside the furnace were on top of each other still. Then a platform was introduced for the pots, separating them from the fire below. Experience taught potters how to control these kilns and raise them to the most suitable temperature. When that temperature has been reached, the fire is slowly extinguished, and the kiln allowed to cool down gradually, since the stress of rapid cooling would crack the pots. An average estimate for the firing period is twenty-four hours – twelve hours to reach the critical temperature and twelve more for cooling.

The method by which a pot has been fired has much to do with its final appearance, particularly when polished or painted. Even the colour of the 'biscuit' (seen best at a fracture) is largely conditioned by the firing. Varying tones in a group of otherwise similar pots are due to different kiln temperatures, or perhaps to varying supplies of oxygen during firing. Surface colour is affected in direct relation to the supply of oxygen and its reaction on the chemical composition of the clay. Plentiful oxygen and a smokeless fire are likely to produce a light-coloured or reddish 'biscuit', while lack of oxygen, or a smoky fire produces dark surfaces and dark 'biscuit'.

Early pottery in Sumeria rose to a splendid excellence. As we talk today of Wedgwood and Sèvres, so we can describe Tell Halaf and al 'Ubaid wares, the most distinctive of the earliest painted pottery in Sumeria, named after the sites at which they were first identified. Tell Halaf ware in particular is extremely satisfying, both in the shapes of its pots, which were built up by hand, and in their decoration, which includes abstract patterns as well as delightful, stylized animals. Tell Halaf pots, for all their 6,500 years, would not look out of place in any exhibition of modern applied art.

Pottery was used in the earliest pre-dynastic settlements in the Nile valley; in common with much primitive pottery the shapes of the pots show them to be copies of utensils made of other materials. This is borne out, too, by the decoration, in which incised lines copy the stitching of leather vessels, or the weaves of basketry. Much early painted decoration simulates the slings or nets in which gourds were carried.

Some parts of the ancient world preferred painted pottery, others chose to perfect single-colour fabrics, their appearance enhanced by polishing or burnishing the surface. Yet there is a constant division of this kind; painted pottery occurs at some time or another nearly everywhere – except in Temperate Europe, which was backward in ceramic development.

Particular styles of pottery have come to be the hallmarks of different societies. Black-topped red ware typifies early Egypt; a wonderful polychrome eggshell ware is the mark of Crete during the Middle Bronze Age; distinctive jugs with a beaked spout spread widely over Bronze Age Turkey; Mycenae is represented by vases with glossy yellow slip and ornament in lustrous red, brown or black paint. This travelled over much of what was then the known world in the days of Mycenae's greatness.

Something of Mycenaean tradition survived the barbarian onslaughts which destroyed the Aegean Bronze Age and influenced the subsequent pottery of Greece, which culminated in the magnificence of the black figure and red figure styles produced by Athens in her heyday. The immense popularity of this Attic pottery can be judged by the area over which it has been found – Italy, North Africa, South Russia, Anatolia, Cyprus, Egypt and the Levant. Yet civilization and its products spread so unevenly that while painters and potters were producing their masterpieces in Athens, peasants in Britain of the Late Bronze Age and the Iron Age were making pottery in every way inferior to the earliest products of Mesopotamia or Egypt.

Many of the crafts practised in remote antiquity are dead; others are dying. But potting survives not as a curious heirloom, but as a flourishing, constantly developing industry; at times that industry has risen to the level of superb artistic creation, as in Sumeria, in Athens and in

China, where noble painted ware goes back to the Chinese neolithic era. (See also *Chinaware*, *Plastics*, *Potter's Wheel*.)

ILLUSTRATION: Pages 222 and 223.

Turn of a switch

ELECTRIC LIGHT, which has so thoroughly and almost universally revolutionized our life in the hours of darkness, is, in the main, produced in two ways, either by the filament lamp or the electric discharge lamp. The filament lamp depends on heating a continuous filament of metal or carbon to incandescent heat inside a glass bulb from which all air has been exhausted or in which an inert gas has been introduced to prevent wasting away of the filament by oxidization. The electric discharge lamp began as an arc between carbon electrodes in air, the carbon being more or less rapidly consumed; it is now more commonly an arc in an atmosphere of mercury vapour or sodium vapour or neon gas inside a glass tube or bulb. The glass container may be coated with fluorescent material to alter the character of the light.

The first practical electric lamp was the carbon arc. This was demonstrated by Sir Humphry Davy at the Royal Institution in London in 1810, but there were no machines to provide the electric current required. In spite of this, the arc lamp, fed by batteries of wet cells, was used for theatrical effects at the Paris Opera from 1846; it was used for street lighting in Lyons in 1855: and even for spotting movements of the enemy during the siege of Paris in 1870. Machines were at first very cumbersome, one of the earliest being designed by Holmes in England to supply an arc light at the South Foreland lighthouse in 1858. Machines were vastly improved, and in 1878 the Avenue de l'Opéra in Paris was lit by sixty-two arc lamps; in 1879 arc lamps illuminated one and a quarter miles of road in London, from Westminster to Waterloo. Right up to the end of the First World War arc lamps were used in ever-increasing numbers for street lighting and other applications in which a light source could still be

tolerated which was unwieldy, very bright, and greedy of current; and which demanded frequent attention. The arc lamp was obviously no use for the home.

The aim of many early experimenters was 'the division of electric light', by which they meant the production of light sources small enough to be manageable in the home. Many experiments were made from 1840 onwards. The fact is that no filament lamp could last a sufficient length of time to be economical in use, until the discovery of the technique of exhausting the lamp bulb to a fairly high degree of vacuum. The critical invention was the Sprengel air-pump of 1865, which was greatly improved by Sir William Crookes ten years later. With this instrument Sir Joseph Wilson Swan in England produced a practical carbon filament lamp in 1878 and Edison in America an even better lamp a few months later in 1879. These lamps were successful and were soon greatly improved; even so they were only about one-sixth as efficient as arc lamps.

Carbon was not a good material for filaments, and at the end of the century research was directed towards making filaments of metal which would be both fine enough and strong enough. Tantalum was used with some success in 1905, but William David Coolidge in the U.S.A. in 1909 invented a means of improving the ductility of tungsten by roasting and hammering; this gave what is still the best of filaments. Efficiency was improved by coiling the filament and putting it in an atmosphere of inert gas (argon) in 1913. In domestic sizes the filament lamp is now more than half as efficient as the old arc lamps, while in very large sizes, such as lamps for lighthouses, a filament lamp may be appreciably more efficient than the arc lamp.

The production of the light-bulbs for the filament lamp is a complicated business of considerable magnitude. Up to about 1920 almost every glass bulb had to be blown by hand, and thousands of glass-blowers were engaged in this monotonous task. The Westlake automatic bulb-blowing machine was developed in America, but it was many years before it was satisfactory. By 1920 the machine was capable of producing about 60,000 bulbs in a twenty-four-hour day. Later versions of this machine would make

100,000 bulbs in the same period. However, another American development, the ribbon machine, forms the bulbs out of a fast-flowing ribbon of molten glass at such a speed that it can make up to 1,000,000 bulbs of the 60-watt size in twenty-four hours. The output is so great and the consequent services to keep the machines going are so complex that an installation containing only two ribbon machines is enough to fill a fairly big factory of 100,000 square feet.

Automatic machines mount the filament assembly, exhaust the air, insert the argon gas and seal the bulbs. The 'pip' or sealing end once so familiar at the end of the old glass globe, where it was vulnerable to damage, is now concealed within the brass cap. Another refinement is the frosted or 'pearl' lamp, in which the frosting is now on the inside of the globe. Before 1925 the frosting was on the outside, where it picked up dirt, which was difficult to clean off and which seriously reduced the efficiency of the lamp. A human hair is half as thick again as the filament of tungsten wire for a 230-volt, 100-watt lamp, and yet the permissible variation in diameter is only two-and-a-half per cent. If a difference in size as great as one tenth the thickness of a human hair were permitted, it might lower the average life of the lamp by several hundred hours. In the latest 'coiled-coil' lamps the coiled filament wires are coiled a second time on a relatively thick centre wire of material less chemically inert than tungsten. This centre wire is later dissolved away by acid.

Discharge lamps and fluorescent lamps have presented new problems in manufacture. As early as 1709 Hawksbee noticed that a discharge of static electricity would give a glow in a very imperfect vacuum, and in 1867 Alexandre Becquerel put willemite crystals into a glow discharge tube and noticed that they fluoresced. In 1895 Moore, in the U.S.A., produced a discharge lamp consisting of a glass tube filled with carbon dioxide and excited by high-voltage, high-frequency electric currents. It was nearly ten years before these tubes were commercially successful: they were made in lengths of 100 or 200 feet. Meanwhile in 1900, also in the U.S.A., Cooper Hewitt introduced a mercury-vapour tube working on ordinary voltages which was not unpopular, particularly for photographic studies. The neon tube, so familiar today, was introduced by Claude in France in 1910, but it was used on a very small scale for the first decade or so of its existence. All these tubes suffered either poor efficiency or poor quality light, or both. In 1932 the high-pressure mercury discharge lamp in a quartz tube (to resist the effects of discharge) and the sodium lamp in a special glass tube resistant to the chemical effects of sodium vapour were both introduced in Great Britain. The efficiency of the mercury lamp was more than one-and-a-half times that of the carbon arc, the efficiency of the sodium lamp higher still, but the light given out by both tubes left much to be desired: the mercury light was a hard blue and the sodium a not very pleasant yellow. Research followed into the possibility of transforming the quality of the light by means of fluorescent materials, and in 1939 the first practical high-efficiency fluorescent tubular lamp was introduced in Britain, the result of work over many years in various parts of the world on the materials that can be excited by an electric discharge. These researches continue, and lamps have been progressively improved ever since. (See also *Lamp, Torch, Candle, Dynamo.*)

ILLUSTRATION: Pages 116 and 117.

All knowledge in outline

ENCYCLOPAEDIA as a term for a compendium of knowledge belongs to the modern era. Thus in 1620 Johann Heinrich Alsted published his notable *Encyclopaedia septem tomis distincta*, which ran to 2,543 pages.

However, works of the nature of an encyclopaedia have been compiled since the time of Plato, and modern encyclopaedias are very much a part of the intellectual tradition of Europe. The earliest encyclopaedia we have, vastly influential in the Middle Ages, is the elder Pliny's *Natural History*, dedicated to the Emperor Titus in A.D. 77. Pliny himself stated proudly that it contained 20,000 facts. Though he interpreted it widely, Pliny dealt with only one branch of knowledge, whereas the typical encyclopaedia attempts to present on a large scale knowledge in all its aspects. One may mention from the Middle Ages the huge *Speculum majus* compiled by the French Dominican friar Vincent of Beauvais (c. 1190–c.1264), setting forth all that his world could be said to know.

Alsted's *Encyclopaedia* of 1620, indexed, but in Latin as the *Speculum majus* had been in Latin, marked both the end and the beginning of an era. Very soon after Latin ceased to be the universal language of scholarship, and in the making of encyclopaedias as tools of the mind, an alphabetical arrangement of subjects began to find favour – a symptom, like more efficient indexing, of a new taste for order and reason. Several alphabetical encyclopaedias appeared in French in the second half of the seventeenth century. This was an era of scientific advance, which saw the foundation in London of the Royal Society. In 1704 John Harris (c. 1667–1719), clergyman, mathematician and Fellow of the Royal Society, produced his alphabetical *Lexicon technicum; or, An Universal English Dictionary of Arts and Sciences.* Among his contributors he numbered Isaac Newton (then President of the Royal Society) upon acids.

Harris died without a penny, but his encyclopaedia had a distinguished progeny in English, leading first of all to Ephraim Chambers's two-volume *Cyclopaedia; or, an Universal Dictionary of Arts and Sciences* (1728), which he dedicated to King George II and which in turn led directly to the most famous encyclopaedia of all time. A French version of the *Cyclopaedia* was planned, and then abandoned when the wise and energetic Denis Diderot conceived and undertook a new encyclopaedia altogether, which was duly published in twenty-eight volumes between 1751 and 1765 after obstruction and difficulties of every kind. This was the *Encyclopédie; ou, Dictionnaire raisonné des sciences, des arts, et des métiers.* Diderot made it into a compendium of all recent speculative and practical knowledge, and it was one of the great instruments of the liberation of modern thought. Under *Encyclopaedia* Diderot himself wrote: 'The purpose of an encyclopaedia is to collect the knowledge scattered over the face of the globe, to set it down in order for our contemporaries and to pass it on to future generations, so that the labours of the past may influence those of the future, so that

our children may be better informed, and happier in consequence, and so that we may not die without deserving well of humanity' – inspiring words which later editors of encyclopaedias have not always remembered. The fame of Diderot should not altogether obscure memory of Ephraim Chambers, a freethinker who composed his own epitaph for a memorial in the cloisters of Westminster Abbey, saying that in shade and in light, neither learned nor wholly ignorant, he had lived a life devoted to letters.

From the merely practical point of view Diderot's *Encyclopédie* was inferior to Johann Heinrich Zedler's *Universal-Lexikon* in sixty-eight volumes (1732–1754). This was far more comprehensive than any previous encyclopaedia, and even included biographies of people then alive. In 1771 the first edition of the *Encyclopaedia Britannica* by 'a society of gentlemen' was published at Edinburgh in three volumes. But it rejected history, geography and biography – even of the dead. One of its virtues was to include good copperplate engravings.

From this time onwards the encyclopaedia developed rapidly as a scientific conspectus of all knowledge. The second edition of the *Encyclopaedia Britannica* (1777–1784) was vastly improved and more than three times as long. At Leipzig, between 1798 and 1808, Brockhaus's famous and excellent *Konversations-Lexikon* made a first appearance, and directly influenced similar works in England, America and Russia. The progeny of Brockhaus, though, contrives sometimes to imitate its brevity and neglect some of its intellectual virtues. The *Encyclopaedia Britannica* (which is now American owned) set a fashion in titles – even in encyclopaedias as national projects, full-length encyclopaedias now tending to be too expensive for private enterprise. The large and thorough *Enciclopedia Italiana* (1929–1937), though conceived and executed under the Fascist regime, is remarkable for many excellences, including the illustrations. Marked here and there by Soviet peculiarities, a vast Russian encyclopaedia, the *Bol'shaia sovetskaia entsiklopediia* in sixty-five volumes, was published between 1927 and 1947. The *Encyclopédie Française*, to be completed in twenty-one or twenty-two volumes, began publication in 1935, though it is unusual in following the classificatory rather than alphabetical principle. The scheme is too complicated for easy reference. The Turkish Government since Kemal Ataturk's revolution has also sponsored its *Inönü ansiklopedsisi*. English-language encyclopaedias have lost their earlier lead, and have shown an unfortunate tendency to sacrifice detail and scholarly apparatus and to restrict their range of enquiry, as though in deference to the imaginary figure of the 'Average Man'.

In China a tradition of encyclopaedic compilation from Chinese literature of all kinds goes back for several hundred years. The encyclopaedia launched in the early years of the eighteenth century at the behest of the emperor K'ang Hsi runs to a stupendous number of volumes.

ILLUSTRATION: Pages 262 and 263.

F

New teeth for old

FALSE TEETH have a double importance – they are masticators and they are a means of preserving the countenance. As they have come into general use, so the face of old age has changed. The witch-face of the chapfallen mumbling hag, for example, has disappeared, at any rate from urban civilization.

The earliest set of false teeth, or substitute teeth, of which we have knowledge was found in a grave at Sidon, and dates from Phoenician times. The four lower incisor teeth had been replaced by four others, two of which were probably taken from the jaw of another person. The four teeth are strung together with gold wire, the ends of which are twisted round the two canines. In Greece during the classical period artisans used gold wire to anchor loose teeth (this is still

done in the Indian bazaars), and they sometimes replaced missing teeth with teeth taken from other mouths. The most numerous specimens of early artificial teeth are from Etruria. The Etruscans were adept at making gold bridges. Each tooth was surrounded at its base by a gold ring, with an extra ring for each of the two natural teeth on either side of the gap. The rings were soldered together to form a continuous bridge. Human teeth were used, or else artificial or semi-artificial teeth carved from the teeth of the ox.

These general principles were applied in all the early civilizations. For example, the Roman medical writer Celsus (first century A.D.) described how loose teeth were bound to their neighbours with gold wire, and at a much later date the Arabian physician Albucasis or Abū-l-qāsim, who lived in Spain and died c. 1013, described a similar procedure.

For a long while advances in artificial dentistry appear to have accompanied the development of French aristocratic society. The works of the great French surgeon Ambroise Paré (1510–1590) contain references to the making of artificial teeth of bone, or of 'ivory from the hippopotamus or walrus'. Paré's pupil, son-in-law and successor at the French Court, Jacques Guillemeau (1550–1613), went much further. He too gives instructions for tying loose teeth together with gold wire, and says that gaps in the mouth may be filled by artificial teeth, also tied in by wire. Ivory teeth, though, tend to become yellow, and he recommends walrus ivory and also gives a recipe for the first mineral substitute in the making of artificial teeth; this consisted of wax, mastic, white coral and prepared pearls.

Pierre Fauchard, in his great work on dentistry *Le chirurgien dentiste, ou traité des dents* (1728), had much to say about artificial teeth. He developed the use of the crown, and for this purpose he used either natural teeth or ivory. The crown was fixed to the root by a wooden pivot. In making a denture Fauchard did not employ an impression of the mouth. The denture, carved from the long bone of an ox or from ivory, was worked on until it fitted. Springs were used to keep dentures in place, but in some cases they fitted by atmospheric pressure.

Eighteenth-century dentures were not pleasant

things to wear. Thus George Washington wrote in 1798 to his dentist John Greenwood, in Philadelphia, to complain of his sore mouth, and of the 'pouting and swelling appearance' given to his lips, the upper lip being forced out 'just under the nose'.

The development of the crown was an important step. Fauchard removed the crown of the natural tooth down to, or even beyond, the gum, and the pulp cavity was cleared and then filled with lead. The prepared artificial crown was then fixed to the lead by a dowel. What was probably the first gold crown was described by Pierre Mouton in 1746, and later developments gradually led to the shell crown of gold, and then – but only after considerable advances in dental technology – to the gold crown cast from a wax mould.

The French chemist Duchâteau conceived the idea of making artificial teeth from porcelain (see *Chinaware*) re-invented in Germany in 1709. After unsuccessful attempts, he collaborated with the dentist Dubois de Chemant, who made him a satisfactory porcelain denture. In 1788 Dubois de Chemant exhibited dentures of baked porcelain. The Italian Fonzi first made individual teeth of porcelain. Between 1810 and 1840 great advances were made in England, France and the United States in the manufacture of porcelain teeth, which rapidly displaced substitute teeth or teeth carved of ivory and other materials. Of these porcelain teeth perhaps the best was the English Tube Tooth, first made by Claudius Ash in 1838, which had a tube of precious metal fused in the centre. This tooth could be easily fixed to a pivot in the root.

Another development was the introduction about 1850 of the 'banded crown', which gave additional fixation by means of a gold band round the root of the tooth. These banded crowns were popular for many years. They formed the two extremities of the bridge which bore the artificial teeth. Such 'crown and bridge work' was a dominant feature of dental prosthetics in the second half of the nineteenth century. The first 'fixed bridge' – that is, one in which the artificial teeth were attached to a gold bar on their posterior aspect, each end of the gold bar being fixed into a prepared cavity in the adjoining tooth – was said to have been made by

Bing of Paris in 1869. Early in our century doubts began to be cast on the crown as a focus for sepsis and the evils which arise from it; after extensive investigations by William Hunter of London crown and bridge work gradually fell into disfavour.

Despite the long history of false teeth, there was still some way to go before mankind was equipped with a satisfactory removable denture. All depended on suitable materials. As a base for the teeth, a substance or substances were needed which could be moulded easily and which would last and withstand conditions in the mouth. Also a way had to be devised of obtaining an exact impression of the shape of the mouth. For taking the impression plaster of Paris was suggested in 1844, and in 1857 the Englishman Charles Stent used the first compound material. For accuracy's sake, choice in the end fell on colloid materials, a common mixture now for this purpose consisting of an emulsion of agar-agar, waxes, resins and water.

Making a suitable base was more difficult. First of all the French used gold for this purpose, though fixing teeth to the gold base was a slow process. In 1847 Edwin Truman, who had overcome the difficulty of a protective covering for the Atlantic cable by suggesting gutta-percha, now introduced the same material as a base in dentistry. In 1850 Harrison of Portsmouth introduced tortoiseshell as a base; but this was the century of the development of rubber (q.v.), and instead of gutta-percha, Charles Goodyear (1800-1860), the inventor of vulcanization, introduced vulcanized rubber for the base, and for a long while this was the customary material.

The smile of false teeth became general only after the First World War. In place of Goodyear's vulcanized rubber, many new substances were tried. Of these the thermo-plastics include cellulose, and vinyl and styrol resins; after heating and setting they may again be softened by heat. The other resinous substances used in dentistry are the thermo-setting synthetic resins (see *Plastics*); the most modern plastic for dental bases, methyl methacrylate or polymerized acrylic resin, was introduced about 1935.

ILLUSTRATION: Page 82.

Objects of power

A FETISH now means to the anthropologist a material object in which a spirit is thought to reside, or through which a spirit may act. The word derives from the Portuguese *feitiço*, charm or sorcery. When they discovered West Africa, the Portuguese called *feitiço* the various charms and talismans used by the natives of the coast. The term soon had a wide currency, although in some districts, such as the Niger delta, these objects were also called *ju-ju*, after the French *joujou*, a toy or doll.

Obviously, 'fetishism' covers a wide variety of beliefs and institutions, even when defined in this rather narrow sense. In West Africa personal fetishes are the most common; these are small objects consecrated by the *oganga* or witch-doctor, so that a spirit takes up residence in them, and gives the owner the benefit of its special guidance and protection. Small hollow objects are usually selected, and their cavities are filled by the *oganga* with a variety of substances chosen on the principles of sympathetic magic. To give bravery or strength, some part of a leopard or an elephant will be included; for cunning, part of a gazelle; for wisdom, a portion of human brain; the heart, on the other hand, conveys courage, and the eye, influence. These various substances are each of them thought to lure some appropriate spirit, which will take up residence in the fetish and help the possessor in its particular way. The materials selected for the fetish are mixed by the *oganga* with other ingredients, such as the ashes of certain medicinal plants, pieces of calcined bones, gums, spices, resins and filth. The preparation takes place in secret, with music, dancing and the invocation of spirits through mirrors or limpid water, after which the mixture is smeared over the fetish stick or bone, or stuffed into the shell, bead, etc. Special fetishes may be prepared for special purposes, such as victory in war, safety on a journey, success in love, profit in a business deal.

A second type of fetish is that which belongs not to an individual but to a village or a district, and which has the power to inflict sickness, disaster or even death. Unlike the personal fetish, it produces effects which are harmful and to be feared. A group of fetishes of this kind, consisting of wooden figures of men and animals, used to be found in the Portuguese district of Kabinda, near the mouth of the Congo. They were known as Zincauci Zi-bacici, and into each of them the *nangas* (priests or fetish-men) had introduced one or other of the human passions. However, all systematic connection between the operation of the fetishes and the particular passions with which they were imbued had long been lost sight of at the time when the fetishes were suppressed; all the natives cared about was their reputed power to work evil. Each nail driven into the fetish by the *nanga* represented a vow or spiteful wish. The unfortunate persons who suffered the wrath of the fetish through breaking his vow or from the ill-will of his enemy, could obtain relief only by paying the *nanga*, in his turn, to withdraw the nail. These fetishes kept whole districts in a state of misery and fear, and about 1892 the Portuguese Government organized raids to suppress them. As a result, one of the most powerful of these fetishes, known as Mavungu, was captured, and ultimately fell into the hands of Miss Mary Kingsley, by whom it was bequeathed to the Pitt Rivers Museum at Oxford. Mavungu was supposed to have one special magic quality: when his *nanga* rubbed his own hands together he became invisible.

Another way of using a fetish is to inveigle into it an unwelcome spirit – usually a disease-spirit – and then to lose or discard the fetish or to neutralize the power of the indwelling ghost in some other way. In parts of Central Africa, for example, the spirit is enticed from the patient's body into an inanimate object, called technically a *keti* or stool. Thereupon the fetish, whether a leopard's claw, a nail or a rag, is driven into or hung on a 'devil's tree', by which operation the disease-spirit is laid.

There are many records also of a fetish being used for divination, and in particular for the detection of crime. Among the Manganja of Central Africa the medicine man was called in on one occasion to fix the blame for a theft. He gave two sticks to four young men, two of whom held each stick. After much incantation and dancing, the men became possessed, or rather they were carried away by the spirits which entered the sticks. After tearing wildly through the brush, they came back to the assembly and dropped the sticks by the hut of one of the chief's wives, who was in this way denounced as the thief.

A special kind of fetish is the family bundle, known in parts of West Africa as the *yâkâ*. This consists of fragments of the bodies of the family dead, especially the finger-ends, and is added to each time a relative dies. In this way the spirits of the ancestors remain immanent in the life of the family circle. They communicate with their descendants by means of dreams, they are appealed to in times of crisis, and their virtues are still available to help and sustain the living. If one of the family should have committed an offence and brought a curse on them all, it is the *yâkâ* which will reveal the culprit, when it is opened, and with the aid of certain ceremonies, will enable the taint to be washed away.

Lastly, a rare but influential type of fetish was that which held the soul of the nation and was a kind of palladium of the realm. Of this sort was the famous Golden Stool of the Ashanti, which came down from the skies into the lap of the king at the behest of a magician early in the eighteenth century. The arrival of the Stool marked the beginning of the greatness of the Ashanti nation. The Stool was ornamented with trophies and it was accorded regal honours, and in 1900 the Ashanti went to war rather than yield the Stool to the administration of the Gold Coast. It remained hidden until 1920, by which time, however, its significance was better understood, and it was left secure in the possession of the Ashanti chiefs.

All these examples have been taken from West and Central Africa, where the phenomena of fetishism are particularly important, and where the term was first applied to the study of primitive religion. However, instances from other parts of the world, like the 'medicine' of the Plains Indian, the witch-bottles of rural England, and the oracular skulls of the Mariana Islanders, recall that fetishes are by no means limited to Africa. Indeed, the belief that spirits occupy and act through material objects occurs so widely in its various forms that it appears to have arisen independently in different times and places, and not to be the prerogative or invention of any particular country or stage of civilization.

ILLUSTRATION: Page 82.

The field

FIELDS we take for granted as a commonplace of life, but they are things involving more than a little of the history of mankind.

First of all a field is a plot of ground cultivated in one piece: the shape of such plots, their arrangement and their dimensions have been governed by the implements used in cultivating them and by the farming system in vogue. Primitive cultivators who use digging-sticks or hoes need not work in straight lines, and so produce plots of a roundish or an irregular shape: they have usually been won by burning the scrub or forest, and were quickly abandoned after the exhaustion of the soil. Unless such fields are outlined by stones picked off the surface, they seldom survive from ancient times in a recognizable form.

Ploughs do make all the difference. Furrows are now produced, and the plot tends to become rectangular, more or less. In peasant cultures it has often been a convention that each individual plot should represent the amount of work done by one plough-team in one day, or else half such a unit. The result has been some rough uniformity in the area of such plots, though the proportion of length to breadth depends on what is considered to be the most desirable furrow length, short furrows making squarish plots, long furrows making narrow, strip-like plots.

In Europe, right up to modern times, two contrasting field-systems have been in vogue, square-plot and strip; and the square-plot system is the earlier, developed in southern Europe in a warm, dry climate in which it was desirable to conserve moisture by pulverizing the soil. We know from classical writers that this was done by cross-ploughing – *i.e.* ploughing in two directions at right angles to one another, so that the two sets of furrows as they cross pulverize the soil pretty thoroughly. This cross-ploughing can only be done in fields which are more or less square or oblong; and we have evidence that this field-system had spread northwards as far as Holland by the sixteenth century B.C. and as far as Denmark by the fourteenth century B.C. Here the actual marks made in the subsoil by the point of the plough in cross-ploughing have been preserved under certain exceptional conditions – for example, underneath a burial mound containing datable grave-goods. This square-plot system does not seem to have reached Britain till about 800 B.C., when it was introduced by immigrants from continental Europe.

The other system, the strip system, must have been developed in northern Europe, probably in response to the wet conditions which prevailed after 400 B.C., though it is doubtful whether strip ploughing was undertaken before the beginning of our era. The underlying principle was to dry out the soil – to attempt to reduce moisture by undercutting the sods and turning them over and so exposing the undersides to the sun and wind. Cross-ploughing defeated this aim. So came the longer furrows (which meant less time spent in turning the plough) and the narrow, strip-like plot.

This system was spread through northern Europe by the expansion of the Germanic peoples after the fall of the Roman Empire. It was introduced to Britain in the fifth century A.D. by the Angles and Saxons, superseding the square-plot; and in the form of the Open Field – an aggregate of such strip-like plots, forming one half or one third of the total arable of the community – it became characteristic of England in the Middle Ages. In the Open-field System acrestrips, under rotating ownership, were scattered throughout the Common Field, and bundles of three strips, each with its length ten times its breadth, formed 'furlongs', groups of furlongs forming in turn each of the large 'felds'. As economic conditions changed at the end of the Middle Ages this cumbersome feld-system was gradually abolished, and the furlongs, were enclosed by hedges to make the 'felds' now so characteristic of the English countryside. The next stage comes with the adoption of mechanical means for drawing the plough. Tractors (q.v.) do not tire like oxen and horses; and the old convention that the plot represents the day's work for one plough goes by the board. So new fields have appeared wherever fresh ground can be broken up – fields of vast size with still larger furrows.

Two other points. The outline of ancient fields is frequently preserved by the formation of 'lynchets', which are terrace-like banks along the upper and lower edges of the field. Lynchets are formed as the upper edge of each plot on sloping ground is denuded of its soil under the influence of ploughing, frost and rainwash, the soil accumulating along the lower edge. The relation of such lynchets to other datable structures may enable the field itself to be dated.

Besides *furlong*, which is a 'furrow-long' or the standard length of a furrow (220 yards), another word in common use today owes its origin to the English Open-field System; this is *acre*, which originally meant a cultivated plot (like the Latin *ager*), and then was the name given to an individual strip in the Common Field, of fixed length (a furlong) and breadth (four rods). The rod, too, was the goad with which the ploughing oxen were prodded. (See also *Plough*.)

ILLUSTRATION: Page 22.

One to 64,000,000,000

FINGER-PRINTS, so important to police in the detection of crime and to bureaucrats in the control of those who would evade bureaucracy, have been utilized now for just over half a century.

Our finger-tips are constantly and involuntarily making these prints because of the tiny sweat-pores on the patterned ridges. Indeed, a magnifying glass of ten magnifications will just reveal what the plant anatomist and microscopist Nehemiah Grew (1641–1712) was probably the first to notice – that 'every Pore looks like a little *Fountain*, and the sweat may be seen to stand therein, as clear as rock water, and as often as it is wiped off, to spring up within them again'.

But Grew did not observe what is now a commonplace, that 'in each individual' (to quote the current edition of Gray's *Anatomy*), 'the lines on the tips of the fingers form distinct patterns unlike those of any other person'. This uniqueness of a man's finger patterns, and so of his prints, may have been known to the Chinese. The evidence is not conclusive, though from an early period they were well acquainted with finger-patterns and frequently signed contracts and documents with an inked impression of the finger-tip.

In the West, two men, independently of each other and of any Eastern knowledge, realized that finger patterns could be a means of identification. These were Sir William Herschel (1833–1917) and Henry Faulds (1843–1930). Herschel, when he was a civil servant in India, began to take what he called 'sign-manuals' of contractors, pensioners and convicts. The first palm-prints and finger-prints he recorded, with oil-ink, in 1858, were those of a Bengali village contractor. Herschel discovered that finger-tip designs do not change in a lifetime. As early as 1877 he attempted to have a system of recording prints

Fig. 11. Finger-prints of identical twins.

accepted in Bengal, as a deterrent to tricksters and as a means of identifying criminals.

Faulds was a medical missionary in Japan. In 1878 or thereabouts finger-prints on some ancient Japanese pottery suggested to him that 'bloody finger-marks', as he wrote in a letter to *Nature* in 1880, might lead to the 'scientific identification of criminals'. Faulds had once worked with a firm of shawl manufacturers arranging, classifying and numbering an immense variety of patterns. The whorl-patterns of Paisley shawls helped to sharpen his eyes to the not dissimilar whorls on the human finger.

Some months before his letter appeared in *Nature*, Faulds had written to Darwin about

finger-patterns; Darwin handed his letter to Francis Galton, who was then working on the laws of heredity. Galton must also have read the letter in *Nature* and the letter which it elicited in turn from Herschel. It was Galton who established the uniqueness of the individual's ridge patterns, and made suggestions for a workable police system. In *Finger Prints* (1892) he calculated the chances of duplication. The improbability of one finger-pattern in one individual coinciding with one finger-pattern in another individual he found to be 1 to 2^{36}, or 1 to about sixty-four thousand millions: 'When two fingers of each of the two persons are compared and found to have the same minutiae, the improbability of 1 to 2^{36} becomes squared, and reaches a figure altogether beyond the range of imagination; when three fingers, it is cubed, and so on.'

Finger-printing was quickly adopted, first of all by the Argentine in 1891. In 1892 the La Plata police caught a murderess by means of her prints. Scotland Yard took to finger-printing in 1901, abandoning the cumbrous and less certain anthropometric system of Alphonse Bertillon, chief of the Paris Police Identification Service, who followed the principle of the great Belgian statistician, L. A. J. Quételet, that the measurements of no two persons are alike. This system required careful measurements of parts of the head, fingers and limbs. It was far from fool-proof. In America, in 1901, a negro convict named West, arriving at jail at Leavenworth, Kansas, denied having been there before. After some enquiry he was confronted by a negro astonishingly like himself. His Bertillon measurements were similar – and his name was also West! But the finger-prints of the two men were different.

There have been many refinements in finger-print technique; in Sweden a method has even been devised for developing invisible prints left on a book twelve years before. But finger-printing begins to go further than its inventors would ever have approved in an age of liberalism and liberty. American visa regulations demand the visitor's finger-prints blackly and stickily taken in American embassies. The American army and navy finger-print their personnel. In the Argentine every person has had his prints taken for ten fingers by the time he reaches voting age. In 1937 the Conservative M.P. Sir (then Mr) Rupert de la Bère asked the Home Secretary to consider a national register of British finger-prints and the Foreign Secretary to consider the desirability of thumb-prints on every British passport. He received dusty answers.

Making a light

The **FIRE-DRILL, TINDER BOXES** and **STRIKE-A-LIGHTS** were among the many devices of obtaining fire, that prime necessity of human culture, before the invention of matches.

Of devices for getting fire by wood friction, which require skill, patience and even hard work, the commonest is the fire-drill; a hardwood rod is rotated rapidly until it drills a bed for itself on a piece of soft wood, which is known as the 'hearth'. The rotation can be by hand, or by the aid of a bow, in which the thong joining the ends of a bow-shaped piece of wood is passed round the drill in a loop. If the bow is then worked backwards and forwards with a sawing action, the thong rotates the drill. However the rotation is done, the important point is that the hardwood drill should bore into the softwood hearth, producing considerable heat by friction and also a quantity of powdered wood, which at last begins to smoulder if wood and air are sufficiently dry and the operator sufficiently skilled. At the right moment the operator blows on the smouldering heap, adding to the glowing mass small quantities of easily combustible material, such as plant down, which at last breaks into flame.

The same principle applies generally to the fire-saw, in which the hearth, instead of being drilled, is cut by a sawing motion, using a hard split cane or a sharp piece of wood. A less common method is that of the fire-plough, in which the hearth is gouged out by continual rubbing with a ploughing or digging action. One popular misconception is that these methods were to be found only in tropical countries. In fact, the fire bow-drill was the method used by the Eskimos.

Fire generated by wood friction sometimes became associated with religious practices, in which it was distinguished from the more efficient method of getting fire from flint and steel. The Brahmins in India, for instance, generated holy fire, using nine different kinds of wood in the ceremony.

A nodule of iron pyrites struck with a sharp flint, or even two such nodules struck together, will give a spark. This is the primitive method preceding the flint and steel, which give a spark which is much hotter, and therefore easier to manage. Many early writers, including Virgil, who, in the *Georgics*, referred to 'man learning to strike the lurking fire from veins of flint', and Shakespeare, who said, 'The fire in the flint shows not till it be struck', were under the impression that it was from the flint and not the steel that the spark emanated. In fact, the hard cutting edge of the flint slices off a tiny piece from the iron surface, and the energy of the blow can only be dissipated in the form of heat, which is sufficient to raise this tiny piece of iron to incandescence (in time the iron was worn away by the flint).

A lump of pyrites with signs of apparent use was found in excavating the mesolithic site of Star Carr in Yorkshire (c. 7000 B.C.). These excavations also brought to light bracket fungi of the kind used till recently for making the German tinder or 'amadou', prepared by boiling, drying, and heating the fungi and impregnating them with saltpetre. German tinder was hawked all over Europe, and was commonly sold by druggists. Some of the bracket fungi at Star Carr had been sliced, perhaps for making tinder. A sliced specimen was exhibited at the British Museum. Flint with iron pyrites has also been found among the grave goods in Bronze Age barrows in Great Britain.

Iron, first smelted and worked by the Hittites about 1400 B.C., greatly improved matters; and mankind could now make his fire easily enough with tinders such as dried plant down, dry touchwood, charred rag or amadou.

It is not difficult, with a little practice, to make the spark fall on to the tinder, which can then be made to glow brightly by blowing on it. In the sixteenth century a flint and steel device was first applied to small arms, and the flintlock pistol of the seventeenth century, in which a specially shaped piece of flint was triggered on to a hinged steel flap from which a spark shot on to the gunpowder below, was adapted very quickly for making fire, and may be looked upon as the ancestor of the modern petrol lighter. In the next two centuries tinder pistols became increasingly common and progressively less expensive. Nevertheless, the majority of people had to be satisfied with the ordinary domestic tinder box, which was simply a container for flint, steel and charred rag tinder. Tinder boxes were most frequently required during the hours of darkness, and quite apart from the frustration caused by damp tinder which would not ignite and the difficulty of performing the operation of dropping the spark on to the tinder in the dark, there was the further problem of actually finding the tinder box itself. Boswell, the biographer of Dr Johnson, described this vividly in one of his memoirs; the fire had gone out; he could not find the tinder box and he had to sit in the dark until the watchman came round and gave him a light from his lantern.

To get the tinder to the glowing stage was relatively easy; to get the actual flame out of it was by no means easy without a sulphur match, which became a common domestic article in the seventeenth and eighteenth centuries. These matches were quite easy to make, since sulphur readily melts into a glutinous mass into which the ends of slivers of wood can be dipped. The work was frequently done in the household, in which the preparation of the tinder was usually the charge of one of the housemaids. She dried cotton rags before the fire and charred them by setting them alight and extinguishing them before they were consumed. In damp climates, such as that of Britain, tinder had to be heated every three days or so, and oftener in wet weather. It was necessary for it to be absolutely dry if it was hoped to coax it into flame from the smouldering stage without the intervention of a sulphur match. Sulphur matches or 'spunks', as they were called, would ignite easily from smouldering tinder and were practically impossible to extinguish until all the sulphur had been burnt away. For this reason only a tiny coating of sulphur on the end of the match was usual. When blowing on the tinder to ignite the sulphur match, the nose was brought so close that it was very easy to inhale enough sul-

phur dioxide to be unpleasant. Nevertheless these matches were regarded as an indispensable convenience, and their disadvantages were hardly worth consideration.

Tinder boxes were contrived in a wide variety of forms; some domestic tinder boxes were simply crude containers of hardwood, of all shapes and sizes; some, for carrying about on the person, were beautifully finished in costly materials. There were also tinder bags and pouches; North American Indians carried tinder pouches elaborately embroidered with beads. In Tibet, the *chuckmuk* was a common article of wear for the more important tribesmen. It was usually a decorated skin pouch with the fur outside and with the steel forming the bottom edge of the pouch. The rank of an individual could be guessed with fair accuracy from the value of his *chuckmuk*, which was carried on a leather strap.

Fire steels, which were known as 'strike-a-lights', were also of many kinds, varying from the simplest types, often made out of an old file, to elaborately decorated examples sometimes clamped in brass ornamental holders. Spanish fire steels were particularly sought after in Europe. The main requirement in a steel was to provide a firm hand-grip which would enable it to be held rigidly for striking by the flint. It was for this reason that many of them were inverted U shape. Some of the more elaborate Eastern types were jewelled and damascened, while tinder holders might be of gold, richly worked. These were the exceptions, but they showed that even the wealthiest potentates regarded the possession of the means for making fire as a necessity. (See also *Matches*.)

Fighting fires

The **FIRE-ENGINE** in its manual form goes back to the Greek mechanician Ctesibius of Alexandria in the second century B.C. and was based on his invention of the force-pump.

Described by Vitruvius in his *De architectura* (c. 27 B.C.) and by Heron of Alexandria in his

Pneumatics perhaps in the first century A.D., it consisted of a two-cylinder force-pump which pumped water into a vessel rather like a soda siphon. The air in the upper part of the vessel was compressed, and the water was expelled by the pressure through a tube which dipped below the water level. The delivery end of the tube had movable joints so that it could be pointed in any direction. The use of an air vessel enabled the water pressure to be maintained, so that the water issued at

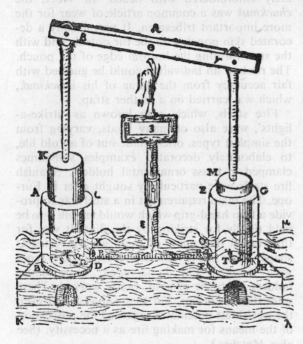

Fig. 12. Force-pump of Ctesibius.

a steady rate, instead of in a series of intermittent jets at each stroke of the pump.

In the Middle Ages the engine was unknown, and fires had to be extinguished by means of buckets of water. By the sixteenth century hand-squirts or syringes were being used. A set of fire-fighting equipment illustrated in Agricola's *De re metallica* of 1556 consists of a squirt, three buckets, a sledge-hammer and two firehooks. The latter were used for pulling down burning roofing (such hooks for thatch were frequently kept in

English villages. One still – 1954 – hangs ready on a wall in the main street of West Lavington in Wiltshire). Jacques Besson in 1568, in his *Theatrum instrumentorum et machinarum*, depicted a large squirt, mounted on wheels, and worked by a screw, an arrangement which would give a continuous stream of water while the charge lasted.

In the sixteenth century the fire-pump was re-introduced, but, curiously enough, without the refinement of the air vessel already known to the Romans. An illustration in the *Von gewaltsamen bewegungen beschreibung* (1615) of Salomon de Caus, the French engineer who worked in London and Germany, shows such an engine. It consists of a pump mounted in a tub on a sledge. Two men work the pump handle, a third directs the stream of water issuing from a tube with two rotatable joints, and the fourth member of the crew replenishes the water from a bucket.

In 1657 Hans Hautsch of Nuremberg re-introduced the air vessel and constructed an engine worked by twenty-eight men, which was capable of throwing a jet of water to a height of eighty feet. The engine was described in English in an account published in the *Philosophical Transactions* of the Royal Society in 1676; but it was not used in the Great Fire of London in 1666, which was fought with squirts and buckets, and naturally stimulated a concern for fire-engines. Many inventors were active after that disaster. One of the most successful engines was designed by Richard Newsham in 1721, and remained the basis of manual engines. In the eighteenth century it became customary to mount fire-engines on wheels, which was obviously more convenient than the earlier practice of using a sledge. In the nineteenth century the larger manual fire-engines used by fire-brigades were horse drawn. The fire-hose, which brought the water to the required point and greatly increased the effectiveness of the fire-engine, was invented by Jan van der Heiden, artist and also General Fire Master of Amsterdam. The leather hose introduced by him in 1673 was used not only for delivery but for suction, so that chains of men were no longer needed to bring up water in buckets to feed the engine.

The first steam fire-engine was built in 1829 by the railway engineer John Braithwaite and the Swede John Ericsson. These two were joint competitors in the locomotive competition of 1829 which George Stephenson won with his 'Rocket'. Although their fire-engine worked gratuitously at several fires in London with great success, it met with determined opposition from the managers of the Fire Brigade, and it was not until 1852 that steam fire-engines were permanently adopted in London. In 1863 an international competition was held, which was won by Merryweather's 'Sutherland' engine, an example of which is preserved in London in the Science Museum.

In these engines the pump only was driven by steam, the operators getting up pressure while the engine was being drawn to the fire by horses. A steam-propelled fire-engine was made in 1860, but another forty years went by before self-propelled engines came into favour. This was reasonable, since there was an inevitable delay in starting these self-propelled machines in the fire-station – unless steam could be maintained by an auxiliary boiler in the fire station.

However, by this time the steam fire-engine had already been made obsolescent by the invention of the internal-combustion engine. The motor tractor had already been used for drawing steam fire-engines, and in 1904 the Borough of Finchley, in the suburbs of London, acquired the first self-propelled petrol-motor fire-engine to be used by a public fire-brigade. In this machine, now in the Science Museum, the motor was used both for propulsion and for driving the pumps.

ILLUSTRATION: Pages 24 and 25.

Flames of fire

FIREWORKS, of a kind, preceded the invention of gunpowder. These were no more than patterned displays of fire, for which there is evidence both in the West and the Far East. Thus a Chinese poem of the seventh century A.D. says:

Flames of fire move round the wheel,
Peach blossoms spring forth from the falling branches.
Clouds of smoke move around the house,
And the fairy lake reflects the floating lights.

Conceivably these fireworks were made with gunpowder, but it does not seem probable, there being no firm evidence (Wang Ling, 'The Invention and Use of Gunpowder in China', *Isis*, Nos. 109 and 110, 1947) that gunpowder had been invented or developed in China by the tenth century A.D.

Both in Europe and China the extensive use of gunpowder in fire displays followed its use in war, as an incendiary if not as a propellant. China has total priority. The Chinese were using gunpowder as a war incendiary by A.D. 969, after which they were certainly making fireworks and giving entertainments with them by A.D. 1103. A full description exists of a splendid many-coloured display of that year.

European evidence for using gunpowder goes back to the thirteenth century A.D., culminating in a composition suitable for use in artillery by the fourteenth century. After this gunpowder was applied to fireworks by the early years of the sixteenth century, if not before; and pyrotechnic art appears to have developed first among the Florentines and the Sienese. Thus some of the basic terminology of fireworks derives from the Italian – rocket, for example, is from the Italian *rocchetta*. The English engineer Cyprian Lucar wrote in 1588 of fireworks 'for triumph as well as war'; and it appears, as one might expect, that fire effects by gunpowder were added to festivals at which bonfires or fire displays had been customary. There is evidence – see A. St H. Brock's *History of Fireworks* – for the association of fireworks with the old figure of May Day and the May Cycle, the Green Man, a kind of scapegoat (referred to in this volume under *Wreaths*). The fire man or Green Man took part in the water pageants of the Lord Mayor of London, and there is record of green men wreathed in ivy leading a procession to Chester Races on St George's Day (23 April) in 1610 and scattering fireworks as they went. Guy Fawkes Day celebrated with bonfires and fireworks on 5 November seems to be no more than the bonfire festival of Halloween (31 October) All Saints' Day (1 November) and All Souls' Day (2 November) given new vitality by the Gunpowder Plot.

In England firework manufacture was well advanced by the early years of the seventeenth century. The methods of the day are set out in the

Pyrotechnia, or a discourse of artificial fireworks for pleasure of John Babington (1625). Babington's title page shows examples of quite large mechanical displays with serpents and St George and the Dragon, systems of animated figures illuminated with fireworks, an illuminated royal monogram, a device for testing the force of gunpowder and a diagram of the method for filling rockets. After dealing with these and other matters in his book he gives many sets of instructions for special displays such as 'How to make two Dragons to meet each other, from several caves, which shall send forth their fire to each other with great violence' and 'How to make a Bucklar which shall cast forth a hundred fisgigs, every one making his report'.

Fireworks continued to be an essential accompaniment of occasions of national rejoicing. At least one such an occasion has left a legacy which still gives us pleasure, in Handel's *Music for the Royal Fireworks* composed for the London display in 1749 which celebrated the Peace of Aix-la-Chapelle, ending the War of the Austrian Succession.

The provision of the fireworks for these national functions was the business of the ordnance authorities. Private firework manufacture was frowned upon and many restraints were imposed. This merely pushed the business underground, where it went on in volume enough to meet the very large public demand, both for private use and for display in the public pleasure gardens. This unsatisfactory state of affairs persisted until some relaxation was allowed at the beginning of the nineteenth century, by way of the granting of licences for the storing of gunpowder and made-up goods. However, it took the Acts of 1860 and 1875 to bring firework manufacture into the position of a respectable and well-regulated industry, working not only for the frivolities of the firework display, but for more serious demands of peace and war, by way of sound, colour signalling, and the propulsion of rockets. In the U.S.A. firework displays are a feature of Independence Day, July 4th. (See also *Gunpowder, Rockets, Gun*.)

ILLUSTRATION: Plate 6.

Catching the fish

FISHING TACKLE in northern Europe is first found in the mesolithic settlements of 8000 B.C. and later. Then, as in the earlier palaeolithic period, man relied entirely upon food gathering, hunting and fishing. He had not learned to grow corn, he had not domesticated any animal except the dog. But as a fisherman he was skilful enough.

Finds of ancient tackle, preserved either whole or in part, and rock engravings, show that in prehistoric times fish and sea-animals were taken with clubs, harpoons, hook and line, nets, traps and spears (leisters). Man in our time has only improved upon the old techniques. Thus the whaling industry has adopted the ancient harpoon, though the head is made of metal instead of the antler available to ancient fishers, and it is fired from a gun.

Clubs may also be included in the fisherman's equipment, since they perform the vital function of despatching the fish once caught. In recent times, salmon netted in the Severn were despatched with a club picturesquely named the 'Molly Knocker' or 'Knobbling Pin'. Such clubs are found in many regions, made of any available material: rock in the Shetlands, a heavy stone threaded on a rawhide thong among the Eskimos, and wood carved into the form of the salmon is used for battering among the Indians of Alaska.

The very ancient bow and arrow (q.v.) may have been used to shoot fish in prehistoric times, in spite of the difficulties caused by refraction. In the Andaman Islands this is an old-established practice. The unfeathered arrows are four feet long. One type has a shaft of bamboo, tipped by a heavy pointed foreshaft. A barb, made of the spine of the sting-ray, may be added to this; since the coming of the white man and the introduction of iron, metal has replaced this natural barb, although the metal barb retains the shape of the original.

The harpoon was in action as early as the palaeolithic age – against seals so that it can only be classified with 'fishing' tackle in the broadest sense. Wooden shafts have not survived the centuries, but the antler heads were more durable. Barbs were cut along one edge of the head, and the base was perforated for attachment to a line.

Some of these harpoons have been found with skeletons of seals that escaped the hunters to die alone. Clubbing, netting and spearing are other modern methods used in seal-hunting which could have been used by prehistoric man. Certainly the bones preserved at sites in the British Isles show that seal-hunting was a seasonable activity there, even after the introduction of farming about 2,500 B.C. The chief centres in northern Europe were the Baltic lands, the west coast of Norway and north Britain.

Line-fishing is of mesolithic ancestry, which is proved by many finds of early bone fish-hooks at settlements round the Baltic. These may be up to three inches long, and some bear marks made by the drill that was used to separate the hook from the shank. The absence of barbs and the large size of the hooks suggest that they were concealed in a small fish to catch pike. Live bait was also probably used with the small gorges, which are short lengths of rounded bone sharply pointed at each end. With the coming of metal, about 2000 B.C., fish-hooks of modern type made their appearance in Europe. A form of double hook was made in Switzerland about 600 B.C., from a single length of wire twisted into two hooks back to back, joined at the top of the shanks. Curiously, the same idea occurred to Indian fishermen, for similar hooks, two of which are strung one above the other, are used there to catch crocodiles.

Bones of cod are found at neolithic sites, dating to the years after 2300 B.C. in the north and west of Britain, and also at Baltic settlements. Cod is a deep-sea fish, not one that can be caught off rocks, so the men who ate it must have had the use of boats, hooks and lines.

A study of fishing-lines used today in different parts of the world shows the variety of materials which must have been available to early fishermen. As well as gut and rawhide, plant fibres are widely employed, especially in the making of nets and lines. In Malabar, hemp stems are dried, 'retted' in water, beaten into fibres, softened by treading them underfoot, and finally spun into yarn. Even before the introduction of the spindle, fibres could have been rolled on the thigh, to give a similar result. Where it will grow, the coconut is a source of string, the hairs of its husk being twisted into 'sinnet'. In Samoa, a line of sinnet is attached to one form of the attractive Pacific fish-hook, which is made of wood and is backed with pink shell to attract the fish. Mother-of-pearl also serves in this way.

That plant-fibres were made into nets by prehistoric man need not only be inferred from modern primitive practice, since a few fragments of ancient mesolithic nets have survived. On the shores of Lake Ladoga oblong net-floats of pine bark were found, about one foot in length. They had been preserved by waterlogging, and near them were the stones which had been used as sinkers. Beneath some of these lay parts of the net, which proved to have been made either of lime-bast or nettle-fibres. Another find of this kind was made in Esthonia. The neolithic inhabitants of the Swiss Lake Villages also used plant-fibre nets with bark floats, but their sinkers were made of fired clay. Today metal sinkers are used by many primitive as well as civilized peoples, one example being the small interlocked lead rings attached to the nets in the Malay peninsula.

The ancestor of the landing-net could have been suspended on a frame made of a bent green stick. Such a hand-net, with a diameter of rather more than a foot, is used in the Andaman Islands. The Eskimo let down a small net through a hole in the ice. In these circumstances a long handle would be a hindrance (also their only supply of wood is driftwood), so the net is held up by thongs attached in three places to the iron ring from which the net hangs, weighted by a stone. The 'Lave' net of the Severn salmon-fisher may have a prehistoric ancestry. It is attached to the arms of a Y-shaped frame, and the fisherman wades out to meet the approaching fish, clubbing it when he brings the net out of the water. The net for taking salmon with the coracle may well be as ancient as this kind of boat itself, for which a mesolithic origin has recently been postulated. The coracle net was composed of two parts, one of wide mesh through which the fish could swim, the other of fine mesh, bringing it to a stop. Once the fish was in the net, sliding horn rings allowed it to bunch round the salmon, which was hauled up and clubbed.

The use of wicker fish-traps is known in many parts of the world today. From Assam to New Guinea these are made of bamboo, a thorny rattan lining preventing the escape of the fish. In the Cambridgeshire district, a stout basket-work eel trap was baited with a worm threaded on wire. Similarly elongated traps were used in the Severn, baited with rabbit or lamprey. Some prehistoric fish-traps have been fortuitously preserved. There is some evidence for them in neolithic Italy, and paintings in tombs show that even the highly civilized Egyptians did not scorn them. The most ancient traps that have survived are mesolithic and have been found in Danish peat bogs. They were made of birch twigs, plaited with fir, and, like modern forms, consisted of an inner funnel to prevent the escape of the quarry, surrounded by a wicker cage.

Forms of the leister or fish-spear are still in use in some parts of the world, and have indeed only been made illegal in Britain in modern times. The mesolithic leister was tipped with two or three barbed bone points, the bases of which were bevelled so that they could be bound firmly into position. The spears were used ten thousand years ago to catch pike and sturgeon; the skeleton of 'the fish that got away' has been found in Esthonia, with a leister prong lying in the region of its back.

With the use of metal, the antler prongs were translated into bronze, and later into iron. Each was cast with a single barb at the tip. The prongs might be cast together, in a flat trident head, or, in the old way, three were disposed separately round the end of the handle.

A number of specialized kinds of fish-spear were in use on the Severn in the last century and doubtless long before. Pike spears had four barbed prongs, those for trout and flounder had five, and a salmon spear had no less than eight. The flat eel-spear had between three and nine closely spaced prongs, each with a serrated edge. The head was set upon an ash handle up to twenty feet long, which was thrust vertically into the mud, as in mesolithic times, either impaling or wedging the quarry between the prongs.

Streaming on the wind

FLAGS are said to have developed out of standards and banners, a theory which is not confirmed by the study of folklore. 'Flag' also is rather a late word, of uncertain origin. According to the *Oxford Dictionary* it may merely have denoted something which flapped in the wind.

Possibly flags had to do with omens, wind, warfare and the smoke of fires. Fires were sacred; the signs of a burning fire – whether it burnt steadily or fiercely, whether the smoke blew in this direction or that – were carefully observed and regarded as omens. The Welsh name for a bonfire is still *coelcerth*, meaning 'sure omen'. In Celtic warfare, if the smoke of an omen-fire, kindled with rites and incantations, floated towards the enemy's camp, it meant that the enemy would at once withdraw to avoid defeat: the power of the party kindling the fire would spread over the territory which its smoke covered. Wind, no less than fire, manifested supernatural power. Early hunters would have realized that their 'victory' or 'defeat', success or unsuccess, often depended on paying attention to the way the wind was blowing, and early boatmen, in their light craft, certainly looked on the wind either as their 'ally' or their 'enemy'.

Flags bring victory or symbolize victory and are activated by the wind. Dio Cassius in his *Roman History* records that Augustus granted Agrippa, among other distinctions, a dark-blue flag in honour of his naval victory. Gallic horsemen (see Livy, X. 26) fixed decapitated heads of slain enemies on lances so that their long hair waved in the wind. Turks and Tartars used waving horse-tails as flags. The first flag known, the *labarum* of the Roman emperors, small and made of silk, had sometimes tassels and fringes which would increase the effect of its flapping. Before he invaded England, William the Conqueror received a blessed banner from Pope Alexander II, but he appears to have had greater confidence in the raven banner of his Viking forefathers: according to an Anglo-Saxon tradition, at any rate, the Norman enemy was led by a raven-banner which foretold victory when it was floating in the wind, and defeat when it drooped and became limp. A renowned magical flag is the Fairy Flag of Dunvegan Castle in the Isle of Skye. This is an almost transparent piece of faded, fawn-coloured silk, embroidered with curious crimson spots known as 'fairy spots'. According to legend, it was left behind by the fairy-wife of the fourth chief of the MacLeods, when she had to go back to Fairyland. She told her husband, whom she dearly loved, that if it was displayed in moments of need, the flag would save the Clan three times. Twice, so it is said, it brought victory; the third time the flag was ill-used, and the good fortune which had lasted for three centuries came to an end.

Without realizing it, Bernard Shaw magnificently expressed in *Saint Joan* what seems to have been the true explanation of the flag. Dunois is pacing up and down the south bank of the Loire. He looks up at the pennon, which streams in a strong east wind. His boats are down the river and cannot ascend against both wind and current, before 'God changes the wind'. When Joan rushes on the stage, the wind drops 'and the pennon flaps idly down the lance', but Dunois is too much occupied with Joan to notice it. He shows her the way to the church, where she wishes to pray to St Catherine who 'will make God give me a west wind'. A page, picking up shield and spear, suddenly notices that the pennon is now streaming eastward. Excitedly he calls after them, and Dunois and St Joan rush back. He looks at the pennon. 'The wind has changed!' He crosses himself. 'God has spoken.' Kneeling and handing his baton to St Joan: 'You command the King's army. I am your soldier.' From its function in war and victory, it is easy to see how the flag has become an emblem of nations, in the rise of nationalism.

Weather-vanes, on steeples, towers and private houses, are descendants of the flag. The cock, by which they are surmounted on many church towers, was believed to drive away the demons of the night by its crowing. In 1952 it was reported in English papers that at Thames Ditton, in Surrey, the vicar of St Nicholas's Church, 'in cassock, surplice and red and gold stole', ascended the top of the new spire. There he conducted a service and blessed a golden sovereign which was later fixed to the weather-vane.

Besides having a symbolic and emotional significance, flags are the most useful of signals. To the landlubber flag signals, such as those of the sea codes or even an upside-down Union Jack, seem indistinct and tangled images. To the trained eye they bring instantaneous meaning. Flags will probably never become obsolete whatever advances science may offer.

The whopstraw's weapon

The **FLAIL** can claim to be older than most agricultural implements, for it could have been used by hunters and food-gatherers before the development of farming. In the Near East farming is attested by 5000 B.C., but there is evidence that before this date cereal seeds were gathered to supplement the meat supply; and some form of flail was probably used to separate the small seeds from the coarse husk. Early man was probably not too particular about the degree of separation, however. In Britain, even so late as the Iron Age, evidence for this has come to light. Microscopic examination of 'buns' found in excavating the Glastonbury Lake Village has shown that many husks were included with the flour of this comparatively civilized settlement.

The earliest flail was a stick, which has been widely replaced by the superior two-piece 'hinged' flail. In some parts of the world the ancient form has persisted even up to the present time. In the Sudan a T-shaped stick is employed. The stem is about five feet long, the cross-piece, which meets it lopsidedly, a foot long. Ancient Egypt raised this humble tool as high as the right hand of Pharaoh. Sculptures show rulers with the shepherd's crook and flail, crossed on the breast, the latter symbolizing royal scourging of foes and evildoers. Examples of ceremonial flails are found in tombs. One from Tutankhamen's tomb has a handle of bronze, covered with gold and blue glass. The multiple 'swingles', which struck the corn, were of gold-covered wood, blue and green glass, and carnelian.

English hinged flails must have originated in a simpler form, which is still used by the aboriginal Ainu of Japan. The handle of their implement is a five-foot pole, one end of which is pierced. A similar hole is made in the end of the swingle, and a rope is passed once through both holes and knotted.

The two parts of English flails are more elaborately joined. As they have only recently passed out of general use, much information has been recorded about the way in which they were made. In East Anglia the construction of flails was a man's occupation in winter evenings. The staff was cut from an ash or a yew tree, and was chosen for its lightness; it was then steamed over the kettle, and a loop was cut out of the wood at one end, forming the 'cap' or 'runner', through which the hinge material was passed. The weighty swingle was made of holly or blackthorn (elsewhere of crab apple, and other tough woods), and the end was whittled flat to a tongue fitted with a leather loop. For binding handle and swingle together from loop to loop eel skin was a favourite material, and was reputed to be the toughest binding available in nature.

On the farms the thump of flails on the heavy wooden threshing-floors inside the barn and the glitter of the chaff were commonplaces of country life.

'Wide flies the chaff', Cowper wrote,

> The rustling straw sends up a frequent mist
> Of atoms, sparkling in the noon-day beam.

But threshing was the most hated drudgery of the farm worker's existence – hence stories of the piskey or goblin thresher who worked away in the barn with his flail.

The process was admirably described by the Wiltshire poet Stephen Duck (1705–1756), who had been a farm labourer himself. 'Come strip and try,' orders the farmer, 'let's see what you can do' –

> Divested of our cloaths, with flail in hand,
> At proper distance, front to front we stand.
> At first the threshal's gently swung, to prove
> Whether with just exactness it will move:
> That once secure, we swiftly whirl them round,
> From the strong planks our crab-tree staves rebound,
> And echoing barns return the rattling sound.
> Now in the air our knotty weapons fly,
> And now with equal force descend from high ...
> In briny streams our sweat descends apace,
> Drops from our locks, or trickles down our face.
> No intermission in our work we know;
> The noisy treshal must for ever go;
> Their master absent, others safely play,
> The sleeping threshal does itself betray ...
> Week after week we this dull task pursue,
> Unless when winnowing days produce a new:
> A new, indeed, but frequently a worse!
> The threshal yields but to the master's curse.
> He counts the bushels, counts how much a-day
> Then swears we've idled half our time away;
> 'Why look ye, rogues, d'ye think that this will do?
> Your neighbours thresh as much again as you.'

Flails, or 'poverty stocks', are still being used in districts of Norfolk, Suffolk and Cambridgeshire for threshing the beans required for seed. For this they are unlikely to be replaced by machinery since experiments have shown that machines split the seed, whereas the flail does no harm.

In Surrey, the 'frail' or 'thrail' was similarly made of ash and holly or thorn. There, and perhaps elsewhere, it used to be a custom never to touch the straw on the threshing-floor with the hand, but to turn it with the handle of the flail. In other parts of the country the two parts have been joined by other materials in preference to the East Anglian eel-skin. These include strips of raw-hide, loops of pliant green ash, and iron pins and bands.

In most parts of the British Isles the ring of threshers round the staw-littered floor in the barn has been replaced by the threshing-machine (q.v.) in the farmyard or the combine harvester in the field. But the flail has not been forgotten even in this highly mechanized time. The whipping motion of the flail has been adapted to tank fittings to clear paths through minefields: these 'flail tanks' are a curious tribute from the present day to the inventiveness of some peaceful 'village Einstein'.

ILLUSTRATION: Plate 16.

The oldest of wind instruments

The **FLUTE** is no doubt the oldest of wind instruments, and it is the only one in which the sound is produced by the breath of the player striking across a simple hole in the pipe.

All very early flutes were blown across the open end – this type is illustrated in Egyptian and Sumerian art, and it is the same as the *phlogera* still played by Greek goat-herds. An early improvement was to move the hole to the side of the pipe and to close up one end. This not only made for a better tone, but allowed the player to hold the instrument in the more comfortable side position instead of at an awkward semi-vertical angle. Very different are the later recorders, which have a specially shaped mouthpiece. Many flutes were made from bones; both the Egyptian word *sebi* and the Latin *tibia* used of the flute actually mean shin-bone. Few of these bone flutes remain, compared with the large number of wooden and reed instruments that are found scattered among the relics of the world's ancient civilisations.

It is not always easy to determine from ancient illustration what is and what is not a flute. Very early on in the development of instruments it was discovered that by binding two small pieces of cane together a so-called 'reed' could be made which, fixed in the end of a pipe, was an alternative to the simple hole for making the initial sound (in this way children still make squeakers with blades of grass). This instrument is in fact an oboe, and unless shown in some detail it is easily confused with the end-blown flute. The matter is not helped by the Greek habit of referring to flute and oboe impartially as *aulos*. Still, it is reasonably certain that a genuine flute was played by the Sumerians by 2600 B.C. A Sumerian seal of that period shows, rather charmingly, a shepherd playing to his attentive dog.

The instrument first appears in Egypt in the fourth millennium B.C.: a slate drawing shows a hunter attracting his prey by means of a flute. Copious illustration in tomb-paintings and actual remains tell us that the later Egyptians were much interested in the flute, as they were in all musical instruments. They used a particularly long version (still end-blown, with no mouthpiece), so long that the players must in some cases have had difficulty in reaching the furthest finger-holes. A band of seven seated players is painted in one of the tombs of the Pyramids, all playing flutes of different lengths, and possibly accompanying a soloist, who alone stands. Apuleius mentions that similar flutes played a part in the mysteries of Isis; even today the Arabs play a *ney*, which differs slightly from these early instruments.

Europe had both the end-blown flute and the transverse flute in the Middle Ages, the transverse flute deriving probably from Byzantium (to this day the flute is exceptionally popular in the Balkans). It is mentioned in a Greek treatise of A.D. 800 and depicted in miniatures of the tenth and eleventh centuries. By the thirteenth century it is commonly mentioned in French and German writings, but it was still a long while before the end-flute, transformed into the *blockflöte* or re-

corder, with its special mouthpiece, took second place. Bach wrote for both recorder and side-flute, though there is evidence that he preferred the side-flute. Certainly it has a greater brilliance and fullness; in fact it is hard to see how the gentler recorder made itself heard in some of the works of that period.

Today the recorder is heard chiefly in the hands of specialists and revivalists (such as the Dolmetsch family) and in schools, where it performs a valuable service in giving children a simple sweet-toned instrument on which they can quickly learn to play tunes. The transverse flute occupies a position of importance in the orchestra: the normal complement is two, with the addition of the tiny piercing piccolo, and, much more rarely, the breathy and sensuous alto flute. It is easily the most nimble of the woodwind ensemble, owing to the ease of the tone production and the ingenious fingering mechanism introduced by Theobald Böhm (1793–1881). Despite their deceptive simplicity, its clear, cool tones are capable of as wide an expressive range as any wind instrument. Enobarbus's lovely description of Cleopatra seated in her barge implies that for Shakespeare the flute was associated with gentle, amorous sounds, and for Dryden the flute was soft and complaining; today it has also acquired a silvery brilliance and a breathless agility. It is still generally made of wood, though metal flutes are common. Some players compromise by having a metal head to the instrument and a wooden body. The wooden flute gives a deeper, more reedy tone; the metal instrument has a more brilliant, more incisive quality, as would be expected. Concertos have been written for the flute, (including two delightful ones by Mozart), and it was part of the social equipment of many a young gentleman of breeding in the last two centuries; but its best use nowadays is in the orchestra, as with all wind instruments. Here it has been respected and well treated by all composers, classical and modern.

The double flute has disappeared. It was popular with the Assyrians, and the Etruscans, the Greeks and Romans. Nile boatmen still play it, and stray English examples a century or so old can be found occasionally in second-hand shops.

ILLUSTRATION: Page 211.

Quill into fountain pen

The **FOUNTAIN PEN** is basically a goose-quill imitated in other materials. Both the concept and the term are fairly old, the concept of a pen with its own ink supply having been suggested by the hollowness of the quill, which so long preceded the steel pen or metal nibs of any kind (see *Pen*, for the early history of writing instruments). Moreover, the carefully fashioned points of the quill could all too easily be spoilt whenever they were dipped into the ink-pot.

Pepys, the diarist, recorded in 1663 that he had a 'reservoir pen'. 'Fountain Inkhorns' or 'Fountain Pens' are mentioned in print for the first time, according to the *Oxford English Dictionary*, in 1710. Ephraim Chambers in the second edition of his *Cyclopaedia* in 1738 defines the fountain pen as 'a sort of pen contrived to contain a great quantity of ink, and let it flow by gentle degrees; so as to supply the writer a long time, without a necessity of taking fresh ink'. Fanny Burney was also writing her diary, in 1789, with a 'fountain pen'.

The difficulty with these quill fountains was to ensure an even flow. In 1809 Joseph Bramah, in pursuance of what he called the 'fountain or perpetual writing principle', took out a patent ancestral to modern developments. He described a method of making an ordinary quill into a fountain pen by putting a small cork, traversed by a very fine slit, between the point and the hollow ink-holding portion of the quill. The walls of the quill were scraped very thin just where the thumb rested, pressure of the thumb forcing the ink along the cork slit. But the specification also included 'compound fountain pens'. These were made of a thin silver tube tapering to a quill nib. Ink was poured in at the top and sealed by an air-tight cork cap. The nib was supplied, once more, by squeezing the tube, which could also be twisted to control the flow. 'I have proved by experience,' Bramah says in the specification, 'that a tube sufficient to form a moderate sized handle to the pen will, when filled with ink, supply those who write the most constant and with the smallest intermission for at least a whole day.' Bramah as well described a 'sliding piston', which took the place of a 'stationary stopper' on the fountain pen.

Many early designs were variations on this theme. In 1832 John Joseph Parker, another Englishman, patented a fountain pen in which the ink was fed to the nib by a pressure on a piston, and which could be filled by drawing the piston back so that ink was sucked into the barrel. This self-filling pen had, as another novelty, a cap with a wire held centrally inside it. When the cap was put on over the nib, the wire entered the ink delivery passage and prevented leakage. The question of leakage was one of concern to many early pen designers. A small lever stop-cock in the ink passage was used in Scheffer's 'Penographic' fountain pen of 1819. One patent of 1838 described a sliding collar that covered an air-hole in the ink reservoir when the pen was not in use. It was not until about 1905 that the provision of caps for pens became commonplace. Before then there were many designs in which the nibs could be retracted into the barrels to protect them when not in use. It seems odd that the protective value of the cap should have passed almost unnoticed for more than seventy years.

Parker's self-filling pen of 1832 was the subject of many improvements. After half a century's development of rubber (q.v.) the rubber ink sac, so common today, was patented in 1859 by Walter Moseley. The sac was filled by twisting it with an external screw to expel the air, and then untwisting it to suck up the ink. Rubber formed into ebonite also had its share in the development of fountain pens, Goodyear using ebonite first of all for pen holders, and L. E. Waterman in America using ebonite for fountain pens in 1884.

The nib and the duct feeding the ink to the nib were crucial in the development of the fountain pen. Steel nibs were evolved through the first half of the nineteenth century for the ordinary penholder, giving at last the flexibility which was the advantage of the quill pen. But the fountain pen required a nib able to resist attack by corrosive inks, which led to gold or gold-plated nibs, and the tipping of nibs with so hard wearing a metal as iridium. Surprisingly enough, the English engineer John Hawkins had made the first iridium-tipped gold nib as early as 1822. Pressure on the metal nib causes a flexing which tends to draw the ink to the point. However, the main reason for a continuous flow is that the paper is no sooner wetted by ink than capillary action

Continued on p. 179

New-York March, 18, 1829

Dear Companion,

I have but jest got my second machine into operation and this is the first specimen I send you except a few lines I printed to regulate the machine, I am in good health but am in fear these lines will not find you so and the children from the malencholley account your letter gave me of sickness and deaths in our neighbourhood, I had rested contented to what I should if it had been summer season about the health of my family, as it is jenerally healthy during the winter months; but their has ben an unusual quantity of sickness hear this winter, and it has ben very cold in Urope as well as in America, a strong indication of the change of seasonth that I have so often mentioned.— Mr Sheldon arrived here four days ago he went imediately on to Washington and took my moddle for the Patent Office, he will returne hom next week at which time I shall put my machine on sale and shall sell out the patent as soon as I can and return home, at any rate I shall resume hom as soon a the Lake navigation is open if life and health is spared me. I have got along but slow since I have been here for the want of cash to hire such help as I wanted, I have been as prudent as I could, have taken my board with a family from Cayuga who keep a boarding house they are verry good christian people and are kind to me. I pay three Dollars a week for my board.—You must excuse mistakes, the above is printed among a croud of people asking me many questions about the machine. Tell the boys that I have some presents for them. If I had any news to communicate I would print more but as I have none I must close hoping these lines will find you well. I wish you to write as soon you receive this, do not make any excuses I shall like to see it in a ey shape

William A. Burt.

October 15. 1622.   Numb 1.

[55]

A
RELATION
OF THE LATE
OCCVRRENTS WHICH
haue happened in Christendome,
especially at Rome, Venice, Spaine,
France, and the vpper
Germanie.

WITH

Seuerall Letters of the particular late Busi-
nesse which hath happened in France,
before the Conclusion of Peace
was made.

Together

With the Articles agreed vpon betwixt the Kings
Commissioners on the one part, and the
Duke de Rohan on the other part,
in behalfe of the Pro-
testants.

LONDON,
Printed by B.A. for Nathaniel Butter, and
Nicholas Bourne. 1622.

Forerunner of the newspaper. English newsbook of 1622.

Letter written by William Burt on his typographer.

Crüger's azimuth quadrant, 1673.

Telescope from *Selenographia, sive lunae descriptio* (1647), by Johannes Hevelius.

The Lace Maker. Oil by Kaspar Netscher (1639–1684).

Catherine of Braganza, wearing a collar of Dutch bobbin lace. Oil by Dirk Stoop (d. 1686).

Khephren's pyramid, near Gizeh. Fourth Dynasty c. 2850 B.C.

168

Relics of three martyrs, each with a vessel of his own blood. Chiesa di San Giorgio, Monselice, Italy.

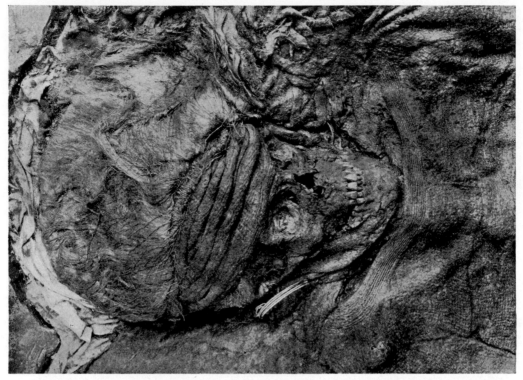

The Skrydstrup woman: detail showing neck of jumper and hair-net.

Clothes: a woman of c. 1000 B.C. in an embroidered jumper, from an oak coffin, Skrydstrup, Denmark.

Corded skirt, jumper and bronze belt-plate from Denmark, Bronze Age.

Prehistoric clothing: checked twill skirt and skin cloak, from Huldremose, Jutland, Denmark. Early Iron Age.

171

A primitive 'pleggenhut' or turf house, from the Netherlands Open Air Museum, Arnhem.

Iron Age farmhouse, Little Woodbury, Wiltshire. Reconstructed in the film *Beginnings of History*.

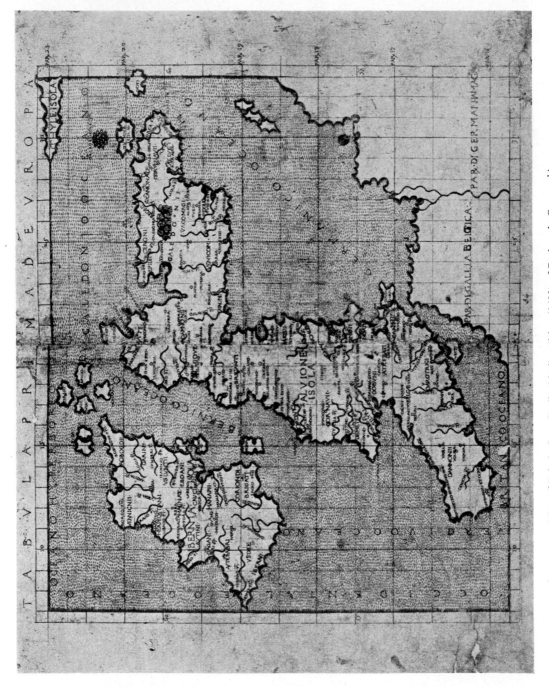

Map of Britain from Berlinghieri's edition (1482) of Ptolemy's *Geographia*.

174

Roman lighthouse at Ostia, the port of Rome, from a relief.

Lighthouse at Cordouan, France, finished in 1611.

From the gallery of the Bishop Rock lighthouse, Isles of Scilly.

A hooded bath, framed in carved mahogany, with shower-bath, c. 1880.

A baroque crib by Guiseppe Sammartino (1720–1793).

178

draws further supplies down the very fine hole in the feed. The barrel of the pen, which holds the ink in a flexible bag, is pierced with small air holes so that there is no difference of pressure to offer resistance inside to deformations of the bag.

Pens have improved with advanced manufacturing methods and newer plastic materials, but there have been no fundamental changes in fountain-pen design in the past fifty years, the new popularity of ball-point pens reflecting no more than advances in the manufacture of points, capillary tubes and inks which are suitably viscous. A ball-point pen for marking boxes was patented in 1888. As for price, a very simple fountain pen with a brass reservoir was marketed in London early in this century for threepence. A few years later, in 1905, simpler but quite effective fountain pens were made to sell at a penny each. In the past from stylus to steel nib, writing tools have influenced the styles of writing and set different artistic ideals before the calligrapher. The modern fountain pen has, on the whole, destroyed calligraphy, making for writing which is swift and slipshod. (See also *Pen*, *Ink*, *Paper*, *Alphabet*, *Typewriter*.)

G

The Tree

The **GALLOWS** and pre-mechanized execution by hanging we owe to the barbaric past of our own ancestors, to judge from the statement made by Tacitus in his *Germania*. With the Germans, he wrote, the methods of punishment varied according to the crime. Some offenders were drowned in bogs with a hurdle over them, 'traitors and deserters are hung from trees'.

Posts and a cross-beam are merely refinements, anything having served, bough, beam, lamp-post,

I

or yardarm; though it may be said that England has never known anything on such a scale of grim permanence as the Gibbet of Montfaucon in medieval Paris, where brick arches forming three sides of a square allowed fifty-two men to hang at a time, under the kites that waited in the air above. The fourth side was a ramp up which the executioner led his victim; he found a gap, placed his ladder, encouraged the victim up the ladder with the help of a leading rope called the *jet*; made all secure, elbowed his man off the ladder, and stood in the stirrups formed by his pinioned arms to shorten the spasmodic movements of his strangling. For medieval or sixteenth-century hangings and gallows turn to the poems of Villon in France –

> The rain's washed over us, we're dried
> And blackened by the sun, and crows and pies
> Have plucked our eyebrows and our beards
> And hollowed out the sockets of our eyes –

or in Flanders to the paintings of Pieter Bruegel, in which gallows stand in corners or against skylines as a perpetual reminder of mortality.

In London, Tyburn developed its own ceremony. Leaving the condemned cell at Newgate in the cart with his own coffin, the criminal halted at St Sepulchre's Church to attend his own funeral service under the tolling bell, and then proceeded with the Chaplain at his ear and the nosegay in his hand to the spot near where Marble Arch now stands. There, if he was notorious enough, the hawkers would be busy selling broadsheets of his 'Last Dying Words'. The cart halted under the 'Tree'; the halter was secured, and the cart drove away, leaving him to dance his way into eternity without assistance, unless the hangman's men were kind enough to drag at his legs.

Not till 1868 did Parliament decide that the time had come to end public hangings and withdraw the ceremony within the walls of the prisons. The public, deciding that it had been cheated, continued to meet outside the prison on execution days and solace itself in imagination. Meanwhile, inside the prison as the statutory hour of 8 a.m. approaches, the whole population waits in silence for the sound of the 'drop'. After it has been heard, pandemonium breaks out as each prisoner expresses in his fashion his execration of society.

The 'drop' is a refinement of eighteenth-century humanitarianism, which is said to have been first employed in 1760 for the execution of Earl Rivers. Its aim is to substitute for the dance of the dying man an instantaneous death by breaking his neck. To do this effectively it is necessary to calculate the right distance (about six to eight feet) according to his height and weight. With a white hood over his head, he stands on a trapdoor. The halter, with a metal eye, is fastened under his chin or behind his ear. The trap opens under his feet, and he falls. The Chief Warder steps forward and opens his shirt so that the doctor may examine him for signs of life. An inquest is held, a formal verdict returned, and the body is buried in quicklime in the precincts of the prison.

Eighteenth-century refinement also brought to an end the old punishment of traitors, invoked for the last time after the Jacobite rebellion of 1745. The victims were first hanged, cut down when still alive, disembowelled and their entrails burnt, their heads cut off and their bodies quartered. The heads and quarters were then taken back to Newgate to 'Jack Ketch's Kitchen' to be pickled, so that they might be exposed on Temple Bar or London Bridge.

Ellwood the Quaker described in his autobiography in 1714 how he saw in Newgate the heads of three traitors, first of all set down among the felons. 'They took them by the hair, flouting, jeering and laughing at them; and then giving them some ill names, box'd them on the ears and cheeks.' Afterwards the hangman put them in his kettle 'and parboyl'd them with bay-salt and cummin-seed', the salt to keep them from putrefaction and the cummin seed 'to keep off the fowls from seizing them'.

The whole sight of the heads and the previous quartering begat, said Ellwood, 'an abhorrence in my nature'.

In spite of eighteenth-century refinements, eighteenth-century legislators also acted on the principle that crime could be discouraged by keeping the example of ferocious penalties before men's eyes, 'gibbeting' (leaving criminals hanging in chains or in the frames known as 'gibbet-irons' until their bodies decomposed) was not recognized by statute until 1752. It had, of course, been practised by custom before, although the Judges always solemnly explained that it was 'no part of the sentence'.

By about 1810 the fifty capital offences known to the Stuarts had grown to more than two hundred. 'Never did I see boys cry so' wrote Greville the diarist in a phrase that Swift would have relished, when 'to their own excessive amazement' several of them were sentenced to be hanged. One child earned the penalty by coveting some paints in a shop window, and smashing a pane of glass to rake them out with a stick. In London and Middlesex 3,680 persons were condemned to death during the second half of the eighteenth century, although only 1,696 were actually executed (mostly for crimes against property).

After 1827 no one could any longer appeal for 'Benefit of Clergy': that medieval survival which had become a legal fiction. Under it many others besides Ben Jonson had owed their lives to their ability to read the neck-verse ('Have mercy upon me, O God, according to thy loving-kindness: according to the multitude of thy tender mercies blot out my transgressions.' Psalm li.) Many more owed their lives to the reluctance of juries to convict.

As the nineteenth century wore on, the security that grew with the new police enabled the reformers to whittle down the list of capital offences, until capital punishment itself was called in question. But, right or wrong, the gallows cannot be made humane; and it is questionable whether the three weeks' wait in the death cell under permanent guard is really to be preferred to the old summary treatment which sent a man to the gallows on the spot, or on the day after his trial was over. (See also *Guillotine, Rope*.)

ILLUSTRATION: Page 120.

From Egypt and Sumeria

GLASS to anyone who is not a chemist is a mystery. Why should opaque and gritty materials like sand, soda and lime, when mixed together in certain proportions and fired, produce the crystal clear, smooth and impervious substance called glass, which can be adapted for so many different uses? Few of us, if asked, could give a plain and factual answer, and it is the more amazing that this wonderful thing was invented as much as 5,000 or more years ago.

We do not know exactly when, or by whom. In Egypt or Mesopotamia over 3,000 years before Christ men had discovered how to make an alkaline vitreous glaze which would adhere, as a surface coating, to stone and other substances. By the middle of the third millennnium B.C. both the Sumerians in Mesopotamia and the Egyptians had discovered that this vitreous glaze could be moulded into small objects by itself without the aid of a core.

At the beginning, so far as we know, the objects made were only small ones – beads and amulets and perhaps pieces for inlay patterns on caskets and furniture – and these glass objects were rare and almost as precious as the stones and gems which they were probably intended to imitate. They were all made by moulding, except the beads, which needed, of course, a hole to string them by, and so had to be made by winding viscous glass round a metal wire, which was withdrawn when the glass cooled.

Nearly a thousand years more were to elapse before the first glass vessels were made. The date is about 1500 B.C., at which time we find vessels in use both in Egypt, under Thothmes III, the famous pharaoh of the eighteenth dynasty, and in the Asiatic countries nearby. Most of these earliest vessels were made by what we call the sand-core process, which was perhaps developed from the technique just described for making beads. It consisted of building up a core of sand, wrapped in cloth round a metal rod and shaped like the inside of the vessel it was intended to produce. Warm viscous glass was applied to this core, either by dipping it in a crucible of glass or by trailing the glass on to the core. When the glass cooled, the metal rod and the core of sand were withdrawn and the vessel was finished by adding base, rim, handles and decorations, as required. This process was useful only for flasks and jugs and other vessels with narrow mouths. Occasionally open bowl shapes were made by pressing glass into moulds; and a third process which was also probably used from the first, though not so

commonly, was one that was borrowed from the makers of stone vases – grinding a vessel out of a cold block of glass, just as if it were a piece of rock-crystal or quartz.

No major change in glass-making techniques took place for another 1,500 years. But the change when it did occur, was revolutionary – none other than the discovery that glass vessels could be made by inflating a solid blob (or 'paraison') of glass with a blowpipe. It is believed that this invention took place in Syria just before or just after the birth of Christ. At that time there were flourishing glass industries of long standing both in Syria and in Egypt. The Egyptian industry, which was centred in Alexandria had by this time moved away from sand-core and was concentrating on moulding and grinding; one of its special lines was the manufacture of the celebrated mosaic bowls formed of sections of polychrome canes of glass fused together in moulds and afterwards smoothed and polished by grinding on a wheel. The Syrian industry, on the other hand, which, like the Egyptian, had long been making sand-core glasses, never really took to the moulding and grinding processes. It was therefore very ready to become a blowing industry once that process was invented, making vessels both by blowing them into patterned moulds and by free-blowing.

Both these centres sent out trained glass workers to Italy, once their respective homelands had been conquered by Rome in the latter half of the first century B.C.; and from the beginning of Augustus's reign great quantities of glass were made by these Syrians and Alexandrians, both in Rome itself and elsewhere in Italy. We even know the names of some of the Syrian makers of the time – e.g. Artas and Ennion – to mention only the two most prominent, for they signed their products.

The invention of glassblowing was, in fact, the last major innovation in glass-making processes, not only in antiquity, but even up to modern times. A Syrian or Alexandrian worker of the first century A.D. would have been as much at home in a modern glass-house as would a Venetian worker of, say, the sixteenth century A.D. The only things that would puzzle him would be the modern machines for mass production. There are still glass-houses in England where the industry makes fine glassware in the old way, although the great majority of modern glass is made by machines which blow the glass into moulds. The human labour force could no longer cope with the enormous quantities required for all the many uses to which glass is put today.

Among the kinds of glass the Romans made, first and most common were flasks for toilet preparations, wine bottles and ordinary table-ware of undecorated glass, mostly green. Quantities of fragments of all these are found on almost every site where Roman remains exist, and quantities of them are also found in Roman burials, for it was the ancient practice to put vessels of glass, as well as of pottery and metal, in the tombs, to contain food and drink and unguents for the use of the dead. In the two first centuries A.D., when burial by cremation was common, glass was even used to make urns to hold the ashes of the dead. Thus Roman burials are the main sources from which complete Roman glasses are derived; glasses found on dwelling sites are normally in fragments.

As well as common plain ware, we have much fine glassware of Roman date, both colourless (for glass workers in Roman times could make as good colourless glass as we can today) and coloured. Richer Roman burials, especially in Italy and certain other main centres of Roman life, such as Cologne, often contain beautiful pieces of glass bearing elaborate cut designs and painted patterns. The cut designs were made either in facet cutting on the wheel or with an engraving tool, or a mixture of both, and they comprise representations of mythological and biblical stories, or scenes of everyday life, as well as geometrical patterns. The painted designs were made usually in enamel paint, fired on, and they, too, sometimes include mythological scenes, though these were more normally confined to animal and vegetable motifs. Some very pretty and attractive glassware was also made with patterns of applied trails and blobs, especially in a variety that was produced about 200 A.D., both in Syria and in Cologne, termed 'snake thread' ware, because the trailed designs are often serpent-like.

Even in the first century A.D. glass was as common, in everyday use, both for vessels of every kind and for ornaments, as bronze and silver. But at the start the shapes were on the whole simple. It was not until late in the second century,

and still more in the third and fourth centuries, that really elaborate and complicated shapes became prevalent.

What happened to the glass industry in the Dark Ages and medieval times? The answer is different in the East and in the West. In the East, both in Egypt and Syria, the tradition of fine glass-making continued without any noticeable break or decline up to the fourteenth century A.D., and beyond. In the thirteenth and fourteenth centuries some of the finest enamelled glass ever made came out of Syrian factories. In the West, on the other hand, the end of Roman power in the early fifth century A.D. brought with it a rapid decline both in the quantity and in the quality of glassware. So much was this so that within a few centuries only a limited number of glasses of any consequence were being made, even in Italy.

During Roman days the western industry had largely been in the hands of glass workers from Syria and Egypt. When Roman rule declined and the barbarian invasions overran the western provinces and Italy itself, the incentive, and even the opportunity, for further waves of Eastern workers to migrate westwards ceased, and so the industry was left to local initiative; and that was lacking. The West had to wait until the thirteenth century when the crusades re-opened contact between East and West, and made it easy once more for workers from the East to come westwards. After that, at Venice and in other centres in Europe, glass works grew up which were again able and ready to turn out the best of wares. So began the modern glass industry of Europe.

In earlier centuries in England, the making of glass was widely scattered over the countryside. 'Glasshouse Wood' is not an uncommon place name for woodland sites where the glass-makers built their furnaces with supplies of fuel to hand. (See also *Chinaware, Earthenware, Plastics*.)

ILLUSTRATION: Pages 78, 79 and 80.

Eyes and no eyes

GLASS EYE is the popular term for the artificial eye, which is now frequently made of glass.

In the course of history artificial eyes have been made of many other substances, including gold, silver, porcelain, ivory, horn, aluminium, vulcanite, celluloid, and, since about 1934, plastic materials, such as methyl-methacrylate. From the wearer's standpoint the principal advantage of an artificial eye is cosmetic – to disguise the unsightly appearance of an empty eye-socket. But it has long been recognized that a properly fitted eye restores the movement of the eyelids and maintains their shape; it also prevents the accumulation of fluids by getting rid of tears through the normal channels and thus diminishes the risk of infection of the socket.

Artificial eyes appear to have been first used in statues and later in embalmed bodies. The final stage was their use in living subjects. Numerous examples occur of artificial eyes fitted to ancient Egyptian mummy-cases. During the early period from about 3000 B.C. onwards the casing of the eye was made of stone, with polished stone to represent the iris and the white of the eye. At a later date the casing was made of bronze. The famous statue of Ra-em-Ké, which dates from the fourth century B.C., had eyes of opaque white quartz; the iris was formed by a shining stud, over which lay a disc of rock crystal to represent the pupil. There are numerous instances of the use of artificial eyes, often made of gold or other precious materials, to fill the orbits of statues in classical Greece and Rome. Such statues are to be seen, for instance, in the Louvre. Although the evidence is not conclusive, it is probable that artificial eyes were also made for living subjects during ancient times. Eye-diseases were very common in Egypt, and a crude type of artificial eye seems to have been used there as early as the fifth century B.C. Such an appliance consisted simply of a rough painting of an eye on a fragment of pottery; this was cemented to skin-coloured cloth, which was itself stuck over the empty socket. The resulting appearance must have been hideous, and septic conditions were doubtless common. The first eyes intended to be retained in the orbits of living persons were frequently made of gold.

Comments on the use of artificial eyes in modern times were made by the great French surgeon, Ambroise Paré (1510–1590). Paré described artificial eyes made of gold or silver, enamelled to represent the natural eye. Where such an eye could not be retained in the socket he advised a metal shield, painted to represent an eye, and attached to a metal band which passed round the head and retained the shield in position.

Many of the great surgeons of the seventeenth and eighteenth centuries describe briefly eyes made of glass. In the manufacture of these appliances the Venetians were at first most successful; but later their superiority passed in turn to the Bohemians and the French. The secrets of the craft were closely guarded, and were handed on from father to son. In 1835 Müller-Uri, of Lauscha in Thuringia, began to make greatly improved glass eyes, and Germany gradually became the source of the finest examples. It was in Germany also that materials such as vulcanite, ivory, and celluloid were first tried as substitutes for the more fragile glass. A special type of glass is required for the manufacture of artificial eyes, and this was made almost exclusively in Germany until 1933, when its exportation was prohibited and Great Britain and the United States were forced to develop the necessary technique. One line of development was the use of plastics.

There are now in use two main types of artificial eye, the 'shell' type, which consists of a simple disc or triangular shaped plate moulded to form a concave surface, like a saucer, on its inner aspect, and the 'reform' type, designed about 1898, in which the thickness of the eye at its central points appears to be very much greater that in the 'shell' type, and which is more frequently used where much of the eyeball has been removed. This eye of two saucers fused at the outer edges and fitting one inside the other, gives a more natural movement and diminishes secretions. Artificial eyes have also been constructed in which the pupil appears to react to light in a normal manner.

The use of artificial eyes is much commoner than is usually realized. In 1939 the estimated number of wearers in Great Britain was 350,000. During the Second World War the numbers rose sharply as a result of bomb injuries and industrial injuries. Shortly after the end of the War it was estimated that, including service casualties, nearly a million persons in Great Britain were wearing them.

On the ocean of air

The **GLIDER,** which has now proved itself as the perfect instrument for the enjoyable navigation of the air, goes back to the wings which brave but reckless men strapped to themselves during the past thousand years or so, before leaping from towers.

Possibly one or two of these early bird-men managed for a short while to hold their wings rigid enough to allow of a floundering attempt at gliding flight. None the less, the first proper glider was a small model built by Sir George Cayley (1773–1857) in 1804. This consisted of a kite attached to one end of a pole – so that its surface was slightly inclined to the direction of flight – and a fin and tailplane attached to the other end. It flew well, and from it developed the gliders of the nineteenth century. Cayley himself built and tested a full-sized glider and launched it with a boy on board just before 1850, but little is known of the event. The French sea-captain Le Bris also built a crude glider shaped after the albatross, with which he boldly but unsuccessfully attempted to glide between 1857 and 1868.

Other, still tentative, efforts followed, each experimenter using the current knowledge of aerodynamics as best he could. But to bring about successful glider flight, a man was needed who could combine theory and practice. Late in the century he arrived in the person of the German engineer Otto Lilienthal (1848–1896), whose work was the last focal point in the history of flying before the birth of the powered aeroplane. Lilienthal looked upon his successful gliding experiments made from 1891 to 1896 as a preliminary to powered flight, and had indeed already built a glider with an auxiliary engine before he was killed in one of his gliders in 1896. Percy Pilcher in England had flown successfully in gliders when in 1899 he too was killed after designing a powered machine which had not been tested.

Lilienthal wrote that soaring machines were 'excellent schooling machines, and that is all they are meant to be, until power, in the shape of an engine working a screw propeller, or any engine working wings to drive the machine forward, is added'.

It was his work and death that finally set the Wright brothers upon their career of triumph in the United States. They made three gliders, in 1900, 1901 and 1902; with the last they achieved an excellent controlled machine with wing-warping (later to develop into ailerons), elevator and rudder. The next step, as all the world knows, was their first powered aeroplane, based upon this glider of 1902, which on 17 December 1903 made the first powered, sustained and controlled flight in history.

It was not until the powered aeroplane had developed into a highly efficient and complex flying machine that pilots turned back deliberately to the glider for sport and relaxation. The excitement of engined flight gave way to the exhilaration of silently riding the air as a soaring bird rides it.

It was in Germany in the nineteen-twenties that gliding as a sport developed on a considerable scale, with every encouragement. After the First World War Germany had been forbidden to make engine-driven planes, so her air-minded young men took to gliding as a means of training and as an end in itself. Gliding offers the supreme poetry of flight, the glider becoming a wonderful soaring machine when weather conditions permit, and when the pilot has learnt to use winds and upcurrents. Gliders have thus been kept in the air for as long as fifty-five hours and have risen as high as 30,000 feet. 'As for me,' says Philip Wills, 'I fly because I am fascinated by the ocean of the air, by its habits and moods, and in learning slowly to understand its curious ways. I suppose you could say that I love the air for itself, as a good husbandman loves the earth or the good sailor the sea.' Those words, written by one of the finest exponents of the art, sum up the feelings and inspiration of glider pilots the world over. (See also *Aeroplane, Balloon, Kite.*)

ILLUSTRATION: Page 67.

The passive music-maker

The **GRAMOPHONE** began with the machine made by Thomas Alva Edison in 1877 which recognizably reproduced words spoken – or rather shouted – into it. He called it a phonograph, conceiving it as an aid (compare the typewriter, q.v.) to the business man, to be used as we now use the dictaphone. The public thought otherwise, quickly realizing its possibilities as a home entertainer; thus the phonograph, like so many other inventions, rapidly escaped from the net of circumstance and intention which brought it to birth.

In Edison's original phonograph a stylus with a rounded point was attached to a diaphragm mounted in a mouthpiece. The stylus rested gently against a sheet of tinfoil wrapped around a cylinder. When the cylinder on its lead-screw was rotated by a hand-crank and someone shouted into the mouthpiece, the vibrations of the diaphragm caused the point to indent the soft tinfoil along a helical track. The screw was then turned back to the beginning and the cylinder was rotated again. The stylus point, in contact with the indentation on the tinfoil, vibrated the diaphragm, and the original sounds were reproduced.

The reproduction was poor, and the tinfoil 'record' could be played only a few times before the indented sound track was obliterated. The immense public interest in the new invention which Edison had patented in 1878 died away, and was only revived by new developments introduced in 1885 by Alexander Graham Bell and Charles Sumner Tainter. For the tinfoil they substituted a cylinder of wax, on which a track was cut varying in depth according to the amplitude of the vibration of the point. This gave records which were more or less permanent, and which were of an acceptable quality. The popularity of the phonograph steadily increased. In 1887 another American inventor, Emile Berliner, introduced a variant of the phonograph. The cylindrical wax record was abandoned for a disc. The recording point was so mounted that its vibrations were in the plane of the recording surface instead of at right angles to it, as in the older instrument. Thus the point cut, and in the reproduction, followed a sinuous track of constant depth, instead of a track varying in depth in a succession of hills and dales. Berliner's instrument was the gramophone; and for a long while it made little headway against the phonograph, though it was victorious in the end; the production of cylinder records ceased with the early nineteen-twenties.

In the older days of the phonograph, people made their own records, though records were very soon put on the market, phonograph and then gramophone now developing, in one sense, as the musical instruments for those who lacked the skills of playing or singing. Thus the camera developed as a means of picture-making for those who could neither draw nor paint. After the First World War the gramophone (which America still calls the phonograph) had to share with the radio set its position as the foremost purveyor of passive entertainment in the home. Yet the gramophone kept its ground; and in effect the two industries combined; a marriage or a symbiosis was arranged between gramophone and radio receiver. This was due to experience gained in the development of radio and then applied to the manufacture of records and the reproduction of sound from them by electrical methods. In electrical reproduction needle vibrations set up varying electrical potentials which are amplified by thermionic valves to produce currents actuating a loudspeaker. This is precisely the method of dealing with the output from the detector stage of a radio set, so gramophone and radio could be incorporated in the now familiar radiogram.

The refined electrical gramophone has demanded, *pari passu*, a refinement of the records. In the early days each record sold was recorded directly by the artist, choir, orchestra, etc. True, a singer or an orchestra would make a dozen or more records at once by performing in front of a dozen or more recording machines. The important step, soon taken, was to make copies from the master recording. The cylinder record disappeared, and the disc record finally settled down to two main sizes, ten and twelve inches in diameter, reproduced to rotate at a standard speed of seventy-eight revolutions per minute, and running from six to eight minutes (counting both sides). To match the delicacy of electrical reproduction, these records are giving way to the long-playing, slow-speed records, with the grooves closer set, which rotate at $33\frac{1}{3}$ and 45 revolutions per minute, are more or less free of needle-scratch and are made of finer and more durable material. Such is the result of more than seventy years of evolutionary experiment. (See also *Musical Box*.)

ILLUSTRATION: Pages 316 and 317.

'From out its rocky clefts the waters flow'

GROTTOES, as garden ornaments or adjuncts, have a long history. They may be pavilions, they may be artificial caves, they may be excavated, they may be piled high, but inside they should glitter. The best of the surviving artificial grottoes are crusted with shells, spar, crystals, bright coal, or mirrors. Inland they often suggest the mystery of the sea, with branches of coral, curious petrifactions, water-worn branches, and the bones of whales.

The origin is obvious, and is most clearly seen in the simplest form of grotto, which we might perhaps call a grot, an embellishment for a garden (enclosing a seat and perhaps a statue) which directly imitates a nook by a rocky stream. The words 'grotto' and 'crypt' alike come from a common source, the Greek *krupte*, a 'vault' or 'hidden place'; and grottoes belong to the tradition of Chinese and European gardening: in both countries they were built for water and the sounds of water, in China also for the whistling and echoing of the wind. Nymphs, according to classical animism, inhabited the grottoes of nature, possessing and sanctifying streams and springs; they were the spirits of rock and water; thus the world-famous Castalian Spring, coming out of the limestone at Delphi in Greece, was owned by the nymph Castalia; she drowned herself in its water to escape Apollo. Diana had her grottoes; according to Ovid

> The chaste Diana's private haunt there stood
> Full in the centre of a darksome wood,
> A spacious grotto, all around o'ergrown
> With hoary moss, and arch'd with pumicestone.
> From out its rocky clefts the waters flow
> And trickling swell into a lake below.

If grottoes, deriving from such ancient traditions, became fanciful and gay, they also retained in themselves an element of the mysteries of rock, water and nymphs.

Accounts of artificial grottoes in the Roman civilization are not specific; and they add confusion through the later word 'grotesque' (*grottesca* in Italian), which seems to have been applied to the paintings – fantastic depictions of men and animals – in the underground rooms of the Palace of Titus. 'Grotesque' thus narrowed to an adjective for the contorted pop-eyed masks which decorate renaissance furniture and architecture. By the seventeenth century grottoes in renaissance Italy had achieved considerable splendour, and the management of cool tricklings of water had been elevated to hydraulic conceits.

A grotto at the Villa d'Este had mechanical birds which flapped their wings and sang by means of water; at the Villa Aldobrandini there were grotto pavilions on each side of the building, in which a centaur with a trumpet, a fawn, birds, Apollo and the Nine Muses sang and played, loudly and disagreeably, by the agency of conduits of air. Visitors who settled themselves resigned to the awful trumpet solo, on the seats surrounding the centaur's grotto, were at the mercy of a hundred little hidden pipes concealed in the fissures of the rocks, which suddenly shot water all over them. The door was closed; a spiral staircase seemed to offer escape, but the ascent was the signal for jets to squirt from all directions, the ceiling, the walls, and the steps themselves. Everyone was soaked. Down the garden another grotto, without conceits, was made of a huge rock in the form of a mask whose open mouth engulfed the visitors. Leafy branches and ivy were trained to form the frowning brows and beard of the monster, the only true grotesque grotto.

At about the same time, similar grottoes were fashionable in France – both Catherine and Marie de Medici built them – and early in the seventeenth century grottoes, water conceits and tunnels proliferated in England. Celebrated water conceits of the kind were contrived by Thomas Bushell (1594–1674), the mining speculator of the Civil War period, at Enstone near Oxford. After this there seems to have been a pause; it is difficult to be certain, because grottoes have always been regarded as trifling by art historians, and in contemporary books which record European architecture, a fountain or a memorial, however small, may often find an honoured place, whereas a grotto, however elaborate and exquisite, will be ignored.

In England, in the first half of the eighteenth century the building of grottoes began once more, inclined at first to the rococo and the gay, beginning then to imitate nature more closely. Alexander Pope, the great poet, built at Twickenham between 1718 and 1724 a grotto which still exists, now only a dull shadow of itself, devoid of its original sparkle of ores from the mines of Cornwall, Germany, Peru and Mexico, and of crystals, fossils and humming-birds. For this grotto stalactites were shot down inside the great cave of Wookey Hole in Somerset. In 1737 Thomas Goldeney started the fine grotto still preserved at Bristol, at the end of an already completed subterranean passage, a grotto complex and most beautifully executed, with a lion's den and a Neptune's cave, a roaring cascade of water, and thousands of shells.

Gay rococo grottoes, inventive, witty and ingenious, were made up to mid-century (and a few somewhat later). Thus the grotto at St Giles's House at Wimborne St Giles, Dorset, was built for an Earl of Shaftesbury in 1751, at the huge cost of £10,000. Here the ornaments include whale bones and oyster shells containing pearls. Rather late in this mode is the grotto made at Ware in Hertfordshire c. 1760 for the poet John Scott, of Amwell, elaborately tunnelled, reaching into a pretty shell-lined room; from this and beside it true and false passages, with and without shells, wind up and down to small rooms with and without echoes. Candlelight shows faintly down long air shafts between these rooms. Scott described how

> 'midst thick oaks, the subterraneous way
> To the arch'd grot admits a feeble ray;
> Where glassy pebbles pave the varied floors,
> And rough flint walls are deck'd with shells and ores;
> And silvery pearls, spread o'er the roof on high,
> Glimmer like faint stars in a twilight sky.

That the grotto about mid-century tended to become more of a direct imitation of nature was partly due to the influence of Chinese gardening and Chinese grottoes, which were described by various writers, notably by Sir William Chambers in his *Design of Chinese buildings ... to which is annexed a Description of their temples, houses,* *gardens, etc.* (1757), Chambers praising the natural taste of the Chinese in the contrivance of 'impending rocks, dark caves, and impetuous cataracts'. Taste was turning outwards to nature; the cave phenomena in limestone districts such as the Peak or the West Riding of Yorkshire were much enjoyed and visited; and, in Virgilian phrase, grottoes were now felt to enshrine 'the genius of the place'. England at this time also produced a notable grotto artist in Josiah Lane (1754–1833), of Tisbury in Wiltshire, a stonemason by birth, 'perfectly ignorant', with 'a genius for this kind of construction'; the rich men of England employed him at two guineas a week, leaving him in the end to die in the Tisbury Workhouse. Josiah Lane's father before him seems to have built several of the finer rococo shell-houses; and may have worked on the splendid intermediate and somewhat formal grotto in the landscape garden at Stourhead, in Wiltshire, which now belongs to the National Trust; this cool and melancholy grotto, enshrining a leaden statue of its water nymph, with lines by Alexander Pope engraved in the stone, is reached by winding ferry steps by the edge of an artificial lake. Symmetrically planned inside, it is dim but not dark, and water flows round the reclining nymph which refreshes but does not deafen. Splendid work by Josiah Lane remains at Bowood (1785), executed for the Marquis of Lansdowne, Wardour Castle (1792), for Lord Arundel, and at Fonthill (1794), for the millionaire author and connoisseur, William Beckford; and his grottoes were imitated abroad, especially in France.

The best grottoes are never an obvious feature of the layout; they neither close a perspective nor are built under a terrace. Instead, the cool darkness of the grotto must be a surprise in the wildest part of the park, found perhaps with difficulty. This is true of Josiah Lane's grotto and caves at Fonthill, or his grotto work, including a cascade and a long cave, at Bowood. The remains of the grotto at Hawkstone in Shropshire are at the end of a long, black labyrinth cut into a steep solid outcrop on a hill, which is reached by narrow paths through forests of rhododendrons. Here there is no water, and the grotto is high and sunny; but the problem of a difficult approach in a cultivated park has never been better managed.

Grottoes in the English manner spread as far afield as Germany and Sweden, and further still; but a story told of Dr Johnson (1709–1784) illustrates the case which gathered strength against these caves of delight and artifice: a lady asked if her new-built grotto would not be 'a pretty cool habitation in summer?' 'I think it would, Madam,' the doctor replied, '– for a toad.'

Nineteenth-century grottoes were different. Tasteful counterparts of the Gorge of the Dripping Verdure at Kung Wang Fu were no longer erected, grottoes were smaller and less Ducal; or else they were constructions built by eccentrics with their own hand – huge grottoes that forbad sleep and food to the builders and devoured a lifetime. Such is the palace of the postman Cheval at Hauterives, in France, a grotto entirely above ground, about eighty-five feet long and over thirty feet high, made of curious stones and rocks, shells and reinforced concrete. Concrete palms sprout above Hindu temples, giants like toy grenadiers enlarged and covered with rough-cast guard the palace in the names of Vercingetorix, Caesar, and Archimedes. It was built entirely by Ferdinand Cheval between 1879 and 1912, in the spare time left to him from a daily twenty-mile round; the swollen and crystallized image of a dream started by a water-worn stone on which he struck his foot. He knew nothing about building, and had almost no tools.

There will always be men like Cheval to build grottoes, the amorphous cities and spires of those who should have been architects much more surely than nine-tenths of the people who are. The aristocratic grottoes, however, are unlikely to appear again. The Festival Pleasure Gardens in Battersea Park, in London, gave us a beautiful grotto blown through with perfumed airs, but on the whole we are now reduced from grotto to rock gardens.

ILLUSTRATION: Page 315.

'Little Louison'

The **GUILLOTINE**, like so many novelties of the French Revolution, was not new, even if it is mechanization applied to death. It bears the name of Dr Louis Guillotin, but developed (so it appears) an idea springing from the fertile inventiveness of the Renaissance.

In the sixteenth century many famous executions in the south of France and Italy, especially of noblemen and ecclesiastics, were performed with the aid of an instrument often called *mannaia*, which resembled the later guillotine either more or less, or exactly. Such were the executions of a certain Demetrio in 1507, described in the *Chronicle of Jean d'Authon*; of Titus Manlius in 1550, shown in engravings both by George Pencz and Aldegraver (with a knife of half-moon shape); of Monsieur de Montmorency in 1632 described in the *Mémoires* of Puysegur; and of Bonasone (in which the instrument is shown on a scaffold and not on the ground). A cut in Bocchi's *Symbolicarum Questionum Libri V* published at Bologna in 1555, shows an instrument precisely like the revolutionary guillotine, even to the triangular blade. Nor was this means of release confined to the Mediterranean, for the Scottish 'maiden' which despatched Cardinal Morton in 1578 seems to have had at least a basic similarity.

Whatever the source of his idea, Guillotin, advocating it to the National Assembly in 1789, promised that 'avec ma machine, je vous fais sauter la tête en un clin d'œil, et vous ne souffrez pas' (I'll take your head off with my machine in the twinkling of an eye, and without hurting you at all.) Strange that so kindly a motive should induce not merely terror, but *The* Terror; and that a public benefactor acting (as his funeral oration declared) from 'philosophical motives' should so bitterly regret that the public insisted on baptizing his machine with his name!

The National Assembly was at first hesitant to share the Doctor's enthusiasm; his proposals were referred to the *Comité de Législation*, and it was not until 1791 that the Committee empowered him to study the mechanical details and construct a prototype. Nor was the Committee disposed to be extravagant in its experiment; and when the carpenter Guedon who was responsible for the 'furniture of justice', showed a conservative prejudice against the new-fangled machine, and presented an estimate of 5,660 livres for building it, his offer was refused. A German carpenter named Schmidt made a tender of 305 francs, and his enterprise was soon rewarded with wholesale orders.

With proper humanitarian and philosophical spirit, the prototype was first tried on live sheep and then on five dead bodies before being put into service. On 20 March 1792 it was formally adopted, and on 25 April the journalist Duplau was able to record with quiet satisfaction: 'Yesterday they tried out the little *Louison*, and cut off a head.' It was first christened *Louison* or *Louisette*, and only later by the voice of the people *Madame Guillotine*.

Its success was immediate, and in 1793 it was ordained that it should be set up permanently on the *Place de la Révolution* (except for the knife which the executioner was to remove after each session, for safety's sake). Moreover, wherever the Revolution went, the guillotine went too, moving in with the armies and the first administrative personnel, the sign and safeguard of progress. At Moulins they placed above it the inscription: 'Tirans, aristocrates, affameurs du peuple, tremblez, je suis en permanence.' (Tremble tyrants, aristocrats, and oppressors: I am here to stay.)

The people were not always grateful; even in 1793 a voice could be raised in the National Assembly – that of Champein-Aubin – protesting and demanding the destruction of the guillotine. Strange that the inhabitants of the Place de la Révolution should not have been sensible of the honour done them, and should have demanded the removal of the instrument of progress, the chief support of liberty, from among them, on the grounds that it constituted a public nuisance – particularly because of the stench and stain of blood and the perpetual uproar of the crowds. Yet so it was; it had to be moved, and a great pit dug beneath it to drain away the blood and the water with which it was cleansed.

The Terror is over, but the guillotine remains in all its beauty and simplicity; its critics remain also, still vocal and still ineffective. Firmly it stands on the cross-pieces that make its base, with the two supports held together at the top by the *chapeau*, and under it the great triangular steel knife weighted to sixty kilos with lead, which makes its descent in three quarters of a second. The victim's body is placed on the plat-

form; the platform rolls forward; his neck lies neatly in the bottom half of the *lunette* (the monocle, if you like); the top half of the lunette, released by a spring, clicks over like a pillory to hold everything in place; the knife descends; the head rolls into the basket; and justice has been done. (See also *Gallows*.)

ILLUSTRATION: Page 121.

'The black dragon lays eggs'

The GUN in its larger sizes goes back to machines which could hurl heavy missiles at an enemy. Such contrivances were employed by the Greeks and the Romans, and were common in medieval Europe until gunpowder came into use as a propellant. Stone-throwing machines were known in China in 707 B.C. In the West the ballista and its variants worked by the propelling force of torsion and were derived from the bow (q.v.); whereas the mangonel and the trebuchet worked by weighted counterpoise. Projectiles were diverse, ranging from stones to combustibles (and on one occasion at least a hive of bees). In China, fire catapults made in A.D. 1000 hurled incendiary projectiles containing gunpowder, which had been developed in the previous century. In 1231 Chinese catapults hurled a pitcher-shaped explosive shell or bomb, filled with gunpowder, and called in Chinese records the 'heaven-shaking thunder-bomb'; and in 1259 the Chinese were at last making a barrelled gun of bamboo, the *t'u huo ch'iang*, or 'rushing-out-fire gun', from which bullets were propelled by gunpowder, and by the last thirty or so years of the thirteenth century guns with metal barrels were first being made in China. The earliest examples to survive belong to the fifties of the fourteenth century. Somewhere about a century later Chang Hsien wrote a poem on the 'iron explosive', clearly referring to gunpowder and artillery:

The black dragon lays eggs big as a peck.
Crack goes the egg, the dragon soars away, the spirit of
    thunder departs.
First it leaps up; light follows; the lightning flash reddens;
The thunderbolt makes a single burst, and the earth is
    cloven in two.

Between the first Chinese cannon made of metal and the first European cannon there appears to be a gap of fifty to seventy years, gunpowder having been applied to artillery in Europe during the first half of the fourteenth century. Cast perhaps by the bell-founders, the first western guns seem to have been made somewhat bottle-shaped with a wide mouth. But owing to the difficulties in the casting technique the first effective cannon were probably those which were built up of a number of wrought-iron bars longitudinally forged into a tube; iron hoops were then shrunk over the tube to make it stronger. These early wrought-iron cannon, which threw a stone shot, were not muzzle-loaders. The breech was arranged to accommodate a separate chamber, which was charged, then firmly wedged between the barrel and a stout block at the rear end of the wooden bed to which the gun was lashed. The largest of the wrought-iron guns, the bombards, were too much for the fortifications of the medieval castle (q.v.), which they rendered obsolete. A surviving example is famous Mons Meg at Edinburgh Castle, which was made before 1479; this weighs five tons and has a length of thirteen feet and two inches, and a calibre of nineteen and a half inches. Some bombards had a breech chamber which screwed into the barrel.

Cannon-founders rapidly improved their methods. Breech-loading bombards of great size were cast in bronze in the fifteenth century, and by 1500 the manufacture of bronze muzzle-loading guns cast in a single piece had been perfected in Germany and Flanders. About 1450 trunnions were introduced – that is to say, projections on each side of the gun to support it on its carriage. These made elevation and movement easier. Muzzle-loading cannon of cast iron were introduced into England in 1543, when foreign craftsmen were employed by Henry VIII to establish the renowned gun foundries of the Sussex Weald, where all was ready to hand. These iron weapons slowly replaced bronze and brass guns, and by the early years of the eighteenth century cast-iron cannon were the principal ordnance on land and sea.

The picturesque names of the sixteenth century gave way towards the end of the seventeenth century to a more prosaic method of classification based on the weight of the relative cannon ball;

so appeared the 3, 6, 9, 12, 18, 24, 32 and 42-pounder guns, which with minor additions were standard until the nineteenth century. The Carronade, which derives its name from the town of Carron in Scotland, where it was first made, became general in the naval and merchant services in 1780. This short-barrelled gun of relatively large bore designed for close engagements at sea ranged in size from a 12- to a 68-pounder, weighed much less than the corresponding cannon, and took a lighter charge of powder. The middle of the nineteenth century saw considerable advance in gun design, the re-introduction of breech-loading, the successful rifling of the cannon barrels by spiral grooves and the early use of cast steel, preparing the way for the complexities of modern artillery.

Small arms lagged a little in the wake of ordnance, because the bow, which had been supreme as a long-distance weapon for so many thousands of years, was not ousted all at once, keeping its military value in the West until the sixteenth century, and later still in the Far East. The crossbow, invented in the classical world and re-introduced in medieval Europe by about A.D. 1100, can be called one of the parents of the new hand gun, which was developed and had been tested in action early in the fifteenth century. Mounted on a stock, made so that it could be triggered, and aimed and discharged from the shoulder, the crossbow was the hand version of the ballista. Since it was looked upon as an infamous weapon, its use, except against infidels, was forbidden by Pope Innocent II in 1139, though without effect (compare our own attitude to chemical warfare or the atom bomb). Even when fire-arms proved themselves, crossbow and bow still had the advantage of silent weapons. Thus a variant of the crossbow, the stone-bow or prodd, designed to shoot stone or lead pellets survived as a sporting weapon until the nineteenth century.

In China hand-guns were being manufactured by 1380. In Europe the hand-gun of the fifteenth century was simply an iron tube, mounted on a stock and supported by a stand. It was fired by applying a lighted match, *i.e.* a cord impregnated with saltpetre, to the touch-hole. Late in the fifteenth century the hand-gun was superseded by the gun fitted and fired with a matchlock; the match, instead of being held in the hand, was clipped to a movable arm actuated by a trigger. Cheap and easy to make, the matchlock continued popular till the latter part of the seventeenth century, although, about 1500, German gunsmiths had produced the more complex wheel-lock, which in principle is like the modern pocket lighter. It consisted of a grooved steel wheel, driven by a spring, which revolved against a piece of iron pyrites, the sparks igniting the priming powder.

The gun needed to be quick and easy and flexible in its handling, and light enough to require no stand; it had, in this sense, to regain the easy handling which had marked the bow for so many thousands of years as a weapon of war or of the chase; such considerations controlled the evolution of fire-arms. In the sixteenth century ignition by flint and steel was introduced with the snaphance, out of which the flintlock developed c. 1600. The powder in its pan at the touch-hole needed to be kept dry. The flint-lock was therefore improved by fitting a pan cover to the pivoted hammer (the steel). When the gun was fired, the flint striking the hammer knocked it back and exposed the powder to the sparks. After two centuries the Scottish clergyman Alexander Forsyth went further and devised (c. 1807) the percussion-lock, in which the charge in the barrel was fired by a detonating powder, itself exploded by the hammer.

Loading remained slow and cumbersome, since fire-arms were muzzle-loading, and powder and ball had to be forced down the barrel with a ramrod. Breech-loading mechanisms were therefore developed in the first half of the nineteenth century. The needle gun of 1841 was the first gun to have ball, charge and means of ignition combined in a single cartridge. The gun had now become a flexible weapon to be refined in detail and varied in type and improved in performance through the next hundred years, from the first rifled breech-loaders to the rapid-firing automatic rifles of our day.

The smallest form of fire-arm, the pistol, first came into being about 1520, and since it was easily discharged with one hand, it was much used by cavalry. In England the carrying of pocket pistols was forbidden by James I in 1616. The various types of pistols were fitted with wheel-lock, snaphance, flintlock and percussion mechanisms. The principle of revolving cartridge chambers to increase rapidity of fire was known as early as the seventeenth century.

One other point should be held in mind. The *t'u huo ch'iang*, or bamboo 'rushing-out-fire' gun of 1259, had done more than introduce to the world a series of killing weapons, large and small. The gun propels its bullet or shell by the rapid use of pressure when a fuel is ignited in its cylinder; which is also no more and no less than the principle of the internal-combustion engine of the nineteenth century. (See also *Gunpowder, Fireworks, Rocket, Bow and Arrow, Blow-gun, Sling*.)

ILLUSTRATION: Page 363.

Charcoal, sulphur and Snow of China

GUNPOWDER, the oldest explosive, developed first in China, is an intimate mixture of charcoal, sulphur and saltpetre (potassium nitrate). Like all explosives, it contains enough oxygen (in the potassium nitrate) to ensure complete combustion without the aid of oxygen from the air. The usual proportions by weight are: charcoal 15 per cent, sulphur 10 per cent, and potassium nitrate 75 per cent, although these proportions may be varied for different purposes.

Incendiary compositions known in ancient times probably contained gums, pitch, oil and sulphur, and continued in use into the Middle Ages. In the West saltpetre is first mentioned in connection with fire-making in the *Liber Ignium*, the Book of Fires for Burning Enemies, attributed to Marcus Graecus, which dates probably from the thirteenth century A.D. This book contains a collection of fire recipes, many of which must have been known for a very long time before, and includes many similar to the recipes of antiquity. However, Marcus Graecus also describes 'flying fire' for making 'thunder' which has some resemblance to gunpowder. It is often said that Roger Bacon invented gunpowder, but his references to it in *De mirabile potestate Artis et Naturae* (1242) show that he was quoting what was common knowledge amongst informed people. The only gunpowder recipe he gives occurs in a passage which some scholars consider not to be authentic; in any case it yields an inferior product.

There can be little doubt that knowledge of gunpowder reached Europe from the Far East, and that gunpowder originated in China, where, in contrast to Europe, there were supplies of natural saltpetre. The Chinese were in possession of gunpowder by the time of the Sung Dynasty in the tenth century A.D. In 969 military use was made of fire-arrows tipped with gunpowder; gunpowder projectiles thrown by catapult were known in A.D. 1000, explosive grenades were invented in 1231, and bamboo guns were made in 1259. The knowledge of gunpowder may have been transmitted to Europe by the Mongols, or else by way of the Arabs, whose name for saltpetre means 'Snow of China'. (See two papers in Isis, 'The Early Development of Firearms in China', by L. C. Goodrich and Fêng Chia-shêng, No. 104, 1946; and 'The Invention and Use of Gunpowder in China', by Wang Ling, Nos. 109 and 110, 1947.)

In Europe, as in China, gunpowder may first have been used for incendiary qualities; but from the time of the European development of the gun in the early fourteenth century, the propellant properties of gunpowder overshadowed all others. The system of society which had depended on the impregnability of the medieval castle and on the military supremacy of the mounted knight now found in gunpowder not only the means of a transformation of the arts of war, but also the instrument of its own overthrow.

Gunpowder is one of the most dangerous explosives to handle. Even in a modern arsenal stricter precautions apply to its manipulation than to that of modern explosives of vastly greater power. The earliest method of making gunpowder by the simple dry grinding of the components was excessively unsafe. The dry mixture quickly separated out into its constituents on shaking in transport, so that the early artilleryman had to mix his powder on the battlefield. It is small wonder that he was enjoined to live a sober and godly life, for he never knew when his next moment might not be his last.

This dry-mixed 'serpentine' powder (so called from a serpentine or S-shaped lever mechanism characteristic of the earliest small-arms weapon capable of being accurately aimed and fired) was very difficult to pack correctly in the gun for reliable ignition. The fifteenth century saw a great improvement: the introduction of wet grinding. This gave a caked product which could be broken up to form 'corned' powder, in pieces of the right size for use in a particular size of weapon. The free space between the grains promoted smoother ignition throughout the charge. Since that time gunpowder has never been used as a powder properly so called, but always in grains of greater or less size.

Towards the end of the eighteenth century gunpowder began to be used in another way: as a bursting charge for shells. A hollow, generally spherical, projectile was fitted with a gunpowder time-fuse, and was filled with gunpowder. The fuse was placed towards the muzzle of the gun and was ignited by the hot gases from the propellant explosion rushing round through the gap between projectile and gun-barrel wall. The length of fuse was adjusted so that the shell burst as it hit its target.

The nineteenth century saw the introduction of big rifled artillery. The gunpowders then in use burned to completion too quickly, so that the projectile received a sudden excessive blow instead of a steady push all the way up the barrel. Guns also could not be designed to withstand this effect, so many experiments were carried out with the aim of altering the progress of the combustion of the powder. General Rodman in the United States was particularly successful in his solution, which was to make the 'powder' in the form of quite large pieces of regular form (e.g. a hexagonal prism) perforated from end to end. In such a structure combustion proceeded from inside as well as out, so that the maximum combustible area was presented towards the end of the explosion instead of at the beginning, as with conventional grains. This gave much improved control of the pressure on the gun.

For hundreds of years the manufacture of gunpowder bore very hard on many people. Charcoal and sulphur were easy enough to come by, but saltpetre could usually be had only from soil which had been much trodden by cattle and impregnated with their excreta. Governments all over Europe made harsh imposts to obtain saltpetre, often refusing to accept money payments in lieu. Thus in eighteenth-century France the saltpetre prospectors had the right to dig anywhere and the right of free lodging and conveyance. The great French chemist, Lavoisier, did valuable work by scientific examination of the natural sources and by the development of artificial saltpetre beds.

In the nineteenth century the opening up of the Chilean saltpetre beds (which provided vast quantities of sodium nitrate which could easily be converted into potassium nitrate) lifted a grievous burden from many rural communities all over Europe. Strict saltpetre collection laws lasted longest in Sweden, the country of Alfred Nobel, the man who did most to overthrow the supremacy of gunpowder.

By 1870 Nobel had perfected his nitroglycerine and dynamite and these began to be used in appreciable quantities as demolition explosives. In 1884 Vieille produced a new propellant, consisting of gelatinized guncotton (nitrocellulose) which was virtually smokeless. One of the chief defects of gunpowder had always been the solid products of combustion which not only fouled the barrels of guns, to the constant exasperation of their designers, but also produced clouds of smoke. In a close-fought engagement it would become nearly or quite impossible to distinguish friend from foe. The new smokeless powders changed not only the means of battle but also its aspect.

Finally gunpowder was superseded as a bursting charge. The finest high-explosive to be used in projectiles was picric acid (trinitrophenol), employed by the French under the name 'melinite' and then by the British under the name 'lyddite'. T.N.T. (trinitrotoluene) and the rest were to follow, though these new explosives were not completely adapted to military ends until after the Spanish-American War of 1898, the last war to be fought entirely with gunpowder. In the First World War gunpowder had only a secondary rôle to play.

Nevertheless there are still military and civil purposes for which gunpowder is either preferable or indispensable, as for example in fuses and priming charges and in some demolition charges. So great, indeed, has been the general increase in the use of explosives that in spite of its relative

decline in importance more of this ancient Chinese composition is manufactured now than ever before. (See also *Fireworks, Gun, Blowgun.*)

H

Poke, pocket, pouch, purse, handbag

HANDBAGS and purses remind us that though things sometimes change their name without changing their nature, it is even more confusing when they do exactly the opposite. We think we know what a pocket is, but the word 'pocket' was in use long before anyone had had the brilliant idea of sewing pockets into clothes. Originally a pocket was a little bag, just as a 'poke' was a big bag ('a pig in a poke'). The little bag (the pocket) was used to carry small objects that a man might want to have with him. It was usually made of leather, and attached to the girdle. It might contain a pomander, or flint and steel for making fire, or money.

In another word it was a purse, a word not in the Middle Ages confined to a receptacle only for money. Chaucer in the fourteenth century describes the leather purse worn at the girdle of the Wife of Bath, and no doubt it served her as a general handbag. Such purses or pouches hung down by thongs, which could be cut from behind – hence the term 'cutpurse' – by the clever thief, as in Bruegel's painting, the *Perfidy of the World*. In the fifteenth century men and women had worn them, sometimes ornamented with gold or embroidery. In the sixteenth century – as Bruegel's pictures show – they were universally worn, usually in the form of a flat bag, the mouth of which was pulled in by tasselled strings. An English inventory of 1510 speaks of 'a tawny bag with tassels of gold and strings of green silk'; and similar objects can be seen in Holbein's portraits of the courtiers of Henry VIII. Towards the end of the century women sometimes wore a purse underneath the skirt.

When breeches replaced trunk hose in the early years of the seventeenth century, it became possible to insert the pocket into the breeches themselves, but it was not until about 1670 that the new style of male dress, consisting of a skirted coat and waistcoat, inaugurated the reign of pockets. Henceforward the male pouch disappears from history. The purse, generally of netted silk, becomes quite a small object easily carried inside the pocket.

In the eighteenth century, indeed, it might have seemed that the pouch had disappeared for ever both for men and women; but shortly after the French Revolution women's clothes became so flimsy that it was impossible for them to contain a pocket, and women's pouches reappeared under the name of reticules, or, as they were sometimes called, 'ridicules'. It was not unusual to wear, under the petticoat, a pair of large pockets attached to each other by tape which tied round the waist. But this was a clumsy contrivance and fashionable ladies preferred to carry a small and elegant bag in the hand.

These were still in use in the late eighteen-thirties, but became less indispensable as skirts became more ample and were made of stiffer material. Even when dresses became somewhat tight in the eighties, the handbag still seems to have been something of a rarity; only to make a triumphant return in 1909–1910, with the advent of the hobble skirt. In such a skirt it was impossible to have any pockets, and very large handbags came into fashion, sometimes carried by absurdly long chains or strings. In the skimpy dresses of the nineteen-twenties a handbag was even more of a necessity, and it has remained in use to carry not only money and a handkerchief, but everything – lipstick, face-powder, mirror, cigarettes, lighter, keys, wallet, cheque-book, diary, letters. It seems unlikely that it can ever be dispensed with as an accessory of women's attire. Leather, and its imitations, has been the commonest material of handbags. Pigskin, snakeskin and crocodile skin make the more expensive bags. Plastic materials are becoming commoner, but generally they still imitate leather.

Blowing the nose

The **HANDKERCHIEF** for mopping the brow and wiping the nose is felt to be a necessity by most civilized people. The Romans are known to have used such a napkin made, as it still is, of linen, but when their Empire collapsed such refinements vanished for nearly a thousand years. The Anglo-Saxons had a 'swat-cloth' – *i.e.* sweat-cloth (Latin: *manipulus*) – and under the name of maniple a similar piece of material survived in the services of the Church, but its form became gradually altered until in the end it bore little resemblance to its cousin, the handkerchief. That the 'handkerchief was not in common use in the late Middle Ages is plain from ecclesiastical remonstrances against priests who blew their noses on their surplices and chasubles.

Early in the sixteenth century we begin to meet with handkerchiefs under that name, but their use was entirely confined to the upper classes. They were carried ostentatiously in the hand, and some of them were extremely rich. Henry VIII used 'handkerchers of Holland frynged with Venice gold, redd and white silk'; and he had others fringed with gold and silver. Among the gifts to Queen Mary Tudor, for New Year 1556, were 'six handkerchers edged with passamayne of golde and silke' presented by Mrs Penne, nurse to the late King Edward VI.

By the end of the century no fine lady or gentleman could be content without a handkerchief. We learn that 'Maydes and gentlewomen gave to their favourites, as tokens of their love, little handkerchiefs of about three or four inches square, wrought round with a button at each corner'. Some scholars have suggested that these buttons were, in fact, tassels, but their use was sufficiently general for 'handkerchief buttons' to be a street cry in London in the reign of Charles I. They are mentioned again as a prohibited import in the time of Charles II.

The seventeenth century is pre-eminently the time of lace (q.v.). Both men and women wore immense quantities at the throat and wrists, and even round the tops of boots. It would have been strange if handkerchiefs had not been influenced by the prevailing fashion. They were indeed surrounded by deep borders of lace and were sometimes extremely costly. When lost they were advertised for and rewards offered for their recovery. The *London Gazette* of December 1672 has the entry: 'Lost, a lawn pocket handkercher, with a broad hem, laced round with fine point lace, about four fingers broad, marked with an R in red silk.' The poorer classes, if they had handkerchiefs at all, had them made of coarser materials such as holland or calico.

In the eighteenth century the almost universal use of snuff offered many opportunities for the display of fine handkerchiefs, and their proper manipulation was considered a mark of breeding. In the nineteenth century the use of the handkerchief spread to all classes. The twentieth, after the First World War, saw a curious revival of the handkerchief as a decorative accessory. The breast pocket of men's suits was now made on the outside, and it was fashionable to show a protruding handkerchief which was sometimes coloured to match the tie. In this case another handkerchief – for use – was carried in another pocket.

In our time cloth handkerchiefs are giving way on the scores of economy and hygiene to soft paper handkerchiefs purchased in the packet and used only for colds in the nose.

'Within the hansom's dry recess'

The **HANSOM CAB** was intended to combine *privacy*, *comfort* and *safety*; key-words which (with *earnestness* and *high seriousness*) express the desires of Victorian England.

Joseph Aloysius Hansom invented a new carriage for a new London. Merchants no longer lived over their shops, but in the distant suburbs of Islington, Battersea, Fulham, and Streatham. The era of railways, of railway termini, of a division into 'City' and 'West End' was beginning; and matrons went shopping in this West End, in its Regent Street, or they took the children to Wyld's Globe in Leicester Square. In the West End young bloods finished the evening at Gatti's or Evans's Song and Supper Rooms, or

crossed the river to the Cobourg or the Surrey – for these and many other purposes, legitimate and illegitimate, a conveyance was needed. A four-wheeler – a 'growler' – might be more commodious for the children and the family luggage, even though the driver would not help with trunks ('I can't leave the hoss, m'm'). But for elegance and speed, as well as comfort and safety, the hansom had certainly the advantages.

But although he gave to the vehicle the immortality of his name, Joseph Aloysius Hansom, like other inventors, was denied material advantage; he claimed that he was promised £10,000, and never had a penny but for £300 paid him for managing the promoting company while it was in financial difficulties. Hansom was a curious character, who oddly recalls at the same time the father of George Eliot and the father of Charles Dickens. Like Robert Evans, he was a carpenter who bettered himself and rose to estate management; and in fact it was while managing the banking, coal-mining, and lands of Dempster Hemming that he invented his cab, and patented it in 1834 on his employer's recommendation. But the enterprises which he touched had a way of going wrong. Architecture was his other love; and Gothic and his Roman Catholic faith went together. For a year he was in partnership with Edward Welby Pugin, but they quarrelled. He built Birmingham Town Hall, but went bankrupt because he went bond for the builders. He parted in turn with his younger brother and his eldest son whom he had taken into partnership. He published *The Builder*, but soon abandoned it. And his cab had the same unsatisfactory fate.

The basic idea of his design was its suspended or 'cranked' axle which passed beneath the body and supported two enormous wheels, seven feet six inches high; the body itself was like an enormous packing case, almost square; and the driver's seat was high up in the front. There were two doors in front, on either side of the shafts. Hansom himself constructed the prototype in Leicestershire and drove it up to London.

While Hansom struggled with the financial difficulties of his backers, John Chapman, secretary of a rival company ('The Safety Cabriolet and Two-Wheeled Carriage Company') got to work and improved Hansom's design. He made the wheels smaller, lightened the body, and (most important of all) transferred the driver's seat to the back of the vehicle, thus giving it what we think of as the typical Hansom balance and line. Other improvements followed as the century went on; the clumsy cranked axle was abandoned for a straight axle running beneath the seat; the windows grew bigger; the wheels acquired rubber tyres.

Hansom's company (having bought out their rival, Chapman) put a fleet of fifty of the new vehicles on the road in 1836 with instantaneous success. But they could not protect their patents

He had left a crop of new problems for the Commissioner of Police of the Metropolis, who in 1853 had taken over the supervision of the Cab Acts. Cabbies had to be protected from 'bilking' passengers, and passengers from exorbitant drivers; distances from place to place had to be measured with a 'perambulator' (a wheel pushed by a handle, with an index that clicked up the miles), and fares tabulated; horses had to be watered and drivers fed; main streets kept clear of 'crawling' cabs in wait for fares; and special arrangements made for railway

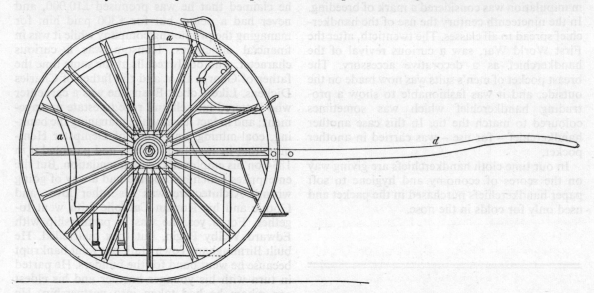

Fig. 13. Hansom's original cab.

or restrain their rivals. By 1896 there were 7,585 hansoms and 3,449 four-wheelers on the streets of London, and even noblemen like Lord Shrewsbury and Talbot and Lord Lonsdale were proud to be the proprietors of fleets of cabs. Meanwhile Hansom himself had given up the road and gone back to architecture in which, it is nice to know, he prospered at last. In 1875 he celebrated his golden wedding with children and grandchildren around him, happy in the knowledge that he had built (at St Walburge's, Preston) the highest spire since the Reformation; and that schools, colleges, convents, churches and mansions by him might be found even in the unexpected landscapes of Australia and South America.

stations. The traffic problems of London had arrived.

In the nineteen-twenties and the early thirties a few once elegant hansoms, turned shabby and drawn by rib-patterned nags, still picked up their fares around Piccadilly Circus, but by that time it was an antiquarian extravaganza to desert the motor taxi for this living fossil of Early and High Victorianism. The last hansom cab left the London streets after 1939. Sometimes a hansom nostalgically re-emerges in Brighton, or in the streets of Sydney, New South Wales. Many have been purchased to hire out to film-makers. But it is scarcely possible now to reconstruct for oneself the exact emotional situation of the young Thomas Hardy in a thunderstorm, in 'town', and in a hansom, as remembered by the middle-aged Thomas Hardy in 1893:

She wore a new terra-cotta dress,
And we stayed, because of the pelting storm,
Within the hansom's dry recess,
Though the horse had stopped; yea, motionless
　　We sat on, snug and warm.

Then the downpour ceased, to my sharp sad pain
And the glass that had screened our forms before
Flew up, and out she sprang to her door:
I should have kissed her if the rain
　　Had lasted a minute more.

ILLUSTRATION: Page 362.

The melodious harp

The **HARP**, says the Leckingfelde Proverb,* 'is an instrumente of swete melodye'; and this characteristic sweetness, scarcely changing in timbre through the centuries, has lulled man's passions and supported the recitation of his heroic deeds from the dawn of civilization. Except for the drum (q.v.), no instrument is of greater antiquity or has changed less; when the Assyrians greeted their homecoming warriors with music and the Sumerians diverted their guests, they did so upon an instrument that is nearly related to the smooth double-action pedal harp that graces our orchestras today.

The earliest harps of all possibly derived from the hunter's bow: the musical hum that followed the arrow's flight would suggest the use of the bow as an instrument, and the musical bow is found in Africa and in Mexico, with or without a gourd resonator to increase the sonority. This is, in effect, a one-stringed harp, stopped by hand like a violin to produce different notes. But the true harp has one string per note only; it was not until modern times that an ingenious mechanism allowed the strings to tighten and relax so that each obtains three notes. The second main characteristic of the harp is that its strings are set

* This poem on musical instruments dating from about 1516–1523 is painted on the roof and walls of the garret at New Lodge, Leckingfelde.

vertical to the sounding-board, unlike those of the zither, the lute and the harpsichord. Horizontal harps, played with the plectrum – a small piece of quill or bone – were well known in ancient times, and they exist as a marginal survival in Ireland; but it is the vertical harp that is the best known, and indeed the best, instrument.

Two slightly different versions were familiar to the ancients: the angular harp, in which two pieces of wood were set at right angles and the strings stretched across the hypotenuse; and the arched harp, the body of which curved gracefully from base to tip, with the strings stretched across as before. The absence of the modern forepillar, completing the triangle of the frame, meant that such harps must be of low tension, and so give a soft, gentle sound.

The harp was much loved by the Egyptians. The many tomb-paintings uncovered at Thebes and elsewhere give a clear impression of its appearance and use, and this is supplemented by the discovery of several actual instruments. This kind of harp was closely related to the Sumerian instrument, and was known in several sizes; the smaller earlier ones were generally played by a kneeling man; by the time of the New Kingdom some were large enough to hold nineteen strings and to require the player to stand up; while the three harps on the wall-paintings of the tomb of Rameses II are six or seven feet high, beautifully decorated with mosaic and paint. There is even enough evidence for an intelligent estimate of the tuning, which certainly differed radically from our diatonic system; of various suggestions the most plausible is that some form of pentatonic scale was used.

The simplicity of the idea of the harp makes it improbable that any one nation or culture was first in the field. The Babylonians were playing eleven-stringed harps by 2500 B.C. The Assyrians decorated their angular harps with tassels, and used a portable version about four feet high, which may have been strung with silk. Small ten-stringed harps prevailed all over the eastern end of the Mediterranean.

The use of the harp by the Greeks is well documented. Not only are there pictures showing harpists on vases, coins, murals and reliefs, but references in literature tell us something of the sound and of the general effect. Plato had some damping things to say about it – not only was it a foreign instrument, a toy of the Eastern barbarians, but its many strings gave it too wide a range of sensory pleasure. The more easy-going lyric poets hymned its pleasures, and a fifth-century vase shows a Muse playing one with evident enjoyment; she is seated, but she holds the harp in the Assyrian manner with one hand supporting the base.

In the British Isles the harp has been known from an early period, and it has long been associated with the Celts. Diodorus in the first century B.C. mentions a lyre-like instrument used by Celtic bards. The medieval Laws of Wales stated a man needed only three things – a chaste wife, a cushion for his chair and a harp – and Dante (1265–1321) in the *Divine Comedy* credits the Irish with a knowledge of the harp. Among the furniture of the Anglo-Saxon ship-burial of Sutton Hoo, now preserved in the British Museum, was a harp, together with its tuning key. A reconstruction of this harp has been made, and played. Chaucer's friar in *The Canterbury Tales* was adept with the harp:

> ... in his harping, when that he had songs,
> His eyen twinkled in his head aright,
> As doon the starres in the frosty night.

The consolidation of equal temperament by Bach brought with it a problem for the harp. No longer could it play modal or pentatonic tunes only, if it was to share in the development of music; but, on the other hand, if it was to have the range of a harpsichord, the number of strings required would be too great for the maker to set conveniently to the player's hand. One solution was to arrange the strings in two banks, another was to include a series of hooks, which, pressing against the strings, raised them by a semitone. From this latter system evolved the Pedal Harp, in which the player depresses seven pedals (one for each note of the octave) one, or two, degrees to raise each string a semitone or a tone. By 1782 Georges Cousineau was working at this system in Paris, but it was not until 1819 that the famous piano-maker Sebastian Erard finally patented his double-action harp, which still serves as the model for manufacturers.

ILLUSTRATION: Page 72.

Stonehenge, Woodhenge, and their fellows

HENGES are ritual monuments which may be called the oldest temples of Great Britain, 'henge' being a convenient though misbegotten name derived from Stonehenge, the world's most famous prehistoric monument.

The Stonehenge that we see grey and solid upon its grassy plain is a later product of building and rebuilding. It began with a circular ditch outside (diameter 320 feet), surrounding a circular bank, in turn surrounding a circle of wooden uprights, tree trunks, now represented by more than fifty round holes under the smooth springy turf. Within this triple circle and also in some of the post-holes cremation burials were made.

This primitive Stonehenge was erected by late neolithic people, early in the second millennium B.C., possibly in the seventeenth century. Charcoal out of one of the post-holes has been dated by the radio-carbon method to 1848 B.C. $\pm$ 275. Similar enclosures have been identified at Dorchester-on-Thames and at Cairnpapple in West Lothian. All contain cremation burials and have yielded pottery of a particular kind. Allied to them and also of the late neolithic period are several more enclosures including two discovered by air photography, at Arminghall near Norwich, a henge which had an oval of large oak pillars sunk seven feet into the ground, and 'Woodhenge', not far away from Stonehenge. Each wooden upright of the six concentric rings at Woodhenge is now marked by a stump of concrete. Within the sixth ring a child's skeleton with the skull split was carefully buried, presumably as a consecration sacrifice. Woodhenge may even have been roofed over.

The Beaker peoples, who had arrived in Britain between c. 1900 B.C. and 1800 B.C., adapted the Stonehenge of bank, ditch and wooden uprights to stone, and they built, or rebuilt, other henges, frequently using stone instead of wooden uprights. The ritual monument of Avebury in Wiltshire is one of their masterpieces, an enclosure of twenty-eight acres within a tall bank and an interior ditch, containing a great stone circle and two smaller circles. One should notice that the chalk plains and downs around Stonehenge and Avebury were grazed by sheep and cattle, which made the district the richest and most populated in prehistoric Britain.

Stonehenge, where the enclosed ground is less than two acres, these Beaker people of the Early Bronze Age appear to have refashioned about 1500 B.C., possibly under influence from Mycenae; they added the two inner circles of stone and the two horseshoes of stone. One circle and one horseshoe are of smaller stones transported from the Presely Mountains in Pembrokeshire. The giant stones with their lintels or cross-pieces are local sarsen from Wiltshire. On several stones

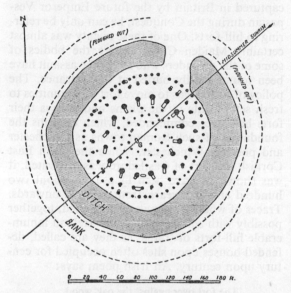

Fig. 14. Plan of Woodhenge.

ancient engraved outlines, including the outlines of Mycenaean daggers, have lately been discovered, the first of them having been noticed in the viewfinder of an archaeologist's camera.

Other ritual circles made by the Beaker people in the Early Bronze Age include the huge thirty-acre enclosure of Durrington Walls in Wiltshire, alongside Woodhenge, and the Knowlton Rings in Dorset. Here there are three circles with an outside bank and an inside ditch, the largest with a diameter of 750 feet. Inside one of the three stands the ruined tower and nave of a twelfth–sixteenth century church of brown stone, bowered in thorn bushes, as if an ancient pagan sanctity was later Christianized. Banked and ditched sanc-

tuaries of the henge type are not known outside Great Britain.

It is natural to ask what kind of religion these temples and enclosures served. One responsible archaeologist has risked a statement: 'Of the nature of this cult we can only guess by analogy that an open sanctuary is appropriate to a sky-god, and that some may have been planned in relation to a celestial phenomenon such as sunrise at the summer solstice.' Another says guardedly that 'in a general way midsummer and midwinter festivals belong to high latitudes where the sun's annual journey from north to south and back is conspicuous'. (See also *Barrows*.)

_____

'Once it was Bruidge's, it was Cathal's'

HILL-FORTS are the surviving defences, more or less circular, which were set up for the most part around ancient farms, villages or small towns. They are widely distributed. In Great Britain, often standing lonely and bare with green rampart and green ditch, or rampart and ditch grown over with blackthorn, they vary greatly in size and were the peculiar product of the Iron Age, starting with invaders from the Continent who began to arrive about 500 B.C. These 'Forts' continued to be built, the form changing and developing, as more and more Continental invaders were dislocated by the turmoil overseas and crossed the Channel to find a new home. The end of the hill-forts, generally speaking, came with the Roman conquest of Britain.

A hill-fort may be a little entrenchment, enclosing less than an acre, or it may be a great system of ditch and rampart enclosing a considerable acreage. At Ladle Hill in Hampshire a fort left unfinished by its builders gives some idea of how the work was undertaken. First of all a shallow trench was cut along the line to be followed by the ditch and bank. Then at several different points round the perimeter the builders began to delve out the V-shaped ditch and construct behind it with the upcast earth a steep-faced bank. Often ditches seem to have been more important

as a source of material for the bank than as defences in their own right. A fort on limestone
country at Chastleton in Oxfordshire has a
stone-built rampart and no ditch; at Chûn Castle
in Cornwall the massive granite defences are
combined only with shallow ditches. This hill-
fort was used by prehistoric tin-miners. Great
skill often went into building the rampart, loose
earth and rubble forming the core, and larger
stones cut from the bottom of the ditch strengthening the face. To bind the bank together successive tips of rubble were sometimes overlaid by
strata of turf. Stout timber uprights were set in
post-holes at regular intervals in the front of the
bank, and between them lengths of wattle fencing
held back the earth. The wooden palisade was
carried up to form a parapet, the top of the bank
becoming a rampart walk.

Building a large hill-fort of this kind was an
immense task. When the sixty-acre fort was constructed at Cissbury in Sussex, some 35,000 cubic
yards of chalk were quarried from the ditch and
about 10,000 timbers, each fifteen feet long, were
cut for the palisade. The fort builders naturally
took what the locality offered them in building
material. If they employed earth usually in the
Lowlands, in the Highland zones of Great Britain earth ramparts are often replaced by massive
dry-stone walls. One group of invaders who settled in parts of Scotland built stone-walled forts
of a very individual kind. The facing walls were
tied together by heavy timbers laid horizontally
at right angles to the face, and the spaces between them were filled with timbers and rubble.
Such a construction was easily fired and once
alight produced a very high temperature, fusing
together masses of stone. By accident or design
most of these Scottish forts were fired in this way,
and are known as 'Vitrified Forts'.

Over the centuries there were changes in pattern. At first a single bank and ditch were enough.
Later invaders built multiple defences with three
or four sets of ditch and bank. One reason for
this change was no doubt the use of the sling,
which has an effective range of about a hundred
yards on the level, making defences in great
depth essential. Huge hoards of sling-stones have
been found in one hill-fort, showing that besieged as well as besiegers used this weapon. As
the most vulnerable point, the entrance was also

elaborated from a mere entry over ditch and
through rampart. Later entrances were set askew,
or the ends of the rampart were turned inwards
to form a bottleneck. Or else outworks were built
completely masking the entrance; of which the
most elaborate version is at the dark-shadowed
Maiden Castle, outside Dorchester.

Some forts were not occupied all the time, but
were resorts in case of danger. Others, we know
from excavation, were permanently occupied;
and some of these were the nearest approach to
towns in prehistoric Britain. When the Roman
historian Suetonius speaks of the twenty towns
captured in Britain by the future Emperor Vespasian during the Conquest, he can only be referring to hill-forts. One of these twenty was almost
certainly Maiden Castle, where the bodies of
some of the defenders who fell in the assault have
been found hastily buried at the entrance. The
policy of Rome was to move fort communities to
fresh settlements in the plains and valleys their
forts had once commanded, which explains the
foundation of such Roman towns as Dorchester
and possibly Winchester. When the small East
Cornish hill-fort of Castledore was excavated, it
was shown to have been in use for about two
hundred and fifty years, from 200 B.C. onwards.
Traces of wooden huts were uncovered, together
possibly with small granaries. In Ireland innumerable hill-forts or 'raths' as they are called, defended houses upon sites often occupied for century upon century. An Irish poem says:

> The fort over against the oak wood,
> Once it was Bruidge's, it was Cathal's,
> It was Aed's, it was Ailill's,
> It was Conaing's, it was Cuiline's
> And it was Maelduin's:
> The fort remains after each in his turn ...

In Great Britain alone, to say nothing of the
rest of Europe, the number of hill-forts is very
great, and much has still to be learnt about them.
In their loneliness and silence they have never
failed to exert a fascination. Later generations
have concluded that such earthworks were the
handiwork of the Devil or the Giants or the
Fairies. Country people have sometimes believed
them to be hollow and to be full of great treasures of gold. The topographer and antiquary
John Leland in the sixteenth century wrote of the

great hill-fort of Dolbury in Somerset 'There is apon the tope of one of the Mendipe Hills a place ancampyd caulyd Dolbyn, famous to the People thus sayinge:

> If Dolbyri dyggyd ware
> Of Gold shud be the Share.'

(See also *Castle, Sling*.)

ILLUSTRATION: Page 23.

Horse brasses and the Evil Eye

HORSE BRASSES are the latest and probably the last amulets which were supposed to protect horses against evil influences. These round brass discs, about three inches in diameter, were fastened, either singly to the forehead of a cart-horse or several together to the martingale. Their designs vary, and include wheels, the sun, the lunar crescent, the eight-pointed star, crosses, hearts, acorns, horseshoes, etc. Some of these patterns, like the crescent and the eight-pointed star, derive from Moorish influence, whereas others, for instance the lion rampant, the fleur-de-lis, etc., are heraldic in origin.

The history of amulets for horses probably goes back to the days of their domestication. Assyrian reliefs show horses with bells attached. In the ancient Orient and in early Italy rattling metal plates, small bells, pendants in the form of ithyphallic men and hands with the fingers spread out were used, whereas, according to Joseph Wiesner (*Reiten und Fahren in Alteuropa und im Alten Orient*), few horse amulets from early Greece have been found. Professor Wiesner traces these types of amulet ultimately back to Shamanism in Central Asia, since the shamans used them for averting evil spirits.

In England horse brasses are not so old as horse bells; they date back only a few centuries, to the beginnings of the brass industry. Their main purpose was to avert the Evil Eye, a belief existing since times immemorial, which we find recorded in Babylonian texts. This belief implies that any object on which the Evil Eye falls would suffer grievous harm, disease and death among men and domestic animals. It is based upon the notion that a ray goes forth from the eye and can wound like a fierce arrow. Shakespeare still alludes to the conception that a man dying of the plague infects the onlooker, for he says in *Love's Labour's Lost*:

> Write 'Lord have mercy on us' on those threes;
> They are infected ...
> They have the plague, and caught it of your eyes.

An early Irish reference to the Evil Eye occurs in the Glossary compiled by Cormac, King of Munster, who died in A.D. 908. In an Irish legend we are told of the Cyclops Balor, whose one eye had become evil by poisonous fumes. His eyelid had to be raised with hooks by four men, and then one baleful glance was enough to enfeeble a whole army. Another Irish legend tells of the witch Cailb, who cast the Evil Eye on King Conaire and predicted his death as it came to pass. And indeed, during the reign of Queen Elizabeth, Irish witches were accused of causing disease among the cattle by the Evil Eye, and were executed for it.

Apart from witches, sorcerers and born *jettatori* (casters of the eye), it is believed that quite harmless people can be roused to casting an Evil Eye by anger, envy or jealousy. Among quick-tempered people – for instance, the Neapolitans – the fear of the Evil Eye is deeply rooted. Fifty years ago F. T. Elworthy collected much evidence for his book, *The Evil Eye*, in Naples and the surroundings; many Neapolitan amulets against the Evil Eye are in his collection, now housed at the County Museum at Taunton, in Somerset.

Two defences against the Evil Eye may be mentioned, both of them supposed to attract the attention of the *jettatore* so effectively that he cannot take his eye away and thus leaves the bearer unharmed.

1. Obscene gestures, among which the 'Fig-Hand' (*mano fica*) is best known; a hand clenched, with the thumb pointing downwards, between index and second finger.
2. Bright and shiny objects, such as red cloth, red coral and horse brasses.

Fig-Hands were cast in silver, or carved in coral and bone; and they were either openly displayed as pendants or carried in the pocket, sometimes in the form of a snuff box. But the gesture alone, whether made openly or secretly in the pocket, was considered to ward off the Evil Eye. In the writer's possession are two photographs as different as can be in time and place: one represents a German portrait, of the middle sixteenth century, of the botanist Hieronymus Bock, from the Odenwald. In his right hand he holds two differently coloured flowers of the same species, whilst with his left hand he makes the gesture of the 'fig-hand'. It would seem that Hieronymus Bock intended to cross – or already had crossed – two plants as well as making the evil-averting gesture. The other photograph was taken in 1936 in Shanghai. It shows an extremely worried-looking Chinese peasant making the 'fig-hand', as though he was scared of the photographer or the camera. Within recent years old countrymen in Ireland have flatly refused to have their photograph taken, in fear of evil consequences. It is also (see *Charms*) a very ancient belief that the likeness of a person can be misused in magic.

Elworthy stated that horses are supposed to be particularly vulnerable to the Evil Eye. A typical story from the Hebrides (Scotland) fifty years ago records that a man was ploughing, when a passer-by from Uist highly praised the two horses. Scarcely had the man from Uist gone on his way when both horses fell down as if dead, though they recovered later. No explanation is known for the special vulnerability of horses; it may be due to their spontaneous and often completely unaccountable behaviour. Suddenly a horse stumbles, it shies, it refuses to go on, it breaks out in sweat, etc.; so horses had to be especially protected against the Evil Eye. A small but particularly fine collection of horse trappings and horse brasses can be seen in the Curtis Museum at Alton, Hampshire. All the specimens were actually used by T. Parfitt, carter to the late Marquess of Winchester. Inferior horse brasses are still being made for arty-crafty ornaments. (See also *Amulet*.)

ILLUSTRATION: Page 260.

Sands of life and time

The **HOUR-GLASS** or sand-glass is a device for measuring an interval of time, in contrast to the clock, which divides the day.

The origin of it is unknown. Possibly it was first made after the manufacture of glass had been re-introduced to the West in the thirteenth century, and it may have been adapted from the water-clock of antiquity, in which water flowed from a bowl through a small orifice in a known time. Paintings of St Jerome by Antonio del Fiore (1430) and the German artist Petrus Christus (1442) show hour-glasses; which are also symbolical properties in engravings by Albrecht Dürer (1471–1528). They may well have developed, like the turret clock, under monastic influence.

Lambeth parish church was given a new pulpit with an hour-glass in 1522. The mathematician and shipwright William Bourne mentions the log-glass in his *Inventions and Devices* (1577). This was used with a log-line to estimate a ship's speed, and continued in use for centuries. Hour-glasses rapidly became one of the symbolic adjuncts of Father Time, and the running sand sententiously equipped the language with metaphors.

Three distinct types were made. The earliest was fashioned of two similar open-necked pear-shaped bulbs of glass. The flow of sand was determined by a hole in a thin piece of pierced brass foil, which was inserted between the two bulbs before they were joined with plaster or wax and a binding of thread. But in this type the joint would work loose and the sand would escape. Damp weather, moreover, caused stoppages.

Towards the end of the seventeenth century a new form appeared. The bulbs were now blown and drawn in one piece, but the glass-blower could not always control the size of the orifice between the bulbs, and in some such sand-glasses the orifice was ground to about an eighth of an inch diameter, and a pierced piece of copper foil was pressed into position, via the filling hole left at the base of one bulb. The hole was sealed by a cloth-covered cork, but damp weather still proved troublesome, and the sand-glass reached its ultimate form early in the nineteenth century; the copper foil disappeared, the glass-blower inserted the sand, drew out the orifice between the bulbs with a proper exactitude, and sealed the second bulb, thus contriving an air-tight vessel.

Sizes varied from two-feet-tall, two-hour glasses used for timing watches on board ship to the three-inch one-hour pocket glass. The most popular time-periods were one hour, half an hour and a quarter of an hour, glasses for a special purpose including the fourteen-second and twenty-eight-second log-glasses, a quarter-of-a-minute pulse-glass used by physicians, a four-stage tea-taster's glass, each stage filling or emptying in one minute, for timing the infusion of tea, and an alarm-glass, mounted in such a manner that at a pre-set time a bell rang. Sets of four sermon-glasses were common: the periods were a quarter, a half, three-quarters of an hour and an hour, and the glasses were mounted on the pulpit in ornate metal cages on swivel stands so that they could be turned upside down. Queen Victoria caused the Royal Chapel to be furnished with an eighteen-minute glass.

The filling was not always sand. Finely powdered and dried egg-shell, fine emery powder, tin dust and lead dust were all used sometimes in an effort to ensure smooth running. As clocks and watches developed into tolerably exact time-keepers, the sand-glass was less needed; and by the eighteenth century it was only maintaining its dignity in church. However, small sand-glasses are by no means obsolete. They are familiar, for example, as domestic egg-timers, and a component of tyre-mending apparatus in garages. (See also *Clock*).

ILLUSTRATION: Page 359.

The dwellings of man

The **HOUSE**, as a thing which man has constructed, goes back far beyond bricks and mortar, and possibly began (in some districts at any rate) as an artificially constructed cave. Palaeolithic man was a cave-dweller, but not so everywhere; and recent finds prove that he can no longer be contemptuously dismissed from architectural discussion as incapable of constructing a home of his own. Pits have been excavated in south Russia and Schleswig-Holstein, the edges of which were marked by rocks and heavy bones of the great mammoth. These are thought to have been placed there to hold down the edges of a skin tent – the predecessor of the North American tepee, a form of home or house well adapted to the temporary accommodation of hunters who were always on the move. On limestone hills among modern vineyards at Dolní Věstonice in Czecho-slovakia two kinds of house, some 25,000 years old have been excavated since the Second World War. One was rather shelter or wind-break than building, a floor prepared with limestone grit, without a roof, probably protected from the wind or driving rain by hides. The other was a hut containing a crude kiln in which pottery pellets and figures had been fired. The hut had a circular wall of clay and limestone grit; upright and oblique posts had supported a roof, possibly of branches, earth, hides and turf, weighed down with mammoth bones.

Remains of temporary encampments have been found on the shores of the Baltic and North Sea, dating from the mesolithic period, 8000–2500 B.C. These are floors of bark and brushwood, laid on damp ground as close as possible to the wild food supply of the swamps and the sea-shore. There is no sign of any structure which could have supported a roof. Northern Europe was then becoming warmer with the end of the Ice Age, and mesolithic man seems to have been more concerned with protection from damp ground than with protection from rain. Also some mesolithic 'pit-dwellings' have come to light at dry, inland sites where wood has not been preserved. At Farnham, in Surrey, holes left by the decay of wooden posts were found outside shallow pits, as if a hurdle screen had been erected as shelter from the wind. Simple 'wind-breaks' of this kind are still found today among peoples at a low stage of cultural development.

Turves have been – and still are – utilized for building, even by people who could use more durable material. The Romans used turves to build the twenty-foot-wide western stretch of Hadrian's Wall on the Solway flats, admittedly only to save the transport of stone from a distance. Turf-built houses were erected till recent times in north-east

Holland. The thick walls were raised entirely of sods, while the ridged turf roof rested upon beams of pine, and sloped down to the ground on either side; the grass growing on the roof made the house part of its surroundings. In the far north, Iceland has had turf-roofed houses since the saga age. A man's enemies came to seek him out in such an Icelandic house where the roof reached to the ground, and to lull his suspicions one of them plucked the grass growing out of the turves to imitate the everyday sound of grazing cattle. Turf has now been replaced usually by galvanized iron, but the turf-roof was well fitted to withstand the fierce wind that cut across the Icelandic landscape. In Holland ground-plans identical with the plan of the modern turf-house or *pleggenhut* are known from prehistoric times; there is no conclusive evidence to affirm their antiquity, but prehistoric man would hardly have neglected such a material, so solid and easily won.

Turves prehistoric man probably used, stone he certainly dressed as a building material, especially under the stimulus of religion. To mention only the most famous examples, the standing stones of the Avebury Circle are roughly dressed, and are forerunners of the huge dressed trilithons of Stonehenge. Both show what early man could do with his stone mauls. Neolithic man used stone for house-building and tomb-building, no doubt employing as often as he could surface stone which had been split by weathering. But he could also have quarried it to some degree, to judge by the methods used today in parts of Africa. There the rock is thoroughly heated with fires, and it splits when cold water is thrown over it. 'Fire-setting' of this kind was employed by prehistoric copper-miners in Austria (see *Mines*). In the western parts of the British Isles and on the wolds in the east, where they have not been destroyed by later farming, ancient 'hut circles' have survived. These are the lower courses of walls built without mortar, much like modern field walls. The small round huts of Dartmoor, with their hearths and cooking-places, may have been roofed by turves supported on stout branches, the lower ends of which rested on the low stone walls.

In the Orkneys a late neolithic settlement has been excavated at Skara Brae. The huts of this settlement were square, with rounded corners; the walls were made of unmortared flat slabs of local stone, and the roofs, which again were probably made of turf, were supported on whale bones, which replaced wood in this treeless region. Covered passages linked hut to hut, and the whole village was smothered with rubbish, presumably tipped over the houses for additional protection from the wind.

In the neolithic age, the palaeolithic technique of 'grinding and polishing' bone was applied to rock. Thus igneous rock was brought into man's tool-bag: using 'polished' stone axes, which were more durable than brittle axes and flint, neolithic man began the deforestation of Europe; the timber he felled to make clearings for his plots he now used in house building. Remains of rectangular neolithic farmhouses have been preserved from many parts of Europe. Some house plans have been recovered from the evidence of post-holes; the butts of the wall-posts and the wooden floors have also been preserved in some localities in which they were waterlogged. At Aichbühl, on the Federsee, in Germany, the early farmers built rectangular wooden structures, perhaps the first in Europe to deserve the name of 'house'. The walls enclosed an area of thirty-three by eighteen and a half feet, which was covered with a wooden floor. This extended into a forecourt at one end of the house. The walls were made by standing split logs, flat side innermost, side by side in a trench. Inside the house an internal wall screened off the kitchen with its hearth and clay oven from the main living-room. In appearance the house must have had something of the look of an English timber-framed and thatched barn.

A separate kitchen was also a feature of the oldest wooden houses of which traces have been discovered in the British Isles. At Haldon Hill, in Devonshire, the rectangular walls of the house were marked by post-holes, and two posts had held up the roof in the centre. The stones that enclosed the wall-posts were probably the foundations of a wall of turf or wattle, no remains of which had survived. The walls of a neolithic house at Lough Gur in Ireland were constructed in much the same way, though the house was more elaborate inside. Within the stone foundations of the walls was a framework of posts, and two rows of posts ran the whole length of the house, dividing it into three parts. Wattle screens would have allowed the house to be sub-divided into several rooms, as well as a kitchen and living-room.

Internal posts were a feature of the wooden 'aisled round house' built by the Celts in Iron Age Britain in the centuries after 500 B.C. Remains of these houses have been found at many British sites. The homestead excavated at Little Woodbury, in Wiltshire, was forty-eight feet in diameter, and shows the typical 'aisle' between the inner and outer walls. Around the hearth were four stout posts, which took the weight of the roof at the centre of the house. The roof was probably made of turves, and sloped right down to the ground, giving this type of house the appearance of a giant cone.

A study of the plans of ancient houses provides some evidence of agricultural diffusion. Farming spread into the Mediterranean from the East, and with it spread what may be described as the ancestor of the farmhouse. The Mesopotamian man had none of the natural building materials which lay so ready to hand in northern Europe. The fertile soil had been deposited by silt-laden rivers, so that neither stone nor trees were to be found. Having nothing but mud to work with, the first farmers in Mesopotamia used it to make the first bricks. The use of sun-dried bricks spread westward with farming into Crete, the outpost of Europe, where the first European farming settlements are to be found, at Knossos, below the Bronze Age palace of Minos. To judge by the ground-plan of these rectangular houses and by a mosaic found at Knossos, the roofs were flat, as they had been further east, where the flat roof helped in the collection of precious rain-water. By contrast, in most parts of Europe the early farmers had too much and not too little rain, and so developed houses with the ridged roof familiar into our own day.

Even with the spread of modern building materials and techniques, the use of natural materials, including turf, timber, stone, thatch (which goes back to the neolithic period, and in the form of straw-thatching is dependent upon farming), mud and clay, has continued into the present, although the older forms of dwelling are vanishing gradually from the landscape into the folk museum. In the meantime it is curious to see how habit dies hard, and dies looking backward, the builder so often using the resources of modern technology to preserve outmoded forms, as in neo-Georgian, or mock Tudor. Still more curious to see in parts of France, Spain, North Africa and the Canary Isles are cave houses dug into the rock, echoing, though in modern shape with windows, doors and chimneys, sewing machines and iron bedsteads, the house habit of palaeolithic man in his caves or cave shelters 20,000 years ago.

ILLUSTRATION: Pages 172 and 173.

I

Ink for writing

INK, a term which comes to us through the Old French *enque*, derives from the late Greek *enkauston* and late Latin *incaustum*, which was the name of the Tyrian purple ink used by Byzantine emperors for their signatures.

The oldest form of ink known is carbon ink, employed in Egypt from the late fourth millennium B.C., and very simply prepared by suspending carbon, such as soot scraped from cooking-vessels or carbon prepared from charcoal, in a sticky solution of water and gum. Egyptian ink of this kind was made in small cakes, like the cakes of modern watercolour. Egyptian palettes with fragments of ink-cakes have survived. Chinese ink, another carbon ink, was also a very early invention, ascribed by tradition to T'ien Chu in the early second millennium B.C.; another tradition ascribes it to the Koreans, who employed carbon ink from at least 600 B.C. The ancient Hebrews also appear to have used carbon ink, which is probably the meaning of the *deyô* mentioned in Jeremiah xxxvi, 18. Modern scholars have suggested that the Hebrews used carbon inks for their sacred writings, and a mixed iron-carbon ink for everyday purposes. In Greek, carbon ink was known as *melan graphikon*, and in Latin as *atramentum librarium* or *atramentum scriptorium*.

The Greeks and Romans wrote with it on papyrus, and made it usually of soot from pitch-pine, or *taeda*, mixed with gum, and sometimes with sepia, from the cuttle-fish (pine soot, with lamp-black from oil of sesame, was also a chief ingredient of Chinese and Japanese carbon ink). This classical ink was much more unctuous than the writing ink we use today, resembling rather the modern printer's ink. Some vinegar was added to make it more permanent, and also wormwood, which was thought to be effective against mice. Another variety, *atramentum tectorium* or *pictorium*, was mainly used by artists.

Carbon inks continued to be used, and are still used, in the Near East – for instance by the Copts for their sacred books, and by the Persians. But in the West, in the Middle Ages, writing with the chemically complex ink compounded of iron salts and galls became more or less universal. The ingredients are galls, copperas (*i.e.* sulphate of iron) and gum arabic, the decoction forming a bluish substance, which exposure to the air converts to black. No doubt it was the use of parchment as a writing material which led to the development of iron-gall ink, since parchment will not hold carbon inks; they wear off, or wash off.

Yet where or when this ink originated is not so certain. A medieval date used to be given, some scholars assigning iron-gall inks to A.D. 1126, which is far too late. For one thing iron-gall ink is actually described in the eleventh century. Moreover out of twelve early vellum manuscripts in the British Museum which were examined in 1935, nine proved to have been written with iron ink, among them both the famous *Codex Sinaiticus* of the fourth century A.D., and the earliest known literary document on vellum, which is a copy of Demosthenes' *De falsa legatione* made in the second century A.D.

The iron-gall inks no doubt developed slowly over several centuries. The kind of iron-carbon ink which was known to the ancient Hebrews goes back to the sixth century B.C., and in the second century A.D. the Hebrews added a new ingredient called in the *Talmud* 'khalkanthon', which seems to be sulphate of copper. Later the *Mishnah* of the *Talmud* does in fact mention iron sulphate, gall-nuts and gum.

Coloured inks were made in remote antiquity.

The Egyptians prepared white, blue, green, yellow, brown and red inks, as well as carbon ink; but, apart from red, they used them for drawing and not writing. This is natural enough. All through the centuries men have tended not to distract the reader from the matter to be conveyed: they have written – or printed – chiefly in the subfusc inks, saving colour, and especially red, for points of emphasis. So today we use chiefly the black and blue-black inks, and red; and typewriter ribbons are either black, or black and red. This is in accord with Egyptian practice. On early papyri the Egyptians often used the red ink they prepared from red ochre or red lead for titles and first lines of chapters, columns, etc. In the Middle Ages it was the same: the red ink then made from vermilion or cinnabar was seldom used except for titles or rubrics (*rubrica*, or red lead, and *minium* were the Latin terms for 'red ink'); though the British Museum does possess one volume of the ninth or tenth century A.D. which is written entirely in red ink. One may add that a good red ink can be made by dissolving carmine in a solution of caustic ammonia (it evaporates rapidly, and has to be kept tightly stoppered), and a still better one by steeping cochineal in hot soft water.

In the Middle Ages this vital liquid of civilization was mainly produced in the monasteries. The monk and writer on painting, Theophilus, in his *De diversis artibus*, probably written in the twelfth century, gives a recipe for making ink from thorn wood. An Italian recipe of the fifteenth century says that iron-gall ink was then known everywhere.

Good writing ink needs a balance of qualities, a permanency, above all; and since no ink is perfect, for centuries the constitution of inks has interested the chemist, and from the eighteenth century onwards much scientific work has been done. One may mention the researches of the English chemist and physician William Lewis (1714–1781), who found that the colouring of iron-gall ink depends not only upon metallic iron, but also upon a reaction produced by a vegetable extract. So by using logwood from the New World, which gives the dye haematoxylin, he improved the colour of writing ink without making it the less permanent. (See also *Alphabet*, *Pen*, *Paper*.)

Gunpowder, coal-gas, petrol

The **INTERNAL-COMBUSTION ENGINE**, which has changed the world, transformed the roads and road travel, delivered us finally from several thousand years of reliance upon horse and ox, and made possible the emergence of aircraft, employs the principle of the gun.

Since it develops power by the combustion of fuel inside its cylinder, it can be called the less militant child of gun and gunpowder and the great-grandchild of Chinese technology. Certainly Denis Papin (1647–c.1712), one of the pioneers of steam and the inventor of pressure cookers (q.v.), and Christiaan Huygens (1629–1695) had given thought to the motive possibilities of gunpowder.

With the steam-engine firmly and a little cumbrously in the seat of power, the idea of generating power in small engines without boilers and the consequent loss of heat between boiler and cylinder made much appeal to inventors. But first came the question of fuel. Gunpowder, with its ultra-rapid build-up of pressure, offered no solution. In 1792 William Murdock, the able assistant of Boulton and Watt, showed the way when he lit his house at Redruth, in the Cornish mining country, with coal-gas. In 1823 Samuel Brown patented the first internal-combustion engine of the vacuum type; in this a gas flame in the cylinder expelled some of the air and was extinguished by a water-jet, causing a vacuum, atmospheric pressure forcing the piston down. Between 1827 and 1832 Brown made engines which drove pumps, a boat and a carriage. In 1838 W. Barnett patented an engine which embodied the compression system; gas and air were pumped into the cylinder, where the mixture was compressed still more by the piston, and then ignited by a permanent gas-flame placed outside the cylinder and lighting the gas inside through ports which opened regularly in a rotating plug-cock. In 1860 the French engineer T. J. E. Lenoir made a horizontal double-acting single-cylinder engine with slide-valves. There was no compression; and the mixture of gas and air was ignited at mid-stroke by an electric sparking-plug. This engine had some success. Several hundreds were manufactured in France, and a few in England by the Reading Ironworks Company, in Berkshire.

It was the German engineer Nikolaus August Otto (1832–1891) who now capped the long process of trial and error and made the decisive advance in 1876 with his four-cycle gas engine, the first to compress the mixture in the working cylinder itself before ignition. An early $\frac{1}{2}$-horsepower engine of this type made at Manchester consisted of a single water-cooled vertical cylinder that had a slide-valve underneath, and used flame ignition. In accordance with Otto's four-stroke cycle, gas and air were sucked into the cylinder during the first stroke of the piston, the out-stroke; the mixture was compressed during the second, the in-stroke, and it was ignited near the point of maximum compression, rapidly expanding during the third, the out-stroke. The fourth, the in-stroke of the piston, expelled the exhaust. The only working stroke was the third, so the crankshaft had to be kept turning by a heavy flywheel during the other three strokes. These engines were easy to handle and took up little space. They were soon popular for driving machines of one kind and another through belts or gears.

The way was soon clear for a variety of engines lighter, more compact and more efficient than others of equal power, starting more quickly and rotating faster. A chief requirement was better fuel. In 1859 oil had been found in Pennsylvania, so petrol – gasoline – was at hand, though it was not at first used by Gottlieb Daimler (1834–1900), when he improved on Otto's work and patented in 1885 his vertical four-stroke gas engine. To this German pioneer we owe much of the development of lightweight, high-speed internal-combustion engines, his early engines running at 900 revolutions per minute compared with about 100 revolutions in the Otto engines. Daimler converted his vertical four-stroke gas engine to petrol, fitting a surface vaporizer to form the combustible mixture of petrol vapour and air.

A new era of transport was now opened. Daimler's first petrol-driven motor carriage ran successfully in 1887, and within two years he had devised the V twin-cylinder petrol engine. In 1902, a year before the first successful powered flight made by Orville Wright and Wilbur Wright at Kitty Hawk, Charles Manley in America had devised the first radial aeroplane engine.

A cycle which began with Chinese gunpowder and Chinese bamboo guns was now complete. (See also *Gunpowder, Motor Car, Aeroplane, Steam-Engine*.)

ILLUSTRATION: Page 358.

The democratic metal

IRON, the fundamental material of modern civilization, has been called the democratic metal, since its ores are so plentifully and readily available in so many parts of the world. Yet man had to wait many centuries before he discovered methods of smelting these ores.

Since prehistoric times man had found and used lumps of meteoric iron. Its celestial origin was well known to the ancients, many, like the Egyptians, calling it 'the metal from the sky'. However, they did not connect it with the many coloured iron ores, some of which they valued as precious stones; and they could not work it because of its high nickel content, which gave it the qualities of steel. With great difficulty they sometimes managed to cut and grind nuggets into some shape. Thus the tomb of Tutankhamen, who lived about 1355 B.C., contained two small amulets made of meteoric iron.

The obstacle to smelting the iron ores was the melting point of iron, which is considerably higher than that of copper, lead or antimony, the metals to which the Bronze Age smith was accustomed. When he smelted their ores, these metals would run from his furnace or collect at the bottom. The chemical process of separating the iron from iron ores was fundamentally the same, but the particles of iron thus formed would solidify at once and remain embedded in the slag unless the temperature was very much higher than anything the ancient smiths could produce in their primitive furnaces. We can be certain that the early smith did try to smelt iron ores, which he knew and which are described in many texts; but the result must have been a most disappointing cinder-like mass of slag with a multitude of tiny particles of iron, and no stream of molten metal to be cast like copper or bronze.

The only way of converting this mass into a solid piece of pure wrought iron was to heat it again and again in the smith's fire and hammer it, thus removing the slag and forging the iron particles together; this technique took many centuries to develop. New tools and new furnaces had to evolve, but even then iron would be much more expensive to make than the copper and bronze already in use.

Iron could hold its own only if it had superior qualities; which was indeed so. During the repeated heating and forging particles of charcoal were diffused into the surface of the iron and gave it steel-like toughness. The early iron tools and implements have therefore a core of wrought iron and a skin of steel; it was this steel which made iron tools so much better than bronze tools. Combined with the ready availability of iron ores, it explains the rise and spread of the ancient iron industry.

The experimental stage lasted all through the second millennium B.C. Small pieces of wrought iron were made during the refining of certain gold ores or by smelting such ores as bog-iron and shaping them into amulets and the like. By 1400 B.C. the new technique and its tools and implements took their final form. The Greeks knew that the Chalybes, a mountain tribe of northeastern Asia Minor, had been the first to start producing iron with a steel-like surface, hence the Greek *khalups* for steel. Independently of such traditions, we have documents to prove this, such as the letter addressed to the King of the Hittites who ruled Asia Minor, by the governor of the eastern provinces stating that the iron dagger he ordered was not yet ready but would be so in a month's time. The Egyptian king Amenhotep II received from the king of the Hittites a steel dagger which he cherished as a precious gift and which is possibly identical with a dagger found in the tomb of Tutankhamen.

From the documents it would seem that the Hittites monopolized the secret manufacture of iron tools and weapons for some while. However, fortuitous political circumstances led to a breaking of this monopoly. About 1200 B.C. the Hittite Empire was invaded by tribes from the Balkans, and their power was smashed. This invasion caused many peoples to migrate southwards and eastwards, invasions which the Egyptians could stem only with the greatest difficulty. When these migrations in the Near East are over, we find specialists in iron metallurgy all over this area. Thus the Kenites of Old Testament fame who lived in Midian on the Red Sea, opposite Mount Sinai, exploited the rich iron ores of their locality. (Moses married a wife of Kenite extraction.)

Farther to the north iron-working tribes, including the Hurrians, begin to provide the Assyrians and Babylonians with ingots of the new

Fig. 15. Blacksmith's shop, Attic vase, sixth century B.C.

metal. In the palace of Sargon II (800 B.C.) a few hundred tons of iron ingots were found. The Assyrian State bought iron in the form of such ingots and had them fashioned into tools and weapons by smiths, who often bear Hurrian names and who must have been immigrants induced to bring their expert understanding to Assyria.

The coming of iron had a profound influence on ancient society. Once the secret of its manufacture became known, it spread rapidly, since iron ores abounded in so many places. During the Bronze Age the shortage of tin had always impeded the use of metal tools and weapons on a very large scale. Now such tools could be made quite easily and locally. Furthermore, iron metallurgy was soon carried to a much higher degree of perfection. It was found that steel could be hardened by plunging the red-hot metal into cold water. The hardness and brittleness of this steel

could be controlled by gently heating the hardened steel at not too high a temperature. This process of annealing would take away some of the hardness as well as the brittleness, making the metal more tough and ductile. By a subtle interplay of such techniques the quality of the iron could be varied at will. Thus, though wrought iron and steel are really iron-carbon alloys, it was the conditions of forging and annealing, not the percentage of carbon, which determined the qualities of the product in the first place. Bronze Age techniques, such as alloying and casting, faded away into the background. The Iron Age smith is characterized by his forge, his hammer and tongs and his anvil.

The ready availability of iron made it possible to provide even the common soldier with iron swords, daggers and helmets. Here at last was a metal that was tough enough for ploughshares; ploughs could cut large sods and go deeper into the soil, thus improving the harvests and farm economy in general. Axes and hoes of iron were now in good supply, and the drainage of swamps and the felling of trees could be attempted on a much larger scale. (The deforestation of many tracts in the Near East, such as the cedar-forests of the Lebanon, became serious during the first millennium B.C.). New tools were invented, as well. Up to 1000 B.C. sheep were plucked, and the tufts of wool were spun into yarn and then woven. Shears – that is, two knives joined by a metal spring – were not possible in bronze, but iron had the necessary elasticity, and iron shears now allowed sheep to be shorn and a sheep's fleece to be produced as a unit. Shears developed into scissors, which could be used to cut one's hair or cloth. Formerly a garment had to be woven as such. Now the art of tailoring was invented, cloth was produced which was then cut with the aid of scissors and fashioned at will in greater variety of shapes. Iron nails, bolts and nuts came to be used in carpentry and engineering, and they supplanted older forms of joining pieces of timber by mortice and tenon. The first step was taken on the long road to assembling machinery from standard parts. The Assyrian kings started to use iron pickaxes to hew their roads in the mountain passes of the north, and so pacify Armenia, making trade and transport easier.

Iron metallurgy went westwards. Homer's great

epics are a curious picture of a Bronze Age society described by a poet of the Iron Age who sometimes lacks the technical knowledge for portraying a past era. By 1000 B.C. iron metallurgy had arrived in Italy; it now crept slowly northwards and westwards until the Iron Age is heralded even in far-away Britain by 300 B.C. The exploitation of the iron ores of Noricum (the present Styria), Elba and Spain provided the Roman Empire with the iron tools and weapons it required, the weapons being forged by smiths in the cities of the Po valley and in the neighbourhood of Rome. In the fourth book of Aristotle's interesting *Meteorologica* (c. 340 B.C.) he says that 'wrought iron melts' under heat. But it is unlikely that ancient charcoal-fired furnaces could heat iron to its melting point (1600°C.). The word 'melts' can, however, be interpreted as 'becomes soft', the state of iron ready for forging.

Wrought iron and steel were long the only forms of iron produced on a larger scale. Some steel was made by a crucible process, probably invented in India, and was forged into strips to be fashioned into swords of superior quality, with 'damascene' patterns on the blade. Not until the thirteenth century A.D. were furnaces advanced enough to produce molten iron. The secret lay in the blast of air from bellows activated by water-wheels: the iron could now be maintained at high temperatures long enough to absorb a sufficiency of carbon, and so to liquefy. Adequate supplies of cast iron now meant that the old Bronze Age technique of casting could at last be applied to iron as well. New possibilities could be tried out; guns could be cast, and cannonballs, which at last made the invention of gunpowder a revolutionary factor in warfare.

Such were the principles of manufacturing wrought iron, steel and cast iron up to the eighteenth century, when smelting iron ores with coke was developed by the Darbys and when the old processes were gradually improved or new ones to work poorer and contaminated iron ores were discovered. The great revolution of the nineteenth century was the discovery of large-scale processes for making cast steel, the alloying of steel with small quantities of such metals as nickel, tungsten and molybdenum and the application of the microscope and other scientific tools to the control of such techniques. (See also *Mines, Bronze*.)

K

An optical toy

The **KALEIDOSCOPE**, a tube containing bits of coloured glass, etc., which arrange themselves in beautiful and ever-changing shapes (Greek *kalos*, beautiful; *eidos*, form; and *skopeo*, I see), was one of the most popular inventions of the last century.

Devised in 1817 by Sir David Brewster, it was soon in everybody's hands, admirably fitting in with the Regency taste in elegant coloured bric-a-brac. 'Every person who could buy or make

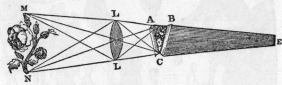

Fig. 16. Brewster's Kaleidoscope.

one', runs a contemporary report, 'had a Kaleidoscope. Men, women and children, rich and poor, in houses, or walking in the streets, in carriages or on coaches, were to be seen looking into the wonder-working tube, admiring the beautiful patterns it produced, and the magical changes which the least movement of the instrument occasioned.' However, the instrument could be made so easily that the patent rights were violated, and Brewster missed the fortune it might have brought him. He had discovered the principle on which the effects of the kaleidoscope depend, while engaged in experiments on the polarization of light by successive reflections between plates of glass. We all know that we can form several images from one object by using two mirrors. If inclined to each other at an angle of 90° they give three images of an object placed between them, the images and the object being apparently placed at the four corners of a rectangle. If the mirrors are inclined to each other at an angle of 60°, five

Continued on p. 227

PLATE 9

FUNERAL PORTRAIT, 3rd century A.D., from the Fayum, Egypt (see *Picture*).

PLATE 10

KITES, from a colour print by Ando Hiroshige (1797–1858).

The Fluting Shepherd-boy, also by Hendrik ter Brugghen.

Playing end-flutes. *The Fluting Pageboy*, by Hendrik ter Brugghen (1578–1629).

211

Doll's House – the famous cabinet house in the Rijksmuseum, Amsterdam, made c. 1700, probably for Petronella Brandt-Oortman.

Drawing-room, from the Rijksmuseum doll's house.

213

Fixed prayer-wheel. The Tibetan monk has just given it a spin.

Turning a hand prayer-wheel in Tibet

Gallows matchbox of 1824.

William Burt's 'typographer'; early typewriter of 1829.

Earliest dated example of printing – the first section of the Chinese Diamond Sutra, A.D. 868. The Buddha talks to his disciple Subhūti. The colophon reads, 'Reverently made for universal free distribution by Wang Chieh on behalf of his two parents on the fifteenth of the fourth moon of the ninth year of Hsien-t'ung (11 May 868).

Newspaper printing on a ten-feed semi-rotary machine, 1860.

Printing-press, from a *Dance of Death*, 1499.

Page from the Gutenberg Bible, probably 1455.

Crib by Arnolfo di Cambio (c. 1232–c. 1310), in Santa Maria Maggiore, Rome. This is the oldest surviving crib. The figure of the Madonna belongs to the sixteenth century.

220

Bagpipes in medieval England. A fourteenth-century statue-bracket, Beverley Minster, Yorkshire.

Earthenware – a *li*, or tripod cooking-pot from China (Chow dynasty c. 1027–256 B.C.).

Egyptian earthenware. Painted jar c. 4000 B.C.

Before the steam-engine: making and using elm-tree pumps to drain mines, from Agricola's *De re metallica*, 1556.

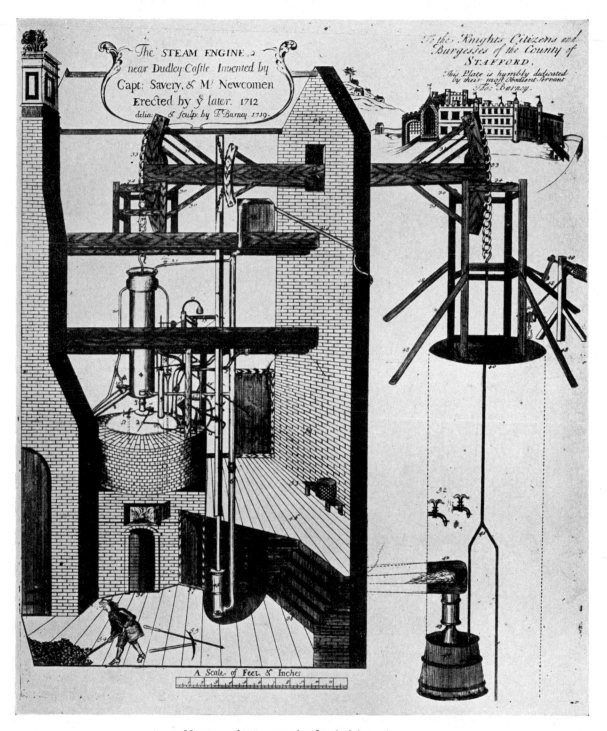

Newcomen's steam-engine for draining mines.

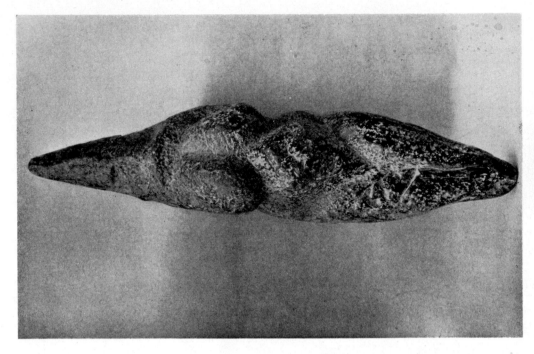

Upper palaeolithic fertility figure from Savignano sul Panaro, near Modena (height 8⅞ in.).

Upper palaeolithic sculpture: the fertility figure of the 'Venus' of Willendorf (height 4⅛ in.).

PLATE 11

A COACH IN ROME, detail from *Piazza del Campidoglio*, by Bernardo Bellotto (1720–1780).

PLATE 12

DETAILS FROM THE EARLIEST KNOWN CARPET, frozen in a Siberian burial mound,
Pazyryk 5th—4th century B.C.

images are produced which, with the original object, show a hexagonal arrangement.

It was these symmetrically arranged images which suggested to Brewster the kaleidoscope, in which (usually) two long, narrow mirrors are placed lengthways in a tube, inclined to each other at 60°. One end of the tube is closed by two parallel plates of glass, the outer one ground-glass, the inner one transparent, leaving between them a space in which are placed small pieces of coloured glass, pieces of twisted glass of varying curvature, small glass tubes partly filled with coloured liquid, etc. At the other end of the tube is a small eye-hole or, in better instruments, a convex lens. On looking into the tube one sees the images of the pieces of glass so reflected that beautiful symmetrical coloured patterns are produced, of infinite variety, for with every movement of the instrument the pieces of glass rearrange themselves in new combinations.

According to the inventor, the express object of the kaleidoscope was less to amuse than 'to exhibit and create beautiful forms and patterns, of great use in all the ornamental arts'. In conjunction with a magic lantern, the images could be enlarged on a screen, affording entertainment to a number of people at the same time.

As with almost every popular invention, the primacy of Brewster's discovery was disputed by people interested in getting the patent set aside; they alleged that Athanasius Kircher had described the effects of repeated reflections in his *Ars Magna* (1646). However, there is only a superficial resemblance between Brewster's kaleidoscope and Kircher's instrument (to be met with also in the books of several later writers on optics), which consisted of a many-faceted piece of cut-glass in a tube, through which one could either see patterns or project them on to a screen.

Around Scottish thighs

The **KILT** seems a primitive form of dress, surviving, as much else survived, such as the bagpipe (q.v.), on the periphery of Europe; but there is a

singular absence throughout the Middle Ages not only of any pictorial record but also of any written description of distinctive costume in Scotland. It is not until we come to the sixteenth century that we find, in the *Chronicle* of Lindsay of Piscottie, a description of what he calls 'the Reid-Shankis or Wyld Scotes' (*i.e.* Highlanders), who, he says, 'be clothed with ane mantle, with ane schirt, fashioned after the Irisch manner, going bair-legged to the knee.'

George Buchanan, writing in 1582, tells us that 'they delight in variegated garments, especially striped, and their favourite colours are purple and blue. Their ancestors wore plaids of many different colours, and numbers still retain this custom, but the majority now, in their dress, prefer a dark brown, imitating nearly the leaves of the heather, that when lying upon the heath ... they may not be discovered by the appearance of their clothes.' It would seem that Buchanan failed to distinguish between the 'hunting tartan' and one worn on ceremonial occasions.

So much for the material of which the kilt was made. There is considerable controversy concerning the origin and antiquity of the kilt itself, some writers declaring it to have been almost unknown before the sixteenth century. Originally it seems to have been a large mantle of one piece, belted round the body, and thence called 'the belted plaid'. One of the most recent authorities, Mr George F. Collie, tells us that 'it consisted of a plain piece of tartan, two yards in width by four to six yards in length. The plaid was placed upon the ground and folded neatly into pleats, until its length had been reduced to about five feet, leaving as much at each end unpleated as would cover the front of the body, with full overlapping. The plaid being thus prepared, the wearer would lie down on it, so that the lower edge was level with his knees.' He then folded it about him, fastened it with a leather belt and threw the remainder of the plaid over his shoulder.

What we now call the kilt is simply the lower half of this, with the pleats permanently sewn. The upper part became a loose, and, finally, merely decorative plaid over the shoulder, kept in place with a brooch. The 'little kilt' came into use in the early eighteenth century and was worn until the law of 1746 prohibited the use of Highland dress altogether. The law was repealed in

1782, and there was a notable revival, stimulated no doubt by the battle banners of Highland regiments and also by the Romantic Movement. When George IV visited Edinburgh in 1822 there was a tremendous display of Highland dress, in which the King himself joined. The kilt is now recognized all over the world as the national dress of Scotland, and each clan is proud of its particular tartan, even if some of them are of no particular antiquity.

Kites, hawks and aeroplanes

KITES originated in China in the remote past, probably before 1000 B.C., and they are widely flown in the East and the Pacific. In Europe, though the Greeks and Romans had something of the kind, and though dragon-shaped kites appear to have been known and flown in the fifteenth century, it seems that they were only popularized in the sixteenth and seventeenth centuries by direct Chinese influence by way of Holland, when East and West came into a closer relationship.

In England, kites were pictured in John Bate's *Mysteries of Art and Nature* in 1635. Their English name (not found in print until the seventeenth century) they owe to the kite, with its peculiar forked tail and soaring flight, which was one of the most familiar of British birds, although now almost extinct. The Italians call them *aquiloni* (large eagles) and in Germany the kite is *drachen*, or 'dragon'. The kite indeed has been made in many forms – from bird shapes and dragon shapes, elaborately painted and articulated, to the simplest lozenge or triangle. In the East the kite has been more than a toy of elegance and fascination. It was in demand for magical purposes, to fend off evil spirits. Flutes and whistles and reeds were attached to make sound kites or musical kites; a Chinese general of the Han dynasty (202 B.C.–A.D. 220) is said to have flown such kites above his enemies in the darkness. They believed their guardian angels were warning them of danger, and fled. Evil has been transferred to

kites, which were then released, by the Koreans and others; and in Siam kites were flown in a yearly festival to call up the right northerly wind which would clear the skies and the weather and dry the ground to make it ready for sowing.

In Europe kite-flying continued to be no more than a game until the eighteenth century, when kites were first employed in meteorology. In 1749 Alexander Wilson and Thomas Melville used the kite to lift thermometers into the air. Three years later, in 1752, Benjamin Franklin made famous use of the kite in his investigations of lightning and electricity. In 1804 the kite took on a more important role: as a simple form of aeroplane in which the surface is inclined to the wind and sustained against the pull of the string, it helped to solve the problems of flight. Sir George Cayley (1773–1857), the aeroplane pioneer, realized its aeronautical nature and constructed the first successful model glider by fixing a kite to one end of a pole, and a tail-plane and fin to the other. Thus the Chinese magical dragon and toy may be called the first true ancestor of the aeroplane.

Kites and aeroplanes have still another link. In Australia in 1893 the scientist Lawrence Hargrave invented the biplane box-kite, a highly stable type which led to an even greater use for kites both as toy and scientific instrument. The box-kite and the biplane glider built by the Wright brothers, combined to dictate the form of the earliest European aeroplanes between 1905 and 1908. (See also *Aeroplane, Glider, Balloon*.)

ILLUSTRATION: Plate 10.

L

A Luxury product

LACE has been defined as a form of ornamental open-work (the word derives from the Latin *laqueus*, a noose), and it developed, so it seems, from the technique of drawn thread and cut-work, and was firmly established in Europe by the sixteenth century. Yet lace has a much greater antiquity. There are indications of netting, drawn thread and cut-work to be seen in the paintings on Egyptian sarcophagi, and specimens of actual lace from Akhmîm, in Upper Egypt, date from the fourth to fifth century A.D.

There are two distinct kinds of handmade lace – needlepoint, and bobbin lace, or pillow lace. Needlepoint developed in Venice, a fitting product of Venetian civilization, from the geometrical drawn thread and cut-work embroidery (*reticella*); it was made with the needle and a single kind of stitch – a looped or buttonhole stitch. First the pattern was traced on parchment. On this design a skeleton pattern of threads was fastened by stitching, and then worked over in buttonhole stitch, forming small 'brides' (*i.e.* ties or bars), some of which were decorated with picots, as in Venetian Rose Point. To this framework the solid parts of the '*toilé*' (pattern) were attached, after which the lace was cut away from its parchment foundation. Raised Venetian Point (Gros Point and Point de Neige) was the richest and most complicated of all point lace. Its outlines were raised so much that it has been likened to sculpture in marble. This effect of relief was obtained by a padding of horse-hair, which was worked over in buttonhole stitch, giving in some instances an effect of double or triple relief. Rose Point was a finer, lighter variation, out of which Flat Point (Point plat de Venise) developed. This, as its name implies, had no relief, and its simple, graceful stems were united by 'brides'. Point de Venise à Réseau, a grounded needlepoint, belonged to the first half of the eighteenth century, its characteristics being a fine *réseau* (net-work ground) and rich '*jours*', or ornamental openwork in the pattern.

Gradually the needlepoint laces of Venice had been superseded by those of France through the efforts in the mid-seventeenth century of Colbert, the French Controller of Finances under Louis XIV. The Venetian lace industry was transplanted to France, Alençon and Argentan becoming notable centres. Alençon point tended to be smaller in scale than its predecessors, with light rococo designs and a *cordonnet* of horse-hair which was covered in small buttonhole stitches outlining the pattern. From about 1700 it may be recognized by a fine looped *réseau*, and it reached the height of its development during the reigns of Louis XIV and Louis XV. Point d'Argentan, a slightly later development, was typified by a hexagonal buttonholed *réseau*. This also had a *cordonnet* of horse-hair outlining the pattern, but the pattern was bolder and larger than that of Alençon.

Brussels point from 1720 closely followed Alençon styles with the difference that its *cordonnet* merely consisted of a strand of threads and was not buttonholed. During the eighteenth century, a bobbin net replaced the needlepoint *réseau*, resulting in an application of small needlepoint sprig motifs to a bobbin ground. However, in the middle of the nineteenth century Point de Gaze was introduced, which was composed of needlepoint on a needle ground. In England before the seventeenth century, lace does not seem to have been made on a large scale. It was imported; and the establishment of lace-making had to await the influx of religious refugees towards the end of the sixteenth century; in the midland counties and in Devon, the foundations were laid for a thriving industry for future generations.

Bobbin lace was constructed in a fundamentally different way. Whereas in needlepoint the solid parts were constructed of looped buttonhole stitches made with the needle, the technique of bobbin lace was to twist and plait numerous threads on the pillow with the aid of bobbins. Thus the *toilé* was composed of threads crossing each other more or less at right angles, giving a woven effect, and the *réseau* was contrived by twisting and plaiting. As Venice was the great centre for needlepoint, so Genoa and Milan were the centres for bobbin lace during the seventeenth century. Genoese lace was heavy in character and frequently scalloped along its borders. Milan lace was worked by a bold design of graceful, leafy stems.

Gradually the Italian bobbin laces gave way to the Flemish lace industry, which became securely established in the seventeenth century. Flemish lace-makers followed the patterns set by Genoa and Milan, but they produced a finer and looser effect, which gave rise to those laces of Brussels and Mechlin. Of these two, Brussels is the most important. A raised *cordonnet* surrounded the *toilé*, which was made in one with the hexagonal plaited *réseau* (the earlier pieces had 'brides'). The pattern of stately and flowing lines of the Renaissance was adhered to until the First Empire, when fashions demanded *semés* or powdering devices and small floral, wreath-like borders. England was eclectic in its lace, owing to the settlement of lace-making refugees; the laces of the midland counties and Devon followed the styles of the bobbin laces of Lille and Brussels during the nineteenth century.

In its more delicate and elaborate forms, lace developed with the elegancies of secular and religious costume. In Venice in 1542 a sumptuary edict prohibited the use of gold and of coloured silks in embroidery, compelling the needle-workers of the city to turn for a livelihood to an elaboration of white-work. As the century advanced, lace was used with abandon on collars, caps, aprons, cuffs, handkerchiefs and the visible parts of linen underwear; even the tops of boots were trimmed with this same costly fabrication; and costly lace continued to be, until the establishment of lace-making by machine in the early years of the nineteenth century.

ILLUSTRATION: Pages 166 and 167.

Lacquer in China and Japan

LACQUER is made from the juice of the tree *Rhus vernicifera*, a native of northern China and one of a poisonous family which includes various sumachs familiar in the garden, and poison ivy. It has remarkable qualities. It will 'take' on almost any material, it is impervious to damp, insects and bacteria. Excessive handling may dull a lacquered surface, but only direct sunlight and dry heat will make it brown and take away its gloss. In 1878 a cargo of works of art returning from Paris to Japan was sunk, and then salvaged eighteen months later. The paintings had turned to pulp, the lacquer ware was bright as ever.

No substitutes, from the insect juice used in Burma to the mineral varnishes of the paint merchant, can match the qualities of lacquer, the exploitation of which by the Chinese began as far back as the Bronze Age. Old Chinese writings record unexpected uses. Lacquer was burnt, the smell keeping off insects or reviving women in childbirth. Possibly, however, it was first employed as a glue and a preservative. To the Chinese and Japanese it was as important as rubber was to the peoples of Mexico.

In China at the beginning of the Christian era lacquer seems to have received special attention from a government anxious to secure luxuries for the court; and it was found easy to transplant and cultivate the lacquer-tree, which was introduced into Japan in the sixth century A.D. Once established there, it produced sap of unusual quality. Normally a tree was tapped after ten years' growth, but master craftsmen were always willing to pay extra for sap drawn from older trees – 150 or 200 years old, if possible. The grey, viscous fluid was run off into wooden bowls from gashes in the bark and the tree left to its inevitable death. For inferior work juice was obtained from the twigs, which were crushed and boiled. Peculiar ingredients were added, if old texts are to be believed, before it was ready for application: lime, rice-flour, pig's blood, egoma oil, plum vinegar, crabs' stomachs (in Sung times workmen poisoned by a long handling of raw lacquer were treated with dishes of crab), cape jasmin juice, whetstone powder – all these figure in the recipes, or are debated as desirable. A text of 1388, no doubt with Buddhist susceptibilities in mind, deprecates adding rhizomes of the lotus.

The sap, boiled and reduced, and mixed with the other ingredients, must be applied in extremely thin coats, each coat being left to dry for twenty hours in the damp atmosphere of a room the walls of which are sprayed with water. Once the coat is dry it is polished repeatedly with charcoal and deer horn before the next application. For an article which is to be entirely lacquered all over, the base is generally a model in thin wood. For sculpture, in which lacquer was used from the T'ang dynasty (A.D. 618–916) onwards, the base was formed of rags laid on a core of clay which was afterwards removed. The smallest lacquer box would require thirty coats. A grand piece of lacquer ware would be given at least fifty or sixty coats. From medieval times in China and later in Japan solid lacquer, sometimes layered in colours, was carved like stone. The thick pieces for such work were built up from many hundreds of layers of sap.

In the first two centuries of the Christian era the lacquer industry flourished in China under the imperial patronage. From the richly furnished tombs of officials in the Chinese colony of Lo Lang in Korea, Japanese archaeologists have excavated a great variety of lacquered articles, from tables to shoes, bowls, toilet boxes, weapons and musical instruments, many of them with their decoration, geometric designs in red upon black, or yellow and green, preserved in its pristine colours. Somewhat later, in A.D. 646, lacquer was officially recognized in Japan, when a government decree directed that all coffins should henceforth be seamed with lacquer and that it should be used to starch the gauze headdresses of court officials. Even a Ministry of Lacquer was established, which in the tenth century was amalgamated with the Ministry of Architecture. The practical uses of the sap were not neglected in China. In the fourteenth century the inhabitants of Hankow were astonished to see a boatman 'flitting up and down the river' with a complement of twenty persons in a lacquer-sealed cowhide boat which he had carried to the capital.

The Chinese remained the masters of carved lacquer. After Han times we know little of the artistic use of lacquer until the period of Hsüan Tê (1426–1435), when a style of carving was established which remained popular through the Ming dynasty and the succeeding Ch'ing dynasty. The red carved lacquer of China was highly prized by the Japanese tea-masters. Yet by the time of Hsüan Tê gifts of Japanese lacquer which were made to the Chinese court enticed Chinese craftsmen to Japan to study the astonishing techniques which had been evolved there. One was the method of superimposing layers of different colours, to be revealed in the carving. Another was to embed metallic dusts at different depths in the lacquer, so as to give subtle gradations of rich colour. The Japanese could imitate the effect of the worn leather of saddles or the imprint of a cobweb, they could build up landscapes in low relief which they set against 'floating sunset gold dust', or they could produce the effect called 'gold in ice'.

European visitors to Japan in the seventeenth and eighteenth centuries were lost in admiration of the richly decorated and gold-splashed lacquer of the time, and had an eye for its practical uses.

In 1669 the traveller Ogilby wrote home that lacquer was 'so beautiful and lasting there is no need for a table-cloth at meals'. From the early seventeenth century only the Dutch had a right of trade with Japan. The lacquered Japanese screens for which there was so great demand in Europe, were traded by the Dutch to English and French merchants at Indian ports and so acquired the name of Coromandel screens. During the Regency period great quantities of Japanese lacquer was imported for furnishing the Pavilion at Brighton. European cabinet-makers also began to imitate Japanese lacquer ware. Cheap imitation has tended to debase lacquer, though in Japanese hands it rose to masterpieces of art fit to be placed beside Chinese jade and porcelain. (See also *Rubber*.)

ILLUSTRATION: Pages 118 and 119.

Lighten our darkness

LAMPS are the most ancient form of lighting, apart from the fire. A hundred grease lamps of stone were discovered in the Lascaux caves in France, where palaeolithic man decorated the wall with his magico-religious paintings some 20,000 years ago. The Sumerians some 4,500 years ago used lamps of gold and alabaster. Pottery lamps were used by the city dwellers of the Harappa civilization along the Indus Valley about the same time; and copper lamps lit the darkness of the Egyptian house. The Athenians had lamps in plentiful supply, remains of more than 10,000 dating from the third to the fifth centuries B.C. having been found by the American School of Classical Studies. The Romans produced pottery lamps on a large scale; and bronze lamps were common in wealthier Roman households, which often had massive standards carrying festoons of lamps. Pliny records that one such elaborate device cost the large sum of 50,000 sesterces.

Early lamps, nevertheless, do not imply illumination as we know it, but rather a pool of light among deep shadows. Whatever their elaboration in material or decoration, they suffered much the same limitation and worked in much the same way. Oil for the flame was sucked up by a fibre wick from a container. This was at first no more than an open saucer in which the wick lay uncontrolled or was floated on the oil. The wick might also be led from the oil by a channel or spout, so that the flame always appeared at the same place. Refinements, as the centuries passed by, included a shutting in of the oil reservoir (as in Roman pottery lamps) so that the oil would not be fouled by dirt or by the bodies of flies and moths attracted by the flame. A technique was even developed, at any rate within the last millennium, of floating the oil on top of water, so that the inevitable dirt from the charred wicks sank right through the oil to the bottom, where it could do no harm. Other refinements in detail included receptacles to catch the drip of unused oil and the provision of tweezers or spikes to pull up the wicks as they burnt away.

Originally twists of fibre, the wicks were greatly improved from the eighteenth century onwards, when the use of cotton or linen rag became more usual. A normal duty of the domestic servant was to twist rags compactly into a wick shape, dip them in grease and singe them lightly, so that they would be ready for use. All the early forms of lamp smoked and smelt, particularly when the oil was running low. Vitruvius in his *De architectura* of the first century A.D. counselled that carved work or mouldings should be avoided in rooms where many lights would be required.

Oils were of various kinds, at first fish oils (which were smelly), including sperm oil; and vegetable oils, including olive oil, which differed greatly in their keeping properties. Probably the best vegetable oil was colza or rape oil, extracted from the seeds of *Brassica rapa*, thousands of acres of which were laid down in nineteenth-century Europe. Colza was so heavy that a clockwork pump or spring pressure was required to force it up the lamp wicks. In England and to a greater extent in America people also used camphor, a mixture of turpentine and alcohol. It burned brightly, with little dirt or smell. Though it was tried extensively between 1830 and 1850, camphor was so volatile and so explosive that it did not survive a reputation for too many disasters.

Before the appearance of this dangerous fuel, there had been little alteration in the amount of light which could be had from a lamp. However, mention must be made of the Swiss physicist Aimé Argand (1755–1803), and the Argand burner which he invented. In earlier lamps the only solution of more light was more wicks. The Argand burner, a great step forward, gave as much light as a dozen ordinary lamps or candles by leading air through a cylindrical wick as well as around it, so that the oil was more thoroughly and effectively burned within a glass chimney. However, it used so much oil in the process that it could be afforded only by the better-off. Almost the ideal answer to the problem of fuel came at last with the introduction of paraffin, or kerosene, constituents of the mineral oil which lies below the earth's surface in various parts of the world. Here was a stable oil which does not deteriorate with time, like most vegetable oils, which rises easily to the wick and burns brightly with little smoke or smell. Small supplies were to be had in Europe and in Burma from about 1852 onwards. New York in 1859 actually imported 10,000 gallons from Burma. However, in that same year Edwin Drake struck oil in Pennsylvania (in what is now the Drake Well Memorial Park), and within twenty years millions of gallons were shipped every year from the United States. Patents for improved paraffin lamps came now by the hundred; and in 1865 the brothers Hinks in England patented the duplex burner. In this improved burner two thin flat wicks protrude a short distance away from each other, burning much better than a thicker single wick. Benjamin Franklin is credited with the discovery of this phenomenon in the case of vegetable oil lamps nearly a hundred years earlier.

In the more modern paraffin lamps wicks are replaced by an incandescent mantle, and the oil is vaporized by the hot gases from the flame before coming in its turn to the burner. These improvements were mainly due to the Austrian chemist Auer von Welsbach between 1888 and 1893, who invented the incandescent mantle, and Arthur Kitson, who made lamps in which the incoming oil is preheated. One consequence of the improvement of lamps has been to reduce the number of fires. A writer in *The Mechanic's Magazine* in 1836 said of the hundreds of fires which occurred every year in London that 'exposed lamps have occasioned serious accidents: but enclosed within glass walls the light is greatly improved, and the chance of accident incomparably small'. Twelve years later, out of 767 fires in London, 237 were due to candles and only three to oil lamps. Sociologically and psychologically improved lighting has had an immense result, whether by oil, gas or electricity, extending man's hours of work and leisure, abolishing the sharp line between night and day. Illustrations to this article show the feeble flickering range of lamps before glass chimneys and the later improvements. (See also *Torches and Candle*.)

ILLUSTRATION: Pages 20 and 21.

The tool-making tool

The LATHE has the importance in technological history of having been one of the few machines which were engaged in commodity production before the Industrial Revolution. After this revolution it became the greatest tool of all: the machine which makes machines.

The earliest form was the pole-lathe, invented probably in Greece. Like the bow-drill, from which it may have developed, the spindle of the pole-lathe is rotated by means of a cord. The top end of the cord is tied to a pliant bough or 'pole'; it is then looped around the spindle, and the bottom end is tied to a treadle under the turner's feet. Press down the treadle, the bough yields, and the spindle turns, in one direction; release the tension and the spindle turns in the other direction. The spindle could also be turned by a rope pulled to and fro by the turner's mate, as with a form of lathe used by the Japanese before their industrialization.

In Great Britain turners were busy with their pole-lathes till recent years in the Chilterns, in Pembrokeshire, Cardiganshire and Armagh, producing table-legs, bowls and platters. In turning such things as a table-leg, the length of wood itself could provide the spindle, and was therefore fitted between the dead points of the lathe. In turning bowls, wheel-hubs, etc., the wood had to be fixed on the end of the spindle, and so necessarily lay outside the spindle bearings. This turning on a 'chuck' needed a stronger frame, and also a motive-power greater than cord, treadle and pole could develop. The Japanese lathe gives a hint of the way in which these requirements were met in ancient times.

One might expect the lathe to have been linked at any rate to the potter's wheel, which was invented in Mesopotamia and used in Crete about 2000 B.C., in Egypt possibly a thousand years earlier. However, for close on two thousand years it did not occur to anyone to turn a harder material than unbaked clay, although the bronze chisels already used by carpenters could take a good edge and would have served admirably for shaping wood on a lathe. Egyptian tomb frescoes depict the painstaking manufacture, by hand, of alabaster vases of exact circular section inside and out. Before the fifth century B.C. the mouldings on the legs of Egyptian furniture were also carved, although they closely resemble the kind of ornament which later was to be turned on the lathe. Stool legs depicted on ivories from Megiddo in Palestine dated between 1250 and 1150 B.C. appear to have been carved as well.

When the lathe appears in Egypt, some time in the sixth or fifth century B.C., it had been introduced, we may suspect, from the Greek world around the Aegean, since in this area its history can be traced a little farther back. Climatic conditions around the northern Mediterranean coast are less favourable for the preservation of wooden objects buried in the earth than either the humid climate of more northerly latitudes or the dry sands of the Egyptian desert. Thus the existence of the earliest turnery can only be inferred indirectly from the shapes of pottery vessels, which must have been ceramic imitations of turnery. In the Geometric period of Greek antiquity (1000–700 B.C.) some shallow earthenware dishes, with curved profiles and close-fitting lids, have just the shape of copies of wooden prototypes developed on the lathe. The pictures painted on the pottery of sixth- and fifth-century Greece leave no doubt of the skill and popularity of the turner's craft, at least as far as furniture is concerned.

Cups with elaborate profiles were also produced on the lathe. None has survived in Greece itself, but a turned wooden kylix of Greek form was recovered from an Iron Age chieftain's grave in Upper Bavaria, belonging to the sixth or fifth century B.C. Its graceful lines and slender ribbing and a loose, solid and irremovable wooden ring contrived round the foot – a turner's *tour de force* – proclaim an advanced stage of technique. We may imagine that this knowledge of turning joined the cultural streams which radiated from the Greek homeland, as much by colonization as by trade, reaching such distant places as the southern parts of France, Germany and Russia, as well as the nearer shores of Italy. In the sixth century B.C. the Greek turner's products, and no doubt knowledge of his machine too, would accompany the very considerable export of Greek pottery to Etruria, thence to be conveyed by the Etruscans to the Celtic inhabitants of northern Italy.

It was Celtic immigrants of the Early Iron Age who introduced the pole-lathe into Britain. In the latter part of the third century B.C. they entered the country from the south-west. At one of their lake villages at Glastonbury in Somerset excavators found a turned wooden tub, twelve inches in diameter with walls five and a half inches high. This would have been a creditable piece of turnery at any period. The Belgic invaders who entered Britain from 75 B.C. onwards must have brought with them knowledge of a lathe capable of very precise work. They turned large pear-shaped urns (some nearly two feet tall) in shale, dividing them into a number of sections made to fit exactly together by means of rabbeted edges. The hardness of shale is sufficient to blunt the ordinary modern chisel very rapidly, and for a time the problem of the tool used by the Belgae in their turning remained unsolved. The excavation of a factory of shale armlets at Kimmeridge in Dorset (where the best jet-black shale is obtained) suggested a solution: for here flint flakes were used, and experiment showed that these were effective in cutting shale on the lathe, although their brittleness allowed them only a short life. So primitive flint was used with one of the earliest of machines.

The Belgae were also masters of a technique allied to wood-turning, the spinning or planishing of thin bronze. In this process which was already known to the bronzeware factories of Capua in Italy, a metal sheet is turned against a shaped mould and with a hard point gradually pressed into the desired shape. Bowls and shield-bosses were manufactured by this means. Spinning of this kind is still carried on in at least one workshop in Great Britain, where noses for fighter planes were made during the First World War, and after the war, samovars.

ILLUSTRATION: Page 313.

'Spirting its little fountain of vivid green'

The **LAWNMOWER** was invented by Edwin Budding, an engineer in the cloth factory of a Mr Lister of Stroud, in Gloucestershire. In the year 1830 Budding patented 'a machine for cropping or shearing the vegetable Surface of Lawns, Grass-plots, &c.' He derived his idea from a small device made for cutting the pile on cloth; and he used to practice with his first lawnmower, in its earliest imperfection, on his own back lawn after dark – to the great mystification of his neighbours.

The first mature lawnmower was manufactured to Budding's specification early in 1831 by John Ferrabee at his Phoenix Foundry near Stroud, and before the end of the next year similar machines were being produced by James Ransome of Ipswich. Twenty years later Messrs Ferrabee and Messrs Ransome showed the only two lawnmowers at the Great Exhibition. They were almost identical with the original; and indeed the earliest mowers were very similar to our present-day machines.

Budding himself was delighted with his invention. 'Country Gentlemen', he says, 'may find, in using my machine themselves, an amusing, useful, and healthy exercise.' But the machines were made in two sizes, and a correspondent of the gardening author John Claudius Loudon wrote in September 1831, 'I have had one of Budding's machines in use, when the grass required it, all this year, and am highly pleased with it. The narrow machine is best for a gentleman who wishes to use it himself, but the wide ones are preferable for workmen.' The small mower cost seven guineas, the larger one ten; and Loudon, who was a gardener with a disinterested passion for progress, expressed the 'sincere hope that every gardener whose employer could afford it would procure a machine and give it a trial'.

Most of those who took Loudon's advice were well satisfied. Mr Curtis, head gardener at the London Zoo, calculated that 'with two men, one to draw and another to push, the new mower did as much work as six men with scythes and

Fig. 17. Budding's lawnmower, 1832.

brooms'. And it was, of course, by scythe and broom that lawns had hitherto been kept in their English perfection. It used to be a tedious business, and Loudon had, years before, worked out with mathematical precision the most economical method of cutting and clearing a large lawn – so that in the end the area was 'studded with heaps of grass sixty feet apart one way, and fifteen or eighteen feet apart the other way'. These heaps were then 'basketed into the grass-cart by a man and a boy with a couple of boards and a besom'.

Under the old system any man with enough practice could become a good mower of lawns. It was the tidying up that was the trouble. But in spite of the obvious advantages of the machine with its grass-box, there was for long among gardeners a conservative party who persisted in the use of the scythe; and down, at any rate, to the Second World War there were many aged men in Great Britain who retained the old skill and could scythe a grass plot perfectly smoothly to the eye and softly to the tread. The tide finally turned, however, with the coming of Lawn Tennis in the seventies. By then horse-drawn mowers

were in use at Kew; and Dean Hole tells of a gardener at Rochester Asylum who used to harness seven madmen to his machine. In the early eighties a Mr R. Kirkham devised a mower propelled by a pedal-driven tricycle, but this never became popular. Rather more successful, but not much more, was Mr Summer's one-and-a-half ton steam-driven mower, patented in 1893. Any future that this last monster might have had was prevented by the perfecting of the internal-combustion engine. In the present century the motor-mower has made the keeping of lawns so simple a matter that in 1939 it was calculated that lawn grass covered more than seventy-five per cent of the total garden area of England.

Edwin Budding's name does not occur in the *Dictionary of National Biography*, nor has any public memorial been put up to him, but everywhere – and especially in England, where lawns flourish as they flourish nowhere else – gardeners are immeasurably in his debt. The noise and the sight of the lawnmower at work have become part of the domestic poetry of modern life:

While the lawnmower sings moving up and down
Spirting its little fountain of vivid green,
I, like Poussin, make a still-bound fête of us
Suspending every noise, of insect or machine ...

Pillars of fire

LIGHTHOUSES appear to have begun as beacons, showing the way into harbour, rather than as lights warning ships from reefs or cliffs of notable danger.

Such harbour beacons were known centuries before the most famous of them, the Pharos at Alexandria, was built by Sostrates of Cnidos, about 300–280 B.C. Several early writers have described it. Strabo, born about 63 B.C., says in his *Geography* that it was made of white marble – 'for the safety of seafarers, for the coast was low on either side and without havens, and had as well shallows and reefs. Those who were sailing to Alexandria from the open sea needed therefore a tall conspicuous sign so that they could set a correct course to the harbour mouth.' Josephus (A.D. 37– c. 95) wrote that the fire on the top of the Pharos could be seen thirty-four miles away. By direct vision this would mean that the tower was 550 feet high, though by reflection from the sky a fire on top of a tower lower than that might have been seen from the same distance.

The Pharos still rose upon its island when Idrisi (1099?–1154), the Arabic traveller, wrote his geographical account of the earth, *Al Rojari*. He remarks that the masonry was so well jointed that the sea was powerless against it; adding (a point to remember about these early beacon towers in the clarity of the Mediterranean atmosphere) that fire was kept going day and night: 'At night it gleams like a star; in the daytime its smoke can be discerned.' Josephus had mentioned that the light warned ships to anchor off Alexandria till daylight because of the difficulties of making port.

The Romans were notable lighthouse builders, setting up towers in Italy at key points such as Ostia (A.D. 50) and the Straits of Messina, and as far afield as the Straits of Dover, which were flanked with a pharos at Dover itself (of which there are remains alongside the church in Dover Castle) and a pharos at Boulogne. Italian trade and navigation caused the erection of a number of medieval towers in the Mediterranean. On the Atlantic coast the rock of Cordouan, at the mouth of the Gironde, appears to have supported a light for more than a thousand years, guiding ships into the estuary which leads to Bordeaux, from which packhorses went across land to the Mediterranean. The lighthouse there now was finished in 1611, with later alterations.

As navigation increased there was a spurt of lighthouse building in the seventeenth century; and the lighthouse, generally land-based still and out of reach of waves, became less frequently a harbour beacon and more often a danger sign, often privately owned and supported by tolls collected from merchants. Sir John Killigrew wrote of his lighthouse at the Lizard in Cornwall in 1619: 'The inhabitants nearby think that they suffer by this erection. They affirm that I take away God's Grace from them. Their English meaning is that now they shall receive no more benefit from shipwreck, for this will prevent it.

They have been so long used to reap profit by the calamities of the ruin of shipping that they claim it hereditary, and heavily complain on me.' The loss of shipping farther west, on the granite isles of Scilly, was enormous; and in 1860 the Brethren of Trinity House obtained a patent for building the Scillonian lighthouse which still stands on the island of St Agnes. Here the coal fire was first lit in October of the same year, after the Trinity House had circularized merchants in Spain, Portugal and the Mediterranean, etc., telling them that the toll would be a penny a ton on foreign ships either way (on English shipping a halfpenny a ton was charged). But lighthouse tolls proved not at all easy to collect. The St Agnes lighthouse was used from 1680 to 1911. Farther out to sea than St Agnes, ships are now warned off the Scillonian reefs by the Bishop Rock lighthouse (1851–1858), which has a full exposure to the pressure and violence of Atlantic waves.

Coal fires gave a diffused and scanty light and were not too easy to maintain. At the Isle of May in Firth of Forth, Scotland, a coal fire at the top of a thirty-foot tower consumed between 200 and 300 tons of coal a year, and every skipful had to be carried up one of four ladders by a watchman who chose the ladder for use according to the direction of the wind. This coal light was maintained from 1635 to 1816.

The lighthouse developed in two notable ways, in position and illumination. Better technique enabled lighthouses to be erected and maintained on wave-swept rocks. The lighthouses set up on the Eddystone, off Plymouth, were among the pioneer buildings; the first Eddystone lighthouse, built in five years (1695–1700), was overwhelmed in 1703. The second, mainly a wooden structure, lasted from 1709 to 1755, when it was burned out. The third, built by John Smeaton, was in service from 1759 to 1877.

Smeaton's lighthouse used for illumination a corona of twenty-four tallow candles. In this it was unusual. Even at so late a period most lighthouses could boast only a few candles, and the lighthouse keepers had to trim their wicks at least once every half-hour. A few years later the whale-oil lamp with a parabolic reflector was introduced for the Mersey lights at Liverpool; and in the United States there were sixteen whale-oil lights round the east coast in the closing years of the eighteenth century. At this time there were twenty-eight lights around English coasts, a few in Scotland and France, and very few elsewhere.

The Argand oil lamp of 1782–1784 gave a light equal to that of twelve candles, but it was greedy for oil. For lighthouses this hardly mattered, and it was quickly brought into use, particularly as both the lamp and its flame occupied little room. With this advantage the revolving light became a practical proposition. One was made at Lancaster, in England, in 1792, and was installed at Walney, not far away. Another was installed in the Cordouan lighthouse in France in 1793. The mechanisms were like those of weight-driven clocks, and their simplicity was such that most revolving lights today are driven in the same way. The characteristic of revolving lights was that they could be made to give intermittent flashes of variable length, from the pattern of which the light might be identified precisely. Glass lenses to make this even easier were proposed in 1759, but it was not until 1822 that various ideas were brought to fruition by Fresnel at the Cordouan light. His simple lens system remains substantially the basis of the modern light, however complicated it may seem. The lens is broken up into a number of concentric glass rings of reasonable size and weight which can be made and maintained much more easily than one great solid piece of glass. It took over forty years to get to this stage from the first attempts by the Abbé Roehm in 1780 to follow up a suggestion made by Buffon.

Electric light was first tried at the South Foreland light in 1858, when a carbon arc fed from a primitive electric generator blazed forth with the hitherto unimaginable strength of 1,500 candlepower. It was not until 1862 that this installation was made permanent, and by 1881 there were only twelve electrically-lit lighthouses in all the world. Oil lamps, after paraffin became common in the 1880s, were mostly preferred. It was not until 1909 that the filament lamp of ductile tungsten was made practical. Soon large filament lamps were being made for lighthouses, and today most new lighthouses use electric lamps of up to 10,000 watts consumption, with bulbs about fifteen inches in diameter; they last for as long as 10,000 hours, but require special generators and appropriate optical systems. The con-

centrated beam of a modern lighthouse lamp is trained so that it dips towards the horizon. Thus in the case of the Lizard lighthouse the direct range calculated from the height of the light above sea-level would be no more than twenty-three miles. In practice, if the weather should be clear, the light is reflected from the upper atmosphere and can be picked up as a 'loom' eighty miles away, or more. In some modern lights there is also a tendency to fix special prisms in front of the main optical panels to divert about a tenth of the light upwards in order to assist pilots of aeroplanes with the same identification signals available to mariners.

ILLUSTRATION: Pages 175, 176 and 177.

M

Magic on the screen

The **MAGIC LANTERN,** from which the cinematograph projector evolved, was first described nearly three centuries ago, by Francesco Eschinardi in 1668.

Athanasius Kircher, inventor, scientist and German Jesuit, also described the 'Lucerna Magica' in the second edition of his *Ars Magna* in 1671. He maintained that he was the inventor, and remarked that the lantern was 'not the work of the Devil, but the result of contemplation'. The lantern had a double convex lens, the light being provided by an oil lamp. A long glass slide with a series of pictures painted on it was placed in front of the lens, and was moved so as to project each subject in turn upon a screen. Through Kircher's book knowledge of the magic lantern became fairly widespread; and in 1692 the scientist William Molyneux, F.R.S., greatly improved its power by adding a condenser to concentrate the light.

The lantern was precisely a magic toy for entertainment. Kircher had used it in a darkened room at the Jesuit College in Rome to give performances of comedies and tragedies, to the great admiration of the audience; and he also mentioned that a Danish mathematician, Thomas Walgenstein, had given public performances of some kind in Rome a short while before, projecting numerous pictures by means of a lantern, which was on sale in the principal towns of Italy.

The slides used in lantern shows gradually became more elaborate, a great variety of them were skilfully painted, and early in the eighteenth century the first mechanical movable slides were made, by means of which figures could be shown in different positions, giving the effect of life and action. Stage plays were performed. Guyot describes in *Nouvelles Récréations* (1770), 'The Sack of Troy', for which slides of different scenery and personages were used simultaneously; they were inserted in different grooves in the lantern, and moved to give the illusion, for instance, of a battle between the Greeks and the Trojans.

Still more elaborate performances were made possible with the Phantasmagoria of E. G. Robertson, an English optician living in Paris at the time of the French Revolution, whose shows were brought to the Lyceum Theatre in London in 1802 by Paul de Philipsthal. After the lights in the auditorium had been extinguished, soft, mournful music was heard, and the curtain rose on a scene of a cave with skeletons and other figures of terror. The music ceased, the rumbling of thunder was heard in the distance, and grew louder; there were sharp flashes of lightning – the impression, in short, of a tremendous storm. Tension grew when the audience saw a light in the air, which gradually increased in size until at length there stood revealed a spectre rolling its eyes and moving its mouth in agony – an image of unutterable despair. This vanished at last into a little cloud, the storm rolled away, and other ghosts rushed up with amazing rapidity and seemed to spring right into the terrified audience, disappearing again to come back clothed with flesh and blood or, as an anticlimax, in the form of some well-known public figure.

The novelty in the arrangement consisted in the use of a double magic lantern which was placed *opposite* the audience, with a semi-transparent screen in between. The double lantern projected one image superimposed on another; and one picture gradually faded out while a new one was slowly brought in. Additional effects were achieved by placing the instrument on wheels; as it approached the screen, the image diminished in size, as it receded it became larger and larger, the brightness of the image being kept constant by turning the wick of the oil lamp up or down as necessary; during the movement of the lantern the focus of the lens was constantly altered, to keep the image sharp on the screen. An ordinary stationary magic lantern was often used as well, to project a landscape into which moving figures were introduced by means of the Phantasmagoria.

Henry Childe, who painted the slides for Philipsthal, revived the idea as a novelty in 1839, but his 'dissolving views' – a great attraction at the Polytechnic Institution up to the mid eighteen-sixties – had nothing to do with ghostly apparitions; they were convincing transformation scenes. A performance consisted of about eighteen different subjects. One of the most popular was a battle between an English and two French men-o'-war. The start of the action was indicated by the appearance of large volumes of smoke from the guns (with sound effects to match), the next slide showed the conquered French ships in a crippled state with their rigging floating on the sea, while the standard flew victoriously from the mast of the English battleship.

Magic lantern shows were a speciality of travelling magicians and showmen in the eighteenth and early nineteenth centuries; often accompanied by two or three musicians, they gave performances at the houses of the well-to-do, particularly where there were children. One of their songs ran:

Vous allez voir! Vous allez voir!
Ce que vous allez voir!
Allons, messieurs, que chacun et chacune
Ouvre les yeux pour mieux apercevoir
Monsieur le Soleil et Madame la Lune.

Voyez, Voyez comme ils tournent les yeux
Tout comme une personne naturelle,
Tout comme une personne naturelle.
Pardon messieurs, une minute ou deux,
Car j'ai besoin de moucher ma chandelle.

From 1840 on the new oxy-hydrogen light provided brilliant illumination – and therefore greater magnification – for the dissolving views, and other lantern shows. Thus at the Manchester Mechanics' Institution in 1858 there were daily lantern shows accompanied by organ music, the slides being magnified to cover a screen thirty feet square. In the eighteen-sixties scenic stage effects by the magic lantern were for the first time employed, at the Haymarket Theatre, in London.

By the eighties and nineties dramatic lantern shows had given way to instructive lectures (chiefly topographical), now showing photographic slides, which had been introduced by the brothers Langenheim of Philadelphia in 1850. This was a highly popular form of entertainment, until the coming of the cinema in the early years of this century. The use of the magic lantern for lectures on geography, natural history, etc., however, went back to the early years of the eighteenth century, when such lectures were first devised by a professor at Tübingen, in Germany.

The now familiar epidiascope, which is simply a modification of the magic lantern for projecting the image of *opaque* bodies, was described by its Swiss inventor, the mathematician Leonhard Euler, in 1753. (See also *Cinema*.)

ILLUSTRATION: Page 356.

Magnet and compass

The **MAGNET**, so familiar to us as a red-painted, horseshoe-shaped toy, and so important in a host of applications from the compass and types of motor and generator to electrical measuring instruments, radar, loudspeakers, television sets, and sound-recording equipment, was known to the Greeks as the *Magnetis lithos*, the 'Magnetic stone' – *i.e.* the stone from the district of Magnesia in Thessaly.

The Greeks were familiar with such hard black pieces of magnetic ore as early as 600 B.C. Thales the Ionian philosopher (c. 624–545 B.C.) held that the magnet contained a soul since it moved the iron. Suśruta, the Indian physician and surgeon of the sixth century B.C., wrote of the surgical employment of magnets: 'A loose, unbarbed arrow, lodged in a wound with a broad mouth ... should be withdrawn by applying a magnet to its end. A shaft of grief, driven into the heart by any of the multifarious emotional causes, should be removed by exhilaration and merrymaking.' The Chinese understood at an early period that a natural magnet, suitably suspended or mounted, always sets itself in the same way to the north–south direction, and they used magnets magically in a form of divination.

It was a Chinese author Chu Yü, very early in the twelfth century, who left the first notice of the mariner's compass, recording that such a magnetic device was employed by foreign sailors between China and Indonesia in the closing years of the eleventh century. So probably the compass was invented by the Arab navigators who pushed east before the Portuguese.

The first compasses consisted of a needle, activated by rubbing it on a magnet, which was fixed to a reed or straw. The reed and its directive cargo then floated on water in a dish. The pivoted needle compass was introduced later in the Middle Ages by the natural philosopher Petrus Peregrinus or Peter of Maricourt, a Frenchman. He described it in 1269 in his *Epistola de magnete*. 'Let a vessel', he said, 'be made of wood or brass or of any solid material and let it be formed or turned in the fashion of a box not very deep ... and let there be fitted over it a lid of transparent material such as glass or crystal ... So let there be arranged in the middle of the vessel itself a slender axis of brass or of silver fitting at its two extremities to the two parts of the box, namely the upper and the lower. And let there be two holes in the middle of the axis in direction at right angles to one another and let an iron wire in the fashion of a needle be passed through one of these holes. And through the other let another wire of silver or brass be passed intersecting the iron one at right angles.'

'By means of this instrument,' Petrus Peregrinus added, 'you will be able to direct your steps to cities and islands and to any places whatever in the world and wheresoever you may be on land or sea, provided the longitudes and latitudes of the places are known to you.'

After the needle had been pivoted, no essential

modification in compasses was made or required until the modern advent of the iron ship driven by engines. The surrounding iron disturbed the needle and means of compensation had to be devised.

William Gilbert (1540–1603), author of the *De magnete, magneticisque corporibus et de magno magnete tellure* (1600), which was the first comprehensive study of magnetism, realized that iron sometimes behaved as a magnet, and he knew how to impart magnetic properties to an iron rod – for example, by heating it, laying it north–south, and hammering it as it cooled – but it was not until the middle of the eighteenth century that it proved possible to make artificial magnets of this kind strong enough to compare with natural magnets.

From the early sixteenth century the natural magnets were known as loadstones, *i.e.* 'journey stones' or 'way stones'. They were fitted into beautiful ornamental cases, with keepers which protected them when they were not in use.

ILLUSTRATION: Pages 318 and 319.

The world upon paper

MAPS of a kind, or various kinds, are made by primitive peoples, scratched in the sand or in the snow, drawn on skins, or carved in wood or bone. They usually indicate in a general way the stages and landmarks on customary journeys, but they show how often the notion of maps must have occurred independently. Thus there is nothing of a common origin about Eskimo maps (which are relief carvings in wood or carved lengths of stick), the charts of South Sea Islanders, and the most ancient of all existing maps, which was drawn on a clay tablet about 2500 B.C. for the purpose of land taxation in northern Mesopotamia (it is now in the Fogg Museum at Harvard).

Maps were made not only by the Sumerians and Babylonians, but in Egypt and early China. They were in frequent use among the Greeks and Romans. The Romans, for example, could see a great map of the world in the Porticus Octaviae, which was set there by the Emperor Augustus. It was based upon a survey begun by Caesar and finished by Marcus Agrippa (63–12 B.C.); and we have what may be derivatives of Greco-Roman cartography in the maps accompanying fifteenth-century manuscripts of Ptolemy's *Geographia*, which was compiled at Alexandria about 150 A.D.

Though the ancient Mesopotamian maps could be accurate, one on a Babylonian clay tablet of the sixth or seventh century B.C. (preserved in the British Museum) shows a Babylonian concept of the world; at the centre is Babylon itself, a circular land mass all around, encircled again by the Persian Gulf. In much the same way medieval maps included conventionalized, generally circular images of the world, centred, as one might expect, upon Jerusalem. A good example is the Hereford Mappa Mundi, made about 1280, and preserved in Hereford Cathedral, a large, boldly drawn map, rich in decidedly uncartographical illustration from the medieval bestiaries.

It is to Ptolemy, after the lapse of centuries, that Europe owed a considerable advance in map-making in the later Middle Ages. Greek manuscripts of his *Geographia* reached the West and were translated into Latin; from 1486 onwards the text was frequently printed and issued with maps engraved on copper or wood. These, based on sound scientific principles but lacking sufficient accurate data, embody the characteristics of maps as we know them. From a slightly earlier period, A.D. 1250–1300, the navigators and pilots of the Italian city-states had begun to chart the coasts of southern and western Europe with the aid of the mariner's compass. These charts, often called portolan charts, concentrate on the coastlines, marked by a close succession of names, and they emphasize islands, deltas, harbours, rocks and shoals. A series of lines, radiating from elaborate compass roses, allowing the bearing of one feature for another to be readily obtained. For the Mediterranean they are remarkably accurate. The normal charts show very little inland topography. More elaborate examples, possibly intended for presentation, are rich in vignettes of cities, banners, and drawings of potentates. The coastal outlines from these charts were rapidly incorporated in existing world maps.

For many years the main source of improvements and extension to the world map were the marine charts drawn by pilots, Italian, Spanish and Portuguese, who accompanied the great explorers on their voyages. The first representation of the Americas is on the world chart painted on an ox-hide in 1500 by the Spanish pilot Juan de la Cosa, who was with Columbus on his second voyage (it is now at the Maritime Museum at Madrid). At the same time the scientists of the Renaissance were developing methods of land survey, and were issuing maps to satisfy the patriotic spirit of the rising nation-states and to assist the growing numbers of merchants and travellers of all kinds. Thus the first maps of the English counties were based on surveys by Christopher Saxton, and were published in one volume in 1579. These fine examples of engravings are strongly influenced by Flemish styles; and it was, indeed, the inhabitants of the Low Countries and more particularly the Dutch – great seamen, traders and financiers – who developed map-making and map-publishing on a large commercial scale. Prominent among the cartographers were Abraham Ortelius (1527–1598), the first to publish a modern atlas, the *Theatrum orbis terrarum*, in 1570, and Gerardus Mercator (1512–1594) who devised the projection so much used by navigators. For most of the sixteenth and seventeenth centuries, the Amsterdam publishing houses of Hondius, Blaeu and Jansson were lords of the European market. Their maps are usually finely engraved with good lettering, and elaborate cartouches. But the scientists of the age of Isaac Newton revealed new facts about the world and devised more accurate survey methods, which made these decorative Dutch maps out of date. In this work of calculating the exact dimensions of the globe, of perfecting the methods of triangulation, and of determining positions by astronomical observations, the lead was taken by French scientists, among whom the Cassini family were prominent. It was on the initiative and through the energy of César François Cassini de Thury (1714–1784) that France was surveyed systematically on a scale of about one inch to one and one-third miles. This was the first modern national survey, and it at once became the model for other European countries.

In 1791, partly as a result of stimulus from France, a regular survey was instituted in Britain, later known as the Ordnance Survey. Its first duty was to lay out the great system of triangles upon which the mapping of the country was based and to produce the map on the scale of one inch to one mile. From this developed the comprehensive series of modern plans and maps of Britain.

Despite the application of air photography and modern science to cartography, much of the surface of the earth is still inadequately mapped. It has recently been stated that only one quarter of the United States has been mapped to 'an acceptable topographical standard', and for the total land surface of the world outside Europe, the fraction properly mapped is probably little more than one-tenth.

ILLUSTRATION: Plate 5 and page 174.

Neither guns nor butter

MARGARINE, the modern substitute for butter and the inevitable fat of the Welfare State, was patented in 1869 by Hippolyte Mège-Mouriès, who was commissioned by the Victualling Department of the French Navy to find an alternative for butter at a time of acute shortage. For his success he was awarded a prize in 1870 by Napoleon III.

Badly fed cows, Mège-Mouriès had noticed, continued to produce milk containing fat, even though the animals themselves were losing weight. From this observation he deduced that the udder converts body fat into the fat of milk. Using beef-suet as a basis, he set about trying to imitate what he thought were the udder's chemical activities. He crushed up his suet with sheep's stomach at first, later with cow's udder, and added a little warm milk. Finally, between warm plates he pressed out a fat fraction with a relatively low melting-point.

Mège-Mouriès called his invention 'margarine' because he thought it was mainly the fatty substance which had been given that name by the French chemist Chevreul a number of years before. The pearl-like lustre of Chevreul's preparation, now known to have been a mixture of stearine and palmitin, caused him to borrow a name from the Greek *margaron*, a pearl.

Manufacturers soon found the stomach and udder additions quite unnecessary, and some of the early success of margarine in America prompted *The Times*, 4 September 1873, to write of English margarine, the raw material of which was 'the fat of horses obtained from the knackers', and to foretell that it would drive genuine butter out of the market.

After the successive adoption of the names 'oleomargarine', 'butterine' and 'margarine', Parliament in 1887 eventually passed the Margarine Act, which clearly defined butter and margarine, and made illegal the mixing of the two.

There have been three major advances in the technique of making margarine. First, other fats, cheaper than those from cattle, were found suitable; secondly, after 1910 it was possible to harden vegetable oils by hydrogenation; and, thirdly, following the discovery in 1927 that vitamin D is produced by irradiating ergosterol, it was possible to add vitamins A and D to margarine without giving it the fishy flavour of cod-liver oil.

It was Sabatier and Senderens, working in France, who discovered in 1899 that hydrogen could be introduced into fairly non-reactive substances with the aid of freshly reduced nickel. Four years later Normann patented a process for hydrogenating fats and oils. Hydrogenation makes lard and butter brittle and crystalline, but vegetable oils and whale oils so treated become firm fats. Thus it is possible to regulate the melting point of margarine so that it is suitable for tropical temperatures or arctic use; and perhaps, one day, there will be summer and winter margarine in the shops, just as there are summer and winter motor oils.

The oils which are hardened into margarine come from plants growing in many different climates. Coconuts are used, also palm, cotton seed and groundnuts from tropical and subtropical countries, as well as olives, soya beans, sunflower seeds, linseed and rape-seed from temperate lands. Whale oil and animal fats are also employed. Margarine production is now a main concern of one of Europe's most powerful cartels, Unilever, and this list of sources of oils gives a slight indication of the width of its interests. However, it is not only output drive and commercial 'plugging' that will ensure a future for margarine: butter is too scarce and too costly for most people. Various governments have hitherto protected dairy-farming by forbidding the sale of coloured margarine; the white, uncoloured fat is very unappetizing. One by one, however, these restrictions are being lifted, both because of pressure from the margarine manufacturers, and because butter shortage or high cost make a cheaper alternative necessary. In 1952, Sir Geoffrey Heyworth, chairman of Unilever, told the annual general meeting:

> The choice ... between margarine and butter will depend upon how much the housewife is prepared to pay for the distinctive flavour of butter. Many people do prefer the flavour of butter to that of margarine, though this may not always be so, for the technique of margarine-making has made considerable progress and is still improving.

One may set beside the words of this great industrial magnate H. W. Fowler's etymological snobbism of 1926 that marj- instead of marg- was 'clearly wrong': 'it was nevertheless prevalent before the war, when the educated had little occasion to use the word'.

Development of matches

MATCHES are among the greatest of the minor boons to mankind, for while it was not difficult to make tinder glow by means of sparks from flint and steel or by wood friction (see *Fire-drill, etc.*), it was by no means easy to complete the stages from glowing tinder to active flame. The earliest matches were therefore a part of the fire-making complex; they were slivers of wood tipped with sulphur which could be easily ignited from the tinder. The Romans knew the ignitible properties of sulphur, but there is little if any evidence that these sulphur matches were common before the seventeenth century.

The next development was to transform the

match itself into the main instrument of ignition without flint and steel. Matches which gave an instantaneous light were devised in the eighteenth century in the form of thin glass tubes, surrounding a wax taper and a small piece of phosphorus (which was not obtained until late in the sixteen-hundreds). These were carried around. To obtain a light one broke the tube, and the phosphorus ignited spontaneously on contact with the air. Matches of this kind were expensive; and were also dangerously liable to break and ignite in one's pocket. In 1786 came the more manageable device of the phosphorus box – in fact a bottle, tightly stoppered and internally coated with phosphorus: sulphur matches were quickly introduced and withdrawn when a light was required. Care had to be taken to re-seal the bottle speedily and effectively each time. More popular than either of these devices was the 'Instantaneous Light Box' introduced about 1810. This time the matches were made by dipping sticks into a mixture of chlorate of potash, gum and sugar. The user had to carry about a small phial of sulphuric acid. For a light the matches were plunged quickly into this and withdrawn. If, in the process, a drop of acid was spilt, it would burn through clothing to the skin. With chlorate matches priced, in those days, at the high figure of a shilling per hundred, the popularity of these dangerous devices is a measure of the difficulty that was experienced in getting a light by other means.

The danger was removed in 1824 by the ingenious device of a Mr Berry of London. His match-box was a tin about five inches by four by two deep, containing (1) a bottle of sulphuric acid, (2) a little turntable to hold matches, (3) a gallows-like structure that could be erected simply by sticking it into a tubular holder, (4) a spirit lamp and (5) a compartment for spare matches. The bottle was sealed by a glass stopper with a conical end that dipped into the acid. To obtain a light, the gallows was erected, a pull on the string lifted up the stopper on the end of which a tiny drop of acid remained, and a match was brought into contact with the acid by turning the turntable. A further turn, and the burning match ignited the spirit lamp. The stopper was lowered again into the acid bottle and the gallows dismantled. No stray drop of acid could spoil the satisfaction of getting a light by a process which did away with the tiresome business of flint, steel and tinder.

However, within a year or two all other contrivances were made obsolete by friction matches. These begin with the 'friction lights' devised in 1826 by John Walker, an English pharmacist of Stockton-on-Tees. To the chlorate match he added sulphide of antimony, and he discovered that if the heads were nipped between a fold of fine sandpaper, they ignited, more often than not, when sharply withdrawn. Walker sold these matches at the old high price of a shilling a hundred, plus twopence for the tin container; but he refused to patent his invention which he regarded as part of his professional service. The news spread, and by 1829 similar matches were being made in London and sold as 'Lucifers'. To these a little sulphur was added to aid combustion. The use of phosphorus on matches was the idea of a Frenchman, Charles Sauria, in 1830; but, like Walker, he sought no patent. Such phosphorus matches were at first dangerously easy to ignite. Many a loaded cart bearing a packet of them among other goods was burnt out because the matches were in the sun, or because the cart jolted badly on the cobbles. The workers making the matches contracted the shocking disease of the jaw and jaw-bone known as phossy-jaw, which could even attack those who used them if they handled the match heads and afterwards put their hands up to their mouths. Red phosphorus, which is not poisonous, was discovered by Schrötter, of Vienna, in 1845, but it seemed impracticable for matches, since it exploded violently when mixed with the other ingredients. Ten years later Lundström, in Sweden, conceived the idea of putting the red phosphorus on the sandpaper outside the box and the other ingredients on the match-head. These matches were called 'safety matches', more from the avoidance of fire risk than out of consideration for the workers, but in fact they were safe in both respects. In 1898 Sevene and Cahen, in France, discovered a harmless substitute for the noxious yellow form of phosphorus in the shape of sesquisulphide of phosphorus, which is equally suitable for 'strike anywhere' matches. These two types, the 'safety' and 'strike anywhere', still rival each other in popularity. The part of the match-stick near the head is usually wax-impregnated to make it burn better.

ILLUSTRATION: Page 216.

'This stinking idol'

The **MAYPOLE** was, and still is, the centre of May-Day celebrations, a life-giving rod set up on the eve of the chief festival of vegetation, farming and fertility, ready for the prime day of the May cycle.

May Day is the day of bringing in 'the May', in English terminology; in Ireland (in Irish May Day is called *lá bealtaine*, the 'blaze-fire', after the strengthening and protective bonfires which were lit on May Eve), it is the day of bringing in the 'Summer' – the English May consisting principally of hawthorn, which was in blossom on May 1st before the changing of the calendar, the Irish 'Summer', including among other plants the May-flower, or marsh marigold, and the rowan-tree. On May Day in various parts of Europe the cattle, which had wintered in the byre, were driven out into the pastures for the first time. The Irish believed that the sun rose early on May Day; and this opening of the year's fertility, both May Day eve and the day itself and all the month, was a period both of rejoicing and of danger. Witches and fairies were active on so stirring an occasion, no less naturally than men and women. The produce of the cattle, the butter and milk, and the cattle themselves needed protection, with the powerful plants of the May or the Summer. For the French and the English it was the hawthorn which had this exceptional power, while the Irish and the people of the Highlands and the Islands, Wales and the North of England trusted, above all, to the rowan-tree (which belongs especially to the upland zone, whereas hawthorn is more typical of the lowlands).

Herrick's famous seventeenth-century poem *Corinna Going a-Maying* bids Corinna mark –

> How each field turns a street, each street a park
> Made green, and trimm'd with trees: see how
> Devotion gives each house a bough,

> Or branch: each porch, each door, ere this,
> An ark, a tabernacle is
> Made up of whitethorn neatly enterwove –

and the Irish, for example, placed rowan over the doors and in the milk-pails and tied it round the churns, and hung it by the hearth to prevent bewitching of the fire. In the Lake District cream was stirred with a rowan stick, and rowan was the material for churn-staffs in the north of England.

Milkmaids danced in London on May Day. Much cream and butter was eaten; horns were blown and used as drinking vessels. Thomas Pennant, in his *Tour in Scotland*, vividly describes Beltane celebrations in 1769, calling them 'a rural sacrifice':

> The herdsmen of every village ... cut a square-trench on the ground, leaving the turf in the middle; on that they make a fire of wood, on which they dress a large caudle of eggs, butter, oatmeal and milk; and bring, besides the ingredients of the caudle, plenty of beer and whisky; for each of the company must contribute something. The rites begin with spilling some of the caudle on the ground, by way of libation: on that, everyone takes a cake of oatmeal, upon which are raised nine square knobs, each dedicated to some particular being, the supposed preserver of their flocks and herds, or to some particular animal, the real destroyer of them: each person then turns his face to the fire, breaks off a knob, and flinging it over his shoulder, says, 'This I give to thee, preserve thou my horses; this to thee, preserve thou my sheep', and so on. After that they use the same ceremony to the noxious animals: 'This I give to thee, O Fox! spare thou my lambs; this to thee, O hooded Crow! this to thee, O Eagle!'

In Westphalia, in Germany, the herdsman rose at dawn on May morning, climbed a hill, cut down the young rowan-tree which first caught the rising sun, and took it back to the farmyard. With a branch of the rowan he then struck the heifer which was to calve over the hind quarters, the haunches and the udder, reciting magical verses (Frazer, *The Golden Bough*) – an account which obviously connects the branch of rowan and the life-giving rod.

The maypole was either birch, elm or pine tree. Thus the Welsh fourteenth-century poet Gruffydd ab Adda ap Dafydd wrote a charming poem *To a Birch cut down, and set up in Llanidloes for a*

Maypole, beginning 'No more will the bracken hide your sturdy seedlings, where your sisters stay; no more will there be mysteries and secrets shared, and sleep, under your dear eaves'. Birch was a powerful tree, used in much the same way as hawthorn and rowan. The Maypole was felled after sunset on May eve; the branches were lopped, except for a leafy crown, and it was heeled. In Elizabethan England it was sometimes dragged from the woods by oxen, according to the angry account left by Philip Stubbes, the Puritan, in his *Anatomie of Abuses* (1583). Men and women went to the woods on May Eve, they brought in the May when the morning came, but 'their chiefest

Fig. 18. Maypole in England, seventeenth century.

jewel they bring from thence is their May pole, which they bring home with great veneration, as thus: They have twenty or forty yoke of oxen, every ox having a sweet nosegay of flowers tied on to the tip of his horns, and these oxen draw home this May pole (this stinking idol rather) which is covered all over with flowers and herbs, bound round about with strings, from the top to the bottom, and sometime painted with variable colours, with two or three hundred men, women and children following it with great devotion. And thus being reared up, with handkerchiefs and flags streaming on the top, they straw the ground about, bind green boughs about it, set up summer halls, bowers and arbours hard by it; and then fall they to banquet and feast, to leap and dance about it, as heathen people did at the

dedication of their idols, whereof this is a perfect pattern, or rather the thing itself. I have heard it credibly reported (and that viva voce) by men of great gravity, credit and reputation, that of forty, three score or a hundred maids going to the wood overnight there have scarcely the third part of them returned home again undefiled.'

In Germany young men carried the Maypole home on their shoulders to the village green or to the market-place, where it was erected. The decoration of the pole with flowers, garlands, etc. had to be finished before sunrise, since the sun destroyed some of the virtue or power of plants. In England and on the Continent, Maypoles were originally set up every year, and were left standing for only a short time. When the deeper meaning of the custom had been forgotten, and when more elaborate decorations had come into use, the poles remained in position for a whole year or even longer. Thus some Bavarian Maypoles have up to sixty carved and painted figures attached to their ladder-like traverses.

Besides the communal Maypoles on the village green or in the market-place, individual Maypoles were sometimes set up in front of private houses, as a symbol of love for sweethearts, as a symbol of fertility for young couples, and as a sign of respect for men holding some high office. On 14 May 1660, Samuel Pepys was at the Hague in Holland and saw there Maypoles 'standing at every great man's door, of different greatness according to the quality of the person'.

Twists of the labyrinth

MAZES, of which there are turf-cut examples of fairly modern date as well as the more recent horticultural mazes, may all have their ultimate source in ancient symbolism and ritual.

The first maze we know of was the Labyrinth, the building at Knossos, according to Greek legend, which Daedalus designed for Minos, King of Crete. Inside it the Athenian girls and youths were sacrificed to the Minotaur. The word *labyrinthos* is probably derived from *labrys,* the double-axe which was the symbol of Zeus of Labranda. The axe was also a sacred object in the Palace of Knossos, which Sir Arthur Evans took to represent the Labyrinth of Greek folk-memory. Apart from the Cretan example, the term 'labyrinth' was applied in the ancient world to three other famous buildings, in Egypt, Etruria and Lemnos. Of these, only the remains of the Egyptian Labyrinth have been discovered. It was built in the Twelfth Dynasty near Arsinoë in the Fayum, its ruins were still extensive in Roman times, and were excavated by Flinders Petrie. This vast two-storeyed structure, built round a series of colonnaded courts, was probably a sepulchral monument. The Etruscan Labyrinth at Clusium was the mausoleum of King Lars Porsena, while the edifice on the island of Lemnos may have been a temple of the Cabiri who were Greek nature deities.

In north-west Europe, labyrinthine diagrams are commonly found inscribed on megalithic monuments, and the passages of chambered barrows sometimes follow intricate winding patterns. One more or less circular maze design in particular had a wide circulation; rock-hewn examples from the Wicklow Mountains and Cornwall show that the pattern was identical with that on ancient coins from Knossos, and on the well-known Tragliatella oenochoë, an Etruscan jar of the seventh century B.C. This cannot be due to coincidence, and points to early commercial and cultural ties between the Mediterranean world and the countries of north-west Europe. Eastwards this traditional Knossian labyrinthine design spread as far as South India, where it is still used in threshold and tattoo patterns.

What exactly was conveyed by the symbolism of these patterns and of the turf mazes is not so easy to say. 'Maze' is derived from a Scandinavian root implying bewilderment or confusion. Confusion of the intruder and limiting the right of penetration to those admitted to a secret is a first and most obvious implication. At the famous Eleusinian Mysteries in Greece the initiate was required to thread his way through a maze. Added to the idea of restricted access to a secret there seems to have been a notion of defence. In ancient Rome they played a 'Game of Troy', described as a 'sacred horse-procession', which was based upon the maze pattern and was connected

closely with the *lustratio*, the ritual confirmation of the defences of the city by a ceremony analogous to the 'beating of the bounds' which has so long been familiar in English parishes. Thus according to Virgil's *Aeneid*, Aeneas watched with pleasure the Trojan youths, including his own son Iulus, performing this game on the plains of Sicily. Riding on horseback, they intertwined in a

Fig. 19. Maze from Etruscan Tragliatella vase.

complex pattern, reminiscent, the poet remarked, of the Labyrinth of Crete. Virgil also says that the game was introduced into Italy by Ascanius (other name for Iulus), who had it performed, doubtless as a foundation ritual, when the defences of Alba Longa were built. The Etruscan jug mentioned above also shows the Game of Troy in progress. The horsemen appear to have come out of the maze, behind which men and women make love. On the maze itself the word *Truia* is written in mirror image. By comparing the pattern of the maze on this jar with Virgil's account, the German scholar Harald von Petrikovits has lately shown how two mounted teams riding the maze would seem to be riding against each other in battle, though they would always just pass each other in adjoining tracks of the labyrinth pattern.

The name Troy is associated with mazes in many parts of northern Europe. Mazes cut in the turf at Somerton in Oxfordshire, Hillbury in Surrey and Pimperne in Dorset have all been known as 'Troy Town'. Turf mazes at Appleby in Lincolnshire and Rockcliffe in Cumberland were called 'The Walls of Troy'. Stone mazes in Norway, Sweden and Finland have names such as

Tröberg, Trojeburg or Trojenburg, and a pebble maze on the island of Agnes in the Isles of Scilly has the same typical Scandinavian design, similar to the Etruscan jug, as well as the usual name of Troy Town. The Troy or Troy Town mazes may owe something to Virgil's story, but the instances of the name Troy in association with a maze seem too numerous and widespread to be due entirely to Roman influence. Possibly 'Troy' for maze – and the Homeric Troy – derive from a common Indo-European root meaning to turn or to make a tortuous movement. Treading the maze was a game in the English countryside, and though it cannot be shown that existing turf mazes are very ancient, these (and the pebble maze at St Agnes) may well have been constantly renewed.

It is curious to find medieval mazes in Christian churches, dating back to the eleventh century, and probably an inheritance from the days of Roman rule. The labyrinth, usually with Theseus and the Minotaur in the centre, was a favourite subject for Roman mosaics (examples are found at Caerleon in Monmouthshire and Harpham in Yorkshire). The church labyrinths of Italy and France are floor designs in the same way. One of the largest now remaining is set in blue and white stones in the floor of Chartres Cathedral. It is usually supposed that these church labyrinths were intended to be traversed on the knees as a form of penance, and they are often called 'Chemins de Jérusalem'; they may also have symbolized the tortuous and hazardous road to salvation. In England they are rare and late; the most famous is one by the west door of Ely Cathedral, constructed by Sir Gilbert Scott during his restorations in 1870.

Garden mazes, of dwarf shrubs or with high hedges, are usually quite different in pattern from the turf mazes or the maze plans of antiquity. They first came into fashion in the sixteenth century; and they may have been known in Roman times. At least, the younger Pliny speaks of having in the garden of his villa in Tuscany a hippodromus, consisting of many paths separated by box hedges and ornamented with topiary work. In addition to the simple hedge maze designed to perplex the visitor, another more elaborate type became popular in the late seventeenth century. In this, winding footpaths penetrated blocks of shrubs and dense thickets, and ornaments and fountains were placed at intervals along the way. The most extravagant example of this kind was the famous labyrinth designed by Jules Hardouin-Mansart for Louis XIV in the small park at Versailles. This has now been destroyed; so indeed with changing fashion have many of the topiary mazes in English gardens. The Hampton Court maze, the most famous and popular of the surviving garden mazes, is also one of the oldest; it was laid out in 1690, probably to replace an older maze of Cardinal Wolsey's time.

ILLUSTRATION: Pages 122 and 123.

A new world of the minute

MICROSCOPES, one of the prime weapons of biology and of the conquest of disease, added immensely to man's experience by revealing a new world of the infinitely small, as the telescope (q.v.) revealed new realms of the infinitely distant. Thus in the seventeenth century, the great age of the foundation of microscopy, the physician and naturalist Henry Power wrote lame but excited and exciting verses on this new revelation –

In the wood-mite or -louse you may behold
An eye of trellice-work in burnisht gold.

Simple and compound microscopes have to be considered, the simple microscope, an instrument of great value and importance in the early days, consisting of a convex lens of short focal length, and so of high magnifying power, mounted in a stand; whereas the compound microscope, optically much more complicated, consists in essence of two convex lenses mounted at either end of a tube. One lens is the 'objective', which forms a real magnified inverted image, the other is the eyepiece which magnifies the image still further. Most compound microscopes have a third lens, the field lens, between the objective and the eyepiece, which increases the field of vision, though it slightly reduces the size of the image.

Objective and eyepiece were first combined to produce a compound microscope at the end of the sixteenth century, an invention for which there are several claimants. From a letter written by William Boreel, Dutch envoy to the French Court, it was apparently invented about 1590, or a little later, by Hans Janssen, or his son Zacharias, who were spectacle-makers at Middelburg in Holland. Boreel says that he saw one of these instruments, which had a brass tube two inches in diameter and eighteen inches long; the tube was supported by three brass dolphins.

In 1609 Galileo devised the telescope which bears his name, and it seems that he realized that, when reversed, it would serve as a microscope. But the nature of the instrument gave it a very small field of view, and Galileo made no attempt to develop it. About the same time microscopes of a primitive type were being used by Drebbel, Thomas Digges, Jan Lippershey, and Jacob Metius, and claims have been made for all of them. There is little doubt, however, that the compound microscope was really invented years before, and that the credit should go to the Janssens.

An early example, the microscope constructed (probably before 1665) by the Italian instrument-maker Campani, is about four inches high, and consists of a vertical tube mounted in a tripod stand. The objective is moved and adjusted by screwing the tube up and down through the top plate of the stand – probably the first application of screw-focusing to a microscope. The eyepiece also has screw-focusing. There is no reflecting mirror, a hole in the lower plate of the stand enabling examination to be carried out by pointing the microscope at the sky or some other source of light.

For many years the microscope was not greatly used or appreciated, though members of the Accademia dei Lincei (the Companions of the Lynx) at Florence were intrigued. One of these, Francesco Stelluti, published in 1625 a small and now very rare work containing the earliest surviving biological figures – of bees, for example – to be drawn with the aid of a microscope. A change came in the last years of the century. From 1665 to 1700 the microscope was employed to great effect by the five 'Classical Microscopists' – two Englishmen, Robert Hooke and Nehemiah Grew, two Dutchmen, Antony van Leeuwenhoek and Jan Swammerdam, and the

Italian Marcello Malpighi. Van Leeuwenhoek apart, all of them probably used both the simple and the compound microscope.

Robert Hooke (1635–1703) published his *Micrographia* in 1665, giving the first descriptions and illustrations of several natural objects, including a plant cell. Thus to the amusement of such men as the poet Samuel Butler, Hooke recorded new information gleaned through 'my

Fig. 20. Campani's microscope.

faithful *Mercury*, my *Microscope*' about the louse. He examined a louse sucking blood from his hand: 'I could plainly perceive a small current of blood, which came directly from its snout and passed into its belly ... there seemed a contrivance, somewhat resembling a pump, pair of bellows, or heart, for by a very swift systole and diastole the blood seem'd drawn from its nose, and forced into the body.'

Van Leeuwenhoek (1632–1723), the draper-naturalist of Delft, used a simple microscope in which the object mounted on a vertical pin could be examined through a tiny biconvex lens mounted in a flat metal plate. He made all his own instruments, and ground his own lenses with superlative skill. Several hundred of his lenses were found among his possessions when he died. The microscope is a crude seeming affair, but with the aid of it van Leeuwenhoek was the first man to observe bacteria and spermatozoa.

Various forms of the simple microscope were developed about the end of the seventeenth century, including the screw-barrel instruments of Hartsocker and of Wilson. Wilson's instruments were very popular. They consisted of a body or barrel of ivory or brass, into the end of which a tube was screwed. The magnifying lens was placed in the upper part of the barrel and an illuminating lens was placed below, in the tube. The object to be examined was pushed in an ivory or bone slide into a slot above the tube and so between the illuminating lens and the magnifying lens. These microscopes were much used for botanical work in the eighteenth century.

In *Micrographia* Hooke had given an illustration of his compound microscope. It possessed several new features. The body was attached by a side ring to a vertical pillar. Coarse adjustment was effected by sliding the ring up and down the pillar, and fine adjustment by a screw thread on the snout. The object was examined by reflected light, focused on to it by a spherical condenser (a glass globe filled with water); and in this instrument he included, possibly for the first time, a field lens, between eyepiece and 'objective'.

Hooke's microscope was the parent of many compound instruments – for example, the important and popular Marshall microscopes first made about 1700. These had a body of finely turned wood (often covered with vellum) which was mounted on a bracket sliding on a vertical brass pillar. Fine adjustment was carried out by means of a screw of the kind which had been devised by the Danzig astronomer, Johannes Hevelius. Instruments mainly of wood, or wood and cardboard, were superseded by all-brass microscopes in the first fifty years of the eighteenth century.

Other improvements slowly accumulated, though for one of importance users of the microscope had to wait till the nineteenth century.

Convex lenses have the defect of chromatic aberration: the lens splits light into components with different foci, producing an image with coloured borders. Several workers attempted to overcome this defect by a combination of lenses. Finally in 1830 Joseph Jackson Lister (father of Lord Lister, the founder of antiseptic surgery) enunciated the law of achromatic foci, and made the first really practical achromatic objective.

Microscope and telescope together had deeply stirred men's imagination in the seventeenth century. Several men besides Henry Power, who found such delicate golden beauty in the eye of the wood-louse, now emphasized that the microscope proved the infinite superiority of works of nature to all human works of artifice. Nehemiah Grew (1641–1712), the microscopical pioneer who was the first to recognize sex in plants, remarked in his *Anatomy of Plants* (1682) on the exquisite fineness of plant tissues as revealed by the new instrument – 'One who walks about with the meanest stick,' he wrote, 'holds a piece of nature's handicraft, which far surpasses the most elaborate woof or needlework in the world.' Another writer imagined both inhabited planets and millions of creatures alive on a grain of sand, so that the giant blocks of Stonehenge were 'as much alive as a hive of bees'.

The primitive microscopes of the seventeenth century had given magnifications of about 100 diameters (Hooke). Today ordinary low-power objectives give a magnification of about 400 diameters. The twelfth-inch oil immersion objective used in bacteriological work gives a magnification of about 1,000 diameters. The electron microscope recently developed, which does not work on an optical system at all, magnifies by 30,000 diameters and upwards, promising to revolutionize histology and the study of virus diseases.

ILLUSTRATION: Pages 320 and 321.

The thing that is hid

MINES, miner and mineral are words at once suggesting the search for ores and metals, yet the first mines go back to an era before metallurgy, to the technological periods grouped together as the Stone Age.

Possibly mining for the raw material of stone tools and weapons began in mesolithic or Middle Stone Age times, in which greenstone, for example, was quarried in Norway. Mines as we understand them – shafts opening into subterranean galleries – certainly belong to the neolithic era, to the search for good quality flint. Surface flint of the chalk districts does not make the best tools, and the more suitable nodules underlie the surface, except at outcroppings. Thus four thousand years ago flint-mining was established in Belgium, France, England and elsewhere. In England the most celebrated of these early shafted mines are to be found at Grime's Graves in Norfolk, where sands and gravel overlie the chalk in which the flints occur.

At such centres mining began to be a profession, and man started upon that long process so well described in the Book of Job: 'he putteth forth his hands upon the rock, he overturneth the mountains by the roots; he cutteth out rivers among the rocks and his eye seeth every precious thing. He bindeth the floods from overflowing and the thing that is hid he bringeth forth to light'. The neolithic miners on either side of the Channel had developed considerable skill. They used digging-sticks, picks and rakes both made of the antlers of the red deer, shoulder-blade shovels, wedges, hammers and rope. They lit the underground darkness with rough lamps hollowed from chalk, and they left pillars of chalk for propping the roof. But it should not be assumed that neolithic man was concerned only with material for his weapons and tools. A variety of minerals also attracted him by their bright colours or peculiar form. There were minerals he could use for cosmetics and pigments; for his pleasure and also for his comfort and his protection, since they were turned into amulets, he collected what we name precious and semi-precious stones. Rock crystal, chalcedony, jasper, steatite, obsidian (a good material for sharp tools) and much else belonged to neolithic man's treasury.

He would thus have been familiar with various ores, including copper ores, the basic material of his next advance, before he learnt how to smelt them. When he did learn the production and use

of metal, his discoveries now involved him in that endless prospecting for ores which has gone on ever since; they impelled him to new surface and subterranean mining, and posed many new problems. Copper-mining in Bronze Age Europe must have been extensive; and we know something of its techniques from prehistoric mines in the Salzburg province of Austria, between Bischofshofen and the village of Mühlbach, which have been examined. Here the prehistoric miner pierced through hard rock by 'fire-setting' – heating the

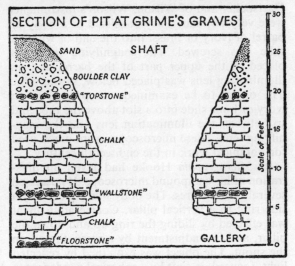

Fig. 21. Shaft at Grime's Graves.

rocks by fire, that is to say, and then disintegrating them by cooling them off suddenly with cold water. This remained the only way of tackling really tough formations until the development of explosives; and its use in Bronze Age mining can be inferred from galleries still black with soot.

The prehistoric miners in Austria employed wooden tools extensively, and dragged the ore on wooden sledges. They knew how to build up wooden staging to lift the fire-setting fires up to the roof. By about 3000 B.C. the miner had learnt the use of wooden props to prevent the danger of subsiding cap-rocks. Pliny in his *Natural History*, in the first century A.D., has something to say of mining in the Roman era – of illumination and lamps which came 'to measure the spells of work, the toilers being for many months without the light of day', of ventilation and bad air and the deadliness of labour in the mines, for which the Romans, like other peoples before them – and after them – used the labour of slaves and war prisoners.

By far the most serious problem throughout the later history of mining was that of drainage, since deeper workings tended to fill with the sub-soil water. The Romans tackled the difficulty by diverting slave labour to treadmills and water-wheels; but drainage limited the depth of mining until the introduction of efficient steam-driven pumps by Newcomen in England early in the eighteenth century. The Royal Society from the start had sponsored the construction of power-driven pumps which would free the mines of water. It is a curious by-product of mines and mining and the water trouble that they were directly responsible for the full development of the steam-engine. For the art of mining in medieval and sixteenth-century Europe, it is a pleasure to turn from page to page of what was the mining textbook, the *De re metallica* (1556), by the German mining expert, Georg Agricola. Lively woodcuts picture all the processes of the time; and Agricola deals even with the discovery of minerals by means of the divining rod (the modern translation of *De re metallica*, by Herbert Hoover and L. H. Hoover contains the illustrations and has lately been reprinted).

The consequences of mining are many of them obvious – and some of them all too obvious – in the metal age. Metals have altered the world politically as well as materially. Ore deposits became coveted possessions at an early period. The goldfields of Eygpt or the iron-mines of the Hittites, the pioneers of the Iron Age, were treasures to be defended at all cost; and the conquest of Spain by the Romans was no doubt hastened by 'the winning of the silver and gold which is there', Spain in due season also hurrying after the gold and silver of Mexico and South America. Since large sums were needed to exploit mines, in the Middle Ages bankers such as the Fuggers and the Welsers financed the mines of Central Europe and Hungary until mining became an important field for the banker and a formative element in the economics of capitalism.

Mines also stimulated the growth of geological science. The ancients carefully studied the char-acteristics of their minerals, their colour, hardness and resistance to acids; and even without any chemical knowledge they managed to build up classifications which were useful. The Assyrians knew no fewer than 120 such minerals which they employed in technology, medicine and magic. The Greeks and Romans knew even more, and tried to find out how they originated. By then there was practical experience enough of mining to guide them to rules about surface finds which would point to lodes further down in the earth. They began to discuss the fossils found in some mines and on certain mountains and their origin. Mining may be credited with a share in the earliest speculations on the history of the earth and the forces of nature moulding its surface, which go back as far as classical times. (See also *Bronze, Iron, Steam-engine*.)

ILLUSTRATION: Page 367.

Urging the rapid car

The **MOTOR-CAR** originated earlier than one might think, beginning and developing before the internal-combustion engine became at last its motivator.

The great increase in trade in the late eighteenth century made many people realize that something more efficient was needed than the horse, trailing in age-old packhorse caravans, or drawing the carrier's waggon, or harnessed to the stage-coach. The stage-coach horse, for instance, worked under such duress that it lived only about three years. Some believed that the steam-engine, now successfully used for draining mines, would propel what the horse had drawn. Thus in 1791 Erasmus Darwin prophesied

> Soon shall thy force, gigantic steam, afar
> Drag the slow barge or urge the rapid car.

The steam-engine was still too cumbersome; yet as early as 1769 Cugnot in France had shown the way by building a mechanically operated road vehicle, which ran under its own power for a short distance. The boiler was not good enough and the machinery needed much improvement.

In 1786 William Symington, afterwards famous for his steamboat the *Charlotte Dundas*, had also built a working model of a steam road carriage.

Trevithick demonstrated his practical steam carriage at Redruth in Cornwall in 1801; and as both the steam-engine and the roads improved, so between 1820 and 1840 many more steam carriages were devised in Great Britain. They naturally resembled the horse-drawn passenger carriages, which by this time were fitted with elliptic springs and stronger wheels. Though Telford and

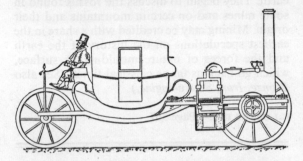

Fig. 22. Symington's steam road carriage, 1786.

McAdam had revolutionized the highways, and though many new inventions helped the pioneers, their difficulties remained formidable. They had only bar-iron and cast-iron to work with, which meant that engine crankshafts, axles and other parts frequently broke. Tools were not well enough developed for good workmanship. There was much prejudice against a revolutionary supersession of horse by steam; some of the new vehicles were wilfully damaged. There was no official support; and to cap everything the new steam carriages were subjected to heavy road tolls.

Mechanical problems were difficult enough – the problem, for instance, of transmitting the power from the engine to the driving-wheels. Cugnot's single front wheel, which also steered his vehicle, had been driven directly from the engine. Walter Hancock (1799–1852), brother of Thomas Hancock the English pioneer of the age of rubber (q.v.) and William Henry James (1796–1873) tried chain-drive, which was flexible and more adaptable; but their chains lacked strength and accuracy, and suffered much from stretch and wear. W. H. James and Sir James Caleb

Anderson (1792–1861) used shaft-drive with a universal coupling in their four-wheel-drive carriage of 1825, thus introducing the cardan or propeller-shaft of the present day (named after the Italian mathematician Geronimo Cardano, who mentioned the universal coupling in his *De subtilitate rerum*, 1550).

Trevithick had apparently been the first to suggest that the speed of the driving-wheels should be varied by gears for tackling hills, and Robert Griffiths (1805–1883) actually fitted change-speed gears on his vehicle of 1821.

For steering, some used pilot wheels in front; others had a swivelling fore-carriage of the horse-vehicle type, in which the fore-carriage was turned by a chain connected to a steering column. It was also found necessary to fit ratchets, or else clutches, to the rear driving-wheels so that one of the wheels could be made free while negotiating a corner. Steering in this manner was somewhat awkward and required great strength; should one of the steering wheels hit a rut or a stone, a severe shock was transmitted to the driver. Part of this difficulty was eventually overcome by adapting an arrangement invented by Du Quet, in 1714, in which the steering wheels were on separate pivoting supports (he had embodied this on a road carriage with sails). The inconvenient ratchets and clutches had to be replaced by something that would be automatic. The solution of this problem was attributed to Onésiphore Pecquer of France, who in 1828 patented the differential gear now utilized on practically all motor vehicles. It allowed the driving-wheels to rotate at different speeds when turning a corner while still taking the driving-power from the engine.

In 1831 Hancock started the first regular road service by steam carriage. His vehicles were good for the time, but they suffered frequent mishaps. Smoke and soot and steam hissing its way through imperfect joints inconvenienced the passengers. Shillibeer's horse-drawn buses, introduced to London in 1829, were more comfortable and successful.

Invention had cleared the way, but little was done with self-propelled road vehicles in mid-century. A few were made in the late fifties and early sixties, such as Rickett's steam car of 1859–1860, which is recognizably a forerunner of the petrol car. Then in 1865 an unfortunate Act of Parliament limited the speed of all road locomotives – traction-engines and passenger carriages alike – to four miles an hour in the country and two miles an hour in towns; a man with a red flag had to walk sixty yards in front.

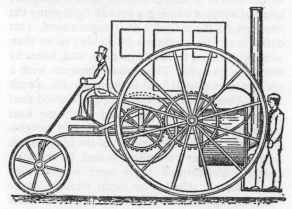

Fig. 23. Trevithick's steam carriage, 1801.

In France, Ravel and Bollée both made contributions. Ravel in 1868 constructed a boiler fired by petroleum, and so was able to devise a much smaller carriage. Petroleum was not well known at the time, and he had to obtain a permit for testing his carriage on the roads. About 1873 Bollée re-invented Du Quet's steering mechanism and also the shaft-drive. He wanted to manufacture his vehicles in large numbers, but there was no demand.

Other advances, nonetheless, helped to transform the situation, notably Bessemer's steel process of 1856, which provided stronger and more reliable materials. By the eighties machine tools and manufacturing methods had much improved. Parts could be made stronger and more accurate; and more cheaply. The 'safety' push bicycle was well developed, and steam-engines were even fitted to push tricycles. Otto in 1876 had made his four-cycle gas engine; Gottlieb Daimler patented his vertical four-stroke gas engine in 1885, and by 1889 produced his high-speed V twin-cylinder engine worked by petrol, which proved a satisfactory unit for propelling cars. Power and lighter weight were now combined; and for this engine Emile Levassor built a new chassis, and one that was in many ways a

departure from the horse-carriage type. In 1891 Levassor devised the layout still usually adopted, in which the engine is in front of the car. A Panhard-Levassor car finished first in the Paris–Bordeaux–Paris race of 1895. This race showed people that horseless carriages – later to be called motor-cars – had come to stay.

In England the 'Emancipation Act' of 1896 removed motoring restrictions, and British engineers were enabled to apply their practical knowledge with enthusiasm. In France and America also development was rapid. The design of all parts, including the electrical ignition system, carburettor, gears, axles, pneumatic tyres, controls, and seating arrangements, was constantly improved. Glass screens, hoods, and side curtains were fitted to protect passengers from the weather. Pneumatic tyres almost entirely replaced solid rubber tyres by about 1904. The four-door saloon car was introduced about 1912. The world entered a new era of transport when mass production of motor-cars was started in 1910. (See also *Steam-engine, Internal-Combustion Engine, Wheel.*)

ILLUSTRATION: Page 75.

Tinkling music

The **MUSICAL BOX** was not the first musical automaton, but it was the first which could be produced cheaply enough for a wide sale. In the Victorian era tens of thousands were exported from Switzerland to every part of the world. Their repertoire reveals the tastes of the age; at first the boxes played selections from opera or dances (which were used by teachers of dancing); then in the middle of the nineteenth century folk-songs and ballads were popular, to be followed by waltzes and finally songs from the music-hall.

For the origin of the musical box one must turn to musical watches, which were invented in the Vallée de Joux in Switzerland in the second half of the eighteenth century.

Taking the watches first, there are two types. In one the comb consists of a number of separate steel teeth or reeds tuned to scale and screwed into the main body of the watch. The teeth are plucked by pins arranged on a brass cylinder in such a way that the plucking produces the melody. In the other kind the teeth or reeds of the comb are secured individually and arranged fanwise following the curvature of the case. There are two sets of them, above and below a disc (instead of a cylinder), which is pinned on both surfaces. The ends of the teeth are bent down at right angles towards the disc.

This mechanism was an advance; it occupied less space and produced a better tone, at any rate in articles so small as a watch. Also the melody could be repeated again and again with one winding of the mainspring. However, the first type prevailed, and became the direct ancestor of the musical box *per se*.

By 1800, miniature musical works of the disc type were being fitted in snuff-boxes, walking-stick handles, fob seals and other *objets d'art*, which were often beautifully enamelled. They were much in vogue during the French Empire. As time went on the snuff-boxes were made larger and lost their original purpose; they became, in fact, miniature musical boxes; and they were fitted with cylinders and laminated combs. The teeth, instead of being separately mounted, were made in groups of three to five or more, each group being screwed into the brass bedplate. By degrees the work ceased to be a branch of watch-making and developed as a separate industry in two main centres, Geneva, where Nichol Frères, founded in 1828, became the largest makers, and St Croix, where E. Paillard was established in 1814. After about 1820 the combs were cut from a single plate, and a box of this period would play two or three or perhaps four airs. The boxes were now twelve inches long; the longer comb and cylinder meant a greater volume of sound and a greater range of tone.

Following the watchmaking custom, the artisans worked in their own cottages. The gear wheels would be produced by one family, the cylinders pinned by another, and so on. The metal used in the comb is reputed to have contained secret ingredients; watchmakers of the time probably knew more than any other craftsmen of the various alloys possible. But the greatest skill was called for in the 'arrangement', as the selection of the tune or repertoire is called, and in

the correct setting of the pins on the cylinder. As far as these go, the best boxes were manufactured between 1845 and 1870.

The Victorian period saw a number of changes and improvements. The early makers found that it took a long while for the vibrations of a tooth to die down; it could not be used during the interval without causing a squeak by tapping the next pin on the cylinder as it came round. This defect was first overcome by having more than one tooth tuned to the same note, and, later, by attaching dampers. The earliest dampers were a narrow strip of quill fixed to the underside of each tooth. About 1830, narrow strips of curved steel proved much better. At about the same time resonators in the form of small lead weights were fixed to the underside tip of the longer teeth to give a greater volume of sound. In the mid-century, air-vibrated reeds were incorporated and, later on, wooden or metal whistles, to be followed by bells, drums and castanets. These elaborated boxes, however, were not of the same high quality as the simpler type. Also about this time models were fitted with interchangeable cylinders, thus greatly increasing the repertoire; here again these were not musically as good as the fixed cylinders. Both Nichol and Paillard produced what was known as the 'Sublime Harmonie', which had three combs, the bass being in the centre to give increased resonance. Boxes were produced twenty-two inches long with cylinders five inches in diameter.

A decline began. About 1850 the home industry gave place to the factory system. Mass production met increased demands for a cheaper box and one with a larger selection of tunes. So quality suffered, in mechanism and case alike. Limitation of the number of tunes was the great disadvantage of the musical box. In the eighties, therefore, the Symphonium was introduced; by means of interchangeable discs, which replaced the cylinder, this gave an unlimited selection of tunes. The Symphonium was followed by the Polyphone and others, until finally in the early nineteen hundreds the gramophone delivered the coup-de-grace.

Note the metal cylinder and then the disc as forerunners of cylinder and disc in the phonograph and gramophone. (See also *Gramophone*.)

N

Newsbook to newspaper

NEWSPAPERS are so much a part of our own lives that it is difficult to realize that the origins of the newspaper go back only to the early years of the seventeenth century, although printing had been invented before the middle of the fifteenth century.

This late development was not due to any lack of demand. The interest in novelty, in news, which St Paul saw as a characteristic of the Athenians, is universal. But governments soon realized the power of the printed word. The success of Luther's revolt against authority was largely made possible by the aid of the printer. The lesson was not lost on secular authorities. Some form of censorship was imposed in every country in Europe in the sixteenth century. In England the publication of news was assumed to be part of the royal prerogative. The legal position was set down by Lord Chief Justice Scroggs in 1680 when the judges were consulted about the regulation of the Press. They declared 'that to print and publish any news books or pamphlets of news whatsoever is illegal: that it is a manifest intent to the breach of the peace, and they may be proceeded against by law for an illegal thing'.

In this cold legal climate there was no hope for the flowering of continuous journalism. Fortunately in times of stability the government did not think it necessary to enforce its prerogative, and in times of crisis it was frequently unable to do so. The publication of isolated newsbooks had occurred in Germany in the fifteenth century. *The trewe encountre*, an account of Flodden published soon after the battle in 1513, may be considered the first English newsbook. Thirty years later Henry VIII suppressed some of the printed accounts of the expedition to Scotland in 1544, but despite setbacks such as this the trade in news continued to increase within the limits set by the licenser and the Stationers' Company. Some 300 news pamphlets printed in London be-

tween the years 1590 and 1610 have survived. In content they range from murders in Hornchurch to floods in Rome, but they contain no home political news that was not officially inspired. Elizabeth's ministers took care to publish an account of the defeat of the Armada, and Ralegh's *Report of the truth of the fight about the iles of Açores* was put out to counter the Spanish versions of the sinking of the *Revenge*.

The circulation of news in Europe at the beginning of the seventeenth century was considerable. It had been helped by the development of the postal services, and also by the rise of written newsletter agencies. The importance of accurate news to international bankers was obvious, and the Fugger newsletters are well known. By the end of the sixteenth century there were in several cities of Europe newsletter writers who were sending weekly reports not only to official bodies but to private subscribers. From 1591, for example, Hendrik van Bilderbeek in Cologne was serving the States General of the Netherlands and through them many Dutch towns, and also clients in Sweden and France. The way was now open for enterprising and resolute publishers to put this news into print.

The earliest surviving weekly newsbooks date from 1609. These are the Strassburg *Relation* and the *Aviso*, formerly attributed to Augsburg, but now thought to have been printed at Wölfenbuttel. The *Relation* clearly goes back before 1609 and the publisher was sufficiently sure of himself to print his name to it. The *Aviso* is anonymous. The lead established by these German towns, no doubt due to their geographical position in the very centre of Europe, was not long maintained. In Antwerp the printer Abraham Verhoeven had been producing newsbooks under licence since 1605. By 1620 his *Gazette* appeared regularly and was consecutively numbered. In Amsterdam the *Courante uyt Italien, Duytslandt, &c.* printed by Joris Veseler, dates from 1618. A year later Broer Jansz. began to publish every week a sheet without title, which was later known as *Tijdinghen uyt verscheyde quartieren*.

These Dutch corantos are especially important because the origins of both English and French journalism are to be found in Amsterdam. The earliest newspaper in English to have survived is a sheet without title printed at Amsterdam by Veseler on 2 December 1620. The issue of December 23 is entitled *Corrant out of Italy, Germany, &c.*, and subsequent numbers bear a similar title. In 1621 Jansz. also published a translation of his Dutch paper, *Courante, or, Newes from Italy and Germany*.

London publishers did not long let these Dutch experts beat them out of their own home market. But they began very cautiously. They issued translations of the Dutch papers, and to disguise their origin better they gave them false Dutch imprints. We can recognize these from the English founts of type which they used. Such papers as the *Corante* of 20 June 1621, 'printed in Amsterdam by Joris Veselde', two papers purporting to come from 'Altmore', and one ostensibly printed at the Hague by Adrian Clarke, a printer otherwise unknown, all come from London. Thomas Archer was probably one of the pioneers in these ventures. In 1621 he was certainly in trouble 'for making or adding to, his corrantos'. By September of that year the first newspaper bearing a London imprint had appeared. This was the *Corante or Newes from Italy, Germany, Hungarie, Spaine and France* printed for N.B., initials which may stand either for Nathaniel Butter or Nicholas Bourne, both of whom were well known later on as publishers of news. Seven issues of this weekly have survived, the last dated 22 October 1621.

All these papers of 1621 and 1622 were, like their Dutch exemplars, single folio sheets of two pages only, each page having two columns. They were modelled on the written newsletter. They contained only foreign news set out in short paragraphs headed by the town of origin and the date of the news. The single pamphlets of news which had preceded these folios had all been small quartos, the usual book and pamphlet size of the time. To this style the newsbooks of 1622 reverted. They were mostly twenty-four pages long. Early in 1622 several publishers had gone into this field of the newsbook and competition had been keen. But by the autumn they had all combined in one syndicate. On 15 October 1622 they happened to have material enough to fill two newsbooks on the same day, and to distinguish them these newsbooks were numbered 1 and 2, the fortuitous beginning of a practice which was observed in subsequent issues and is now one of the main characteristics of the newspaper.

In 1632 Butter and Bourne, the surviving partners in the news syndicate, offended the Spanish ambassador and by a decree of the Star Chamber they were promptly forbidden to publish weekly news. The prohibition lasted for six years, during which time the demand for news of the war in Europe was filled by their semi-annual *Swedish Intelligencer*. In 1638 Butter and Bourne obtained a patent to print foreign news and proceeded to issue three newsbooks a week, one translated from the Dutch, one from the Frankfurt and one from the Nuremberg corantos.

By this time the differences at home between King and Parliament had grown acute. The abolition of Star Chamber in 1641 deprived the government of its chief means of controlling the Press. In November 1641 appeared the first paper to give home political news. This was *The Heads of Severall Proceedings in this Present Parliament*, which soon had many rivals. As earlier in the field of foreign affairs these brief reports of parliamentary proceedings had been anticipated by written newsletters. The outbreak of the Civil War gave an immense impetus to journalism. From 1642 to 1649 on an average ten different newsbooks were published every week. After the execution of the King the Commonwealth gradually succeeded in suppressing all the clandestine royalist journals and from 1656 to 1658 only the official papers were suffered to appear. Richard Cromwell, however, could not control the Press and shortly before the Restoration the first daily was published. This was the *Perfect Diurnall*, which had a brief three weeks' existence from 21 February to 16 March 1660, Sundays excepted.

The Restoration was quickly followed by the Licensing Act of 1662. But the government was not content with a policy of repression. In 1665 it launched an official paper, the *Oxford Gazette*, renamed the *London Gazette* when the Court returned to the capital, which is now the oldest surviving English newspaper. It began as a folio paper with the text printed in two columns. Henceforward almost all newspapers were printed in this form. In 1695 the Licensing Act was allowed to expire and there was a rapid development of thrice-weekly posts, such as the

Post Boy, the *Post Man* and the *Flying Post*. In 1702 the first substantial daily, the *Daily Courant*, was founded. The reign of Queen Anne saw many journalistic innovations, such as the essay paper, containing more comment than news. Governments now realized the need of a Press favourable to themselves: Defoe and Swift were employed to defend the last ministry of Queen Anne. The taxation of newspapers, which lasted until 1855, also began in Queen Anne's day with the Stamp Act of 1712.

The fusion of the essay paper and the newspaper was accomplished in such a paper as the *Craftsman*, a weekly founded in 1727, which also contained a considerable number of advertisements. By the middle of the eighteenth century newspapers included most of the features they have to-day, except for illustrations. But they were still very small, six pages only for the most part, with a circulation counted in hundreds rather than thousands. They were still printed by book printers. As late as 1785 the London *Times* was founded to demonstrate the advantage of printing books by a new method. Power was applied to the printing press in 1814, transport and communications were soon revolutionized, and the way was open that led to the modern newspaper which gives the reader – or a huge number of readers over a wide area – up-to-date news of all the world. Yet the aims of the modern paper go little beyond those which were set down in the first number of *The Times*, on 1 January 1785: 'to facilitate the *commercial* intercourse between the different parts of the community through the channel of *Advertisements*; to record the principal occurrences of the times; and to abridge the account of debates during the sitting of Parliament'.

ILLUSTRATION: Page 163.

Nightdresses, nightcaps, pyjamas

NIGHT-CLOTHES – or special night-clothes – have no great antiquity. It is usually thought that until the end of the Middle Ages at least, both sexes slept naked in bed, and this was probably the general rule. There were exceptions. Contemporary illustrations show that night-clothes were sometimes worn, and especially for such occasions as 'lying-in'. The Lord de Joinville, at the beginning of the fourteenth century, is described as wearing his tunic in bed, but as he was suffering from malaria, this was presumably to keep the body warm during a fit of shivers. In 'The Merchant's Tale', Chaucer describes a man in the fourteenth century as sitting up in bed in his shirt and nightcap. The truth seems to be that in warm weather people slept naked and in cold weather wore their day-shirts or smocks – a practice which continued in country districts until quite modern times. It was only gradually that a distinction grew up between the day-smock and the night-smock, the latter being longer and more ample. Considerations of hygiene had probably nothing to do with it. Sir Thomas More's daughters were no doubt attired in such night-smocks on the celebrated occasion described by John Aubrey (see Aubrey's *Brief Lives*), when his future son-in-law William Roper came 'one morning, pretty early', with a proposal to marry one of them, More taking Roper to the room where they lay in a truckle-bed, whipping off the sheet and revealing them for his choice, with 'their smocks up as high as their arme-pitts'. Men wore nightshirts, and both sexes wore nightcaps, sometimes tied or buttoned under the chin. Men's nightcaps were often of velvet and sometimes embroidered. There is a very elegant specimen in the Victoria and Albert Museum, in London, made in one piece with a lower border embroidered on the reverse side so as to form a turned-up brim.

A certain confusion arises from the Elizabethan use of the word 'night gown'. A stage direction in *Twelfth Night* tells us that 'Malvolio enters in his night gown'; but this was what we should call a dressing gown, a loose and comfortable garment worn by older men as a negligé.

In the seventeenth century the shirt or smock, both for day and night and for men and women, became much more elaborate; it was trimmed with lace at wrist and throat. In mourning the strange custom of wearing black night-clothes was adopted. The *Verney Memoirs* (1651) mention 'two black taffety nightclothes with black capps'. There is mention also of 'six fine night-capps laced, marked V [for Verney] in black silke; four plain capps mark'd in blew silke'. Night-caps continued to be elaborately embroidered until well on in the eighteenth century.

The usual material for night-clothes was linen, of a fineness appropriate to the wealth of the owner, but that other even more luxurious materials were beginning to be used can be gathered from Colley Cibber's play *She Would and She Would Not* (1703), which mentions the lady who would 'steal out of bed ... with nothing but a thin silk nightgown about her'. Perhaps this was similar to the 'modish French night-clothes' referred to in Mrs Centlivre's *Platonic Lady* (1707). On the other hand, there are references to elderly gentlemen wearing flannel shirts, and a character in Smollett's *Humphry Clinker* (1771) wore a quilted nightcap.

Throughout the eighteenth century there was little change in essentials. The nightshirt for men and the night shift for women differed from the day-shirt and the day chemise only in being a little fuller and longer.

In the nineteenth century men's night attire became severely practical. A specimen of 1840 has a plain turned-down collar buttoned at the neck. The jelly-bag nightcap familiar to us in illustrations by Cruikshank was almost universally worn, although Mr Pickwick, it will be remembered, had one that tied under the chin. Women's nightcaps nearly always did so; they resembled babies' bonnets.

In the late sixties, however, nightcaps began to go out of fashion; men's nightshirts remained plain, but women's became more elaborate again, with stand-up collars and yokes, lavishly trimmed with lace. The real revolution in men's attire began in the nineties when pyjamas started to take the place of nightshirts. They are thought to have originated in India, the word coming from the Hindu *pajama*, 'drawers'. Once introduced into England they steadily became more popular, not only with men but with women. A 'combination nightgown' or lady's pyjama of 1886 is described as having frills at knees and wrists, with a high collar and buttoning down the front. An advertisement of 1895 describes 'Ladies' pyjamas in pale blue and white silk mixture, tied round the waist with an encased ribbon and finished at the wrist, ankles and throat with lace; large bishop sleeves; a cascade of lace down the bodice.' Thus night attire in the mid-nineties followed the prevailing fashion for balloon sleeves.

So far as men are concerned, the battle of the nightshirt and pyjamas may now be said to have ended in a victory for the latter; although trade catalogues listed 'gentlemen's nightgowns' reaching to the ankles as late as 1930. With women the issue is not yet decided. Already in 1906 chorus girls in pyjamas were singing 'We won't wear a nightie any more'; but nightdresses have continued to be worn, probably by the majority of women, until the present day. (See also *Bed-clothes*.)

Earth, air, fire, water

NYLON, the ancient philosophers would have said – and with some justification – is made of Earth, Air, Fire and Water. In prosaic modern terms it needs coal products, oxygen and nitrogen from the air, water, and the application of heat in a complex series of chemical processes to provide us with this new plastic material, which is the first completely synthetic fibre and which constitutes a memorial to a great chemist, Wallace Hume Carothers.

In 1928 the American chemical manufacturers E. I. du Pont de Nemours and Company, having decided to extend their provision for fundamental research, brought Carothers from Harvard University, gave him facilities and left him virtually to follow his own devices. He chose to study the subject of polymerization (a polymer molecule is made up of many molecules of some simple substance joined together to form a large molecule of a new substance). He also made plans to examine the internal crystal structure of the substances he made. In 1928 he began the work which eventually led to the discovery of nylon.

The first polymers which Carothers devised were interesting academically but possessed no exceptional properties. Then he introduced a new method of study, using the molecular still. In this apparatus a reaction is carried out in a high

Continued on p. 275

The Blow-gun in Europe. Bird-shooting with blow-gun and crossbow, c. 1475.

Violin, detail from *Eros Triumphant* by Caravaggio (1565–1609).

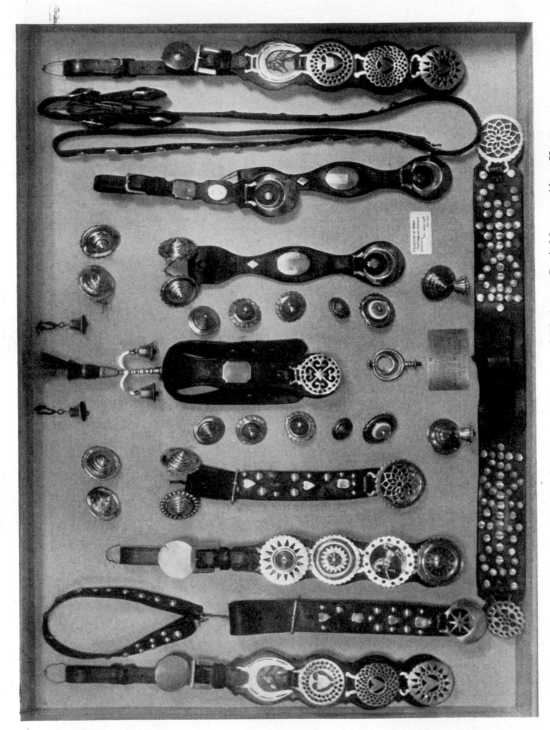

Horse brasses used by T. Parfitt, carter to Marquess of Winchester. Curtis Museum, Alton, Hants.

From horse to tractor: the first internal-combustion engine tractor, designed in 1902.

ENCYCLOPEDIE,

OU

DICTIONNAIRE RAISONNÉ

DES SCIENCES,

DES ARTS ET DES MÉTIERS,

PAR UNE SOCIETÉ DE GENS DE LETTRES.

Mis en ordre & publié par M. *DIDEROT*, de l'Académie Royale des Sciences & des Belles-Lettres de Prusse; & quant à la PARTIE MATHÉMATIQUE, par M. *D'ALEMBERT*, de l'Académie Royale des Sciences de Paris, de celle de Prusse, & de la Société Royale de Londres.

Tantùm ſeries junǎuraque pollet,
Tantùm de medio ſumptis accedit honoris! HORAT.

TOME PREMIER.

A PARIS,

Chez
{
BRIASSON, *rue Saint Jacques, à la Science.*
DAVID l'aîné, *rue Saint Jacques, à la Plume d'or.*
LE BRETON, Imprimeur ordinaire du Roy, *rue de la Harpe.*
DURAND, *rue Saint Jacques, à Saint Landry, & au Griſſon.*

M. DCC. LI.

AVEC APPROBATION ET PRIVILEGE DU ROY.

Encyclopaedia: Title-page of Volume I of Diderot's *Encyclopédie*, 1751.

ACERB, is a Taft between Sower and Bitter, fuch as moft Fruits have before they are ripe.

ACETUM *Radicatum,* is the fharpeft part of Vinegar when the Phlegm is drawn off.

ACETUM *Philofophorum;* fo fome Chymifts call that four Liquor which is made by diffolving a little Butter or Icy Oyl of Antimony in a confiderable quantity of Water.

ACETUM *Alcalifatum,* is diftilled Vinegar faturated with fome Alkalizate Salt.

ACHAMECH, with fome Chymifts, fignifies the Drofs of Silver.

ACHERNER, a bright fixed Star of the firft Magnitude, in *Eridanus,* whofe Longitude is 10. 31. of ♓, Latitude 59. 18.

ACHOLITE, an inferiour Church Servant, who next under the Sub-Deacon, followed or waited on the Priefts and Deacons, and performing the meaner Offices of lighting the Candles, carrying the Bread and Wine, and paying other fervile Attendance.

ACHOR, is a fort of a crufted Scab which makes an Itching and Stink on the Surface of the Head, and is occafioned by a Serous, Salt and Sharp Matter: The difference betwixt an *Achor* and *Favus* confifts in this, that in *Achors* the Holes or Cavities are fmall, and fometimes not vifible; but in a *Favus* they are more large and confpicuous.

ACHLYS, according to fome, is a kind of Darknefs in the Eyes, accounted one of the Species of *Amblyopia,* or Dimnefs of Sight.

ACHRONICAL, is ufed in Aftronomy for the Rifing of a Star when the Sun fets, or the Setting of a Star when the Sun rifes; in which Cafes the Star is faid either to rife or fett Achronically: which is one of the three *Poetical Rifings or Settings.*

ACIDITY, is the Taft which Bodies that are *Acid* or Sharp affect the Mouth with: And thofe Bodies are called

ACIDS, whofe Particles are fuppofed to be longifh, flexible, penetrating, and attenuating; and which have their Points fharp and piercing. And thefe are either *Natural Acids;* which have a Proper Acidity of their own without the help of Art, as Juice of Limons, &c. or elfe *Artificial Acids;* which are made by Fire in Chymical Operations. So that *Acid Spirits* or *Stygian Liquors,* as the Chymifts call them, from their Powers to deftroy or diffolve Bodies, feem to be nothing but an *Acid Salt* diffolved and put into a violent Motion by the Fire: Thefe are called *Acid Menftruums.* You may eafily know whether any Liquor contain in it an *Acid Salt* or not; by dropping fome of it on a little Syrup of Violets fpread on White Paper; or into a Solution of Blue-bottle Flowers, &c. for then the Blue will be immediately turned into a Red or reddifh Purple Colour; whereas if it turn Green, 'tis a fign the Liquor abounds with Salts of an Urinous or Lixiviate Nature; which how to diftinguifh, *fee thofe Words.* The Acidity of any Liquor may alfo be concluded by its being able to deftroy the Bluenefs of a Tincture of *Lignum Nephriticum:* (See *Colours,* and the ways of producing fudden changes of them.)

ACIDULÆ, any Medicinal Waters that are not hot, like thofe at the *Bath* which are called *Thermæ.*

ACINUS, in Botanicks doth not fignifie a Grape-ftone, but the Fruit it felf of all fuch Plants which bear it, in a manner refembling Grapes: It is fofter and more Juicy than a *Berry,* and therefore diftinguifhable from it; as it is alfo becaufe the *Acini* grow in Bunches or Clufters and Berries often fingle.

ACINIFORMIS *Tunica,* is the fame with the *Uvea Tunica* of the Eye.

ACMASTICK *Fever,* with fome, is the fame as *Synochus.*

ACME, in general, fignifies the Height or Top of any thing; the word is more efpecially ufed to denote the height of a Diftemper; many of which have four Periods. 1. The *Arche* or beginning: 2. The *Anabafis,* or the Growth and Increafe. 3. The *Acme,* when the Morbifick Matter is at the height. 4. The *Paracme,* or the *Declenfion* of the Diftemper.

ACONTIAS, a fort of Comets, fhaped like a Dart or Javelin. Its Head is fometimes round, and fometimes oblong or compreffed, and its Tail or Train is flender, but extended to a great Length.

ACOPUM, according to fome Writers, is a Fomentation of warm and emollient things, to allay the fenfe of Wearinefs, occafioned by too violent Labour or Exercife.

ACOSMY, is an ill ftate of Health accompanied with the lofs of the Natural Florid Colour of the Face.

ACOUSTICKS, are Medicines or Inftruments which help the Hearing; as to the latter of which, the ufe of *Otocouftick* Trumpets is now very common; and no queftion Inftruments of this kind are capable of Improvement. Dr. *Hook* in his Preface to his Micrography faith, 'tis not impoffible to hear a Whifper at a Furlong or ⅓th part of a Miles diftance: That he knows a way by which 'tis eafie to hear any one fpeak thro' a Wall of a Yard thick: And that by the help of a diftended Wire the Sound may be propagated to a very confiderable diftance almoft in an Inftant.

ACQUIETANDIS *Plegiis,* is a *Jufticies,* that lies for a Surety againft a Creditor, that refufeth to acquit him after the Debt is paid.

ACQUIETANTIA *de Shiris & Hundredis,* to be free from Suit and Service in Shires and Hundreds.

ACQUITTAL, in Law, fignifies the difcharge of a Tenant from any Entries or Moleftations for any manner of Service iffuing out of the Land to any Lord; that is, above the Mifne. It fignifies alfo, when two are Indicted of Felony, the one as Principal, the other as Acceffary; the Principal being difcharged, the Acceffary by confequence is alfo acquitted.

ACQUITTANCE, fignifieth a Releafe or Difcharge in writing of a Summ of Money, or other Duty which ought to be paid or done.

ACRASY, is the Excefs or Predominancy of one Quality above another in the Conftitution of a Humane Body.

ACRE of Land; its Quantity is 4 Square Roods; or 160 fquare Poles; or 4840 fquare Yards; or 43560 fquare Feet. By a Statute of 31 of *Eliz.* 'tis ordained, That if any Man erect a new Cottage, he fhall add 4 Acres of Land to it.

ACRIMO.

A page from John Harris's *Lexicon Technicum,* 1704, the ancestor of encyclopaedias in English.

Egyptian weight of 100 gold beqa, polished green marble, c. 2350 B.C.

Bone skates from Finland.

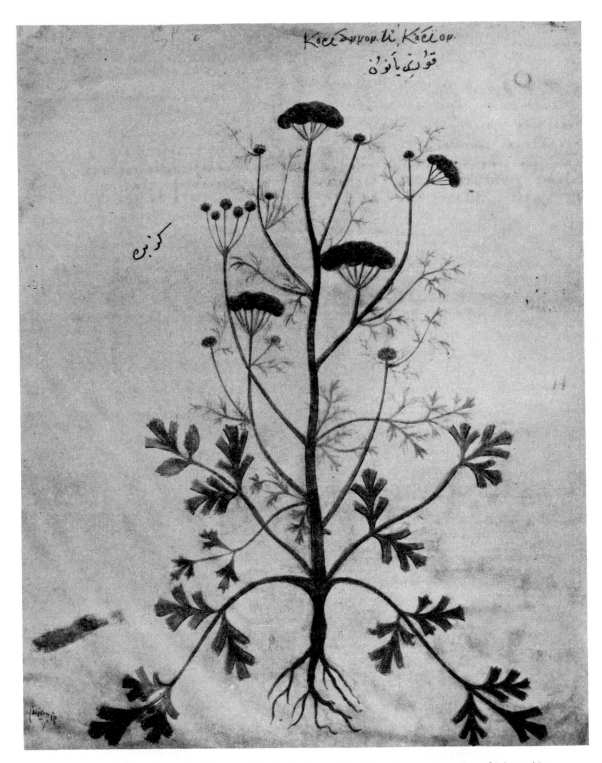

Drugs: Coriander, from the Juliana Anicia Codex (A.D. 512) of the *De materia medica* of Dioscorides.

Drugs: a physician expounds the virtues of plants to his pupils, from a medieval manuscript.

Beehives and Beekeepers. Drawing by Pieter Bruegel, 1565.

270

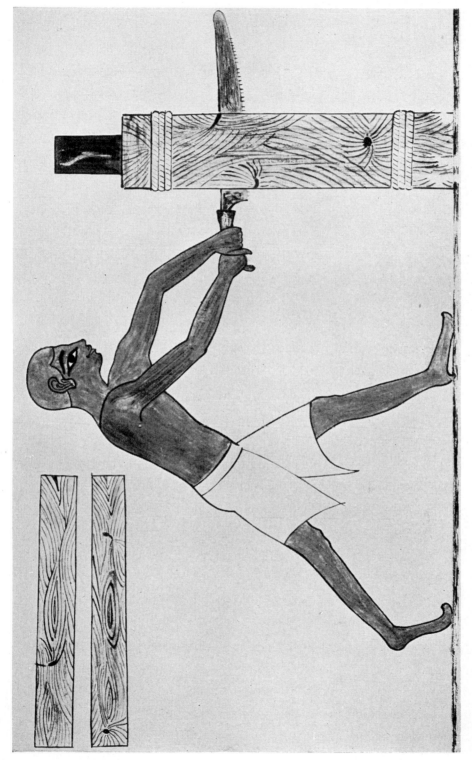

Straight-backed Egyptian saw, painting from the tomb of Rekhmara c. 1480 B.C.

Water-mill with overshot wheels. Detail from *The Water-mill* by Meindert Hobbema (1638–1709).

Table clock. Detail from Holbein's portrait of Georg Gisze, one of the Merchants of the Steelyard (1532).

Double needle telegraph used at House of Commons, 1846.
(Height about five feet.)

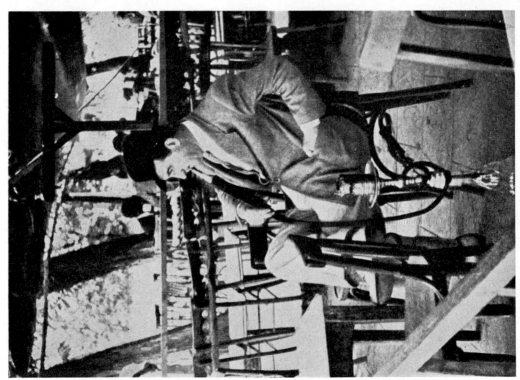

A Turk smokes his hubble-bubble, Istanbul.

vacuum. A cold surface is held very close to the surface of the reacting liquid, so that molecules of any volatile matter evaporating from the liquid are immediately trapped and cannot re-enter the liquid. By this means Carothers was able to get rid of all residual water which had been interfering with the completion of his reactions. The result was the production of substances of very high molecular weight which Carothers called 'superpolymers'. They were tough opaque solids which melted into viscous liquids. If a glass rod were dipped into the melt, a long filament could be drawn out. Then it was found that if these filaments were stretched they developed quite different properties. They became transparent and lustrous, they exhibited a high tensile strength, and were as strong when wet as when dry. Nevertheless the threads were not suitable for manufacture. This was a disappointment, since the du Pont Company had long ago decided to search for a new synthetic fibre. However, Carothers' work had illuminated some fundamental questions of chemistry and the research went on. Carothers decided to concentrate on the nitrogen-containing compounds known as amides. The polyamides he made were still of no use. Spirits flagged, and for some months work was suspended. Then one more attempt was made, this time to make a superpolyamide.

On 28 February 1935, the superpolyamide formed from hexamethylene diamine and adipic acid was made. It was known as '66 polymer' (the polymers were given such code-numbers, which showed the number of carbon atoms in each of the simple starting substances, in this case six in each). Other related types were tried, but 66 was the best fibre-former. Here then was a product possibly valuable in commerce and one stage of the investigation was complete. The next stage was to develop a large-scale manufacturing process, for which du Pont's deployed great resources of money and scientific man-power. Carothers was not to see the outcome. He died in 1937, but the work he had made possible went on. In October 1938 a new textile fibre was publicly announced under the name 'Nylon'.

'Nylon' is a name not restricted to one chemical substance. It applies to a whole group. Here is the definition accepted by the British Patent Office:

N

Nylon is a general term for synthetic fibre-forming polyamides, i.e. organic condensation products which contain a multiplicity of structural units linked in series by amide or thioamide groupings, produced by a process of manufacture in which non-fibre-forming organic substances of lower molecular weight are converted into products of such high molecular weight as to be capable of being formed into filaments, which, on cold drawing, form a true fibre structure recognizable by X-ray examination.

Commercial production of nylon began in 1939 at Seaford, Delaware, after new plant had been specially built to produce in great quantities the starting materials which had hitherto been known only in the laboratory. The first nylon stockings were offered for sale in New York on 15 May 1940.

Many other nylon articles were shown at the New York World's Fair later in the year, but its use by the general public was at first short-lived. After the U.S.A. entered the Second World War the new material proved so valuable that it was employed extensively for military purposes. Its inertness made it valuable in tropical equipment. Its great strength made it suitable for parachutes and glider tow-ropes.

In Great Britain plans for producing nylon had been made by Imperial Chemical Industries and Courtaulds, and a new company, British Nylon Spinners Ltd., began operations in January 1942.

Nylon is a plastic and its method of manufacture resembles that of some other plastics. The starting materials (hexamethylene diamine and adipic acid) which have been made separately, are heated together in an autoclave (a vessel like a domestic pressure cooker on a large scale). The polymerized material which results is then extruded to form a ribbon which, when cold, is chopped up for storage. Later it is remelted and extruded through spinnerets. The fibre formed is then drawn out, and it is this drawing process which gives nylon many of its desirable properties. From this stage on it is available for treatment like any other textile fibre.

The first experimental garments to be made from nylon were stockings, and they turned out to be a sore disappointment. They wrinkled badly in the dyeing process. However, this difficulty was overcome by the addition of a steaming treatment, after which the stockings behaved well.

Nylon can be used in bulk like other plastics,

and it can be made into the thick monofilaments now familiar, for example, in tooth-brushes and as surgical sutures. It is very resistant to chemical attack, it is mechanically tough and it is biologically inert: neither moth nor mildew affect it. Other synthetic fibres may be made, but when future histories of science are written, nylon will have a special place in them as the outstanding illustration of the way individual genius can flourish in the world of industry. (See also *Plastics*.)

King of instruments

The **ORGAN**, '*de tous les instruments le roi*' according to Guillaume de Machault, or a mere 'chest of whistles' in the eyes of disapproving Calvinists, is the largest, the loudest, the most elaborate and the most costly musical instrument devised by man. For centuries it has also been the most important instrumental aid to divine service, thundering its praise in as widely differing places as English cathedrals and synagogues. Though we owe the pneumatic organ to Byzantium, the Eastern Orthodox Church and the sterner Nonconformists are almost alone among Christians in objecting to mechanical aids to worship and excluding all instruments from their churches.

The organ is a set of pipes, fed by a wind chest, and controlled from a keyboard. The first essential, the set of pipes, is simply a magnification of the little pan-pipes (see *Flute*); the second, the wind chest, gives the instrument the semblance of a kind of fixed bagpipe; the third, the controlling system, is a question of mechanics, and it is only in the vast and ingenious elaboration of this that the enormous modern organ differs from its rude forefathers. A large cathedral organ may nowadays have four or five keyboards, scores of stops, and pipes by the thousand. The first stage in

supplying the wind was to employ human labour to compress the wind chest (an obelisk erected at Constantinople as late as the fourth century by Theodosius shows two youths standing rather self-consciously on a huge pair of bellows); the second came when a weight was laid on the bellows, to be raised by hand when all the air had been expired; and the third stage was to provide two pairs of bellows so that the air supply was continuous. These three stages are, of course, indistinctly separated, and the evolution has been gradual. Today organs have many more than one set of pipes; these are brought into action separately or together by means of 'stops' set by the keyboard, and are of almost unlimited range of colour. They are divided into three main groups: diapason, corresponding more or less to the position of the strings in the orchestra; flute, which is the equivalent of the woodwind group; and reed, which is the brass. Unlike the instruments of the orchestra, however, these colours are available throughout the whole compass from deepest bass to highest treble.

The ancient world knew two kinds of organ, hydraulic and pneumatic. Most modern works of reference credit the invention of the now obsolete *hydraulis*, or water organ, to Ctesibius the Greek mathematician, who flourished in Alexandria in the second century B.C.; the evidence is not conclusive, but either Ctesibius or an enigmatic Arab generally known as Murustus may first have built the water organ. Ctesibius invented a water clock as well, which is not to be confused with Plato's fantastic water-driven alarm clock, that blew a note on a pipe every hour; according to the descriptions in Heron's *Pneumatics* (written between A.D. 62 and A.D. 150) and Vitruvius Pollio's *De Architectura* (first century A.D.) the principle was quite different; in the water organ air was forced into the pipes by water under pressure. The tone was said to be so powerful that on a clear day it could be heard up to sixty miles away, and the player had to stuff up his ears to avoid deafness. The Emperor Nero was a notable hydraulist. In modern times the Rev. F. W. Galpin, the great authority on old instruments, has reconstructed a small hydraulis from some Carthaginian terracotta figures, and has even given a public demonstration of its powers.

The modern type of pneumatic organ is perhaps first heard of in detail as the controversial *Magrepha* of the Temple at Jerusalem. The Bible does not mention this instrument, but the Talmud describes it as a chest with ten pipes, each pipe with ten finger holes. However, the true nature of the *Magrepha* is doubtful; some maintain that it was in fact a kettledrum, some a bagpipe, some a bell, and one scholar even states that it was really a large shovel, which was clashed down on the pavement to summon the faithful. The earliest description of a pneumatic organ is by the Emperor Julian the Apostate

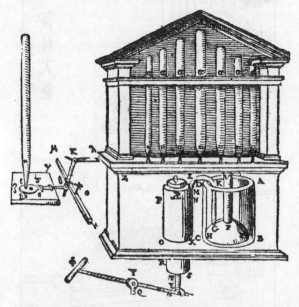

Fig. 24. Heron's water organ.

(A.D. 331–363): 'I see a strange species of reeds... a blast, rushing forth from a cavern of bull's hide, forces its way from beneath ... and a skilful man having nimble fingers stands feeling the yielding rods of pipes, and they, gently dancing, press out song'; and it was at Constantinople that organs were developed. References grow more numerous. Theodoret (c. 393–457) mentions an organ with metal pipes, St Jerome (c. 340–420) describes one in Jerusalem with wind chests of elephants' hides, and Cassiodorus (sixth century) goes into the construction in some detail. The first recorded use in Christian worship is in Spain in 450. By the beginning of the eighth century the organ had

spread as far as England, although the means and route are unknown. It is certainly curious that the organ did not appear in France and Germany until some fifty years later, when Charlemagne's father, Pepin the Short, ordered one from the Byzantine Emperor Constantine Copronymus. Charlemagne himself subsequently received an organ from Harun-al-Rashid.

The early European organs were of two sizes: Positive Organs, which were generally built into the fabric of the church or house that contained them, like the monster that existed in Winchester Cathedral in the tenth century, requiring seventy men to blow it; and Portative Organs, the smaller versions of which were known as Regal Organs and survive today as piano accordions and mouth-organs. The Germans were the first to develop the use of foot-pedals as an extra keyboard, but even in the eighteenth century the pedal-board was still rudimentary by our standards, and it is a mystery how Bach, greatest of organists though he was, managed to play some of the trickier passages in his compositions on the clumsy, short pedals of his organ. England, slow to realize the advantages of pedals, was first with a swell-box, the device that enables the organist to grade his volume from a whisper to a great thunder.

All-electric organs have been made, dispensing with pipes altogether, but although some of these, notably the Hammonds, are useful and even beautiful substitutes, they cannot compete with the majesty of a true organ. There is controversy over the merits of the so-called baroque organ of Bach's day and of the larger, richer and more powerful modern organ. Some scholars claim that only the baroque organ with its simpler, quieter colours and softer tone (due partly to the lower wind pressure) can give a true representation of music of its period; its opponents dismiss the baroque organ as a 'bubble and squeak' affair, and believe that the loss in polyphonic clarity is more than made up for by the richness and strength of the modern instrument.

A notable recent attempt to build an organ that is capable of a baroque effect without loss of richness is the instrument in the Royal Festival Hall in London. Here the use of wind chests of varying pressures has resulted in a beautiful clarity and incisiveness in all departments (a reaction against the woolly weight of most organs of the last hundred years), and at the same time in a healthy power and a wide tonal range.

Least reputable of any is the cinema organ, which supplements its limited resources with effects of chimes, harps, whistles, sirens, thunder, surf, sleigh-bells and broken glass. Small wonder that it has acquired the habit of sinking shame-facedly into the ground at the close of its per-formances. (See also *Piano, Harp, Bagpipes, Violin, Flute.*)

ILLUSTRATION: Plate 1.

P

Papyrus, parchment, paper

PAPER was invented by the Chinese, though our word (which is similar in other languages) derives from its predecessor, the papyrus of the ancient Mediterranean.

The Egyptians wrote on papyrus as far back as the third millennium B.C., and it was the main writing material of the Greco-Roman world for a thousand years. The tall sedge *Cyperus papyri*, from the stems of which it was made, grew in the marshes of Lower Egypt, and in less quantity in northern Palestine. Nowadays this plant grows chiefly in the Sudan and Abyssinia; and also in Sicily, near Syracuse, where it is still made into a special kind of paper.

Though supremely important in ancient civili-zation and human history, papyrus had its draw-backs. Compacted in small sheets with the fibres criss-crossing at right angles, it was brittle; and the supply of the plant was limited geographic-ally. Parchment or vellum, which became the literary writing material *par excellence* of the Middle Ages, also had its drawbacks and advan-tages. It was tougher and more durable than the fragile papyrus, the leaves could receive writing on both sides, and ink could easily be removed for corrections. There were not geographical

limits to the supply of the raw skin from which parchment is prepared; but it was a costly material. Yet it served learning in the western world for well over eleven hundred years – from the time of the earliest vellum codices of the third or fourth century A.D. to the invention of the printing press in Europe about 1450, or rather to the spread of printing on paper in the second half of the fifteenth century.

Fig. 25. Chinese paper-maker, from a seventeenth-century encyclopaedia.

Paper long preceded printing both in China and in Europe, and it would be fair enough to say, no paper, no printing and no printing press. Traditionally – it may be true, in fact – paper was invented by Ts'ai Lun, chief eunuch to the Em-peror Ho Ti, in A.D. 105. Scraps of rag paper of about A.D. 150 were found in China by Sir Aurel Stein. The earliest extant documents on paper were discovered in 1899 in the Caves of the

Thousand Buddhas near Tun Huang, in Kansu province. They are written in Sogdian, the language of a part of the ancient Persian empire. Until recently they were assigned to a period not later than the middle second century A.D., but it has been proved that they belong to A.D. 313 or 314. The good-quality paper of these documents is made entirely from rags of fabric woven of Chinese hemp (*Bochineria nivea*).

The Koreans and the Japanese learned paper-making from the Chinese in the seventh century; the Arabs in the eighth century learned the craft from Chinese prisoners, and Samarkand (now in Soviet Uzbekistan) was the first Moslem city where paper was produced. About A.D. 800 Baghdad and Damascus became important centres of paper manufacture. There are many Arabic paper manuscripts extant, belonging to the ninth century, and made of pure rag (from linen and flax). About 1100 paper was being made in Cairo, and soon after in Fez, in Morocco. At the same time, the Moslems introduced the craft into Spain, where paper-mills were soon working prosperously in Valencia, Toledo and Jativa: in the last-mentioned city a paper-mill is said to have existed in 1134.

The earliest known European document on paper is a deed of Countess Adelaide, wife of Roger I, the Norman conqueror of Sicily, dated 1102. It is written in Arabic and Greek, and preserved in the state archives at Palermo.

In Italy the earliest paper-mills were set up in the later twelfth century at Fabriano in the province of Ancona; where even now the mills are among the most important in the world. It is said that the craft was introduced into Fabriano by people returning from the Crusades. About 1200 Master Polese da Fabriano set up a mill in Bologna. In the early fourteenth century there were about forty mills at Fabriano; water-marking was first invented there. The craft soon spread to France (1248), Germany (early fourteenth century), Switzerland (1380), England (1450), the Netherlands (about the same time). In the fourteenth century paper became the main literary writing material in Europe, and in the course of the next century it gradually superseded parchment.

Paper was made by hand in separate sheets. In 1798 or 1799 a machine was devised by the Frenchman L.N.Robert for making it in a con-tinuous web. In England the first machine for continuous paper-making in bulk was set up in Hertfordshire in 1803 by Henry Fourdrinier (1766–1854), aided by the notable engineer and inventor Bryan Donkin. The substance which the Imperial Eunuch had invented nearly seventeen hundred years before now proved itself more than ever one of the chief vectors of modern civilization, for good and all. (See also *Book*.)

(The translation of the papyrus letter from a boy to his father, which illustrates this article, runs:

This is the fifth time I have written to you, and you have only written to me once, and even then you didn't say a word about yourself, nor have you even come to see me. You promised me 'I will come', but you never come to see if my teacher is looking after me properly or not. He himself asks about you almost every day; 'Isn't he coming yet?' And I just say 'Yes'. So do please come as soon as possible, so that he can start teaching me, which he is eager to do. If you had travelled up river with me I should have been taught long ago, and when you do come, remember all the things I have written about to you so often. Come quickly before he leaves for Upper Egypt ...

P.S. Remember our pigeons.

ILLUSTRATION: Plate 13.

Control by passport

The **PASSPORT** goes back, broadly speaking, to the passes and safe-conducts which have been granted since the earliest times, but what we now mean by a passport – that is, a standardized document, more or less compulsory, issued by governments to their citizens for general travel rather than for particular journeys and withheld when authority so desires, is relatively modern; it belongs to the era of both nationalism and the struggle for political liberties, the growth of the state at the expense of the individual, the organization of the police, the nervous hardening and control of frontiers and the perfection both of the card-index and the card-index mind.

Rulers have a natural itch to control the movement of their subjects, but a need also to protect their servants. In classical times passes were issued by rulers to assist and protect those who were travelling on their behalf; these documents were marks of confidence, hence the name *pisteis*, 'confidences', mentioned in a Greco-Roman papyrus of the second century B.C. When the Roman Empire began to split, passes were required by ordinary travellers; in the days of Theodosius II, Emperor in the East from 408 to 450, it was necessary to have a permit for going from the east to the west part of the empire. In the Middle Ages the vast number of pilgrims from all countries to such centres as Jerusalem, Santiago de Compostella or Canterbury argues a world less stiffly divided, ditched and dyked than our own; and it was a world with a common religious belief, not too conscious of nationality, nor yet fearful, on the whole, of revolution.

Coming down the centuries, it was advisable and sometimes necessary, before the disturbances of the French Revolution and the revolutionary wars, to obtain local passports and passes to ease one's way through foreign countries. It is ironical that in France the first revolutionary Constitution of September 1791 guaranteed among natural and civil rights 'freedom for every man to go and depart without arrest or hindrance'; passports for French citizens were abolished – only to be re-introduced, internal and external, by 1793: the monarchy had needed means of controlling tendencies to revolution; revolution, once in power itself, needed means of controlling counter-revolution.

From the American Revolution and the revolutionary year of 1848, liberty, reform and war and words of objurgation such as 'jacobin', 'democrat' and 'sedition' created a new degree of politicians' and officials' neurosis. A government plain-clothes man, it will be recalled, shadowed Wordsworth, Coleridge and Thelwall in the Quantocks, reporting back to his superiors in London their seditious talk of Spy Nosey, *i.e.* Spinoza; and in parliament the Postmaster-General opposed Rowland Hill's penny post on the ground that it would encourage sedition. The English, however, had no liking for passports. When Harriet Campbell reached Calais in 1817, she remarked in her journal how a man 'followed by about half a dozen attendants in office dressed as soldiers but looking more like monkeys ... lept into the ship and seating himself on a trunk opposite the carriage and demanded our pass-port'. This was a post-war period, and generally speaking, countries, as the nineteenth century settled down, tended to relax passport control, passports remaining documents it was advisable rather than essential to have about one; they were discretionary documents, they might be of help by establishing nationality and identity. The passport has been likened to a pistol in frontier Texas: 'You didn't want it often, but when you did want it, you wanted it very badly.'

Though the U.S.A. in 1856 required its citizens to have passports for overseas travel, foreigners landing in America were not compelled to show passports until 1918. British subjects by this time rarely bothered to ask for passports – unless they were visiting Russia, where officials' neurosis has for so long been so severely epidemic, under emperor or soviet. Cook's *Guide to Paris* of 1906 remarks that 'throughout France the green tickets supplied by Thomas Cook and Son with their travelling coupons are so well known that as a rule there can be no better credential. Passports, however, are useful for obtaining letters addressed *poste restante*, and they will frequently gain admittance to museums when closed against the general public.' Also under 'Passport', the *Encyclopaedia Britannica* of 1910–1911 makes curious reading for ourselves. It defines passport, first of all, by its older signification of a safe-conduct in time of war, 'a document granted by a belligerent power to protect persons and property from the operation of hostilities'. Then, coming to passports in the modern sense, it says, 'Although most foreign countries may now be entered without passports, the English foreign office recommends travellers to furnish themselves with them, as affording a ready means of identification in case of need.'

The First World War changed matters, giving the totalitarian card index its supremacy. The movement of subjects was controlled as a war expedient, and control hardened into a habit. It was in 1914 also that photographs were added to the English passport. The war over, there was a new stiffening of frontiers, and there began a new era of suspicion and control encouraged by fear of communism and the Russian Revolution. Travel became impossible without passports, and the new conditions were reflected in the huge expansion of the Passport Department of the English

Foreign Office. Before 1914 the staff consisted of 'one second division clerk and a doorkeeper, occupying two small rooms near a back entrance'. The department now has branch offices at Liverpool and Glasgow, and a staff varying from 400 to 470 in summer. Also in 1853, no more than 9,409 British passports were issued. In 1953 new British passports numbered about 420,000.

The fee payable for the British passport has mounted, as well. In 1858 it was reduced from 7*s*. 6*d*. to 2*s*., a figure unchanged until 1915, when it became 5*s*., after which there has been a steady rise, to 7*s*. 6*d*. in 1920 and 15*s*. in 1931, a British passport now costing a pound. This document has not always been formed, as it is today, into a neat booklet. In England until 1916, when the book form was introduced, the passport was a single sheet of paper covered with coats-of-arms, preambles and stampings. Thus a surviving British passport, issued in 1884 for a man going to Russia, consists of a large sheet of thin bank paper. This has perforations at top and bottom and seems to have been torn from a roll. Today most passports are in the form of 32-page booklets, the outcome of a League of Nations conference in 1921.

It should be added that no law compels a British subject to have a passport. Circumstances may be compulsive; but whatever he requires elsewhere, a British subject can leave or return to his own country without a passport, though he may be asked to prove his British status. The wording on British passports, 'Her Britannic Majesty's Principal Secretary of State for Foreign Affairs requests and requires in the Name of Her Majesty all those whom it may concern to allow the bearer to pass freely without let or hindrance, and to afford him every assistance and protection of which he may stand in need', still stresses the old protective function of the safe-conduct, but willy-nilly the passport has become to some degree an instrument of control as well as a safe-conduct. One historian in 1927 was already, rather crossly, calling passports 'glorified and expensive identity discs'. The American situation is stricter and more authoritarian than the British. By law a citizen of the United States *must* have a passport either to leave or to enter his country. American passports can be and are refused in the national interest. (See also *Finger-prints*.)

Stylus to steel nib

The **PEN** as one of the major tools of writing, preserves history in its name, which is from the Latin *penna*, the quill feather which was the main pen of the Middle Ages.

Before pens as we know them comes the stylus, the instrument of the earliest written documents which are extant – Mesopotamian clay tablets of the fourth millennium B.C. This broad-headed stylus consisted of a straight stick or piece of reed, bone, hard wood or metal. Assyrian and Babylonian carvings depict scribes holding the stylus in their closed fist and pressing upon the tablet, while the clay was still damp and soft; the scribe impressed the strokes, line by line, with the edge or front of his stylus.

The stylus was also used by the Greeks and the Romans. It was then an instrument of iron, bronze, silver or other hard material, such as ivory, and was used for writing on wood boards or thin wooden tablets coated with wax or polished gesso. The letters were scratched with the sharp point; the other end of the stylus was rounded into a knob, or was flattened and was used to smooth mistakes out of the wax.

In Egypt, from the early third millennium onwards, papyrus was the chief writing material, demanding a different tool, the brush-pen, which was mainly used for cursive writing, and gave to the signs a bolder more running form, thus transforming the monumental hieroglyphic system into a cursive hieratic style. The ink was in the form of small cakes, which were employed as we employ watercolours: the writer dipped the brush in water and rubbed it on the cake.

In China the invention of the *pi*, the writing-brush or pencil, made of hair, is traditionally attributed to Mêng T'ien, a reputed builder of the Great Wall, who died about 210 B.C., but it is likely to have preceded him. Over twenty years ago, F. Bergmann, of Sven Hedin's Central Asian Expedition, discovered a complete and well-preserved Chinese writing-brush, nine inches long, dating in all probability from the beginning of the Christian era. Fine hair brushes are still used by the Chinese for their writing: they first liquefy their ink, then dip their brushes into it. In Europe, fine hair brushes were used mainly for the large capital letters; they were so employed even after the invention of printing, but were discontinued in the sixteenth century. A still finer brush was used by illuminators in applying gold to illumination; it was called in Latin *penicillus*: hence the word 'pencil', which literally means 'little tail'. This type of brush, which artists still use in painting, is made of hog's bristles or finer camel hair, fitch or sable; though 'pencil' is now transferred to the cedar tubes enclosing graphite mixed with clay, or some other solid writing materials, which were first devised in England in the sixteenth century. In the seventeenth century one finds them referred to as 'pensils of black lead' or 'dry pencils.'

From about the third century B.C. the instrument mainly used for writing on papyrus was the reed-pen. Actually this was a length of common reed; at first the writing end was frayed or pulped; later, like the quill pen (see below), it was cut to a point and split; it was sharpened with a knife. Suitable *calami* came chiefly from Egypt, or Cnidus on the south-west coast of Asia Minor. Flinders Petrie discovered in Egypt a number of reed-pens belonging to the Roman period. Some specimens cut like a modern pen are preserved in the British Museum. In the sixth and seventh centuries A.D. the monks of the Christian monastery of Thebes in Upper Egypt were using split reed-pens which averaged an inch in diameter; an unused new pen was just over ten inches long, but pens were resharpened so often that finally they became mere two-inch stumps; one pen, discovered in the Monastery at Thebes, had been lengthened by attaching a piece of wood at the end.

In the late Greco-Roman times reed-pens were used in all the Mediterranean countries and in Western Asia. They continued to be used to some extent throughout the Middle Ages. In Italy they appear to have survived into the fifteenth century. In some countries, such as Egypt, India and Persia, their use lingered on down to our own times. In eastern and south-eastern Asia bamboo canes, cut to about the length and thickness of our pen, are still used for writing.

The quill, made from the wing-feathers of geese, swans, peacocks, crows or eventually turkeys, was in use from the Middle Ages to the nineteenth century. It is uncertain when and where the quill was introduced. It was first mentioned by an anonymous historian of the sixth century A.D., who tells us that the illiterate Theodoric the Great (A.D. 455–526) was provided with a stencil plate through which he drew with a *penna* the strokes which formed the first four letters of his name. St Isidore of Seville (c. 560–636) mentions both the calamus and the quill as being used in his time. Possibly vellum, when it came into general use (in the fourth century A.D.), led to the quill. The flexible pressure of the quill is better suited than the inflexible reed-pen to the hard but smooth surface of vellum.

Metal pens go back to the bronze or silver 'pen-reeds' made by the Romans. A few have been found in Italy, one in England – it is now in the British Museum – and one near Cologne, in Germany; and a metal pen, about two inches long, shaped and slit like a quill, was found not long ago in the so-called tomb of Aristotle, at Eretria (the modern Aletria), the ancient seaport of the Greek island of Euboea. However, metal pens were not greatly used either in ancient Rome or in medieval Europe, since they lacked flexibility. On the other hand, a quill had a short life; each user had to re-cut or sharpen the point with a penknife (a term we still use for the folding pocket knife, though quills have gone out). Attempts were therefore made to find substitutes, or else to give durability to the quill point, or nib. Thus the quill point was gilded (by Watt, in 1818), horn or tortoiseshell tips were attached (J. I. Hawkins and S. Morden, 1823); but such expedients were unsuccessful.

In the meantime, around 1780, a split-ring manufacturer, S. Harrison, of Birmingham, produced a metallic pen for Priestley, the chemist. In 1803 Wise introduced in London the complete steel nib, or rather the split cylinder steel pen. In 1805 Breithaupt (of Cassel, in Germany) marketed silver and steel pens, but they were too heavy, too hard and too stiff. The nib was patented by Bryan Donkin in 1808. Soon afterwards, in 1809, the English engineer, Joseph Bramah (1748–1814), patented a machine for cutting goose feathers into three or four nibs to be used with a pen-holder, and also with a fountain pen. Nib, which had been a word for the point or end of anything (*e.g.* a bird's nib, or bill), including quill pens, now became the name for the new separate device, as the pen divided into nib and holder.

In 1810 the first patent was granted in America to P. Williamson (of Baltimore) for the manufacture of metallic pens. In 1822 J. Mitchell invented the machine-made pen. In 1830 J. Perry (of Birmingham), assisted by Mason, patented his system for producing pens which were so flexible that they could compete with quill pens. This was the birth of the modern pen, and Birmingham became the first centre of the steel pen industry, of which it is still one of the main centres. The advertising rhyme of the nineteenth century for the new steel nibs:

> The Pickwick, the Owl and the Waverley pen
> They come as a boon and a blessing to men

was little short of the truth.

Mass production of steel pens was started in America in 1860 at Camden, New Jersey. Steel pens, however, did not displace the quill scratching its way across the paper until late in the nineteenth century, and soon afterwards the gold-nibbed fountain pen conquered the market. (See also *Fountain Pen, Alphabet, Paper, Ink*.)

Gravicembalo col piano e forte

The **PIANO**, commonest of domestic musical instruments, came very late into being. It only emerged from the rudimentary forms which had persisted since antiquity at the beginning of the eighteenth century, coming to its full development a hundred and fifty to two hundred years later.

Its nature is hybrid. There are three chief ways of obtaining the vibration which causes musical sound – striking a stretched membrane, causing a column of air to vibrate in a tube, and vibrating a stretched string, as it does in the harp and the violin. A string can be made to vibrate in two chief ways, by plucking it and by drawing a resined bow across it. However, since the piano causes a hammer to strike the string, it is a string

instrument, affined to the percussion instruments. The modern keyboard is no more than a beautifully contrived mechanical device for making the striking easier: it is not essential to the nature of the piano and was unknown to the ancients.

The first ancestor of the piano was the delicate little psaltery, the 'psanterin' (translated as psaltery), mentioned in the third chapter of the Book of Daniel – 'when all the people heard the sound of the cornet, flute, harp, sackbut, psaltery and all kinds of music, all the people, the nations, and the languages, fell down and worshipped the golden image that Nebuchadnezzar the King had set up.' The psaltery consisted of a sounding board of four unequal sides, none of them parallel, over which were stretched strings of varying lengths; these were held away from the board by bridges, as in the violin, and were plucked with the fingers or with a quill (*plectrum*). The plucking action makes it basically different from the piano, but its immediate offspring, the dulcimer, owes everything in construction to the psaltery; though the strings of the dulcimer are struck with little hammers, generally spoon-shaped. The psaltery persisted into the Middle Ages, developing into the beautiful harpsichord, and its name survives in various modern forms of dulcimer, such as the Asiatic *santir* and the Greek *santouri*.

The dulcimer originally came to Europe from the East, travelling along the coast of North Africa and so across the Straits of Gibraltar into Spain (one is carved on the porch of the cathedral at Santiago de Compostela, dated 1184). Thence it travelled slowly east again, through France and Italy and the Balkans, so that by 1850 the now much modified form could be found in Turkey together with the native instrument that had come directly from Persia. It is chiefly in the Balkans that the dulcimer is common today, particularly in Hungary, where the *cimbalom*, as the Hungarians call it, has become a national instrument.

Making dulcimer into piano involves only the application of a keyboard, a simple evolutionary step which might well have been made before the eighteenth century. Keyboards in a rudimentary form were known on organs of the twelfth century and even earlier, and with a perfected mechanism and appearance on harpsichords and clavichords of the seventeenth and eighteenth centuries. At the beginning of the eighteenth century these two were the popular keyboard instruments, the harpsichord depending upon plucking by quills for its silvery jangle and upon the use of various stops, like the organ, for variety of tone-colour, the gentler clavichord being simultaneously struck and pressed by metal tangents from below to sketch out its sad tracery of sound. Each is exquisite, but the harpsichord cannot vary its dynamics between loud and soft and the clavichord has neither strength nor brilliance. Something that would have the qualities of both was required. A French attempt in 1410 (the *dulce melos*) and a Dutch invention of exactly two hundred years later proved abortive; and it was not until about 1709 that Bartolomeo Cristofori of Florence provided the first real answer.

Cristofori's piano hammer action, as described in the *Giornale dei Litterati d'Italia* of 1711, is simple: a hinged hammer is made to strike a string by depressing a key; having done so it drops naturally back into position, and when the key is loosed a damper presses against the string to silence it. This beautifully simple mechanism was the model for all later developments. Cristofori improved his action in 1720, and he also added the device whereby the keyboard slips fractionally sideways when required, so that only two of the three strings that go to each note are struck, resulting in a quieter sound. This mechanism is still found in some modern pianos, worked by a pedal with the left foot; in the early days it was managed rather clumsily by two knobs like harpsichord stops. The instrument was given the grandiloquent name of *Gravicembalo col piano e forte* – the harpsichord with soft and loud – which was eventually contracted to pianoforte; today the instrument is almost always referred to, illogically but conveniently, as the piano.

None of the early pioneers had any commercial success with their new musical inventions; and it was the famous organ-builder Gottfried Silbermann (1683–1753) who first exploited the new piano. Yet even he met with rebuffs, notably from Bach himself, who offended the proud maker by complaining of the weakness of upper register and the heaviness of the action. Bach's knowledge of instruments was so great that we may take these criticisms as well-founded. Two

years later the ruffled Silbermann came back with a new piano; this time Bach pronounced himself satisfied, but nevertheless continued loyal to the harpsichord in his compositions. His polyphonic style needed the sparkling clarity of the harpsichord, and it was the changing demands of composition that brought the piano into its own. Romanticism required an instrument that could sing broad melodies with a supporting accompaniment; as the Belgian theorist de Momigny (1762–1838) wrote of the piano, 'it has this advantage that the pressure of the finger determines the force or weakness of the sound: thus it lends itself to expression and sentiment ...'

Mozart first discovered a piano that satisfied him in 1777 in the workshops of the Viennese maker Stein, and from then he never went back to the harpsichord; however, this was still a light, almost harpsichord-like instrument, known as the square piano or fortepiano. It was with Beethoven that piano technique began to stride forward, reaching a peak in Chopin, who wrote for the piano with a deep love and understanding of the sonorities of the piano, and in Liszt, who developed its technical potentialities to such a pitch that his works are still in the highest virtuoso class. Paderewski, Rubinstein, de Pachmann, Rosenthal, Busoni, Rachmaninov – a host of leonine composer-pianists followed as the nineteenth century turned to the twentieth, writing rich, rhetorical, warm-hearted music and playing their massive concertos to enthusiastic audiences all over the world, displacing in popularity the solo violinist and even the enraged primadonna.

Their instrument splendidly fulfilled a century's experiment. The leather-covered hammer of the early fortepianos had given way to a delicately balanced felt-headed mechanism; the antique knobs and knee-pedals had become foot-pedals; the iron frame had arrived from America, allowing for greater strength and tension, and an ingenious system of overstringing made for greater compactness and distributed the enormous stresses over the whole frame (a single string may have a pull of 200 lb.). Musical instruments are suggestive to the composer, but ultimately they have to adapt themselves to his thought. Whatever the future may do to the piano, it has proved itself a noble instrument to which our century and the last are immeasurably indebted. (See also *Violin, Harp, Organ.*)

Picture and statue

PICTURES and **STATUES** are too often embraced and then smothered in the word 'art', although each one of them is a thing effective on its own.

'Things' have been painted and 'things' have been carved through the greatest width of space and time – from the studios of the Left Bank or Greenwich Village to the camping grounds of the aborigine in Arnhem Land; from this year's exhibitions back some 15,000 or 25,000 years to the

Fig. 26. Horse from the cave of Combarelles.

caverns of Lascaux, Les Trois Frères, Font de Gaume and Altamira. Something of a unity contains them all, since the Upper Palaeolithic 'artists' first evolved the techniques which the historic civilizations have refined.

In sculpture they already modelled and carved. They made reliefs, and they made statues in the round. Thus on the floor of the Tuc d'Audoubert cave, in the extreme south of France, figures of animals about two feet long are modelled out of clay in high relief; and recent discoveries at Dolní Věstonice in Czechoslovakia (see under *House*)

have shown how palaeolithic man modelled small animal figurines out of a special mixture of chalky earth and burnt bone, and then baked them, or kiln-dried them. Direct carvings were made in limestone, sandstone, serpentine, in ivory, antler and bone, and no doubt also in wood.

When man ultimately learned to smelt copper and to cast in bronze, he could adapt very old traditions to his new material, as one may see in the vigorous Bronze Age statuettes of Sardinia.

Engravings: techniques of engraving included scratching of an outline on materials, if they were soft enough, cutting out continuous lines, and pecking out lines dot by dot; and engravings have survived on bones, reindeer antler, mammoth tusks, on the limestone of caves and the sandstone of rock shelters, and on flat laminae of stone. Little 'panels' or 'drawing-boards' of stone excavated in the Parpalló Cave, in Valencia, were engraved with animal outlines; or painted with animals, or both engraved and painted. Pecked engravings were made in Sweden and elsewhere in the North on rocks smoothed and polished by the Ice Age glaciers. These belong to a later period. A famous group was pecked on flat rocks by a waterfall above a lake at Glösa, in the Swedish county of Jämtland.

Paintings: 'Carriers' for painting, one may think, were not restricted to the enduring stone slabs or pebbles, the cave faces and shelter faces. The palaeolithic painters of France and Spain would have been as ingenious as the Australian aborigine, whose 'carriers' include not only rock and cave, but other smooth surfaces, from his own stomach and chest to standing trees, and rectangular strips of bark which he cuts and wedges off the eucalyptus. The bark is the first paper or canvas.

For his colour, the Australian sticks to the natural ochres (yellow and red oxides of iron), to pipe-clay, and to charcoal; mixing his pigments with water, and sometimes contriving to add a binding trace of vegetable oil. French and Spanish palaeolithic painters also worked with ochres, and with a manganese black, eschewing any green or blue, and (so far as we can tell) any vegetable pigment.

This limited tradition of red, black, yellow and white continued a long while in the Mediterranean, making for a strong naturalism instead of a weak realism. Greek vase-painters never used more than those few colours, which were also the full palette, according to Pliny, of the great masters of Greek painting. In the Fayum, in northern Egypt, craftsmen were still obtaining rich effects with such limited pigments in the third century A.D., in the panel portraits they made. However, by that time the less provincial parts of the Greco-Roman world had long taken to a much gayer colouring – as one may see in the delicate and delicious wall paintings of Pompeii.

Exactly how the palaeolithic painters 'bound' their colours has not been established; they mixed them with water and then added some kind of oil or fat; or possibly they added white of egg, which would anticipate the glair of medieval art. Australian aborigines make their brushes of human hair or lengths of root frayed at one end. Cave-painters no doubt did the same, also perhaps using pads. Sometimes they must have dried their ochre paste into crayons; and at Lascaux they also appear to have blown pigment on to the designs through a hollow stem or tube, like a commercial artist adding his tone with a spray-gun.

None of our words such as 'art', 'picture' or 'statue', one can be sure, would have conveyed anything to the cave-painters, the quality of whose work varies from the very good to the inept and clumsy. They may have enjoyed painting and carving for their own sake, but they were hunters and food-gatherers intimately involved in nature; the things made by 'art' were probably as necessary to them as hunting weapons or hunting skill: they were hunting magic, as the books always say, also part, one can be sure, of the more complex rituals they lived by.

'Ritual and life: without the former', it has been written of Australian aborigines, 'life would cease; and without the latter, the necessity, the urge, for ritual would not exist. But ritual implies art', and the Australian expresses through art what he calls the 'dreamings', the secret, mythological life uniting him to his ancestor figures and cult heroes; through art he gives visible expression also to the 'shades' or souls of the totemic animals he is tied to. The Australian has ritual chants which express the 'dreamings', and he will sing or chant these 'dreamings' *into*

his carving or his painting, into the designs he paints on his own skin –

Even though an artist executes a bark painting especially for us at our camp, as does happen in Arnhem Land, he withdraws in spirit from ordinary camp life while he does so. Putting away for the time being its troubles and pleasures, he becomes the medium through which the 'invisible things of this world', the 'shades' of the totemic species, and of the cult heroes and 'gods' are expressed on bark. The primitive brush is a conductor's baton drawing the theme of the chant-song, which is pulsating though his mind, out of an orchestra of ochres, pipe-clay, charcoal and bark. (A.P.Elkin.)

Animals carved on spear-throwers have to do with success against those animals. Bull walks behind cow in the French cave of La Mairie, at Tayjat: so the artist is concerned not only for successful kills, but also for the fertility of his animals and a plentiful supply of them, so that there shall be future kills. Small figures of women from Dolní Věstonice in Moravia, Lespugue in France, Savignano in Italy or Willendorf in Austria are all shown as pregnant: the hunting group is concerned for the pregnancy of its women and for the continuance of the group.

So much can easily be discovered from palaeolithic art. Yet there may have been much linking the palaeolithic hunter to his art images which these images can no longer reveal – there may have been greater ritual complexities to do with the 'dreamings' and the 'shades'.

Only initiates are allowed to visit some of the cave 'galleries' in Australia; so it was, no doubt, with many of the galleries deep in the caves of France and Spain. Such a ritual causation for art persisted long after the Old Stone Age. Egyptian tomb sculptures and tomb paintings, for example, may be 'art' to ourselves as we examine them; but they provided the Egyptian dead with the personal life and the services and adjuncts of life they needed in the next world – a funerary art. That was the be-all of Egyptian art, inspired, maintained and developed by the cult of the dead. The lively image of Plate 9 may seem to us only a portrait now as it hangs on the gallery wall; but once it was a 'life': it was not made to flatter the subject's vanity; but to cover her mummified face. (See also *Dolls*.)

ILLUSTRATION: Plate 9 and page 226.

'So vile and stinking a custom'

The **PIPE** – the smoker's pipe – is one of the few articles of everyday life in Europe that have travelled to us from the West instead of from the Near East.

In the New World the early explorers and commentators found that smoking had its use in religious and medical ceremonies. Like other narcotics, tobacco appeared supernaturally strong. Benzoni, who published his *Travels in America* in 1565, described the way in which medicine men in Hispaniola cured patients by intoxicating them with tobacco smoke. Mexican Indians still employ tobacco or tobacco smoke in rain ceremonies; and the ancient Mexicans had come to smoking their pipes for pleasure and release.

Cigars and cigarettes also originated in the New World (*tabaco* originally meaning 'cigar', not the dried leaves). The Tewa Indians in their pueblos in New Mexico make cigarette papers out of corn (maize) husks, smoking the cigarettes in their underground kivas or ceremonial houses; and with other peoples tobacco is much wrapped up with myth and magic.

Judging by its attraction, also, for primitive hunting peoples in the New World whose way of life seems to have changed little in thousands of years, pipe-smoking must go back far beyond the classic civilizations of North America and South America. Far and wide American pipes had the bowl and straight stem which we have imitated, though they varied much in detail and in material. Thus the bowl of an Indian 'peace pipe' might be fashioned, like an example in the Horniman Museum in London, out of red stone (catlinite), while the stem was carved out of wood and bound in human scalp.

The Haida Indians of British Columbia, famous for their lofty totem poles, carve their wooden pipes with totemic figures. Pipes which are both pipe and tomahawk, the handle of the war-axe making the stem, are a curious example of rediffusion. They were first devised in Europe by enterprising manufacturers, who exported them to the Indians.

The Tlingit Indians of Alaska and British Columbia returned the compliment in a manner of speaking when they made pipe-bowls out of the spent cartridge cases of the white man. The stem was attached to the foot-bone of a bison, and the cartridge case was inserted in the bone. The Tlingits and the Alaska Eskimos also carve pipes from walrus ivory.

William Harrison recorded in his *Great Chronologie* that in 1573 'the taking-in of the smoke of the Indian herbe called Tabaco, by an instrument like a litle ladell, whereby it passeth from the mouth into the hed and stomach' had become very popular. A 'little ladle' not inaccurately described the early clay pipes, in which smallish bowls sloped forward; it was not until the end of the seventeenth century that the bowl assumed the familiar upright position.

Having crossed the Atlantic, pipe and tobacco began the conquest of all the world. Travellers carried them both to Africa, to Asia and to the Pacific islands. The new devotees of the Indian weed either copied the white man's pipe, with a few local variations (thus the Maoris made wooden pipes which combined the immigrant design with their own ancient style of carving), or else they contrived altogether new adaptations. In New Guinea, for example, pipes consist of a short, thick stem of bamboo with no bowl, or rather with a bowl which has dwindled to a piece of cane just large enough to take a rolled tobacco leaf.

Water-pipes, which are smoked across Asia and in China and across Africa, were adaptations aiming for cool and clean smoking. The first form was probably the *narghile*, now confined to India and Persia, which consists of stand and container, and preserves a memory of the time when a coconut or round-bottomed gourd, requiring a support, was used to hold the water. In the more widespread hookah, which Turks in European dress smoke in Istanbul cafés, the water-vessel stands by itself on a flat base. This form, in several variants, ranges from Turkey and Egypt through Africa and into China. In Africa the container may be made from the long, twisted horn of an antelope. In China, on the other hand, a beautifully decorated water-pipe has been devised which is only eighteen inches long and can easily be carried about.

Now that smoking is under such severe assault by doctors, it is ironic to recall the supposed medicinal virtues which first recommended tobacco in the sixteenth century. Harrison had written of its use 'against Rewmes and some other diseases ingendred in the longes and inward partes'. A more important factor making for the popularity of pipe and tobacco was the belief that smoking gave protection from the plague.

Woık for Chimny-ſweepers:
OR
A warning for Tabacconiſts.

Deſcribing the pernicious
vſe of *Tabacco*, no leſſ: pleaſaı̨t then profitable for all ſorts
to reade.

Fumus patriæ, Iɡne alieno Luculentior.

As much to ſay,

Better be chokt with Engliſh hemp,
then poiſoned with Indian Tabacco.

Imprinted at London by T.Eſte,for Thomas
Buſhell,& are to be ſould at the great North
dore of Powles. 1602.

Fig. 27.—Title-page, *Work for Chimny-sweepers*, 1602.

Yet the counter-attack was furious. In 1602 the anonymous author of *Work for Chimny-sweepers or A warning for Tabacconists* argued against tobacco medicinally, morally, religiously and hygienically; it had been 'first found out and invented by the divell, and first used and practised by the divels priests' (*i.e.* the Indians), not forgetting to observe the filthy state of tobacco pipes and the 'swart and sottish tincture' that 'cleaveth so fast to the inward part of the Pipe,

as hardly by any meanes but by the extreme heate of the fire it may be cleared from thence.'

King James I soon after castigated smoking as 'so vile and stinking a custom', imitated from 'the barbarous and beastly manners of the wild, godless and slavish Indians'. But the smoker and his pipe have survived all onslaughts.

ILLUSTRATION: Page 274.

New substances from the chemist

PLASTICS is an unfortunate word, though now an unavoidable one, for the products which are a mark of our age and among the greatest advances in technology since the prehistoric development of pottery and the very early invention of glass.

If it were used literally 'plastics' would have to include bitumen, clay, rubber, etc., but by consent the term is restricted now to products which consist of organic (*i.e.* carbon) compounds obtained in two ways – either by modifying substances which occur naturally (cellulose, for example), or else by synthesizing compounds of a new type altogether. But even that restriction of plastics to carbon compounds needs easing a little with the development of new substances based on silicon.

Physically there are two chief classes, the thermoplastic kinds which can be heat-softened and reshaped over and over again, and the 'thermosetting' kinds which undergo a chemical reaction when they are heated and are 'cured', *i.e.* they acquire a permanent set when they are cold.

The pioneer plastic was celluloid (nitrocellulose). In 1833 Henri Bracounot had experimented with the action of nitric acid on sawdust and cotton, and had tried to make coatings with his product. In 1846 Christian Schönbein, professor of chemistry at Basel, made the first fully nitrated cotton which attracted attention chiefly for its explosive properties. Products with different percentages of nitrogen were less violently explosive and, working with these the English chemist Alexander Parkes (1813–1890) succeeded in making successful coatings from solutions between 1855 and 1865.

Celluloid was first applied with commercial success in 1865, when John and Isaiah Hyatt in the U.S.A. won a prize offered by the firm of Phelan and Collander for an ivory substitute for making billiard balls. The key to the successful fabrication of cellulose nitrate was the introduction of camphor as a 'plasticizer'. Such substances, which promote the manifestation of plastic properties, are among the essentials of the technology of plastics.

Many developments followed the production of celluloid. In 1884 Hilaire de Chardonnet made an artificial silk from cellulose nitrate. It was quite unwearable, since it was liable to take fire, and attempts to render it non-inflammable were not successful. However, the experiments pointed the way to future progress. Goodwin, Reichenbach and others produced continuous flexible sheets of celluloid and so enabled George Eastman of Rochester, New York, to perfect the first roll-film for the camera, and others to develop the motion-picture film. Inflammable or no, cellulose nitrate remained the standard base for 35-millimetre professional ciné-film for many years, because of its dimensional stability. Only recently has it begun to be replaced by cellulose-acetate-butyrate. 16-millimetre film has been made on 'safety-base' (cellulose acetate) for much longer, because the dimensional requirements are not so stringent. Celluloid is still the material preferred for some products, including table tennis balls and plastic coverings which have to be stretched over metal, *e.g.* over the steering-wheel of a car.

Early on cellulose acetate, which like celluloid is thermoplastic, was investigated as a non-inflammable substitute. It came into general use in the First World War as an aircraft 'dope'. After the war, makers of cellulose acetate with plant on their hands had to find new outlets. One consequence was the rise of the acetate rayon textile industry. Cellulose acetate is a valuable material where high impact strength is required (*e.g.* in safety goggles and gauge glasses). It replaced celluloid in the sandwich type of safety glass. Casein plastics made from the coagulated protein of milk had a useful life, but are now made only into small articles like buttons.

All the plastics just mentioned are modifications of a natural substance. The other plastics, often referred to loosely as 'synthetic resins', from the resin-like character of some of the early experimental materials, are all built up from comparatively simple chemical substances. This may happen either by 'polymerization', in which many small molecules of one substance join to form one big molecule of a new substance; or by 'condensation', that is, by the reaction between many simple molecules with a loss of volatile components. The big molecules formed by polymerization are generally like long threads, while those formed by condensation are generally cross-linked into net-like structures.

The most extensively used of the 'synthetic resins' are the phenolic plastics evolved from 1907 onwards by the American, Belgian-born chemist Leo Baekeland (1863–1944), whose name has contributed to the familar term 'Bakelite'. They are thermosetting and are used with many types of filler, such as wood-flour, cotton or asbestos, selected to confer special properties on the finished article. Phenolic plastics were also applied very early on to making laminated products, in which sheets of wood or paper are impregnated with the plastic. This has provided many valuable new structural materials.

In schemes of researches chemists have often made resinous or polymeric substances incidentally, and they remained unexploited. Many of these have now been re-investigated to see if they have desirable properties. An example is the polymer of vinyl chloride, which after being known since the middle of the nineteenth century was studied again in the nineteen-twenties. After many failures two types of polyvinyl product were contrived. Polyvinyl chloride is now familiar as the PVC of insulated wire and lightweight rainproofs to which it is fitted by its rubber-like properties. It has also been used in the 'cocoon' method of sealing up machinery for storage and in new types of paint.

The earliest plastic developments owed much to the enterprise of individuals, but since modern applied research requires the resources of large industrial organizations, the newer plastics are inevitably associated with the great chemical combines – polyethylene or 'Polythene', for example; this is made from ethylene, one of the simplest of chemical compounds, though years of research with equipment of great complexity were required to perfect the means of its polymerization.

By the beginning of the Second World War enough of this curiously wax-like substance was being made to have a vital influence on the development of radar, in which its exceptional electrical properties were invaluable. Polystyrene, another substance with desirable electrical properties, has also been developed industrially, styrene having been available since it was produced in quantity for the manufacture of one of the types of synthetic rubber during the Second World War.

Transparent plastics like the now familiar 'Perspex' came into their own during the war, with the acrylic resins in the lead. Polymethylmethacrylate was the most used, vast quantities going into aircraft windows. One never knows how to predict the applications of any plastic; thus the acrylic resins used in aircraft first became prominent as a material for artificial dentures, while the polythene used in radar has turned out to be admirable for making talcum-powder sprays.

While chemists have provided the right substances, physicists and engineers have brought plastics from the test-tube to the counter. Machinery for moulding plastics has been developed from a capacity limited to a fraction of an ounce of moulding powder at one time to a capacity of many pounds. Several methods of fabrication are employed, compression moulding, for example, which involves heating and compressing the substance in one cavity, injection moulding, in which the substance is separately heated and forced into a prepared cavity, and extrusion, *i.e.* forcing the heated plastic through a shaped nozzle.

Many people still think of plastics as substitutes – and often inferior substitutes. This is a mistaken and an untenable view. The very ease of the fabrication of plastics does make it all too simple to turn them into shoddy articles, but with plastics it is possible to devise articles which could not be made in such numbers or in such forms or with such properties in any other way. Every new material man has exploited or developed has in part provided him with a substitute for an old material, and, in part, offered him potentialities which cannot be explored and realized all at once. That is an old story, familiar from the prehistoric evidence when stone tools gave way to bronze, or bronze to iron, and it is very true of plastics. (See also *Nylon, Earthenware, Chinaware, Glass*.)

Ace, King, Queen, Knave ...

PLAYING-CARDS were familiar in Europe by 1360, but where or how they originated is not at all certain.

Without evidence, they have been claimed for China, for India and vaguely for the East. Gipsies have also been credited with introducing cards into Eastern Europe for fortune-telling. But gipsies did not reach Europe until 1417, long after cards were first known to the Italians; as for India, cards were probably taken there by the Portuguese colonists in the sixteenth century. Perhaps one should also mention the theory advanced by St Bernard of Siena (1380–1444) and by other ecclesiastics – that playing-cards were invented by the devil. This still has its devotees, an ungrateful theory since cards have provided mankind with much innocent release and have canalized their impulses of aggression.

The oldest cards extant are Italian tarots, painted emblematic cards, which first appeared, without numerals and without names, in Venice. Whatever the origin of the emblems, these cards were probably meant for instructing and diverting the young, not for adults. The figures on the Atouts (trump cards) were the Mountebank, the female Pope, the Empress, the Emperor, the Pope, the Lovers, the Chariot, Justice, the Hermit, the Wheel of Fortune, Force, the Hanging Man, Death, Temperance, the Devil, La Maison Dieu, the Star, the Moon, the Sun, the Judgement, the World, and the Fool. However, suits, distinguished as 'cups', 'swords', 'money' and 'batons' (clubs), were added to the original band of twenty-two atouts; the cards in these four suits were numbered, and the pack was then used for playing *tarocco*, the first of all European card games. Such numbered cards existed certainly by 1377 and probably before.

All early cards were elaborately painted and there are tarocco packs decorated delightfully by quattrocento artists with tooling, gouache and illumination in gold and silver. Sets were decorated in this way by Antonio di Cicognara, who also painted the choir books in Cremona cathedral; and in 1392 the French craftsman Jacquermin Gringonneau was commissioned to paint for Charles the Mad of France that famous pack of tarocco cards responsible for the tale that cards were invented for the amusement of this king in his attacks of insanity.

As cards spread through Europe, they quickly changed. They had become a main instrument of gambling, and for this a pack of seventy-eight (ninety-seven for the Florentine game of *minchinate*) was unwieldy. So one of the four 'coat' (or 'court') cards in each suit was discarded. The atouts were abolished, all except the Fool, who survives with us as the Joker. Thus the pack was reduced to the present figure of fifty-two, the Joker apart. Several countries introduced their own suit-marks. Spain and Portugal were satisfied to retain the Italian cups, swords, money and batons, but Germany, the Netherlands and parts of northern Europe adopted hearts, bells, leaves and acorns. France took to hearts, diamonds, spades and clubs, which were handed on to England.

Painted cards were unsuited to shuffling and dealing and only the rich could afford them. By 1425 the Germans were stencilling cards; before long they were printing them from wood blocks and then from metal plates. French wood-block cards of the fifteenth century (such as the King of Diamonds, named after Charlemagne, reproduced in Plate 4) were printed several cards to the sheet and then cut up by the purchaser.

Since the fifteenth century there has only been one change of importance. In France early in the nineteenth century double headed figure cards appeared for the first time. This change to cards which can be recognized the moment they are thrown on the table was sensible and inevitable, and the double-heads soon crossed the Channel, though it was some while before they were generally adopted. Indeed, court cards with whole-length figures were still being printed for some of the famous clubs in England as late as 1875.

ILLUSTRATION: Plate 4.

The speeding of the plough

The **PLOUGH** is by no means as old as agriculture itself, nor is it an essential part of it; it is rather one of the earliest mechanical improvements introduced to increase the supply of food. Before the world-wide spread of modern European culture the plough was confined to an area which comprised practically the whole of Europe and of southern and eastern Asia, with Egypt, Abyssinia and parts of North Africa; even today there are large areas of the world where it is not used at all.

Before the days of the plough the ground was cultivated with digging-sticks and hoes, which are, in general, the implements still usually employed by primitive cultivators. A digging-stick is a strong, pointed staff, the ancestor of the spade, the garden fork, and the angular digging-sticks such as the Hebridean *cashchrom*. From the hoe, with its blade of hard wood, metal or stone, set at an acute angle to the handle have been derived the pick and the mattock.

It could hardly be expected that digging-sticks would leave much evidence of their use in ancient times, but there is plenty of evidence of the early use of hoes. For instance, hoe-blades of flint or chert have been found in the remains of the predynastic cultures of Egypt and Mesopotamia, and there is proof that the people of the Danube valley used stone-bladed hoes for agriculture in the third millennium B.C.

Our knowledge of the ancient plough has been derived from contemporary representations left by ancient peoples, especially those of Mesopotamia, Egypt, Greece and Rome, from crude pictures carved on the face of rocks in the Italian Alps and in Sweden, and most of all from actual specimens of the wooden plough which have been preserved, in whole or in part, in the peat-bogs of northern Europe.

The plough is believed to have been developed by adapting either a digging-stick or hoe so that it could be dragged continuously through the soil. This invention is not likely to have been made independently at different times and in different places, though it is possible that, once the principle of traction had been established and the knowledge of it diffused, it may have been applied by some peoples to the digging-stick and by others to the hoe; which would account for the two chief types of primitive plough which are not only found in antiquity, but have survived in use to the present day.

Ploughs carved on Mesopotamian cylinder-seals and drawn in Egyptian paintings are the earliest evidence we have. The seals and paintings date from rather before 3000 B.C. – that is to say, they belong to the early Dynastic period of both regions, when society was beginning to be organized on an industrial basis and when it was necessary to produce a surplus of food for feeding workers who were not themselves engaged in agriculture. Also without the plough corn could scarcely have been grown on a scale large enough for export, so that its invention was also necessary to the rise of the first city civilizations. As it was said of old that the plough was the gift of the gods, we may suspect that the inventors of it were the priests; they were the employers of the time, and the plough would have increased the supplies of grain for taxation and export.

According to Dr Carl W. Bishop, the plough may first have been developed from the digging-stick by tying a cord to it a little above the pointed end; one worker would then keep the point of the stick in the ground, another would pull on the cord and so drag the point through the soil, making a continuous furrow. Then, it is suggested, for reasons to do with fertility magic, a cow or a bull was tied by the horns to the digging-stick and made to share with the men the labour of drawing it. When it was found that the ox pulled more steadily, and was just as effective in fertilizing the soil with its manure, human traction gave way to ox-traction, and the cord was replaced by a pole, which was attached to a yoke tied to the horns. This theory of the genesis of the plough is based on the earliest contemporary drawings. In the rudimentary plough thus contrived and evolved the digging-stick became the combined stilt and share-beam; the type is conveniently distinguished as a *spade-plough*.

The crook-plough, on the other hand, is essentially a very large hoe, dragged through the soil by a specially elongated handle, and having a stilt added at the rear to enable the ploughman to guide it and steady it. This may have been the product of a hoe-using people who had learnt the advantage of the spade-plough and adapted the principle of traction to their own implement.

Both of these types of primitive plough spread widely over Asia, Europe and northern Africa as far as India and China. The original focus may have been in northern Mesopotamia, but soon after 3000 B.C. the plough is found as far west as Greece and as far east as India. In the Italian Alps it is depicted very frequently in rock-drawings attributed to about 1400 B.C., and evidence has been found proving the existence of the plough in Denmark by 1400 B.C. and in Holland by 1600 B.C. So far as we know at present, the plough did not reach Britain till shortly after 1000 B.C., nor did it penetrate to China until 300 B.C. The crook-plough was the type favoured in Crete, Greece and northern Germany, while the spade-plough was preferred in the Italian Alps, Denmark and Sweden. Actual wooden specimens, datable by pollen-analysis, have been found in the peat-bogs of Denmark and north Germany, and the method of ploughing with them is clear from the Swedish and Alpine rock-drawings. These show that a team of two oxen was normally employed, though larger teams are occasionally depicted; the ploughman guides the plough by its stilt, while the driver walks backwards in front of the beasts, calling them on. Similar primitive ploughs and teams are still in general use in the warm, dry lands of southern Europe and north Africa. In northern Europe, especially since the deterioration of the climate that took place about 400 B.C., heavier, wetter soils had not merely to be broken open, but the sods had to be turned right over in order to be dried out. This led to the development of ploughs with larger and stronger frames and special devices for turning the sods over, or in some cases for turning them to right or left at will. Plough-shares of wood or iron were introduced during the last 400 years B.C., and iron coulters appeared about the end of that period. Mould boards and wheels were added to some ploughs at a much later date. The further development of the plough was regional, and depended on local factors such as the character of the soil. Ox-teams in the Middle Ages in England consisted nominally of eight animals, but in practice probably four or less. Ploughing with oxen is still common in southern Europe; in England a last team of six oxen was still ploughing in Sussex until 1926. The use of horses in England was giving way to tractors before 1939. Scarcity of labour and need of more crops during the shortages of the Second

World War soon led to an immense increase of mechanized ploughing and a great decline in the number of horses. (See also *Fields*, *Tractor*.)

ILLUSTRATION: Page 27.

Cushions of air

PNEUMATIC TYRES (known as 'rubber tires' in America), allowing vehicles to create, so to say, much of their own road surface, absorbing unevenness, reducing friction and increasing the comfort and safety of passengers as well as the ratio of performance to horsepower, have been the greatest development in the wheel since its remote invention in the Middle East.

Early in the nineteenth century several minds realized the value of some form of springy, non-rigid tyre, but it was left to the English railway engineer and inventor Robert William Thomson (1822–1873) to suggest the use of inflated rubber tubing. Transport had been revolutionized by steam, McAdam had introduced scientific road-making and harder surfaces, and much attention had been paid to the uses of rubber by Hancock, Macintosh, Goodyear and others. In 1844 Good-year patented vulcanization; in 1845 Thomson took out a patent for what we should call tyres, or rather for a combination of an inflated rub-berized cushion with a double covering. 'My said invention', he wrote in the specification, 'consists in the application of elastic bearings round the tires of the wheels of carriages, for the purpose of lessening the power required to draw the carri-ages, rendering their motion easier, and dimin-ishing the noise they make when in motion. I pre-fer employing for the purpose a hollow belt com-posed of some air and water-tight material such as caoutchouc or gutta percha and inflating it with air, whereby the wheels in every part of their revolution present a cushion of air to the ground or rail or track on which they run.' He called his cushion an 'elastic belt'. It was to be made of 'a number of folds of canvas, saturated and covered on both sides with india-rubber or gutta percha in a state of solution'. The belt was then to be 'sulphurized' (*i.e.* vulcanized), and

fitted with a canvas cover inside 'a strong outer casing of leather'. A pipe for inflating the 'elas-tic belt' went through the tyre of the wheel and was 'fitted with an air-tight cap'.

It was reported in 1846 that a set of Thomson's tyres had been fitted to a brougham and had run for over 1,000 miles, but after this nothing more was heard of the invention. Solid tyres of one kind and another were still preferred, Thomson himself in 1867 patenting solid rubber tyres for a traction engine of his own design. Such tyres before long were commonly used on bicycles and other vehicles, and were only modified in 1884 by the invention of a cushioned tyre in which an air space was left in the solid rubber.

Independently of Thomson's forgotten inven-tion, John Boyd Dunlop (1840–1921), a busy veterinary surgeon of Belfast, now took the cru-cial step, by devising a pneumatic tyre which he patented in 1888, 'for bicycles, tricycles, or other road cars'. He called his invention 'a hollow tyre or tube made of India-rubber and cloth, or other suitable material, said tube or tyre to contain air under pressure or otherwise': Dunlop stated in his autobiography that he had never ridden a bi-cycle himself, though his small boy had known the agony of bumping on a solid-tyred cycle round the hard, stone-paved streets of Belfast. A bicycle with the new tyres was advertised in the *Irish Cyclist* on 19 December 1888. 'New Pneu-matic Safety,' it said, 'vibration impossible.' The paper made a facetious comment, little realizing that a revolution had now begun in world trans-port. 'We note the advent of a new Pneumatic – News room attic – bah – a new Pneumatic Safety. "Pneumatic", something to do with air, isn't it? Quite right too, we like to see new ideas well ventilated.'

Though Dunlop knew nothing of Thomson's previous work, a chain of causation and endea-vour and circumstances naturally connected the two inventions. There was now a more immedi-ate reason for applying the invention, and Dun-lop's tyres immensely improved the comfort and speed of bicycling; they were quickly popularized and developed. Another big step forward was taken by C. K. Welch in 1890 when he patented a tyre which was wired to the rim of the wheel and could easily be taken on and off, whereas Dun-lop's original tyre was stuck to the wheel.

In 1895 pneumatic tyres were first fitted to a motor-car, and cars could now ride smoothly into general use. Various modifications and improvements were inevitable. The wear of tyres was greatly increased by S. C. Mote's discovery in 1904 that rubber was made more tough by an admixture of carbon black, which soon became the common practice. Between 1916 and 1920 the woven casing of the outer covers was discarded. The constant flexing of tyres meant that the cotton threads crossing at right angles rubbed against each other, weakening the cover and causing failures. 'Cord' fabric was now substituted, consisting of parallel threads or cords with only just as many weft threads as are required to hold the cords together. This change helped in the development of giant pneumatic tyres for lorries, buses, etc.

Modern life without the pneumatic tyre, which supports the aeroplane when it takes off or lands no less than it carries the farm tractor through the muck, would now be unthinkable. The limit of development has not been reached; among recent innovations is the tubeless tyre – the pneumatic tyre so built that it can hold air under pressure without an inner tube. (See also *Rubber, Coaches, Wheel.*)

ILLUSTRATION: Page 370.

'Stamps to be used separately'

POSTAGE STAMPS, though such an obviously good idea as labels for the prepayment of the delivery of letters, were invented little more than a hundred years ago, and had then quite a laboured birth.

In the eighteen-thirties postal reform was canvassed in Great Britain. The services of the Post Office were antiquated and expensive, and largely beyond the reach of the poor. Postal fees were calculated by distance, and the dues were collected on delivery. An era of industrial expansion and of revolution in transport by the new railways demanded easier and cheaper communication; and in 1837 Rowland Hill published *Post Office Reform: Its Importance and Practicability*, a pamphlet which analysed postal economics and stated a compelling case for uniform penny postage, prepaid. Hill's plan was opposed, mainly by the Post Office, and among others by John Wilson Croker in the *Quarterly Review*, who maintained that it would be 'only a means of making sedition easier'. In Parliament the Postmaster-General pronounced that 'of all the wild and visionary schemes which he had ever heard of it was the most extraordinary'. However, the penny post was accepted unanimously by the Cabinet and established by Act of Parliament in 1839, coming into force in January 1840, when a half-ounce letter could be sent anywhere in the United Kingdom for a penny.

Stamps were Rowland Hill's solution of the problems of prepayment. In his pamphlet he had written of 'a bit of paper just large enough to bear the stamp, and covered at the back with a glutinous wash, which by applying a little moisture might be attached to the back of the letter'. He had also had in mind stamps printed on envelopes, but on second thoughts the postage stamp seemed to him a more ingenious and more flexible expedient. The Treasury, unsure that stamps were the best solution, had invited suggestions for a means of prepayment, offering prizes of £200 and £100 and receiving more than 2,000 replies. But in the end the authorities decided to issue two devices for the reformed postal service, Rowland Hill's bits of glutinous paper – 'stamps to be used separately', as they were called in a Treasury minute – and wrappers shaped like envelopes. They were, however, afraid of forgery, since the forgery of bank notes at that time was on the increase. So stamp and wrapper were to be engraved after designs by artists, with such complications of craftsmanship as might baffle the forger.

The wrappers, in which the greater faith was placed, bore an allegorical design on the front, picturing the dissemination of mail to all lands; the designer was the Anglo-Irish artist William Mulready, R.A., a doyen of the Academy, celebrated as a draughtsman. For the adhesive labels or stamps a drawing was commissioned from the less eminent artist Henry Corbould. It was to include Queen Victoria's portrait, which was another ingenious notion from the clear analytic mind of Rowland Hill. He was not thinking solely of doing honour to the Queen; since everyone would be so familiar with her likeness, he thought that the slightest deviation in engraving by a forger would produce a change in expression which would be discernible at once. The model chosen for the head was the City Medal engraved by William Wyon, the chief engraver of the Royal Mint, to commemorate the Queen's visit to the City of London in 1837; this profile was also familiar from the new coins. Charles Heath, engraver to the Queen, cut the die for the new stamps, and Jacob Perkins, of the firm of Perkins, Bacon and Petch, bank-note printers, of Fleet Street, who made the stamps, invented new security measures, including a special engine-turned background for the royal head which could not be reproduced without the knowledge of complicated calculations; in addition, each stamp was to include two letters of the alphabet in such a way that a different combination of letters appeared on each of the 240 stamps in every sheet. The new devices came into use with some delay on 6 May 1840, four months after the launching of the penny post. A poem about the 'Mulreadies', as the wrapper-envelopes were called, appeared in *Punch* in 1842, satirized Mulready's design, with Britannia despatching winged messengers, his Indians, his Chinese and ships, reindeer, and a nude workman hammering a hogshead. But the poem tells one much of how people felt about the new postal revolution:

Hail! O Mulready! Thou etcher of penny *envellopes*!
How can we praise the ethereal air of the garment
That hangs down behind from the shoulders of Mrs
  Britannia?
What is the thing that is perched on the top of her
  helmet?
Is it a wasp, with its head cut off, stuck on its tail, there? ...
Mighty Britannia! enthroned on her 'tight little island',
Sending abroad o'er the earth, to its uttermost quarters
Air-swimming angels – celestial 'General Postmen',
Types of the swiftness enjoined by the 'new penny post-
  age'.
Some does she send from her right hand, and some from
  the other
One to the region where Penn shaketh hands with the
  Indians –
A symbol that now, when so cheap is the postage of
  letters,
We'll see ev'ry hand on the face of the earth with a Penn
  in it.

One flies into Lapland – and one into Turkey –
And one to take part in a snug Chinese committee.
Praise we the symbol of ships sailing up against moun-
  tains,
Showing that nothing on earth can retard our progressing.
Praise we the thought that could show us the terrible
  vastness
Of the consumption of ink from the 'increased facilities' –
Showing that now it is sent, not in bottles, but hogsheads!
Great is thy genius, Mulready! and thou shalt live ever,
By Fame handed down to posterity in an *envellope*!

The stamps proved immensely popular, issued at first only in the two denominations familiarly known to collectors as the Penny Black and the Twopence Blue. Both had the same design, one of the boldest, simplest and most agreeable in the history of postage stamps, and a design which was to remain in use for forty years.

Correspondence increased enormously with stamps and the penny post, with benefit to the Post Office; and stamps soon began to appear in other countries. The list of first comers is surprising, since it was not the leading countries or governments of the period that were most speedily off the mark.

March 1843	Zürich
August 1843	Brazil
October 1843	Geneva
July 1845	Bâle
July 1845	New York
August 1847	U.S.A.
September 1847	Mauritius
January 1849	France
July 1849	Belgium
November 1849	Bavaria

After the first ten years the list grew rapidly; and today about 200 countries are active in the issue of stamps. For fifty years, stamps followed the style which had been set by the English. Some stamps bore armorial devices or decorative numerals in place of a head, but all were of a utilitarian design only for postal purposes. In 1892 the United States broke with tradition and issued stamps to publicize an event – the Columbian Exhibition at Chicago which marked the 400th anniversary of the discovery of America. A long set of sixteen stamps each pictured an incident in the life of Columbus; and it was now realized that stamps were a possible means of propaganda.

Stamp collecting, the world's most popular hobby, began early, having its origin perhaps in the attraction of stamps, not so much as miniature works of art, but as symbols of travel and distant countries. It was in full swing by the eighteen-sixties, though satirized at first by *Punch* –

> When was a folly so pestilent hit upon
> As folk running to collect every spit upon
> Post Office stamp that's been soiled and writ upon?

For rare stamps the highest prices ever paid are $40,000 for the 1 c. British Guiana of 1856, of which only one specimen is known, and £5,000 for the 3 sk. Sweden of 1857, printed in yellow instead of green.

ILLUSTRATION: Page 307.

A primal invention

The **POTTER'S WHEEL,** which seems to us so elementary, is one of the earliest applications of a mechanical principle to an industrial process, making for greater speed and efficiency.

In human history it deserves comparison with the machine developments of the Industrial Revolution. Like the still earlier advent of metallurgy (see *Bronze*), the invention of the potter's wheel was a step towards eliminating the family as an economic unit which was self-contained, producing its own food, its own clothing and its own household equipment for daily life. In fact, special craftsmen were now coming to the fore, who lived by exchanging their manufactures for the surplus food grown by the rest of the community. Significantly the wheel spread at first from its original home, which was Mesopotamia, only to those societies which were more or less urbanized; it did not become the stock-in-trade of less advanced cultures until nearly 4,000 years after its invention.

Its presence in Mesopotamia in the early fourth millennium B.C. has been inferred with absolute certainty from the character of the pots recovered in the 'Uruk' occupation levels in the ancient city mounds of Sumeria; and it appears that the potter's wheel and the earliest wheeled vehicles emerged together more or less, the wheel of the vehicles perhaps suggesting the potter's wheel. By 3000 B.C. wheel-made pottery had become universal in Mesopotamian cultures, whence it was diffused eastward to the cities of the Indus valley, and north-west into Syria and Anatolia. It appears in the second city at Troy before 2000 B.C. In Egypt, perhaps because the ease of water transport discouraged the early development of wheeled vehicles, the potter's wheel is a late arrival; it was not certainly in established use until the Old Kingdom, in the Third Dynasty, *i.e.,* about the middle of the third millennium B.C.

In essence this wheel is no more than a circular platform mounted for free revolution. The most primitive type, known also as a 'tournette', consisted of a disc, probably of baked clay, on a vertical pivot. It could be rotated only by turning the disc itself, a task which had either to be done by the potter (which left him only one hand free to work his clay) or by an assistant. This 'slow-wheel' probably persisted, as it did in Egypt, for a great while, but it was replaced in time by the 'fast wheel', in which the wheel itself was not directly revolved. Power was supplied either by the potter or his assistant, the potter working a treadle with his left foot or turning with the ball of his left foot a second disc fitted to the pivot, more or less at ground level. A more sophisticated device relieved the potter of this heavy work; his assistant turned by handle an independent wheel mounted vertically in a frame, and the power was conveyed to the pivot of the potter's wheel by an endless belt.

Before the wheel came into use, pots were all built up by hand, normally by the women of the household. It was a slow, laborious job. Hand-made pots lacked such fine symmetry, and it was impossible to fashion walls of a uniform thickness. Hand-made vases in antiquity depended far more on the design of prototypes in other materials – gourds, leather vessels, wooden containers. So the invention of the wheel 'released' the potter; he was stimulated and freed of limitations, and it was the wheel which established aesthetic standards for pots as pots, not as imitations of something else. The use of the wheel does not end with 'throwing' or shaping the pot. When the surplus water has dried out, the pot goes back to the wheel for 'turning', the potter working on the surface with special tools to make it perfectly regular, to produce mouldings and perhaps to polish or burnish it. Potter's shops painted on Greek vases make it clear that the wheel was also employed in the painting of vessels. A paint-charged brush was held against the revolving pot. Many Mycenaean vases and Cypriot vases of the geometric period are decorated with encircling bands of paint so regular that they must have been applied on the wheel, sometimes with a multiple brush.

Making very large vases presents special difficulties to the potter, who gets his best results by building the big vessels up in sections, each one of which is thrown separately on the wheel. The sections are dried, stuck together with slip (diluted clay) and 'turned' on the wheel to smooth over the joins. To assemble such a vessel depends on measuring each section very accurately. Greek potters used the method. Their Archaic and Classical Attic masterpieces, so superbly proportioned, make it certain that they worked from a 'blueprint' design elaborated beforehand.

One should add that the potter's wheel had reached the Greek mainland in the Middle Bronze Age (it had found its way to Crete, where it was in use soon after 2000 B.C., either from Egypt or Anatolia). Wheel-made pottery from Mycenae was being distributed over a large part of the Mediterranean and Levantine world in the latter half of the second millennium B.C. The break-up of the Bronze Age world, which affected the central and eastern Mediterranean at the end of the second millennium, greatly slowed down the spread of the potter's wheel in Europe; Greek, Etruscan and Phoenician colonists eventually diffused it through the Mediterranean, and at last it penetrated north into Europe, though not until the Iron Age was well advanced. For example, in Britain there is not a sign of wheel-made pottery before the Belgae arrived from the Continent and settled in south-east Britain about 75 B.C., using wheel pottery of a very distinctive type.

Wheel-made pots only became general in Britain after the Romans had imposed their imperial cultural unity. Even so, the Dark Ages that follow the collapse of the Western Empire set back the clock in this as in much else; in Britain, pottery became very much scarcer, and a high proportion of it, once more, was made without a wheel. Even medieval pottery in England was mostly made on the slow wheel, which is shown by the pot shapes, vital very often, yet somewhat gawky. (See also *Wheel, Earthenware, Chinaware*.)

'Hail! the Jewel in the Lotus'

PRAYER-WHEELS are particularly a symbol of Tibet and of Buddhism in Tibet. Almost every family, rich or poor, owns a hand prayer-wheel. Vast rows of wooden ones line the walls of monasteries, to be spun by pilgrims and by travellers as they pass on their journeys. Scattered through the country, even in the most remote and inaccessible places, there are also prayer-wheels in various sizes operated by wind or water.

The hand prayer-wheel is usually made of bronze. Some of the wealthier families own wheels made of silver, or of silver overlaid with gold and studded with precious stones. However, the basic design is the same in all cases. A wooden handle, covered with bronze or silver, is attached to a metal shaft which enters a cylindrical box. The shaft is tipped with a conical metal cap to prevent the cylinder from spinning off. Inside the metal cylinder are coiled paper ribbons, printed with symbols and prayers. The usual prayer is *Om Mane peme hum* – 'Hail! the Jewel in the Lotus'. The cylinder, too, is engraved outside with sacred symbols. From one side of the cylinder there hangs a chain carrying a metal weight. A slight flick of the wrist spins the wheel, and the centrifugal force of the weight carries on the motion. The wheel must be spun clockwise.

The purpose of the prayer-wheels is tied up with the Tibetan Lamaist belief of merit. The Tibetans believe that by the invocation of these

sacred prayers or mantras, they are freeing themselves of any likelihood of being born in a lower
form in their next incarnation. Their aim is to
reach the bliss of Nirvana; if they earn more and
more merit during each rebirth they may eventually be released from the cycle of birth and
death, and so reach their goal of Nirvana. Thus
each turn of the prayer-wheel, by hand or by
wind or by water, is one more step towards
Nirvana.

Some of the more religious people in Tibet
have wheels so made that the shaft turns on an
ivory or stone cylindrical base attached to the
handle. The continuous spinning of the shaft
wears through the stone or ivory and after many
years bores its way through completely. The piece
of ivory or stone is then highly prized, and considered to be impregnated with merit. The owner
strings it and wears it as an amulet, and earns
considerable respect.

Nobody is quite certain when the prayer-wheel
was first brought into use in Tibet, or knows
how the present types and shapes have evolved.
It is certainly a strange fact that prayer-wheels,
especially those driven by wind or water, should
be so highly developed in a country where the
use of the wheel for other purposes was never
exploited. Beyond his mountain passes the modern Tibetan may ride his bicycle or even his
motor-bicycle; but his country is still one of
mules, horses and donkeys carrying their load on
their backs.

It has been suggested that the prayer-wheel
symbolizes the Buddha's message to mankind
and is thus the wheel metaphorically which was
set spinning by the Buddha for man's salvation.
However that may be, wheels of worship are not
confined to Tibet, to Asia, or Buddhism, or
the Buddhist countries. There are prayer-wheels
in Japan. In the ancient world there is record of
wheels turned by the worshippers in Egyptian
and in Greek temples; and wheels have not been
unknown to Christianity: Æthelwold, bishop of
Winchester from 963 to 984, had in his cathedral
a wheel hung with bells which was spun on
saints' days; wheels hung in churches in Brittany
are spun in honour of saints, much as by another
act of symbolism one buys and lights a candle.

ILLUSTRATION: Pages 214 and 215.

A 'philosophical supper'

The **PRESSURE COOKER** goes back,
unexpectedly, to the seventeenth century. In 1680
the French-born Denis Papin, 'excellent mechanic,
philosopher, and physician', exhibited to the
Royal Society in London his 'new Digester or
Engine for softening Bones'. On 12 April 1682
members of the Royal Society (Papin among
them) sat down to a meal cooked in this engine.

John Evelyn describes the occasion in his
diary:

I went this afternoone with severall of the Royal
Society to a supper which was all dress'd, both fish and
flesh, in Monsieur Papin's Digestors, by which the hardest
bones of beefe itselfe, and mutton, were made as soft as
cheese, without water or other liquor, and with lesse than
8 ounces of coales, producing an incredible quantity of
gravy; and for close of all a jelly made of the bones of
beef, the best for clearness and good relish, and the most
delicious that I had ever seene or tasted. We eat pike and
other fish bones, and all without impediment; but nothing
exceeded the pigeons, which tasted just as if bak'd in a pie,
all these being stew'd in their own juice, without any addition of water save what swam about the Digester, as *in
balneo*; the natural juice of all these provisions acting on
the grosser substances, reduc'd the hardest bones to ten-
dernesse ... This philosophical supper caus'd much mirth
amongst us, and exceedingly pleas'd all the company. I
sent a glass of the jelley to my wife, to the reproch of all
that the ladies ever made of the best hartshorn.

The principle of the device is that the temperature of steam rises with pressure. In the modern
domestic cooker a pressure of 15 lb. to the square
inch is usually the maximum. Papin required
higher pressures, bones softening greatly at 35 lb.
to the square inch and almost disintegrating at
50 lb. His boiler, therefore, acted fiercely by
means of its strength and heaviness; and it was
equipped with a steam safety-valve controlled by
sliding a weight along a lever. These high pressures were dangerous, owing to the crudeness of
engineering techniques in Papin's day; in later
cookers a pressure of only two or three pounds
per square inch was used. About 1800, heavy cast-
iron cooking-pots were made with flanged lids.
A conical weight fitted into a conically seated
hole at the top of the lid. When pressure ex-

ceeded two or three pounds per square inch, the weight was sufficiently raised for steam to escape until the pressure fell again to less than that which would support the weight. The lids were secured by twisting them under retaining lips, as in some modern cookers.

The disadvantage of these early cast-iron cookers, apart from danger at high pressures, was their great weight; and pressure cookers became practicable in the home only with the advent of supplies of the very much lighter aluminium in our own century. The risk of bursting has now been made negligible, since modern methods of inspection reveal a potentially weak component; and resilient packing rings have been developed to effect a steam-tight seal between lid and bowl.

Since not all dishes require the same treatment, the steam pressure of some cookers can now be varied by a simple adjustment. But this needs to be as accurate as possible. In general, pressure cookers give the best results when the cooking time is reduced to about a third of ordinary boiling time. Steam is so much more penetrative at pressure that it makes most foods more tender, but it may also alter them in consistency to a degree which the cook must be able to regulate. In Papin's bone softener the meal John Evelyn enjoyed in 1682 must have needed only a very short cooking time. Steam at such high pressure would quickly have disintegrated any meat, and the process must have been a critical one, making no allowance for the long slow cooking which some dishes require. Industrial pressure cookers of the present day are more like Papin's original apparatus, with the addition of the most accurate means of control.

Some products, such as canned salmon, are deliberately cooked at such a pressure that the bones soften to the point of edibility.

ILLUSTRATION: Page 309.

Printing, Chinese and European

PRINTING in Europe may or may not have been influenced in its origins by the Far East, but it is certain that printing was first of all practised in China. There it emerged from a variety of techniques, impelled by several distinct political and social forces. One cannot seize the moment when impressions from seals and stamps, and rubbings and squeezes from engraved stones, led to the multiplication of literary matter by similar but perfected means.

The essential materials, paper and ink, had been manufactured for many centuries before they were used by the printer. Something resembling ink – in China this always consisted of lamp-black and gum suspended in water – was used for writing over a thousand years before the beginning of the Christian era, as is testified by marks on some oracle bones from Anyang, the capital of the Shang dynasts, who ruled c. 1523–c. 1027 B.C. In the Han dynasty (202 B.C.–A.D. 220) ink was used for writing on the slips of bamboo which constituted one kind of the official stationery. If we may believe the Chinese annals (and these are nearly always shown to be reliable when a means of independent checking exists), paper was invented in the year 105 B.C., the credit for the discovery going to a palace eunuch called Ts'ai Lun, who reported the novelty to the Emperor and later was deified as the patron god of paper-makers. It was made from hemp, either fresh or obtained from fish-nets and old rope, and from mulberry bark. It was the last which gave (and gives) Chinese paper its special character, for it made possible a paper at once thin, strong, soft and beautiful. A dressing of gypsum and starch is said to have been used even in the pre-Christian period to improve the surface for the reception of the ink. Paper rapidly ousted the bamboo tabs, silk and a near-paper made from silk, which had previously served for writing.

Since no single person can be credited with the invention of printing, we may look for its origin among motives and minor techniques which appear to lead towards it. Confucian philosophy and education seem inseparable from the printed text with its commentaries. Confucians were behind the great flowering of official printing in the Sung dynasty (A.D. 960–1279). Since A.D. 175 it had been a Confucian custom to carve the classics periodically in stone in order to establish an authentic and improved text. During the T'ang dynasty (A.D. 618–906) authorised ink-rubbings were issued from the engraved stones. The Confucians believed that actual printing was the invention of one Fêng Tao, a prime minister in the middle of the tenth century, when China was divided under the rule of five dynasties. Fêng Tao suggested that wood be substituted for stone in making the customary record of the classics, for his state could ill afford the more enduring material. Whatever is the truth of this story, there began in the tenth century a classical revival, sustained by printed texts, which compares with the European renaissance some five centuries later. Under government direction or patronage a steady stream of books appeared – classics, commentaries, histories, memoirs, dictionaries – of such excellence that for later bibliographers the Sung dynasty remained the classical age of printing. Over-printing in colour, with exact registration, was employed for such works as almanacs and a famous history of architecture.

After the Mongol invasion, in the thirteenth and fourteenth centuries, popular novels and dramas were printed in large numbers. The development of book illustration in line engraving took place in the Ming dynasty (1368–1644), soon to be followed by the invention of coloured prints from the wood-block.

The other force behind the early development of printing was Buddhism. It seems that even before the time of Fêng Tao printing was known in the small state of Shu (Szechwan). The earliest reference to block printing is in an account by Liu Pin of his visit to Szechwan. The output was mostly books of divination and non-canonical writings for the poor and ignorant, 'smudgy and illegible'. Paper money was also printed. The earliest known printed book is the Diamond Sutra, Buddha's discourse on the unreality of phenomena and personality, and one of the most popular scriptures of Mahāyāna Buddhism. The copy of this book which Sir Aurel Stein obtained at Tun Huang on the north-west frontier of China is dated A.D. 868 and has as frontispiece a woodcut depicting the Buddha pronouncing his discourse to the aged disciple Subhūti. The duplication of brief texts and devotional icons (as other material recovered at Tun Huang shows) was a common method of accumulating merit. Printed charms and votive offerings were sold at the temples (Latin indulgences were one of the first fruits of European printing). As for the Diamond Sutra found at Tun Huang, Wang Chieh had copies of the work printed 'for free general distribution in order to perpetuate in deep reverence the memory of his parents'. The book consists of a roll sixteen feet long with six sheets of text and one illustration. There was also found at Tun Huang a folded book with pages as we know them, dated A.D. 949. But for the persecution of Buddhism in China in 845 and the destruction of thousands of monasteries, it is probable that we should know much more about the development of printing, in which Buddhists seem to have had a considerable start over the Confucians.

The earliest Buddhist printing of all survives in Japan. In 770 an Empress ordered the manufacture of a million miniature wooden pagodas, each to contain a text of about thirty painted characters, of which a few are still preserved in museums and temples.

The printing described so far was executed from wooden blocks, one to the page, on which the characters were carved to stand in relief. This is the method of printing which remained in favour in China and Japan until the advent of the linotype machine. Printing with movable type, in Europe synonymous with printing itself, was in China never more than a minor variation. In the eleventh century Wang Cheng invented movable type of clay, and later on experiments were made with wooden type; presumably these methods were quickly abandoned, for the histories say little about them and no books recognizably printed with movable type have survived from an early period. In Korea the idea found more favour. The Koreans developed the technique of printing from movable type, and in Ming times it was reintroduced into China, but in spite of some official encouragement it never came into general use. Special difficulties faced the Chinese in this matter. It was difficult to carve and handle a fount which for learned texts might amount to 10,000 different characters, and could not usefully be kept under 5,000. Altogether apart from this, movable type could not give an individual rendering of a text to the satisfaction of a people so sensitive to calligraphic beauty. The page-block could moreover be rapidly carved, and at a small cost in labour. At the present time the disadvantage of a system of writing which renders the typewriter all but impractical must be acutely felt, but it would be chaos in China if a system of romanized spelling were adopted overnight. For irreducible linguistic reasons the 'good old characters' will be retained for a long time.

The invention of printing in Europe by movable type is usually ascribed to Johann Gutenberg (c. 1397–1468), though claims are also made for the Dutchman Lourens Janszoon Koster (c. 1370–c. 1440) and the Italian Pamfilo Castaldi (c. 1398–c. 1490). Several men in different countries were no doubt working on the same problems and driving toward the same conclusions, but printing certainly spread in Europe from Gutenberg's activities and his pioneer work in Strasbourg or Mainz.

Compared to Chinese ideographic writing, the alphabetic system was the more flexible and convenient and favoured a rapid development of printing once the first steps had been taken and the principle of movable type had been established. The crux, therefore, was not a method of printing – which already existed in Europe, in seals and block-prints – but a method of making letters which could be arranged in words, printed, dismantled and then reassembled to make other words. Movable type could be cut in wood, but this was too laborious: type had to be cast in metal, and so printing was really invented when a mould had been made which could be adjusted to cast, to a certain degree of perfection, letters as thin as i and as wide as w. The whole process involved no new principle, process or alloy, no newly-observed law of nature: it was, as so often in the history of invention, a matter of endless patience and of the continual application of common sense and ingenuity to surmounting first this and then the next small difficulty. For example, it was necessary, in order to counterfeit the irregularity of writing, to have many variants of each letter; and in the forty-two-line bible which Gutenberg probably finished in 1455, at Mainz, there are 240 small letters, compared with about forty (including accents and ligatures) used in modern gothic type.

There can be little doubt that it was Gutenberg who introduced the adjustable metallic mould. Once cast, in type-metal which is an alloy of fairly low melting point, the letters of exactly the same height from the face to the base of the stand,

could be wedged in an iron frame with low space bars in between. On the even surface, inked with a leather dabber, a sheet of slightly damped paper was laid; and another flat surface was brought down on the paper with pressure derived from turning a wooden screw such as was well known in Gutenberg's time as the operative part of a wine-press. When the pressure had been applied and released, the damp paper, now containing a clear imprint of the type faces, was hung over a cord to dry, like washing on a line.

A man and a boy usually combined to operate these early presses. Between them they might print 150 impressions in an hour. Their work was lightened very early on by the addition to the press of the tympan and frisket. The tympan was a hinged flap, cloth covered, on to which the paper was laid. The frisket was a hollow iron frame, hinged to the tympan, that retained the paper in position while the tympan was rotated so that the paper was held in position over the type face while pressure was applied. With this simple improvement the printing press remained practically unaltered for 300 years.

Of Gutenberg's first book, the forty-two-line or Mazarin Bible, there exist about thirty copies and many single sheets, out of an edition which consisted probably of 210 copies. It shows how printing, so to say, was born perfect, as it had to be. The printed copy had to be as efficient as the hand-written copy; and a fifteenth-century missal, like a clipper ship in the nineteenth century, was the culmination of centuries of craftsmanship.

After the early years, the next significant improvement in the printing press was made in 1799 by Charles Stanhope, third Earl Stanhope (1753–1816), scientist and Fellow of the Royal Society. His press was made entirely of iron, and he devised a system of levers whereby increased pressure could be obtained within a precisely limited stroke. This gave better work on a sheet double the previous optimum size. The number of sheets that could be printed per hour rose at the same time to about 200, a figure gradually increased to 250 as successive designs of iron press were introduced. One of the most successful was the Columbian devised in America by George Clymer in 1817.

Inking was still by dabber, even though in 1810

a leather-covered inking roller was tried by Friedrich Koenig in Germany. The difficulty was to devise a roller that was soft and yielding and would not set hard. In 1813 this was achieved in England by Bryan Donkin (1769–1855), who made a roller from a mixture of glue and treacle that was little different from the rollers still employed.

However much it was elaborated, the flat-bed press, in which a screw brought pressure to bear on a type face drawn into position horizontally after the paper had been set upon it, was very limited in output, 250 sheets an hour seeming to be the maximum. A cylinder machine was patented in 1790 by William Nicholson, but never built. This patent anticipated many later developments. In 1814 The Times* was printed at the high rate of 1,100 sheets an hour on a machine designed by Koenig in 1811. It had a cylindrical platen, or pressure device, with tapes to guide the paper, and inking rollers. In 1827 Edward Cowper and Augustus Applegarth led the paper by means of tapes beneath one roller, and in reverse beneath another, so that the paper was printed on both sides; this raised the production of The Times* to 5,000 sheets an hour. In 1835 Rowland Hill, of penny post fame, made a true rotary machine fed from long rolls of paper, but the Customs and Excise refused to permit its use for newspapers, since the stamp duty required that each sheet should be printed and stamped separately. The semi-rotary machine using flat sheets of paper was therefore developed to a fine degree of perfection, and in 1848 an Applegarth machine was made in which nine cylinders worked in unison, with paper sheets fed to each. The Times* was produced on these machines at the rate of 16,000 sheets an hour. The Daily Telegraph was printed in 1860 on a ten-feed semi-rotary machine designed in the United States.

In modern rotary machines the output is commonly 40,000 complete newspapers of eight pages, per hour, folded and delivered ready for despatch. For book work, 2,000 sheets, printed on both sides, may be delivered from one machine in an hour. Each sheet may contain thirty-two book pages.

* Of London

ILLUSTRATION: Pages 218 and 219

Pyramids of Egypt

The **PYRAMID** is Pharaoh's tomb. It derives ultimately from the heap of earth piled up above the grave, magnified a thousand times and stylized into a shape of profound religious significance.

The earliest royal tombs of Egypt were covered by an oblong mass of mud bricks with sloping sides. King Zoser of the third dynasty (about 2560 B.C.) was the first to give permanence to his funerary monument by using stone and he was likewise the first to build a tapering structure, 204 feet high, over his grave. But this did not possess a smooth outline; it rose in six unequal tiers or stages – hence its designation: the Steppyramid. Forty years later king Sneferu, of the fourth dynasty, built the first true pyramid, and his son Khufu, whom the Greeks called Cheops, erected the great pyramid of Gizeh, in which the simple geometric form becomes fantastic beyond belief by dint of its sheer mass and scale. It stood originally 481 feet high. The sides of its square base were orientated to the points of the compass and measured 755 feet, with a difference of 7·9 inches between the longest and the shortest sides. It covered an area of about 13 acres.

The pyramid of Khufu is a solid mass of stone except for the narrow passages leading to the burial chamber. The stone was quarried on the east bank of the Nile and ferried over to the Western Desert in the summer, when the great river was in flood, husbandry at a standstill and the valley covered by a sheet of fertilizing water. Herodotus records the tradition that 100,000 men were annually levied for three months during twenty years to carry out the work. Now only the rough core remains. Originally the pyramid was covered with a casing of the finest limestone, long ago looted by the stonemasons of Cairo. The fragments of the casing which survive at the base, where sand protected them, are fitted so marvellously that the joints are well-nigh invisible.

The methods of the builders are as difficult to reconstruct as their intentions. Skill and manpower counted for more than mechanical aids, which were of the simplest. The builders used tools of hardened copper and probably raised the blocks by means of huge temporary ramps of mud bricks and wooden rollers, wedges and cradles. A sarcophagus cut from a single block of limestone or granite was built into the burial-chamber, and after the interment the entrance passage was sealed and the structure was never entered again.

The great pyramid of Gizeh is merely the most splendid of the royal tombs. Remains of over sixty other pyramids are preserved. From about 1600 B.C. onward the kings were buried in a valley of the Western Desert at Thebes, and their tombs were carefully concealed and not marked by monuments. But the ruins of 130 later pyramids survive in the Sudan, where Ethiopian kings, claiming to be true successors of the Pharaohs, maintained Egyptian traditions in a barbarous fashion well into Roman times, as in the royal cemetery at Nuri.

All the later pyramids were smaller and less extravagantly built than those of the fourth dynasty. They consisted generally of a rubble or mud brick core with a casing of hewn stone; the latter has now disappeared and the weathered cores stand as shapeless hillocks crumbling in the desert.

The pyramid was part of a large architectural complex, with its entrance in the valley at the foot of the western cliffs. Here a temple formed the vestibule of a walled ramp or passage which led up to the desert plateau and ended in a second and larger temple built up against the eastern face of the pyramid enclosure. In the depth of the temple, where it abutted against the enclosure wall, and in the axis of the pyramid, a huge 'False Door' marked the spot where the living communicated with the dead king. The barrows of northern Europe offer interesting analogies.

During the fifth and sixth dynasties (from about 2400 B.C. to 2200 B.C.) a strange and fascinating miscellany of texts was chiselled on the walls of the passages within the pyramids and also of the burial chambers. Some of them seem to have been part of the funerary ritual, others accompanied offerings or magically effected such offerings by their mere presence; others were spells protecting the king's body or, more often, his surviving self on its journey into the Hereafter. Incoherent if considered as a whole, and often obscure, they represent the earliest large body of religious writing in the world. They also throw some light on

the conceptions which underlie the construction of the pyramids.

The immense effort spent on the burial of Pharaoh was justified by a belief that was hardly shaken during the long course of Egyptian history – the belief that in the person of their king a god, the Son of the Sun, had taken charge of the people. Nor did death necessarily interrupt his beneficial activities. The form of the pyramid had a cosmological significance and played its part in a funerary ritual which aimed at achieving the king's transition from this world to the Beyond with the fullest possible retention of his powers. It is probable that the function of the pyramid could be explained in more than one way; we know that a multiplicity of meanings did not present an intellectual problem to the ancients but was appreciated as an enrichment of their experience. It is certain, in any case, that the form of the pyramid was in some way related to the sun, or rather to the god who became manifest in the sun but was the creator of the universe and the begetter of Pharaoh. It is highly probable that the pyramid represented the Primeval Hill upon which the Creator had taken his stand when he emerged from the Ocean of Chaos to create the world. The Primeval Hill, as a centre of vitality and creative force, was an appropriate place for the divine king's resurrection after the crisis of death.

Whatever precise dogmas found expression in this astonishing type of building, its foundation in contemporary thought and feeling can be gathered from such texts as the following, in which the death of King Amenemhet I (about 2000 B.C.) is grandiosely announced: 'The god entered his horizon. King Amenemhet withdrew to heaven. He united himself with the sun-disk and the divine body coalesced with its sire.' Though the pyramids have received minute study from reputable archaeologists as well as the 'Pyramidiots', who tried to predict the future from pyramids' measurements, they can still offer surprises. Only recently, and at the foot of the Great Pyramid of Gizeh itself, troughs containing two huge funerary boats, probably of Khufu, were found accidentally by a road engineer. (See also *Ziggurat, Barrow*.)

ILLUSTRATION: Page 168.

Q

How corn was ground

QUERNS are early devices for grinding grain by hand, consisting of two stones, an upper moving on a lower. In the more ancient saddle-quern the lower stone is elongated and may be saddle-shaped, the upper stone being pushed backwards and forwards on the lower with both hands. A one-handed variety is sometimes distinguished as a 'grain-rubber'. In a rotary quern both stones are circular; the upper stone is pivoted on a spindle projecting from the centre of the lower stone and revolves on it; an aperture in the upper stone admits the grain, and a handle is usually provided for turning it.

The study of querns has been much neglected in the past, and very much remains yet to be learnt about their evolution and typology.

The saddle-quern may be a development from the primitive pestle and mortar or the rock basin, designed for grinding rather than crushing small seeds. It has been found widely distributed in both hemispheres, but, with few exceptions, only among agricultural peoples. It was the only 'mill' of ancient Egypt, of the Old Testament and of Homer, and is still widely used by African peoples. It appeared in Britain with the Neolithic (food-producing) culture about 2000 B.C., and survived there till the first century B.C., when it was superseded by the rotary quern.

The rotary quern cannot have been derived directly from the saddle-quern, but may have been an adaptation from the large revolving donkey-mills that appeared in the Mediterranean world about the fifth century B.C. These last must have been invented by some educated engineer to facilitate the supply of flour to the urban communities of the Greco-Roman world on a commercial scale. So far as the present evidence goes, rotary querns had appeared in southern Europe before the second century B.C., but none are certainly known to antedate the donkey-mills. It is very probable that the rotary quern may have been produced as a portable version of the donkey-mill for the use of armies in the field or of sailors on long voyages. The idea would readily be taken to their peasant homes by discharged soldiers and adopted as standard domestic equipment, replacing the saddle-querns, which were less efficient, and rubbed down the fingernails of the women who operated them. At any rate at least two types of rotary quern have been distinguished in the Mediterranean basin – an eastern type, high and narrow, with sloping grinding surfaces and radial horizontal handles; and a western, Iberian type, with flat grinding surfaces and vertical handles. The former was brought to southern Britain in the first century B.C. by Celtic immigrants with the La Tène culture from Gaul; the Iberian type seems to have reached Ireland at an earlier date and may have spread later to western Scotland. Other types were in vogue in the Rhineland, where they were made from the local lava and exported to Britain during and after the Roman occupation.

Wherever these querns were introduced they underwent local development with a view to increased simplicity and efficiency. In general, this took the form of an increase in diameter and a decrease in the height or thickness of the stones, with a corresponding reduction in the downward slope of the grinding surfaces, where this existed.

Querns continued in use throughout the Middle Ages, but they were generally prohibited by the lord of the manor, whose milling rights in the manorial water-mill or wind-mill were thereby infringed, and who sent his servants to search out and break up all offending querns. Their use nevertheless continued in parts of England till comparatively recent times, and in Ireland, Shetland and the Western Isles of Scotland till the present century. They are still used in North Africa.

If wheat is first thoroughly dried by heat, an efficient rotary quern will grind from 5 to 10 lb. in one hour, depending on the skill of the operator and other factors. Undried grain is most difficult to grind, and there is evidence that preliminary drying was the usual practice. Yet it was hard work which the women disliked and wished on to beneficent elves; just as there are folk stories of elves flailing the corn, so Robin Goodfellow, as one may recall from *A Midsummer Night's Dream*, would come to the house and 'sometimes labour at the Quern'. (See also *Water-mills*, *Windmills*).

ILLUSTRATION: Page 26.

R

From radio to radar

RADIO, as with so many developments that have profoundly affected the lives of civilized peoples, began in laboratory experiments remote from the thought of practical applications. Unexplained observations gradually accumulated from 1780 to 1888; work was done on electromagnetic waves by Clerk Maxwell and later by Heinrich Hertz. Guglielmo Marconi (1874–1937) knew of Hertz's laboratory successes from his tutor, Professor Righi, and began his own experiments in 1895. He had obtained contracts for supplying short-distance shipping information to Lloyds and results of the Kingstown Regatta to a Dublin newspaper in 1898. In December 1901 he announced to an incredulous world that he had received signals in Newfoundland from Poldhu in Cornwall. By 1907 he was operating on a limited scale a public transatlantic radio telegraph system.

Early radio transmitters depended on the crude, but controllable, effects following the passage of a powerful spark between electrodes. There were no amplifiers. Sir John Ambrose Fleming, in 1904, produced a thermionic valve which was a very sensitive and stable detector, but was incapable of amplification. The American, Lee de Forest, in 1907, added a third electrode or 'grid' to such a valve, thus obtaining an instrument capable of amplification, but he did not publish his researches until 1913, by which year Meissner, in Germany, had actually used the Lieben-Reiss relay of 1911 as a generator of oscillations and an amplifier. The importance of these developments would be hard to overestimate, since one of the most crippling features in early radio developments was the difficulty of getting reliable signals at long range; the currents received at any distance were so minute without amplification that they could hardly be detected. The First World War stimulated the development of valve (or tube) amplifiers, war requiring rapid communication. The telegraph and telephone had been hailed as great advances in this respect, but the ability to communicate without intervening wires was doubly welcome. Developments in the war period were great, but signalling was almost exclusively in code.

The transmission of speech and music by radio dates back to 1906, when R. A. Fessenden (who claimed to have heard speech, even if poorly articulated, by radio in 1900) used a high-frequency alternator as a power source at Brant Rock, U.S.A. The cost was high, and the quality range very poor, so that regular broadcasting was not at the time in contemplation. The war of 1914–1918, though it advanced radio in other respects, was doubtless responsible for delaying anything so frivolous as transmissions of music. It was in 1921 that a station at Pittsburgh, U.S.A. and another at Writtle, England, began regular transmissions. The power of the Writtle station was only one quarter of a kilowatt, and when the British Broadcasting Corporation was incorporated in December 1922 a chain of eight stations with $1\frac{1}{2}$ kilowatts capacity was erected within a year. There were also eleven relay stations, each of 120 watts – a power that may be compared with that of a domestic 100-watt electric lamp. By 1924 the Daventry station of the B.B.C. was of 25 kilowatts capacity.

The quest for more and more power in broadcasting was by no means an unmixed blessing. The 500-kilowatt station could swamp all its neighbours and blanket reception from afar over a wide area. Dictatorships were quick to seize on these qualities which they hoped to turn to their own advantage. The inevitable outcome was a power race, of which the effects, particularly in Europe, are still to be found in poor quality reception.

The Second World War was as prolific as the First in advances in the art of communication by radio. Outstanding were the developments by Watson-Watt and his colleagues, who began by researches into the reflection of radio waves from the ionized layers of the upper atmosphere discovered by Kennelly and Heaviside in 1902 and at a higher level by Appleton in 1925. It is the multiple reflections from these ionized layers and from the earth's surface that make it possible for short-wave signals to be heard after passing completely round the earth, whereas it had originally been thought that they would leave the earth altogether at the visual distance from the aerial to the horizon. Watson-Watt argued that if such waves could be reflected from an ionized layer they might equally be reflected by a conducting surface such as the wings and fuselage of an aeroplane. Confirmation of this theory was obtained in 1935, but the detection and accurate registration of these minute reflections posed mechanical and electrical problems of what at one time seemed almost insuperable complexity; but in war the support was forthcoming for the prosecution of researches, however costly; and from these came radar, valuable in war and a boon in peace-time navigation.

Another war-time advance was the discovery of the peculiar properties of the rare substance germanium as an amplifier and rectifier. Amplifiers of great efficiency, long life and very small size are made possible by the germanium valve. Radio, in this case, comes to the aid of telephony, since such amplifiers will be sunk at intervals as part of the first transatlantic cable telephone. (See also *Television, Telegraph, Telephone.*)

The coming of railways

A **RAILWAY** has been defined as 'a way or road laid with rails (originally of wood, in later times usually of iron and steel), on which the wheels of wagons containing heavy goods are made to run for ease of transport'. Or put another way it has been said that 'railway' is a concept of three elements: the wheel, a prepared track and means for lateral constraint of the motion. Either

definition throws the origin of the idea back into the past, long before the era of steam and the locomotive.

It has been claimed that grooved stone roads known from ancient Malta, Greece and Assyria were deliberate rut-systems. But the first evidence for railways comes from the sixteenth century, when tracks with wooden rails were used in the mines of Germany and Eastern Europe. The railway, in fact, belongs to the age of metals and mining, and such tracks are described in detail and illustrated in Agricola's mining treatise *De re metallica* (1556). The trucks shown by Agricola had flangeless wheels. They were kept on the line by a large pin, fixed to the bottom of each, and running in a groove between the tracks. But in Transylvania trucks had wheels with flanges; they ran on wooden rails which had rounded tops and were mounted on sleepers. Lines of rail were connected to each other by points, with a movable tongue. Here is the germ of the modern railroad.

No one knows when railways were introduced into England, which was to be the country of their greatest and most striking transformation. As one might expect, the early ones were associated with coal-mines, and in 1597 a wagon-way – the first one to which there is a reference – ran from the pits at Wollaton and Strelley, in Nottinghamshire, to the river Trent. By the middle of the eighteenth century a network of horse railways extended over the valleys and uplands round the Wear and Tyne.

Ralph Allen, deputy postmaster of Bath, and organizer of postal services in the West of England, laid a railway from the quarries above his house, Prior Park, to Bath. By the middle of the eighteenth century some of the great railway engineering works which have helped to make the English landscape had already been constructed. The Causey Arch, built in 1727, had a single 104-foot span. Nearby was a railway embankment 100 feet high, with a base 300 feet wide.

By the end of the eighteenth century iron was beginning to take the place of wood for rails. Many of the early iron railways transferred the flanges from the wheels to the rails, which were L-shaped and known as 'plates'. This system died out by 1810 or so, but not before it had given us the word *platelayer*.

Continued on p. 323

PLATE 13

PAPYRUS LETTER, 3rd century A.D. from a schoolboy to his father
(for translation, see *Paper*).

PLATE 14

CHRISTMAS TREE, from *King Nut-cracker* by Heinrich Hoffmann, translated by J. R. Planché (1853).

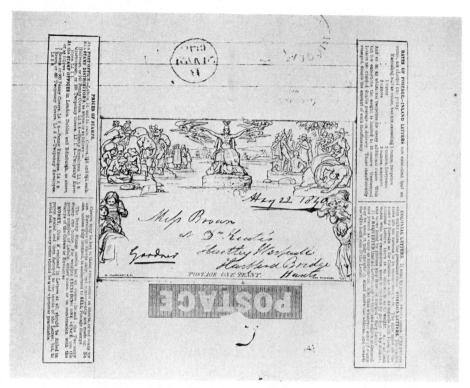

Mulready's wrapper-envelope, 1840.

Baird's original television apparatus, Science Museum, London.

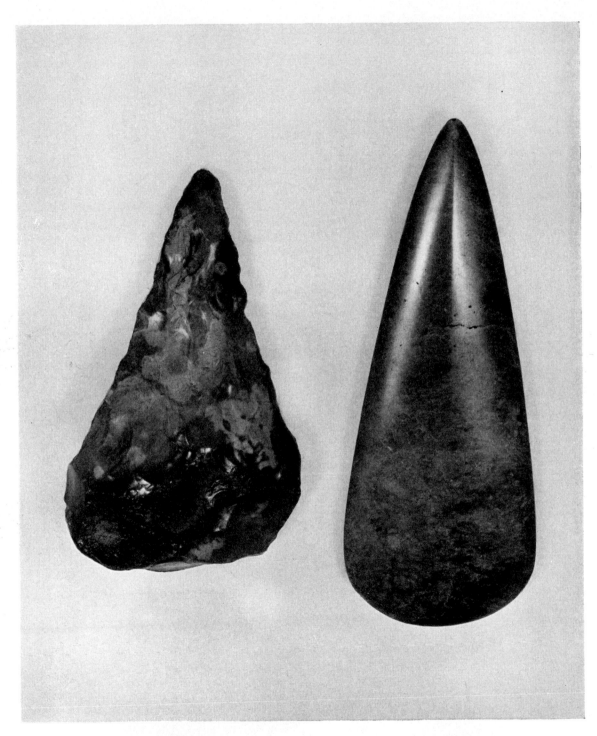

Stone Tools: neolithic axe of greenstone and flint hand-axe found at Black St Mary in 1690.

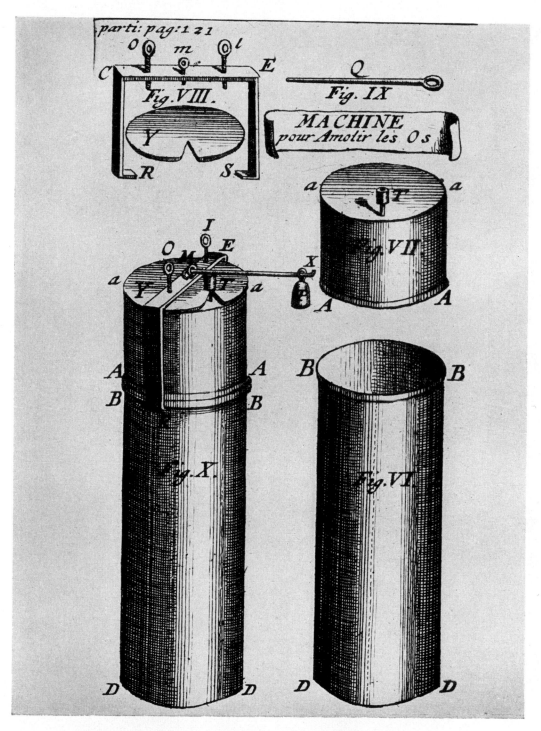

parti:pag:121

Fig. VIII.

Fig. IX.

MACHINE
pour Amolir les Os

Fig. VII.

Fig. X.

Fig. VI.

Pressure cooker. Diagram from Denis Papin's *La manière d'amolir les os*, 1688.

Flint sickle, as used by neolithic farmers, from the film *The Beginnings of History.*

Bronze: reconstruction of the technique of bronze casting and smelting during the Bronze Age.

Divining-rod in use for finding metals, from Agricola's *De re metallica*, 1556.

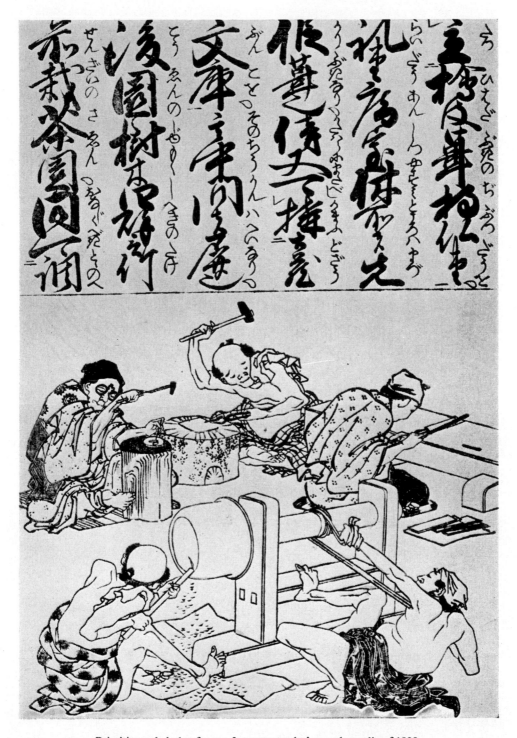

Primitive pole lathe, from a Japanese trades' encyclopaedia of 1828.

A ziggurat reconstructed.

Remains of a ziggurat in the Land of Elam between Shush and Shushtar.

Castles: Henry II's tower keep of the twelfth century surmounting Dover Castle. The base of the Roman lighthouse can be seen alongside the church.

Entrance to the grotto at Painshill, Park, Surrey.

315

Gramophone: a replica of the pioneer machine – Edison's phonograph of 1877.

16
XYLOPHONE SOLOS BY CHAS. P. LOWE.

12000 Home, Sweet Home, with variations
12001 Wood Nymph Galop
12002 Edison Polka
12003 Carnival of Venice, with variations
12004 Du Du Medley, with variations
12006 My Old Kentucky Home
12008 Firefly Galop
12009 The Mocking Bird
12010 You'll Remember Me
12011 The Suwanee River
12013 Robin Adair
12018 Leonora Waltz
12020 Dancing in the Sunlight

One who has not seen the modern Graphophone, known as the Universal and designed especially for use in dictating letters, has no idea of the perfection reached in the talking machine. It is simple and compact in construction and made to run by clockwork or by electricity as desired. Such a Graphophone greatly increases the capacity for work of any office.

SONGS BY LEN SPENCER.

Mr. Len Spencer, the most versatile artist ever engaged in record-making, is exclusively employed in our service. He combines the gifts of comedian and vocalist to an unusual degree.

Part of a page from the first Columbia gramophone catalogue, c. 1898.

Loadstone in ornamental case; Russian, eighteenth century.

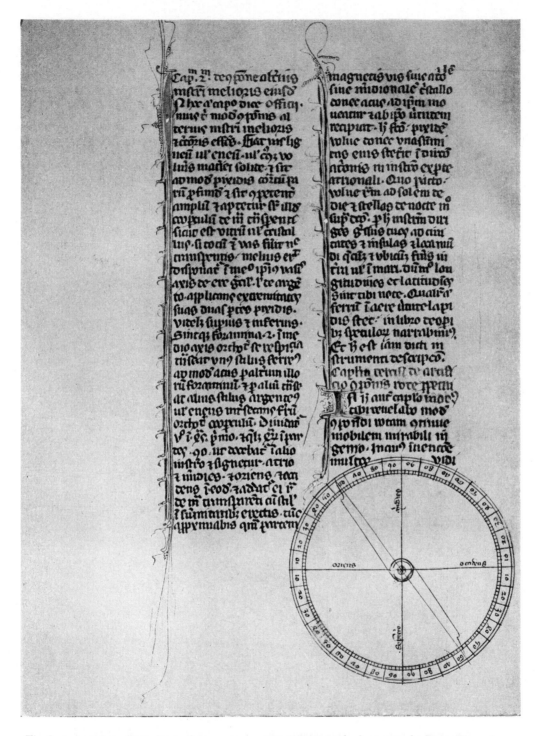

The first pivoted needle compass, from a manuscript of the *Epistola de magnete* by Petrus Peregrinus.

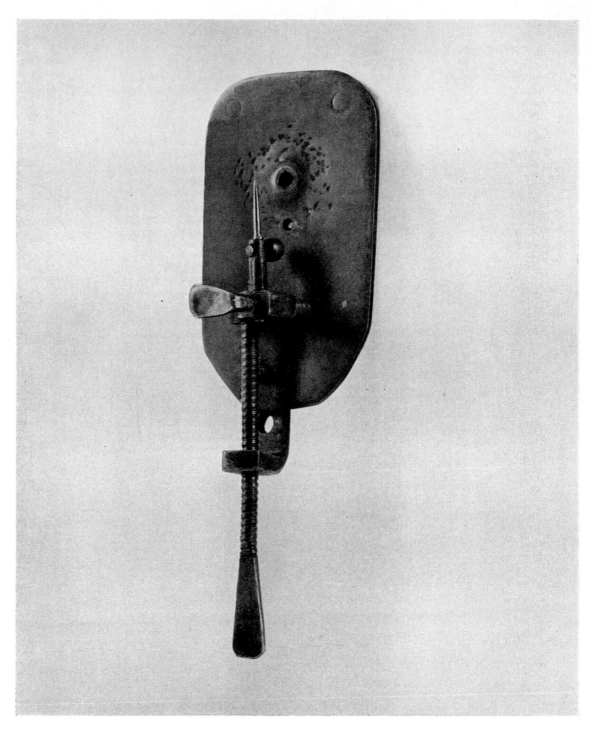

Facsimile of the simple microscope used by Antony van Leeuwenhoek (1632–1723).

Marshall compound microscope, c. 1700.

A Tower Mill, Heckington Lincolnshire.

Moulin le Brande Stacke at Arneke, Nord, France.

PLATE 15

FINDS FROM A BEAKER BARROW, 1814. Oil ascribed to T. R. Guest.

PLATE 16

WIELDING A FLAIL, detail from *Chairing the Member*, by Hogarth (1697–1764).

Iron rails, wrought-iron boilers and high-pressure steam, accurate machine tools – these were the concomitants of the steam locomotive's introduction on railways in the early nineteenth century, in place of the horse. The mercurial, erratic, inspired engineer, Richard Trevithick (1771–1833), who was reared in the Cornish mining industry and who devised the first high-pressure steam-engine, built in 1803 the first locomotive in the world to run on rails. He launched it at Penydarren in South Wales, on Monday, 13 February 1804. Oliver Evans (1755–1819), the great American engineer who invented the high-pressure steam-engine independently of Trevithick, foretold before his death the transformation of railways from local mineral lines to a system of passenger transport by steam. 'A carriage,' he wrote in 1812, 'will set out from Washington in the morning and the passengers will breakfast in Baltimore, dine in Philadelphia, and sup at New York the same day. To accomplish this two sets of railways will be laid so nearly level as not in any place to deviate more than two degrees from a horizontal line, made of wood or iron, on smooth paths of broken stone or gravel, with a rail to guide the carriages so that they may pass each other in different directions and travel by night as well as by day.'

It was Trevithick who had taken the vital step to make this true; but Samuel Smiles, in his *Lives of the Engineers*, has successfully bamboozled the world into supposing George Stephenson to have been the inventor not only of locomotives but even of railways themselves. He wrote in his belief that invention was inseparable from thrift, sobriety and piety, qualities by which Trevithick was not distinguished. Smiles was helped in his deception because it was not until 1830 that the first publicly renowned steam railway, from Liverpool to Manchester, was opened. Stephenson was the engineer in charge of construction. The celebrated Stockton and Darlington Railway, opened five years before in 1825, was a coal railway, carried no passengers except a few in horse-drawn carriages, and did not strike the public imagination of the time.

The Liverpool and Manchester Railway held a competition for locomotives (including one propelled by a horse driving a kind of self-propelling treadmill) in 1829. Stephenson's *Rocket* won,

P

though it was probably not the best engine on show. The Liverpool and Manchester was opened in 1830, by the Duke of Wellington. One of his guests, the economist and statesman William Huskisson, was run down by a locomotive and killed. The first locomotives, particularly those before 1830, were regarded as mechanical horses, with a special kind of life of their own. To this day locomotives are *stabled* in *sheds* and conducted by *drivers*. They run on *roads* or *tracks*, drawing *wagons*, *coaches* and *carriages*. A locomotive of 1812 was named *Iron Horse*, a term which has now become a cliché.

By the forties most of the main lines we know had been laid or planned. By the fifties, or at most by the sixties, the great English railway bridges had mostly been built – the Saltash, the Britannia, the Newcastle High Level, the Border. (We had to wait until 1886 for the Forth Bridge, in Scotland.) Railways progressed by chaotic planning, cut-throat competition, and wild speculation, till the country was covered by a crisscross of lines that looked in places like the skein of wool tangled by Alice's kitten.

Rising speeds, elementary signalling, makeshift brakes, incredible working hours and poor pay brought a crop of accidents that one would have supposed might have daunted the bravest. But nothing could stop the railways booming. Automatic brakes brought an end to the age of accidents and made possible the nonetheless highly dangerous railway races to the North between the East Coast and West Coast routes, and to the West between the Great Western and the London and South Western. By 1900 running times sometimes equalled and even exceeded those of 1939. Even today we rarely attain to 1939 speeds.

It is sad to think that by 1954 Britain no longer had pre-eminence in railways. Today the English railways are well-organized (allowing for the difficulties) but dull. It is to France that we must turn to see railways at their twentieth-century best – steam, diesel and electric. The trains thundering south at prodigious speeds from the Gare de Lyon to the Mediterranean and the frontiers of Switzerland and Italy have stirred the imagination of engineers all over the world. (See also *Roads, Steam-engine*.)

Clean chin or beard?

RAZORS are connected so intimately with beards that one cannot be discussed without frequent reference to the other. Abundant evidence for the use of razors in antiquity can be gleaned from sculpture, vase-painting, etc. We can admire not only the fine curly beards of kings and warriors on Assyrian reliefs and the beards of Greece recorded by Attic vase painters, but also the clean chins of sculptured Egyptian monarchs and of Minoans represented in bronze or ivory.

Occasionally, classical literature provides information of a kind not deducible from material objects. In his play *The Thesmorphoriazusae*, written in 411 B.C., Aristophanes has produced a scene of pure farce about shaving. The main character, Euripides, has learned of a plot by the women of Athens to murder him because of his revealing treatment of them in his plays. He plans to introduce a friend disguised as a woman to a festival at which no men are allowed, to learn their plans. His friend, like every other Athenian of the day, is bearded, and so must be shaved. Euripides starts by asking his friend Agathon, the tragic poet, for a razor – a sally at Agathon, who had a reputation for effeminacy, of which shaving was very much a symptom at this date:

Euripides:	Agathon, you must have a razor on you somewhere? One would be a godsend to us just now.
Agathon:	Help yourself – take it out of its case.
Euripides:	That's most kind of you. Now, Mnesilochus, sit you down, and puff out that right cheek of yours.
Mnesilochus:	Ooow!
Euripides:	What *is* the matter? I'll stick a gag in your mouth if you don't keep quiet.
Mnesilochus:	Ouch! Ouch! Hi! Oooh! Help!
Euripides:	Now, where on earth are you off to?
Mnesilochus:	I'm going to take sanctuary with the Gods – Heavens, you don't think I am going to stay here to be cut to pieces?
Euripides:	You're going to look a bit of a fool with just one side of your face shaved, aren't you?
Mnesilochus:	I couldn't care less if I do.
Euripides:	For heaven's sake, *please* don't let me down. That's it – come along over here.
Mnesilochus:	What a fool I am.

Euripides:	Now, keep still, and hold your head up. Now where are you wriggling off to?
Mnesilochus:	Oooooooh!
Euripides:	What are you moaning about? It's working out very nicely.
Mnesilochus:	Oh dear, Oh dear – what a fool I am being. Just fancy me having to go and do my military service with no beard.
Euripides:	Now, there's no need to fret. My word – you do look handsome. Like to see yourself?
Mnesilochus:	All right, bring the mirror if you like.
Euripides:	See?
Mnesilochus:	Good Lord! That's not me – that's Kleisthenes!
Euripides:	Now, stand up a minute and keep your head up, so that I can give you a singe.

So the farce goes on. Little wonder that the elder Pliny in the first century A.D. recommends for cuts inflicted in shaving a styptic application of spiders' webs.

In searching for the ancestry of the modern razor, it is almost impossible to determine when and where a man first used a knife-blade to scrape off the hair on his face. Equally inscrutable are the exact motives, ritual or psychological, underlying the act, though women's hairless faces may have had some part in the story. Archaeologists have identified as razors certain flint blades found at pre-dynastic sites in Egypt, and therefore some 5,000 years old; and flint persists into the early dynastic period in the form of short blades with neatly rounded or squared edges. The tradition of flint razors was strong enough in Egypt for the earliest metal blades to copy their shape. One Egyptian metal type, resembling a wide, two-edged knife with a short tang for the attachment of the handle, is similar to razors that have been found in early Sumerian graves, where they always occur in pairs, too badly preserved to reveal whether they had been sharpened on both sides. In tombs of the Early Bronze Age in Cyprus, at the end of the third millennium B.C., similar tanged razors frequently accompany the dead. In Cyprus, and in many other areas during the Bronze Age, the hair also appears to have been removed by tweezers, whose very presence as an alternative gives some idea of the painful process that shaving must have been.

In Crete, blades of obsidian, sharp as the glass it resembles, and very probably used as razors, have been found at Knossos as late as the end of the Middle Bronze Age, but soon after this metal razors are in use, the shape of one type resembling, on a small scale, a butcher's cleaver. This pattern was also used by the Mycenaeans. In Sicily, double-edged metal razors are found which have an indentation at the bottom, a feature common to many types of razors found in Europe during the Bronze Age. Handles of Early Bronze Age razors from Denmark are decorated with human or animal heads. As the types develop, the blades tend to become convex, bulging out in a wide sweep on either side of the handle. Razors which appear in Britain during the Late Bronze Age are of this kind; the long cutting edge may have made it possible to shave without having to stop in the middle to whet the blade. Quite a different pattern occurred in Upper Italy in the Late Bronze Age and Early Iron Age: razors with a twisted wire handle riveted to an almost rectangular blade, in which there is a nearly round aperture: perhaps a finger fitted into this to help guide the razor.

The indirect evidence for the existence of razors in antiquity helps to fill a good many gaps; if we cannot always be certain of the precise types of blade in use at certain times in certain places, there is plenty of information to show where razors were used and where they were not. All the men portrayed on the famous 'Standard of Ur' are clean-shaven, though some other sources show bearded Sumerians. Egyptians are usually, but not always, beardless, as innumerable statues and tomb-paintings show; the aggressive-looking Hittites who appear on so many reliefs within the wide sphere of their influence in Turkey and North Syria are clean-shaven. Minoan art, where it portrays human beings, might be said to have idolized youth, and beards would be lacking anyway. But representations of older men show the custom to have been universal.

At Mycenae, however, some men wore beards. Of the five gold masks which Schliemann found in the Shaft Graves, three represent bearded men, in appearance not unlike the bearded face engraved in profile on the magnificent gem recently found in the new series of Shaft Graves at Mycenae.

Vase-paintings, terracottas and sculpture make it clear that to the Greeks beards were the dis-

tinguishing mark of a fully adult man and of certain gods. Apollo, and later Hermes, were thought of as being at the threshold between youth and maturity, and are represented as beardless, though sometimes with the 'first down of youth'. Yet razors were familiar enough then to add metaphors to the language. In the *Iliad*, Nestor can address Diomedes with the words 'To the razor's edge have things now come for all the Achaeans, whether there be bitter death for them, or whether they shall live.' The same metaphor is used by prose writers such as Herodotus, as well as by the tragic poets. Creon, in the *Antigone* of Sophocles, is warned by the blind seer Tiresias that his conduct has brought him to 'the razor's edge'.

Under Alexander, fashions changed; it is obscure whether the habit of shaving was introduced by Alexander himself or his Macedonians, or whether it was the result of the closer contacts with the East. Aristotle was one of the first to adopt the new custom, no doubt because of his intimate association with the Macedonian court as Alexander's tutor. His brother-philosophers evidently ignored his example, and felt there was a necessary connection between beards and learning, for several writers are found passing remarks such as Dio Chrysostom's 'Cultivation of a beard does not make a man a philosopher'.

In Rome, razors were at least available as early as the days of Tarquinus Priscus, when the augur, Attus Navius, confounded his king by cutting a whetstone in half with a razor. The practice of shaving, however, did not become general with the Romans until the second century B.C., when an otherwise undistinguished member of the renowned family of the Scipios brought a barber to Rome from Carthage. From then onwards until the time of the Emperor Hadrian the Roman male was clean-shaven, and the growing of a beard was a sign of great grief or distress. The Emperor Augustus grew his beard after the announcement of the destruction of Varus and his three legions in the Teutoberger Forest in north Germany. Suetonius reminds us that a razor could have more than one use when he relates that the half-mad Emperor Gaius ordered his father-in-law Silvanus to kill himself by cutting his throat with his razor.

Hadrian grew his beard, it is said, to cover

certain blemishes on his face, but the bearded habit now spread throughout the Empire and persisted, no doubt to the detriment of barbers and makers of razors, until the time of the Emperor Constantine in the early fourth century A.D. (See also *Safety Razor*.)

ILLUSTRATION: Page 76.

Reaping machine to combine-harvester

REAPING MACHINES were first described by Pliny the elder in the first century A.D. Used in the lowlands of Gaul, these were carts with close-set teeth or knives projecting on the fore-edge, pushed by oxen through the corn. The attendant carried a tool for clearing the knives; the heads of corn fell into the cart, leaving the straw standing in the field.

Some time after the end of the fourth century these elementary machines seem to have fallen into disuse; and the idea was at last revived in 1785 by a correspondent who submitted translations of the accounts of Pliny and Palladius to the Royal Society of Arts in London. Many machines were devised in which, once again, the knives were pushed forward, or rotated, or given a scissors or sideways action. Most of them were not required in that era of cheap labour, but in 1826 the Reverend Patrick Bell, of Carmyllie, Scotland, produced a reaping machine which was demonstrated two years later to forty or fifty landed proprietors; it 'cut down a breadth of five feet at once, was moved by a single horse, and attended by from six to eight persons to tie up the corn; and the field was reaped by this force at the rate of an imperial acre per hour'. The price was between thirty and thirty-five pounds, which, it was claimed, could be saved in a single season; but the machine had limited sales, in spite of such features as a collecting reel, scissors action and sideways delivery band, all worked by gearing as the horses pushed it through the field: labour-saving was not regarded as important, or even desirable. Sickle and scythe

still held the field, as for the previous seven thousand years or more.

The same fate seemed likely to befall the reaper demonstrated in America in 1831 by Cyrus Hall McCormick. It was in some ways similar to the Bell reaper, although it had been invented independently, and at trials it proved its efficiency over and over again. Nevertheless sales were anything but spectacular until the rush to the Californian goldfields in 1849, which denuded the farmlands of the U.S.A. of a great deal of male labour. The McCormick reaper, made in the inventor's factory at Chicago, enabled many farms to carry on, although six to eight persons were still required to follow the machine gathering and binding the corn into sheaves. In 1851 a sheafing mechanism which held the cut corn on the machine until enough had been collected to make a sheaf was invented by Hurlbut. Fewer workers were now required behind the reaper, and America was thus able to export large quantities of wheat at high prices to Europe, and particularly Britain, when the Crimean war of 1854 cut off Russian supplies. From 1861 to 1865 the U.S.A. was itself torn by the ravages of civil war, which stripped the farms of their men. Salvation lay in the reaper: there was no famine, and 200,000 bushels of surplus wheat were exported to Europe. The later drift of labour to the towns was largely counteracted by the binding table of 1858 invented by another American, Charles Wesley Marsh. The wheat was raised by the machine on to the table, handy for a seated man, and tying the sheaves was no longer a backbreaking task; 25 per cent less labour was now required. The full effects of this invention were not felt until the late eighteen-sixties. In 1878 the American farmer John Francis Appleby patented the Appleby twine knotter, which tied the sheaves mechanically and again increased capacity of the reaper just as the industrial growth of the United States began to attract more and more labour into the factories. Many inventors had tried to devise a twine-knotter, and Appleby's invention was preceded by a knotter which bound the sheaves with wire – which was difficult, and even dangerous to deal with afterwards. The great feature of his knotter was the beak, said to have been suggested to him by the sight of a little girl playing with a Boston terrier.

A skipping-rope fell loosely over the dog's neck. It shook its head and backed away; the rope slipped off its nose – ready knotted.

The reaping machine of 1878, now operated by a single labourer, was said to do work equivalent to that of forty men with sickles. Between 1850 and 1900 the proportion of country dwellers in the United States fell from 94 per cent to 60 per cent, because of the great industrial upsurge. Yet the wheat crop, increasingly gathered by mechanical means, multiplied six-fold in the same period (though the intensive cultivation of huge fields designed for machine cropping led to disastrous 'dust bowls' in the prairie states). S. Giedion, in his *Mechanization takes Command* (1948), quotes appositely a statement of Californian agriculturalists in 1926: 'We no longer raise wheat here, we manufacture it ... We are not husbandmen, we are not farmers. We are producing a product to sell.'

In Australia machines had been developed which were just 'headers', like those of ancient Gaul, the long straw being left on the ground. John Ridley, who made such a machine in 1843, added a beater to thresh the grain, which had later to be winnowed. Another Australian, McKay, combined a separating fan in a patent of 1884. Huge 'headers' drawn by steam tractors or as many as thirty or forty horses appeared in Michigan in the eighteen-seventies, but in 1899 the Canadian firm of Massey-Harris made smaller and better models based on Australian practice. They exported several hundred to Australia. The next step came ten years later, when the same firm developed a combined thresher-harvester which did not have to leave long straw uncut on the ground. The modern combine is little different in principle, though much improved in performance. The grain is cut; the ears are separated from the straw, which is ejected at the back of the machine to be picked up later; the ears are riddled, the chaff is blown away by a powerful fan and then the grain is separated into first grade, second grade and weed seeds to be burnt. A field of corn can be 'combined' while still too wet for harvesting by other methods, though the grain has to be dried afterwards. With the combine harvesters, straw is crushed and crumpled, so at last becomes useless for the old craft of thatching. (See also *Sickle and Scythe, Threshing Machine*.)

The 'fridge' in the kitchen

The **REFRIGERATOR** for preserving food in the home began with devices for the manufacture of ice – for producing, so to say, a mechanical winter in the warmth of summer.

It was the old practice to collect ice in the winter months and store it in ice-houses. Thus underground ice-houses of the eighteenth century may often be seen in the grounds of English country houses. Methods of storage improved, and naturally ice was commonly used until our own century.

The first man to produce ice by mechanical means was the eminent Scottish physician and chemist William Cullen (1710–1790), who wrote in 1755 *An Essay on the Cold produced by Evaporating Fluids*. Cullen made use of a powerful vacuum pump to bring about the rapid evaporation of water in an enclosed space at ordinary temperatures. The heat required for evaporation was absorbed from the rest of the water, so lowering its temperature and causing it to freeze.

Since considerable quantities of water vapour had to be removed at low suction-pressures, Cullen's machine was not very efficient. It was improved by another Scottish scientist, Sir John Leslie, who introduced a flat dish containing sulphuric acid under the receiver of the air-pump, the acid absorbing the water vapour (*Annales de Chimie*, 1811). The system was next improved about 1850 by Edmund Carré, with a machine which had to be replenished frequently with fresh acid, owing to continual dilution of the acid by water. In 1878 F. Windhausen devised a machine in which the dilute acid could be concentrated and used again. In 1883 a dairy company in Bayswater in London was using an improved version of Windhausen's machine to make about twelve tons of ice a day (*Journ. of the Soc. of Arts*, 1883).

The refrigerator as we know it begins with Jacob Perkins, who patented a vapour-compression machine in London in 1834. Ether was compressed by a single-acting vertical compressor, and the heat of the compression was removed by passing the fluid through a coil immersed in water. The ether was then allowed to expand through a valve into a chamber near the bottom

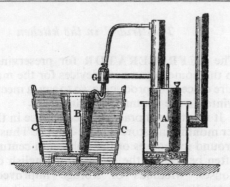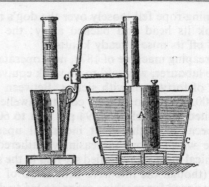

Fig. 28. Carré's artificial ice machine.

of a cistern of water; the low temperature produced by the evaporation of the expanding ether was thus transmitted to the surrounding water. Perkins's apparatus was sounder in principle than in operation, and twenty-one years went by before it was made effective by James Harrison of Australia (British Patent No. 747 of 1856).

Ether was one possible refrigerant. About 1876 Professor Carl von Linde of Munich introduced refrigeration by the compression of ammonia, designing a machine substantially unaltered to the present day, although new refrigerants have been introduced. Ammonia is still common for industrial plants, but since it is poisonous, safer materials have been developed, particularly for domestic use. Thus one family of new refrigerants, introduced in 1932, consists of a group of fluorinated hydrocarbons.

Low temperature could be produced not only by vapour compression but by the absorption of vapour, a system which goes back to 1860, when Ferdinand Carré introduced his Artificial Ice Machine. This consisted of two vessels. One contained a strong solution of ammonia, the other at first was empty and surrounded by cold water. The ammonia solution was heated by a stove, and the ammonia gas driven off into the second vessel, where it condensed and gave up its latent heat to the water outside. After a while the ammonia solution became very dilute, whereupon the stove was removed, and the ammonia vessel was also surrounded by cold water. As a result, the condensed ammonia in the second vessel began to evaporate, and in so doing exerted a refrigerating effect, the ammonia gas being reabsorbed

by the now weak solution in the first vessel. It was an intermittent operation, but Carré also designed a continuously operating system; a modified form of ammonia-absorption machine in which the condensed ammonia is made to evaporate by contact with a stream of hydrogen, was devised some thirty years ago in Sweden, and is much used for domestic refrigeration since it involves no moving mechanical parts.

Though refrigeration was devised and developed to produce ice, obviously it was possible to stop short with producing cold – a cold storage chamber, which did the work of ice with more efficiency and without the mess. Refrigeration, like vacuum-cleaning, had also developed as industrial plant: the problem was also to reduce refrigeration to the domestic refrigerator – to the now familiar 'fridge' – as it was to reduce vacuum-cleaning to the vacuum-cleaner (q.v.). This was done between 1910 and 1920, in the United States, the first kitchen refrigerators having the familiar look of the old kitchen icebox. (See also *Thermos Flask*.)

Relics of the dead

RELICS appear to have had a pre-Christian origin in Greece, where the cult was chiefly based on the idea that those who had risen to heights of perfection could still influence the living who visited their graves or had contact with their belongings.

In Greece (according to Pfister's *Reliquiemkult im Altertum*) veneration was accorded to the relics of mythological founders of dynasties, of local heroes who were regarded as demi-gods, and of strangers such as Oedipus who had fled from their homes and found a place of refuge elsewhere. We seldom hear of particles of relics, mostly of the entire mortal remains at rest in the grave. Only in exceptional cases was the peace of a grave ever disturbed.

Heroes who died abroad in the Greek colonies or on the expeditions of Alexander the Great were taken home for burial, either immediately after their death or later. Legendary accounts of such 'translations' are rare, but a few records of the Hellenistic period leave no doubt that the dead heroes were translated so that the living might derive benefit from their remains. These were supposed to afford protection in warfare, in pestilence and in famine.

Christianity changed the older concepts. The Apostles, saints and martyrs were not worldly heroes; they were not concerned with earthly fame, but with the Kingdom of God. The cult of relics in the grave gradually became the exception; the exhibition of relics became the rule.

From the middle of the fourth century it was customary to build churches in memory of the martyrs and to translate to those churches their earthly remains, which were usually placed under the altar. In fact, it was soon widely held that no altar was complete without relics. Churches and cities and emperors and kings vied with one another and with private persons in obtaining such treasures. The English monk Ælfric (955–1020) recommends in his *Homilies* that the sick should expect healing rather from holy relics than from 'unhallowed practices or accursed enchantments or witchcraft'.

It became a general practice to exhume the dead and divide relics into innumerable bits and pieces. Pilgrimages were encouraged not only by countless reports of miracles due to relics, large or small, complete or fragmentary, but also by the magnificent processions in which they were carried. The most humble pilgrim could receive a blessing by touching the venerated shrine in which the relics were placed; or he might bring home such desirable gifts as a little earth from the Holy Land or some dust from the Casa Santa of Loreto in Italy, the house, it was believed, of the Virgin Mary, which angels had transported aerially from Nazareth to Loreto in the thirteenth century. The magnificent reliquaries made to hold the precious items were of ivory, crystal and precious metals. Their shape varies a great deal, ranging from elaborate miniature replicas of churches to replicas of heads, hands, legs, and busts. Others are in the form of small crosses and medallions and contain tiny fragments, sometimes of several saints, which could be worn as amulets.

The sense of wonder went remarkably far at times. Thus when Frederick Barbarossa was besieging Milan in 1162, the bones of three men were discovered in a church. They were at once equated with the bones of Kaspar, Melchior and Balthazar, whom legend, and only legend, had created out of the 'wise men from the east' described so simply and without detail or number or names in St Matthew's Gospel. Around the bones, translated to Germany, arose not only the cathedral at Cologne, but much of the city's medieval importance and prosperity.

The blood of saints and martyrs was also regarded as powerful. After the execution of Charles I, a few of his devotees gathered his royal blood in handkerchiefs, and a number of miraculous cures were recorded. At a famous Breton place of pilgrimage, St Anne d'Auray, the clotted blood of two priests executed by the Germans in 1944 is on view, together with the bullets which killed them.

It is fair to add that the veneration of relics in more or less degree continues when objects associated with some great man, his chair, his palette, his pen, his manuscripts, his bath sponge, etc., are preserved behind glass in a modern museum.

ILLUSTRATION: Page 169.

Winding or straight

ROADS, in the sense of metalled or paved roads, belong to a late stage of civilization when central government and public finances made them possible, and when wheeled traffic made them necessary.

Tracks and trails are as old as mankind and possibly much older, since herds of wild animals are known to travel along certain well-defined trails like the migration routes of birds. Primitive man travelled to barter his products with neighbours, to get new supplies of special stone and flint from certain quarries. He drove his flocks of cattle and sheep to the summer meadows on the mountains and later in autumn back again to the valleys along well-trodden paths. When he travelled he was apt to avoid the wet and swampy areas in the valleys or the steep hill-slopes, gradually tracing a well-defined track along the high ridges. Such are the ridgeways of the English downs and indeed of many other countries. Near his sanctuaries he might even go further and mark the road with large upright stones – witness the megalithic 'avenues' in Brittany and at Avebury.

It was rare for him to do much else, though he made the crossing of swamps easy by building short stretches of log-road, many of which have been found on the present German–Dutch border (wooden roads of the Bronze Age have also been recognized in the marshlands of Somerset); such 'corduroys' inspired Roman engineers to build similar roads so that their armies could cross more difficult regions.

In early historic times transport by land was chiefly confined to luxury goods carried by beasts of burden or men. Mass production was still unknown and local production was consumed locally except for a few very expensive items of craftsmanship, which were traded abroad. If such things as corn, olive oil, wine, timber, minerals or metals had to travel, they were usually transported by ship; and the few overland tracks led to the nearest port and the sea. Metalled roads existed only in certain cities, where they led from the city gate to the palaces and temples on the processional routes or the route of the king's progress in the celebration of military triumphs or religious festivals. Sometimes (in Assyria and in Egypt) these slab-pavements extended beyond the city gate to temples in the plain. But most city streets remained unpaved litter heaps.

The need for a good road-system was first felt by the Persian kings, who, after establishing their rule over the whole of the Near East in the fifth century B.C., tried to amalgamate the conquered nations by establishing a good uniform coinage and linking up the distant parts of their empire by a messenger service. They had the most important tracks swept and levelled; hostels were built at distances of fifteen to twenty miles, where the messengers could find fresh horses, food and shelter and military protection. One of these lines of communication ran for some 1,500 miles from the western shore of Asia Minor to the capital at Susa; and the distance could be covered by swift horses in relay in ten days, at a speed not to be surpassed until well into the nineteenth century. A few stretches of Persian road were slabbed, but otherwise the roads were not metalled in any way. Alexander the Great, when he conquered the East, profited by this track-system, and his successors, such as the Ptolemies of Hellenistic Egypt, established similar messenger services in their country which carried not only state papers but also private letters and goods. We have time-tables of several of these services, the example of which was to be followed by the Roman state.

Road-building by the Romans begins early in Roman history. In 312 B.C. the blind censor, Appius Claudius, in charge of the public works, gave Rome its first aqueduct and also started to pave the great highway, henceforth named the Via Appia, which led south into the district of Campania and thence to Brundusium, the present Brindisi, where one could cross the Adriatic and travel to Macedonia and beyond. This was the first of a series of highways which finally covered the whole of the civilized Roman world. In the days of the Empire one could travel for 1,200 miles on the road system from York in Britain to the banks of the Euphrates, and even further south into Egypt or along the north coast of Africa.

These Roman roads mostly served armies, civil servants and merchants. The well-organized *cursus publicus* transported mail and passengers in light vehicles or on horseback very quickly. Road-horses and hostels were efficient and provided for all the needs of travellers. Road transport of merchandise, on the other hand, was still hampered by the inefficient harness evolved for the slow ox and useless for the swift mule or horse. Transport was therefore exceedingly expensive, the price of goods doubling for every hundred miles of road, and it was usual to take goods by short stretches of road direct to river and sea, a fact which is evident when one looks at road-maps of Roman Spain or other provinces of the Empire. Curiously we have no Roman textbooks on road-making, though excavation, information in texts about the construction of floors and references in Latin poets (among them Statius) tell the story well enough. Heavy stone setts were the foundation, above which four strata rose up to the *pavimentum* of stone slabs. Such roads were three to five feet thick, and have been aptly described as 'walls on the flat'. (In Britain the Roman roads were not usually paved, but built up as metalled causeways.)

Building such a system of roads required capital and man-power on the imperial scale, the Roman soldier often doing the job as a fatigue. However, in the later years of the Empire it became more and more difficult to finance either the messenger service or the road repairs, even though the burden of traffic was light by our standards. After the fall of the Roman Empire the cost of roads and repairs was fatal to road construction for century upon century. The medieval kings tried tolls and statute labour, without success. A few brick-and-cobble roads were built in the Middle Ages and some Roman roads continued in use; but road transport could scarcely develop beyond the packhorse without scientific attention once more.

The beginning of modern road-building can be traced back to 1623, when Nicolas Bergier, a lawyer at Rheims, published a book on Roman road construction based on the references from Latin authors and prompted by his discovery of the remains of a Roman road in his garden. This book attracted much attention, and the French minister Colbert made plans for the proper technical education of engineers who would build roads and bridges. His plans were finally realized in the early eighteenth century, when the famous *École des Ponts et Chaussées* was founded, the pupils of which rebuilt the roads of France scientifically. The eminent English road-builders such as Thomas Telford (1757–1834) and John Loudon McAdam (1756–1836) preferred to educate their pupils by practice.

Napoleon saw the strategic value of roads quite clearly, and repaved and rebuilt the roads of many European countries, introducing the new scientific building methods. Macadamized roads of broken stone properly drained did good service to the nineteenth century, smoother surfaces greatly increasing wheeled traffic, and preparing the way for motor cars. The realization that tolls were unwelcome and could not maintain an elaborate network of roads was another great advance: it became evident that the state had to finance roads by taxation. Motor-cars demanded still smoother surfaces, and the roads now taken for granted in Europe, and especially in Great Britain, were made possible by the discovery of Portland cement, and by the advent of coal-tar, rock asphalt and petroleum bitumen. All these materials provide an even surface able in varying degrees to withstand the suction of the pneumatic tyre, the new force which now causes wear and tear in place of horseshoes and the bounce of hard wheels. There are other drawbacks and limitations to a scientifically planned network such as the Romans laid down or such as the Nazis built in the *autobahnen*, both of them for military rather than civil reasons. A glance at the Ordnance Maps of England will show how the majority of minor English roads, now so firmly surfaced, wriggle and turn and twist upon the natural lines of the ancient paths and tracks which they follow, instead of taking the shortest practicable distance. (See also *Railway, Canals, Wheel.*)

ILLUSTRATION: Page 362.

Reaching extreme altitudes

The **ROCKET**, one of the earliest of man-made flying objects, and the one by which man himself will leave the earth in his space voyages, was invented in China. The Chinese had gunpowder by the tenth century A.D., and the rocket appears to go back to the Huo Yao Pien Chien, a kind of fire-arrow described in A.D. 1040 in an official account of Chinese military weapons, which says that five ounces of gunpowder were fixed to the end.

The gunpowder rocket reached Europe, and was used in 1379 in the fighting between the Venetians and the Genoese for Chioggia in the Adriatic. Rockets were employed on and off in war during the next four centuries, though they were more familiar in firework displays (which were usually under the control of ordnance authorities). By 1805 Sir William Congreve, son of the comptroller of the Royal Laboratory at Woolwich Arsenal, had devised a practical rocket weapon, in time for the Napoleonic Wars, in which the Allies used his rockets with effect – rockets were in action at Waterloo. In 1807 the Cornishman, Henry Trengrouse, invented the life-saving rocket which conveys a line to ships in distress.

As guns became more accurate, military rockets, which had been established as an auxiliary to gunfire, dropped out of the scene, only to return with resounding and frightening success in the Second World War, in the shape of small weapons for attack on the ground and in the air, and as giant projectiles driven by liquid fuel. It was the German V.2 that revolutionized rocketry, becoming in 1942 a weapon which could reach a target 220 miles away, after careering sixty miles into the upper air and reaching a speed of 3,600 miles per hour on the climb.

The V.2, and all modern liquid-fuel rockets, which are so much more powerful than the old solid-fuel powder rockets, derive from the work of a remarkable but little-known American scientist, Robert H. Goddard, who made his first liquid-fuel type in 1926. He had planned such a vehicle for some while, and the paper he published in 1919, *A Method of Reaching Extreme Altitudes*, marks the beginning of modern rocketry. (See also *Gunpowder, Gun, Fireworks*.)

With a thousand uses

ROPE and **STRING**, its small brother, have a history distressingly obscure in relation to their importance in human affairs. Rope is so essential to our activities, whether between ocean liner and tug or neck and gallows, that we could scarcely do without it; yet the power of rope to survive, unlike that of stone tools or earthenware pots, or metal weapons, is slight; and of the thousands of millions of miles of rope and string produced by ancient rope-makers, a few pitiful fragments alone have endured.

The essence of rope-making has hardly changed at all; and since it is simply an enlargement of the making of thread, rope and cloth may well have developed together. Fibres are isolated from the raw material, laid parallel in equal lengths and twisted into a yarn. Twisting three or more of these yarns together produces a 'strand'; and a rope is made by 'laying' together three of these strands, a cable by 'laying' three ropes. A ropewalk is needed, in the open air, in a long narrow covered shed, or in a cave (as formerly in the Peak District), since the spinner attaches fibres to a hook on the spinning-wheel, and walks slowly back as wheel and hook revolve, feeding the fibres from a supply wrapped round his waist, and taking care that the resulting yarn keeps a uniform size. He needs the ropewalk again for forming the strands and laying the ropes.

Bone needles found in palaeolithic deposits make it clear that some kind of thread was used, probably for stitching skins together; but likely enough the thread was gut or sinew. Palaeolithic hunters used the bow and arrow, which points to an early need of strong cordage for the bowstring, though bows are strung with various materials in different parts of the world, including hide and sinew.

In the subsequent mesolithic phases string or twine must have been made, since there is abundant evidence for fishing nets and fishing lines. A mesolithic deposit from Lake Ladoga in Finland yielded fragments of a net made of lime bast, the fibrous inner bark of the lime tree, which the salmon fishermen on the Severn and English farmers used for rope seven thousand years later. Nettle fibre then, as in the historic era, was probably twisted into fishing lines and twine for nets. Most of the evidence for ancient nets and fishing lines is indirect, consisting of net floats and sinkers and fish hooks.

Rope was used in neolithic centuries by the flint-miners at Grime's Graves, in Norfolk, where rope marks were left in the flint walling of the shafts; cord must have been required for tying the dead in the crouched position characteristic of Beaker burials in Britain in the years after 1800 B.C.

The Sumerians clearly had rope and twine. Clay net sinkers have been found in Sumerian excavations, and the model of the earliest sailing boat yet known, from a Sumerian tomb of the al 'Ubaid period at Eridu, of the beginning of the fourth millennium B.C., shows how anciently rope was required on the water.

Egypt, though, has produced more evidence for ancient rope than any other area. Cords of reed are known in the Badarian culture of pre-Dynastic Egypt, from which early date ropes of flax and of halfa fibre are known. During the First Dynasty grass rope was made (hay and straw ropes have been made by European farmers in our day – and not only for thatching); and from the Old Kingdom there is at least one example of a rope of camel hair. The favourite Egyptian material was fibre from the date-palm. Two hundred bundles of this fibre specially for rope-making are mentioned in a late Egyptian document. Tomb-paintings and statements by Theophrastus and Pliny show that the Egyptians twined rope out of papyrus. Bits of papyrus rope, of uncertain date, have come to light from the Tura Caves in Upper Egypt, which are limestone quarries. One piece was eight inches round, and consisted of three strands, each of forty yarns, in each of which were seven fibres.

The most spectacular use of rope – and papyrus rope – recorded in the ancient world comes, not from the Egyptians, but the Persians. In 480 B.C. Xerxes bridged the Hellespont to bring his vast invading army from Asia to Europe. According to Herodotus, the basic unit of the two bridges was a ship – there were 360 ships in the one and 314 in the other. Abnormally large anchors were used to moor them in two lines and they were linked by cables: 'They assigned to each bridge six cables, two of which were of white flax, whilst four were of papyrus. Both kinds were of the same size and strength, but the flaxen was the heavier, weighing no less than a talent per cubit.'

The victorious Greeks carried these cables home; and dedicated them in their temples.

Bits of rope of the Roman period, with a diameter of five-eighths of an inch, made up of three strands, are found occasionally in the ancient copper mines not far from Soloi in Cyprus; they are preserved in the muddy silt, and with the rope there are sometimes wooden pulleys. The Romans needed rope for the ballista – for instance, the *ballista fulminalis*, which fired a large arrow. The author of *De rebus bellicis*, about A.D. 370, described this as a type of ballista surpassing all others in range and power. 'With an iron bow erected over the groove from which the arrow is fired, a strong rope is drawn back by an iron hook, and when released fires the arrow with great force at the enemy. The very size of the machine does not allow this rope to be drawn back by the strength of soldiers' hands; but two men haul the rope back by pressing upon the spokes of two wheels.'

In Rome watching performances on the tight-rope was already a most popular entertainment. Terence in 165 B.C. complained of having no audience for one of his comedies because of the superior attraction of a tight-rope walker nearby. Greeks were most accomplished performers, and 'tight-rope walker' was one of the many terms of abuse which the Romans liked to use of the Greeks. A fresco from Pompeii depicts a man and a woman, both naked, dancing on the same rope, each with a drinking vessel in hand. It is even on record that in A.D. 166 a young man fell from the rope at a public show. This so distressed the Emperor Marcus Aurelius that he humanely ordered nets to be spread under the performers. Even elephants, it is alleged, were trained to the rope.

Roman rope twined out of hemp has survived, for instance, from Roman wells, dug in Saalburg fort (second to third century A.D.) near Bad Homburg in Germany; a reminder also of the benefit of rope for hanging, a common practice among the Germans, according to Tacitus (see *Gallows*). The Tollund Man recovered from a bog near Silkeborg in Jutland in 1950, and now preserved, in his extraordinary perfection, in the National Museum at Copenhagen, had apparently been hanged before he was thrown into the bog. But his date is uncertain – he is evidence for rope and execution at some point in a wide span of years between 400 B.C. and A.D. 400. (See also *Spindle*.)

A world material

RUBBER, which is present in the milky juice or latex of many species of plant, was first exploited by the peoples of the New World. Together with maize, potatoes, tomatoes, quinine and cocaine, it is among their major gifts to human welfare, though it was a long while before methods of manufacture were invented and the remarkable potentialities of rubber were fully realized.

The Aztecs and other peoples of Central America and South America were acquainted with rubber which the Aztecs called *olli*, long before the arrival of the Spaniards, tapping various rubber-yielding plants, and collecting the latex for more purposes than one would imagine and for purposes one would not guess at all. Cult figurines were made of rubber, it was burnt to bring rain, the black smoke suggesting rain-clouds, it was smeared on the face; priests mixed it with the blood of children who had been sacrificed, and drank it, it was taken or applied as medicine; and above all rubber was fashioned into hard, high-bouncing balls for the ceremonial or religious game of *tlachtli*, presided over by the god Xolotl, and played in stone-walled courts decorated with religious paintings. *Tlachtli* was played by chiefs in person, and by professionals on their behalf. Players wore hip-leathers, and hand-leathers and leather vizors (not unlike the accoutrements of an American footballer) and tried to direct the large balls with their elbows, their legs, their hips or their posteriors into two stone rings set upright into the walls of the long court, which had the shape of a capital I. There was much gambling on *tlachtli*. One famous game also was played between Montezuma and the chief of Texcoco, to test predictions, disputed by Montezuma, that Mexico was to be conquered by strangers. Montezuma lost.

Rubber was soon noticed by the Spaniards. Thus the Italian geographer Pietro Martire d'Anghiera in his book *De orbe novo*, published in 1530, was actually the first European to mention rubber, writing (at second-hand) of trees in a valley of what is now Venezuela, which were remarkable for their products: 'From one of these trees a milky juice exudes in a short while when a wound has been made in the branches. Left standing it thickens to a kind of pitchy resin.' He also described the ball game at Tenochtitlán (Mexico City) and the manufacture of the balls from the juice of a vine, wondering 'how these heavy balls are so elastic that when they touch the ground, even though lightly thrown, they spring into the air with the most incredible leaps'.

Two centuries went by in which no one paid rubber the compliment of much attention – at least in Europe. In the New World rubber had had its more pedestrian uses. It was employed as a gum for fixing feathers in articles of feather dress. Shoes were made by dipping clay lasts into latex. Montezuma's dwarfs and hunchbacks had worn rubber boots which gave comic effects of falling and staggering; and by Indians and Spaniards clothing was waterproofed with latex, though this waterproofing would go soft in the hot sun.

To the European world a stimulus came at last from the reports of two Frenchmen, Charles-Marie de la Condamine (1701–1774) and François Fresneau (1703–1770). De la Condamine was a member of a French scientific expedition sent to determine the length of an arc of the meridian in South America. Soon after his arrival in Quito in 1736 he sent a report on rubber to the French Academy of Sciences. Later he met Fresneau, who wrote a detailed memorandum in 1747 on rubber in French Guiana, the species of tree which the natives tapped (including *Hevea brasiliensis*), and the uses to which the latex might be put. A very minor property gave rubber its usual English name. Joseph Priestley, in his *Familiar Introduction to the Theory and Practice of Perspective* (1770), mentions in a footnote a substance (*i.e.* rubber) which would rub out lead-pencil marks; it was this use which popularized caoutchouc, to give rubber its older name of Indian origin; and an English encyclopaedia of 1778 says that it was 'popularly called rubber and lead eater'.

By the early part of the nineteenth century, boots, clothing and surgical articles were being made from rubber, but these still suffered from the disadvantage that they became soft and sticky in very hot weather and hard and inelastic in very cold weather. The chemist Charles Macintosh (1766–1843) sought to overcome this by interposing a layer of rubber between two layers of cloth, the material being used for making waterproof clothing; hence the word 'mackintosh', now spelt with an inserted 'k'. He took out his patent in 1823. In 1839, the American Charles Goodyear (1800–1860) went a step further, and a vital step: he discovered that when rubber is heated with sulphur, it becomes more elastic and is not affected by normal changes in temperature. The process was subsequently termed 'vulcanization', after Vulcan, the god of fire. Goodyear's discovery was the beginning of the modern rubber industry, and at last transformed rubber into a basic material of our civilization. While Goodyear was working in America, Thomas Hancock (1786–1865) was developing processes and machinery for the manufacture of rubber in England. In 1842 Hancock was shown a piece of Goodyear's vulcanized rubber. He detected sulphur in it, and after some experiments, found that rubber could be vulcanized by heating it in a bath of molten sulphur. When the heating was prolonged, a hard product, now known as ebonite or vulcanite, was produced, consisting of rubber in combination with 32 per cent of sulphur. This has been familiar in fountain pens and the mouthpieces of tobacco pipes. Hancock patented his process in 1843. A few years later, at the Great Exhibition of 1851, a variety of vulcanized rubber articles were shown. These included waterproof clothing, footwear, belts and braces of elastic fabric, and airbeds. The most notable rubber exhibit was Goodyear's suite of rooms made of ebonite and furnished with ebonite furniture.

By the time of the Great Exhibition, one of the most striking inventions involving rubber had been made when R. W. Thomson in 1845 patented his pneumatic rubber 'carriage wheels'. But for the fuller story from Thomson to Dunlop, see *Pneumatic Tyre*.

Recently many synthetic rubbers have been made; these are not 'superior' to rubber as an all-round substance though some of them may excel in one aspect, such as resistance to oil, temperature or corrosion. The discovery of the 'silicones' (a useful hybrid of silica and organic compounds) has produced a 'silastic' rubber which will have a versatile technical future.

ILLUSTRATION: Page 370.

S

An item of convenience

The **SAFETY-PIN**, one may like to recall when buying a card of safety-pins, has a respectable antiquity, going back to the Bronze Age.

Though one does not know where it was invented – perhaps in Mycenaean Greece, or in Italy or Sicily, or even in Denmark – the safety-pin developed from the ordinary straight pin, beyond which in turn there is an obvious natural prototype in thorns. Straight metal pins were used for

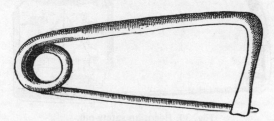

Fig. 29. Late Mycenaean safety-pin.

fastening clothes in Sumeria; but then pins work loose, and the unguarded points jab into the body. So the safety-pin was required; and it was duly invented or duly evolved as one of the minor triumphs of the early age of metals.

In essence it is merely the long straight pin doubled into two legs, so that the pointed leg (the 'pin') is the shorter, the sharp point fitting snugly and safely into a loop twisted from the end of the other leg, which becomes the 'bow'. Properly fixed, the pin now can no longer move forwards or backwards, or work loose, or do damage. Other refinements were made. The simple safety loop was hammered flat, and the tip was turned up to form a little trough for holding the pin point. This is the 'catch-plate'. Also a mere doubling of the pin into two legs did not supply tension enough to keep the point firmly in the catch-plate, so the bend was replaced by a round turn forming the simple coil-spring we still know.

The earliest type, called by archaeologists the 'fiddle-bow' pin, was close to modern safety-pins. It has been found in graves on the Greek mainland which belong to the latter end of the Bronze Age, somewhere about 1300 or 1250 B.C. In this type bow and pin are parallel and are separated by little more than the width of the coil-spring. Safety-pins very similar in design were in use in Italy at much the same date, and in Central Europe as well; while in Bronze Age Denmark safety-pins made in two pieces instead of one also occur more or less at this time. Denmark and Greece were at opposite ends of the amber route, so it is more than a coincidence that in both countries during the thirteenth century B.C. people should

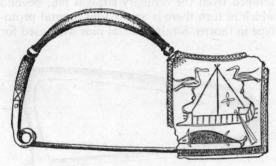

Fig. 30. Boeotian safety-pin.

have started fastening themselves up with the same or a similar device.

The earliest safety-pins were made of bronze or silver or gold wire, and can hardly have been used with heavy cloth, though safety-pins and straight pins may have been employed in conjunction, the straight pins still doing most of the work. With the safety-pins the Bronze Age innovators may also have fastened light wraps or the like. In Homer's *Odyssey* safety-pins seem to be mentioned when Antinous offers Penelope 'a broidered robe, great and very fair, wherein were golden pins, twelve in all, with well-bent clasps'. But Homer does not say how they were fixed. The first simple fiddle-bow pins were quickly improved. The bow was altered until it was no longer parallel with the pin, and so could embrace a bigger fold of cloth. Also the pin or the sharp-pointed leg was fashioned so as to take more strain without coming adrift from the catch-plate.

Safety-pins – or fibulae as they are called by archaeologists – went out of use in Greece by the end of the seventh century B.C. In their time they had developed most splendidly of all into the fibulae of Boeotia, in which the catch-plate was large and square and engraved with geometric designs or delightful long-legged horses recalling similar animals painted on Attic vases of the eighth century B.C. Safety-pins, in fact, for more than a thousand years of their existence were items with the personality which comes from handicraft. The modern safety-pin is a factory debasement and a mere convenience.

From Greece fibulae spread eastward through the Greek islands (they were specially popular in Rhodes) as far as Syria and Palestine, while from their focal points in Italy, Central Europe and Denmark they became fairly widely diffused through Bronze Age Europe. They did not reach Britain until the fifth century B.C. at the beginning of the Iron Age when Halstatt invaders introduced them from the Continent. Archaeologists, it may be added, hold the prehistoric safety-pin in special affection: it is a useful indicator of chronology, since there are now few types to which a fairly close date cannot be assigned.

Brooches also descend from the fibula, the emphasis shifting from the utilitarian to the ornamental. (See also *Buttons, Zippers*.)

'The form of the common hoe'

The **SAFETY RAZOR** comes late in the history of shaving, though it was called forth inevitably by the perils of the ruthless blade of the straight razor, either in one's hand or in the hand of the barber.

In Paris in the eighteenth century Jean-Jacques Perret, a master cutler, contracted skin diseases from going to the barber's shop and being cut about the face, so in 1762 he conceived the idea of adding a wooden guard to a straight razor, on the analogy of the carpenter's plane in which only a short section of the blade projects from the surface. He described and illustrated the invention in his book *L'Art du Coutelier*. But his razor was sold at a price beyond the means of the ordinary man, and it can never have been widely used.

Safety razors in their usual modern form with a guarded blade set across the handle were devised by William S. Henson of London. In 1847 he took out a patent for what he called 'Certain Improvements in the Construction of Razors for Shaving'. Henson's invention was twofold. According to his specification his 'comb tooth guard or protector' was attached to ordinary straight razors, or to a razor 'the cutting blade of which is at right angles with the handle, and resembles somewhat the form of the common hoe'.

The term 'safety razor' was not used by Henson, and took a long while to emerge. Knight's *Practical Dictionary of Mechanics* in 1875–1876 describes a 'guard-razor', which had 'a brass frame or guard to prevent persons whose hands are tremulous from accidentally cutting themselves'; and according to the *Oxford English Dictionary* 'safety razor' first appeared in print in 1893.

Henson, at any rate, devised the safety razor as we know it – in principle, at least, since his new razor had one drawback: he used a small hollow-ground blade, which had to be fixed in a separate holder for stropping.

Sharpening razors had always been a skilled and tedious job; and it was King C. Gillette, of Boston, Massachusetts, who found the solution in 1895, when he proposed to mass produce blades of the wafer type so cheaply that they could be thrown away when they were no longer sharp. The wafer blade, which requires less steel than the hollow-ground blade and is easier to make, was no new invention at this time. As early as 1814 Rhodes and Champion, of Sheffield, had been making a (non-safety) razor consisting of a wafer blade held in a frame. Gillette started production of his blades in 1901, and in less than twenty years the safety razor had become the predominant tool for personal shaving, though in skilled hands the old straight razor may give a closer and smoother shave, working better into the angle between upper lip and nostrils. Wafer blades are now made from continuous strips of steel, each weighing 30 lb. and long enough for 12,000 blades. These strips are passed through a series of machines in turn, being wound from one spool to another. The strip is perforated and shaped as it goes through a press, rolled to remove burrs, then toughened, blued and tempered – tempered hard at the cutting edge and softer along the centre to allow the blades to bend in the razor. After the maker's name has been etched on the strip, it is lacquered and passed through a machine in which the cutting edges are rough ground, fine ground and honed. This machine finally cuts the blade off the strip. Last of all the now separate blades are fed into a machine which wraps them. The disappearance of the Victorian beard and side whiskers and next of the Edwardian moustache can perhaps be correlated in part with the spread of safety shaving, Gillette having thus altered the male physiognomy of the world.

Dry shavers are the next stage in the story of the smooth face. The master patent, which is the origin of all modern dry shavers, was taken out in 1913 by G. P. Appleyard, of Halifax, who described 'a power-driven shaving appliance' which 'comprises a fixed cutter A, having finely serrated edges, co-operating with a reciprocating blade B'. The reciprocating blade or moving cutter 'may be rotated or oscillated and actuated manually, mechanically or electrically'. The modern dry shaver, electrically operated, in which the hairs pass through holes or slots in a thin metal plate and are then sheared off by the moving cutter, completes the history of shaving, from the Stone Age to the Age of Electricity and Steel. Here at last are no blades to be purchased and consumed or sharpened, or thrown away by a philosophy of waste, no paraphernalia of soap and brush and hot water, no cuts, no blood, no cottonwool and no styptic stick. (See also *Razors*.)

From flint to steel

The **SAW** in the mythology of the Greeks was attributed variously to Talos, Perdix the nephew of Daedalus, and Daedalus himself. It is said that Talos, the strange metal man made of bronze who was guardian of Crete, found that he could cut wood with the jaw-bone of a snake, and so was led to making a metal saw in which the teeth of the snake were imitated by indentations in the metal blade. The resemblance between the saw and a jaw-bone set with teeth is strikingly illustrated by the saw made by the aborigines of Western Australia, which consists of a stick partly covered with hard gum in which is set a row of sharp stones or flakes of glass.

Be that as it may, our own saws have a clear enough ancestry from flint to copper and bronze, copper and bronze to iron and steel. The saw, in fact, is one of the primeval instruments. Roughly serrated flints have been found of late palaeolithic times. In the mesolithic period flint flakes were more exactly serrated into little saws, and a mesolithic flint saw from Star Carr in Yorkshire may be seen in the British Museum. Neolithic saw-flints or saw-flakes were common.

Metal saws followed as a matter of course. Thus copper saws have been found in the Early Dynastic levels of Ur and of Egypt, taking the metal tool back to about 3000 B.C. Planks of wood used in early dynastic coffins in Egypt must have been sawn; and in Sumeria the tool must have been important in fashioning the earliest wheeled vehicles. Copper saws were also familiar to the carpenters of Mohenjo-daro in the Indus Valley.

Sumerian saws were fixed into the handle by a narrow tang, and they had curved cutting edges and a curved back. The Egyptian saw, ancestor of our own types, had usually a straight back. and was also tanged, as one may see from the painting of an Egyptian carpenter, c. 1480 B.C., on the walls of the tomb of Rekhmara, Thebes, The curved wooden handle which the carpenter grasps with two hands remained common for ages to come, and is still fitted to smaller saws. Carpenters who lived in the Somerset lake or marsh villages in the Iron Age a thousand years later were using short iron saws, straight-backed and straight-bladed and set in curving handles of a similar kind, with a pronounced knob. The tang was fastened to the handle by two iron rivets. Excavations in Battlesbury Camp, a hillfort on the edge of the Wiltshire chalk downs above Warminster, produced several iron articles which were used somewhere between 100 B.C. and A.D. 100. Among them was the iron hub of a chariot wheel and a short iron saw with two rivet holes. The sixty-six teeth of this saw were set in

alternate pairs upon either side of the blade, which gave an easier clearance through the wood.

The earliest metal saws have simple straight teeth: they scraped rather than cut their way through wood, both by pulling and pushing. In cutting saws the teeth are raked forward or backward for push-cutting or pull-cutting. The push-cutting saw demands a tougher blade than the ancient smiths could always contrive, and the majority of the cutting saws of antiquity cut only on the pulling stroke. Flinders Petrie stated that such pulling-saws with the teeth sloping began to be made about 900 B.C. Roman saws were of this kind; so were the Somerset lake village saws and the Battlesbury saw of the British Iron Age. The knob of the handle gave the hand something to pull against and the rivets kept the tang from dragging out on the backward cutting stroke.

Some of the difficulties of making a strong saw blade were overcome by the early invention of the frame-saw, in which thin blades are held under a tension they would not otherwise possess. The Greeks were using such saws by the beginning of the fifth century B.C. and they were common in Roman hands.

ILLUSTRATION: Page 271.

Chain-stitch and lock-stitch

The **SEWING-MACHINE** is so much a piece of home equipment that we forget both its industrial and social importance, and also the degree to which it has delivered women from work in the home and from the endless, enervating drudgery of the sweat-shops. Spinning, which had occupied so much of women's time, was mechanized in the eighteenth century. Mechanization of sewing and of the making-up of clothes freed women still more for other occupations and interests, led to the mass production of cheap clothing; and was in several ways a factor of social revolution.

Thomas Saint in London in 1790 patented a machine for sewing leather – 'for stitching, quilting or sewing', to be worked 'by hand, by a Mill,

Steam Engine or other power'. Nothing came of it, and the machine was forgotten until the patent was discovered accidentally in 1874, by which time the sewing-machine had been re-invented and established by others, chiefly in America. Ill fortune was also to attend the French tailor, Barthélemy Thimmonier, of Saint-Étienne, who invented a chain-stitch sewing-machine in 1829. A chain-stitch is formed from a single thread, the stitches being linked by passing each stitch through a loop in the previous stitch; it can very easily be pulled out, a property with advantages and disadvantages.

Thimmonier's machine was practical, though the barbed needle tended to tear the fabric. His Parisian clothing factory in which eighty machines made army clothing was wrecked by fearful and indignant tailors. Thimmonier persisted, improved his machine, but failed to impress it upon the world.

In 1832 or thereabouts the New Yorker William Hunt invented a more important machine, using a needle with an eye at the point. This carried an upper thread through the cloth, forming a loop. A second thread was carried through the loop by a shuttle, so that the two layers of cloth to be sewn together were securely united by an efficient lock-stitch. Hunt met with opposition, and his machine dropped out of sight. In 1845 – independently, so it appears, the New Englander Elias Howe devised another lock-stitching machine with a curved needle moving through the cloth at the end of a swinging arm; he demonstrated that his machine could work five times as fast as a skilled seamstress. It was rather complicated, though, and expensive, and it had one serious defect: the cloth was held on pins projecting from a metal strip, which moved along with each stitch. After a short length of seam had been sewn the operator had to remove the cloth and place the next length on the pins.

A more famous name now appeared – Isaac Merrit Singer (1811–1875), able mechanic and able business-man. This New Yorker in 1851 patented a machine which is recognizably the ancestor of the sewing-machine, whether hand-driven, treadle-driven or electric, which is so familiar today in every home. The needle moved up and down in a straight line; the cloth lay on a cloth plate, and was held by a presser foot from above against a wooden wheel which moved intermittently under a hole in the plate, so thrusting the cloth forward after each stitch. Howe promptly challenged Singer for infringing his patent on the shuttle and the eye-pointed needle. The defence that these inventions had been anticipated by William Hunt did not succeed, since Hunt had failed to protect them by patent.

Invention followed invention. Between 1849 and 1854 Allen Benjamin Wilson improved sewing-machines by a number of skilful devices, which are embodied in most of the modern lock-stitchers. He replaced the shuttle by the stationary disc bobbin which supplies the under thread. The upper thread, brought through the cloth by the needle, was carried by a rotary hook round the disc, interlocking the threads. Also he devised the four-motion feed, in which a claw rises through a hole in the cloth plate pushing the cloth along.

Wilson's machine was small, neat, and much lighter than the Singer. However, Singer, Howe, Wilson and others combined and exploited their patents with the greatest success until the patents expired in 1877. Between them, they had given women in the homes of the world one of the most valuable of all labour-saving instruments, and one which was quickly adopted and appreciated.

Many devices and inventions made their way more slowly. Women were already blessed with the water-closet, but the bath h. and c., electric lighting and power, gas and electric cookers and fires, central heating, vacuum cleaners, washing machines, electric irons, tinned or canned food, and refrigerators, were all either later developments or later inventions in the new conquest of drudgery. (See also *Spindle*.)

The seaman's aid

The **SEXTANT** is one of a family of navigating and astronomical instruments which includes the astrolabe, the quadrant, the octant, the forestaff and the backstaff. They are – or rather were, for all but the sextant are now obsolete – device, for measuring the separation of two distant objects. The height of the sun above the horizon is the measurement most frequently made with the sextant. From this it is possible, with other data, to find the time of day or the geographical latitude of the observer. On board ship this measurement of the sun's altitude, 'shooting the sun', is made at regular intervals.

The earliest astronomical measurements were probably taken by holding the arm at full length and seeing how many fingers, or spans, covered the space between two distant objects, a crude method the results of which depended on the length of the observer's arm and the size of his hands. More accurate results were obtained when the human arm was replaced by a wooden staff and the fingers by a cross-piece of wood. This constituted the cross-staff, also called the forestaff or Jacob's staff. The great navigators of Portugal in the fourteenth and early fifteenth centuries, such as Vasco Da Gama, and Bartholomew Diaz, who first rounded the Cape in 1488, took with them the cross-staff as a principal aid to navigation. Columbus also used it when he crossed the Atlantic to America four years later. It must have been a trying implement to use, since the observer had to hold one end of the staff near his eye and look toward the sun, moving the cross-piece up and down the staff till it covered the space between the sun and the horizon.

Matters were eased when the English navigator John Davis (c. 1550–1605) introduced the backstaff, which is described in his book *The Seaman's Secrets* (1594). With this, the observer stood back to the sun, no longer running the risk of being blinded, and moved the shadow which the sun cast on a small piece of wood, into line with the distant horizon.

Of the two other early instruments, Gunter's quadrant, devised by the English mathematician Edmund Gunter (1581–1626), and the astrolabe, which was known to later Alexandrian and early Arabic scientists, and was first constructed in the eighth century A.D. by Ibrāhīm Al-Fāzārī, the Arabic astronomer, neither one depends upon a sight of the horizon to find the direction of the sun or a star. Gunter's quadrant has a plumb line which gives a true indication of the vertical direction, and the angle between the direction of the distant body and the vertical is measured. The astrolabe, because it hangs freely from a loose ring, takes up a vertical position and allows inclinations to the vertical to be measured.

Late in the seventeenth century, in the remarkable early or foundation period of the Royal Society, it was suggested by the great Robert Hooke, F.R.S. (1635–1703) that by the use of a mirror it would be possible to reflect the sun until it appeared to be superimposed on the horizon; then by observing the tilt of the mirror the angle between sun and horizon could be found. This is the basic principle of the sextant. John Hadley (1682–1744) embodied it in a practical instrument in 1731. It was called Hadley's octant, or sometimes Hadley's quadrant.

The confusion of names is easy to explain. Until Hadley's time instruments were named 'quadrant', 'sextant' or 'octant' according to whether the graduated arcs which were used for the measurement of angles, extended over a quarter (90°), a sixth (60°) or an eighth (45°) of the complete circle of 360°. When a mirror is used, the angle turned through by the mirror is only half the angle measured; so that to measure an angle of ninety degrees, which would require a quarter or quadrant, without a mirror, only requires an eighth, or octant, when a mirror is used – *i.e.* in Hadley's instrument a graduated octant measures a quadrant of a circle. In the modern sextant, which works on exactly the same principle as Hadley's octant, the arc is graduated over a range of about sixty degrees or a sextant of the circle, but the instrument measures angles up to 120°.

More than twenty years had to go by before Hadley's new instrument was popular with ships' officers. The use of the sextant is not, of course, confined to objects in the sky or to navigation at sea. By measuring the angle between top and base, it can be used on earth for finding the height of a tree, a building or a mountain. In the air, a special type, the bubble sextant, is employed in aeroplane navigation. But there is little doubt that with the growing use of radar and radio methods of navigation, in the air and at sea, the need of the sextant will decrease until it becomes as obsolete as the astrolabe.

Its immortality is assured, nevertheless; in 1752 the astronomer La Caille considered these instruments to be so basically important in his own science and in navigation that he gave the name of Hadley's Octant to a group of stars in the southern hemisphere. There is also a constellation Sextant.

ILLUSTRATION: Page 164.

Sickle and Scythe

The **SICKLE**, for cutting grain crops, a specialized form of knife, and the **SCYTHE**, which is an enlarged form of sickle with a longer handle (a 'sneath') and a longer blade, for cutting grass close to the ground, are two of the primal implements of man's civilized history. Indeed, the sickle is one of the few implements which can be traced back to its origins in the times immediately before the earliest beginnings of material civilization in the Near East.

So far as we know at present, the first to make sickles were people of the Natufian culture of food-gatherers, who inhabited caves in Mount Carmel in Palestine probably between 10,000 and 5000 B.C., and collected the wheat and barley which is believed to have grown wild in their neighbourhood. They constructed multiple knives by setting a row of sharp flints in a groove along the edge of a carved, straight, tapering bone, which also served as a handle. Some of the flints show polish along their edges, which is due to friction with the siliceous stalks of grain-bearing plants or grasses, and which is found in all later flint sickles that have had much use. The complete implement reminds one of the jaw-bone of a grazing animal, a resemblance which may have been intentional seeing that the one was intended to serve much the same purpose as the other, 'eating up' the cereal. Any magic involved may have been reinforced by the animal head which was carved on the end of the handle.

In Egypt a similar kind of flint sickle has been found in a granary pit in the Fayum, dating from pre-dynastic times; in this implement the flint teeth were set in a straight wooden stick. In dynastic Egypt the flint teeth were set in the concavity of a curved or angular wooden handle – and here one has the prototype of the curved sickle of all subsequent times – of that sickle, for instance, which is part of the emblem of the U.S.S.R. Sickles of this last type, dating from about 2000 B.C., have been found in Alpine lake-villages and in Spain. They exhibit a crescentic row of neatly trimmed flint teeth fixed end to end in a curved or L-shaped wooden handle. We now begin to find in the Alps a new development, which may or may not have been due to the skill and initiative of the European peoples: crescentic flint blades supplanted the row of flint teeth. These crescentic blades were developed and perfected in Scandinavia, where they must have been mounted in similar curved wooden handles, although no original handles have survived. But since the crescent of flint could stand by itself, no longer requiring the embrasive support of the handle, we find modifications appearing – both in flint blade and wooden handle. One horn of the crescent is straightened to form a kind of tang, and the handle is shortened so that it does no more than secure this tang. The result appears as a slightly curved flint blade projecting at right angles from the end of a straight wooden handle – the angular sickle. In practice any suitable long sharp-edged flake was more often employed in this kind of sickle than a carefully worked blade; a specimen, complete with its wooden handle, found in a bog at Stenild in Jutland, shows how these flakes were hafted and employed. Here again the polish resulting from prolonged use in cutting straw is found on a large proportion of these Scandinavian blades.

The sickle evolved still more. Flint was gradually replaced by bronze during the second millennium B.C. and bronze gave place to iron about the fifth century B.C. in northern Europe. Flint had been shaped by skilful chipping, the bronze was cast, and the iron was wrought – processes which influenced the shape of the tool and its method of hafting. At first in Scandinavia bronze crescents were cast and hafted like the flint crescents, but these soon died out, and were replaced by bronze versions of the angular sickle. In Britain this last developed a socket, for sockets were a British specialty in the Late Bronze Age.

When iron came in, the British iron sickle, accordingly, had wings beaten over the handle to form what is a socket, in effect, while its Scandinavian cousin developed a tang placed at right angles to the blade. Each preserved the angular form, but it was the enlargement of the tanged sickle in Scandinavia and other hay-producing areas that led to the scythe, that old symbol of time and transience – *Ah me! I sigh to see the scythe afield*; and it was the qualities of wrought iron that made this enlargement possible.

In central Europe the crescentic flint blade led on to a semicircular form of sickle, first in bronze and later in iron with a tang. The great disadvantage both of the angular and semicircular sickles was their lack of balance; this caused the point of the blade to turn downwards towards the ground. As a remedy the tang of the semicircular sickles came to be bent in such a way that the line of the handle passed through the centre of gravity of the blade, thus producing the balanced sickle as we know it today. Some of the flint sickles of Egypt were balanced in this manner; but the earliest metal examples of the balanced sickle appeared in Austria and Transylvania about the beginning of the Christian era, since when the sickle has been little modified.

The short-handled scythe, derived in Scandinavia from the angular iron sickle and in central Europe from the semicircular sickle, also appeared about the beginning of the Christian era, while the long-handled scythe was developed under the Romans. The scythe was balanced differently from the sickle by bending the long handle (or sneath) near its middle, so that the line of the nearer half of the handle passed through the centre of gravity of the whole implement.

Primitive sickles are more efficient than might be thought. In a series of experiments using copies of ancient sickles Axel Steensberg of Copenhagen found that it took only two or three times as long to reap a certain area of barley as it took with a modern sickle. This was of no account in primitive economics, especially when it is remembered that much less grain was cultivated and had to be harvested than in later times. (See also *Reaping Machine, Lawnmower*.)

ILLUSTRATION: Pages 310 and 369.

Silks from China

SILK is always considered to be a Chinese invention, though it is not quite certain that the Chinese were the first to make a fabric from the cocoon of a moth. Something of the kind may have been known in Assyria and India more than three thousand years ago, and the transparent fabrics of the island of Cos, which scandalized Roman moralists, were certainly a form of silk. In Cos, however, the silken floss was plucked from the cocoons, and then spun and woven. Sometime in the second millennium B.C. the Chinese had certainly discovered that it is possible to unwind the entire silk thread from the cocoon and to weave it in single or multiple strands. They domesticated the species of silk-yielding moth which feeds on mulberry leaves and is now universally used in sericulture. Each cocoon gives six to eight hundred metres of thread.

The Chinese themselves attribute the invention to a legendary ruler over four thousand years ago, and there is evidence that silk was being made in the last few centuries of the second millennium B.C. Casts of the silk fabric they were wrapped in appear on the corroded surface of numerous bronze vessels from tombs of that period. A still more curious chance has refrigerated and preserved Chinese silk in solid blocks of ice formed anciently in the tombs of nomadic chieftains in southern Siberia. Some of these fabrics of the late fifth or early fourth century B.C. were of untwisted silk thread compactly woven, having forty warp threads and fifty-two weft threads to the centimetre.

From the second century B.C. a considerable trade in silk developed with the western world along the caravan routes of Central Asia, but the secrets of domesticated silk production were successfully withheld by the Chinese for many centuries to come. The Greeks and Romans called the stuff *serica* and its makers the *Seres*, both terms ultimately derived from the Chinese word *ssŭ*. They had no direct contact with the Chinese, for silk reached the Mediterranean by the hands of many middlemen, and the states of Parthia and Seleucid Syria lay across the route and formed a political iron curtain. The Seres were at various times thought to be brown-skinned, fifteen feet tall, and cheerful of disposition though inclined to be gruff with strangers. Moreover, they lived to immense ages. From Alexandria and Antioch silks were traded all over the Roman Empire, where they became a common luxury by the beginning of the first century of the Christian era. Since 56 B.C. when the soldiers of Crassus saw the fluttering silk standards of the Parthians, silk had also become important to the economic prosperity of the eastern part of the Empire. Political disturbance, less in the remoter sectors of the long silk-route than in the states immediately west of Assyria which were bitterly inimical to Rome, caused fluctuations of price and supply. In A.D. 16 the Roman Senate passed an ineffectual decree forbidding men to wear silk, 'ne serica vestis viros foedaret', lest it should soften the male population. In A.D. 79 we hear that silk was unravelled in Alexandria and the thread rewoven into thinner stuff. Imperial example varied. Caligula wore a silk chlamys. Aurelian forbade his wife a purple mantle of silk – but only from motives of economy. The puritanical prejudice of old Rome was passing. After the seat of imperial government had been transferred to Constantinople in A.D. 330 the silk trade flourished more than ever. St John Chrysostom complained in a sermon that people who did not wear silk were mistaken for monks.

In A.D. 355 Sharpur II of Persia conquered Roman Mesopotamia and marched into Syria. This restricted the imports of raw silk cloth to Rome and led the Constantinopolitan government to interfere in the silk trade, partly to exploit an easy monopoly and partly to ensure supplies for the court. The results were depressing, and the need for the local cultivation of silk became more urgent than ever. The secret of the process had leaked out from China to the Central Asiatic state of Khotan in the fourth century A.D., but it had not gone farther west. However in A.D. 552, according to the Byzantine historian Procopius, two monks arrived at Constantinople and presented the Emperor Justinian with eggs of the silk moth and some mulberry seeds which they had smuggled through Persia in a hollow staff. They brought with them information on breeding the moths and preparing silk, and within a few decades the demand for silk was met by western production; and the profits and romance

of the silk route, which had linked the two greatest states of the world for more than six centuries, now came sharply to an end. The Persians began to produce silk at about the same time. Islam by its conquests spread the silk craft along North Africa to Andalusia; and from Constantinople it had passed direct to Italy.

In China silk from the beginning had furnished the clothing of the well-to-do. It was praised for its warmth in winter and its coolness in summer. In Han times it was used for writing on, and had probably already become the characteristically Chinese ground for painting. From the Siberian finds already mentioned, and from others made at Palmyra, we know something of the patterns woven in China between 400 B.C. and A.D. 300. These were frequently based on rhomboid shapes and diagonal zigzags such as arise in compound cloth-weave. Chinese silks, mostly of the fourteenth century A.D., have survived in the West as ecclesiastical vestments. The vestments of Pope Benedict XI (d. 1304) which were recovered from his tomb at Perugia in the nineteenth century, contain brocade woven of silk with flat strips of tough paper covered with gold leaf. Damasks were also exported from China to medieval Europe. Both damasks and brocades must have an older history. Chinese silk tapestry originated in the T'ang dynasty.

Two patterns used in Chinese silks of the fourteenth century were very influential in Europe: the pointed-oval unit of design (which itself may have been influenced by earlier Byzantine styles) and an asymmetrical arrangement of tendrils. Both were copied in the weaving-shops of Lucea and Venice. By the seventeenth century the Chinese were exporting to Europe silks designed to customers' specifications.

Swift on the ice

SKATES made of different materials have been used since ancient times in northern and central

Europe. There is archaeological evidence for prehistoric skates made of the bones of the big domestic animals in Pannonia (the modern Hungary) during the Bronze Age and in Sweden during the Viking Age.

In Hungary, Germany and the northern countries into the modern age it was the metacarpal bone of horse or ox from which skates were fashioned. The bone was split. Holes at either end admitted the thongs by which the skate was tied to the foot, and the skating surface was actually the rounded side of the bone. Skating for pleasure goes back long before the era of Dutch paintings or winter landscapes by Bruegel: young Londoners amused themselves on the frozen Moorfield marsh in the time of Henry II, according to the description of William Fitzstephen in his twelfth-century *Vita Sancti Thomae*: bones tied to their feet, they pushed themselves, he says, with a spiked staff, sliding on the ice as swift as birds in the air or arrows from a cross-bow. This spiked stick thrust between the feet is also shown by Olaus Magnus in the *Historia de gentibus septentrionalibus* in 1555 (Olaus Magnus had shown two skaters on the Gulf of Finland in the map which he printed in 1539). It was difficult to get a start on bone skates without a stick, though the stick was also an aid to propulsion. Sometimes the skater had a couple of sticks to which he fastened a sail for greater speed over the ice, in a favourable wind.

Contrivances similar to these bone skates seem to have been worn in some areas even on hard icy snow. Thus a Persian writer of the thirteenth century describes people in the country called Jura (*i.e.* the Voguls, living on the eastern side of the Urals) running on snow with the aid of ox bones. The medieval traveller William of Rubruquis also recorded in the thirteenth century that the Ulryankhes (*i.e.* the Soyots) west of Irkutsk fastened smooth bones to their feet for moving over icy snow fields; and in the last century the Cheremisses on the upper reaches of the Volga still used wooden skates for snow travel.

Bone and wood gave way to iron, and then to steel. Before the development of the skate made altogether of steel and screwed to special boots, the metal runner was fixed to a wooden plate, which in turn was strapped to the foot. Just as 'ski' comes to English from the Norwegian, so

skate, it may be mentioned, has been borrowed from the Dutch *schaatzen*.

ILLUSTRATION: Page 265.

Running on the snow

SKIS, though we also use them now for sport as we use sledges and skates, were anciently developed as a necessity of life; and a necessity of life they remain where the snow lies long and thick through the winter.

They originated in the northern part of the Eurasian continent, where the earliest examples have been found in the peat bogs of Finland and Sweden and have been dated by pollen analysis to the second and third millennia B.C. Two prehistoric rock-engravings which depict ski-running have also been found, one on the Wyg river near the western shore of the White Sea, and the other on the shore of Lake Onega. The oldest words for ski – which in Finnish is *suksi* – belong to the Finno-Ugric and Samoyed languages. *Ski* in Norwegian and *skida* in Swedish (the same as the English *shide* for a piece of split wood) meant first of all a splinter or lath cleft from a log.

More than a hundred ancient skis, of various dates and types, have been found in the Finnish and Swedish bogs – mostly Finnish. The material was pine or spruce (in contrast to the birch used later on in these Fennoscandian areas), the ski being cut from the outer curve of a curved tree; and they vary in length from 300 cm. to 80 cm., in breadth from 20 cm. to 10 cm. Probably the smaller ones were used by women and children.

Neolithic, Bronze Age and Iron Age skis are known. Skis later than the Iron Age can often be dated by the carved ornament of the upper surface. Skis can be distinguished, too, by different ways of attaching them to the foot. Some Siberian peoples, including the Samoyeds and Chukchees, used a ski in which the attachment is fixed to holes bored vertically through the ski – an arctic type which was also familiar in the west, to judge from a specimen recovered from a North Swedish bog. In another primitive type a space for the foot is hollowed out of the wood; on either side raised wooden tongues are left, each bored with a hole to take the thongs. The oldest known ski of this kind, from southern Finland, dates from the beginning of our era. This type is used, or has been used until recently, by several peoples in the Soviet Union, including Russians, Syryens, Estonians, Latvians and Lithuanians; it is also known in the Polish Carpathians, in Carinthia, and in southern and mid Sweden. The third and most highly developed type goes back, remarkably enough, to the neolithic period. In this the thong passes across the foot space (which is thicker than the rest of the ski) through a horizontal hole. Modern sporting skis have been made in the same way. This third type belonged anciently to Fennoscandia, and has also been employed by eastern Finno-Ugric peoples living on either side of the Urals.

The oldest skis were even and smooth on the under-surface. When the thaw started, sealskin or skin from the legs of the wild reindeer was fastened to the under-surface to prevent the soft snow from sticking. For their long hunting trips the Lapps of the Kola Peninsula and many Siberian peoples still run on skis fitted in this way. At the end of the Bronze Age a ski type was developed in which the under-surface was grooved: hairy skin was fixed in the groove, protected by the raised borders of wood on either side. It was found that these raised borders helped straight running, so grooved skis were also used without skin; and eventually the groove on the under-surface was reduced to a finger's breadth, as on racing skis. Seven or eight centuries ago the groove was still about three fingers wide.

Somewhere about A.D. 1000 at the latest skis were invented in which the kicking ski of the right foot was considerably shorter than the running ski of the left foot. Probably this development made for greater speed in hunting reindeer, elk and wolf. Such skis were common over much of Finland and in central Sweden; they survived here and there in the modern age; skis of equal length triumphed at last when the technique of the ski stick was changed. To a late date ski-runners used only one stick, fitted at the lower end with a wooden disc or ring. The first record of skiing with two sticks, which greatly improved the speed, goes back to 1615, in northern Finland. The reindeer herdsmen of Lapland and some peoples of the U.S.S.R. use the single stick even now. In the southern part of the ski area, especially in the U.S.S.R., sticks were never used, the ski-runner holding on to cords fastened to the points of his ski.

Ski troops were known in the Swedish-Finnish armies in the sixteenth and seventeenth centuries. Four thousand ski men took part in the campaign of 1610, which extended as far as Moscow. The Finnish national epic, the *Kalevala*, also describes the ski-running of one of the heroic characters as he chases the elk of the forest god Hiisi (the translator has wrongly used snowshoe for ski):

On his back he bound his quiver,
And his new bow on his shoulder,
In his hands his pole grasped firmly,
On the left shoe glided forward,
And pushed onward with the right one ...
Chased the elk upon his snowshoes,
Glided o'er the land and marshes,
O'er the open wastes he glided.
Fire was crackling from his snowshoes,
From his staff's end smoke ascending ...
Forward pushed, his strength exerting,
And the first time he shot forward,
From before their eyes he vanished.
Once again he speeded onward,
And they could no longer hear him,
But the third time he rushed onward,
Then he reached the elk of Hiisi.

The long, broad ski was already becoming antiquated in the more thickly populated regions of the north in the nineteenth century, especially where there was a network of roads. But in the forests and in the fells they have always been used for travel, hunting, lumbering and reindeer herding. Some decades ago a good pair of skis was held to be worth a milking reindeer.

In the north ski-racing (and in Norway ski-jumping) began in the last century; and the short, narrow sports skis which are now used everywhere, were developed in 1920. Instead of the primeval spruce or pine, or the later birch, ash, hickory and other hardwoods are now employed.

Ski-ing has now established itself as an internationally popular sport, whose exhilarations and excitements are no longer the prerogative of the wealthy.

ILLUSTRATION: Page 266.

Sledges in the North

SLEDGES, the most ancient of vehicles, probably originated in the skins of animals on which hunters lugged the flesh and fat of their kills home across the snow. Sealers in the gulfs of the Baltic sometimes use skins in that way even now, when they make trips in early spring to the ice-fields. Lapps also make occasional use of reindeer skins as if they were sledges.

For snow traffic built-up wooden sledges have been employed since early times not only in the northern parts of Eurasia, but in Alaska, Canada and Greenland. Finds of sledge-runners, usually of fir wood, in the bogs of Finland and Sweden (one example has also been discovered near the Urals) lead to the surprising conclusion that the sledge may antedate the invention of skis (q.v.) by many thousands of years. Thus pollen-analysis shows that a sledge-runner from Heinola in Southern Finland – the oldest known – dates from about 6500 B.C., from the mesolithic period. This belonged to a two-runner sledge, and was nearly twelve feet long and six inches wide. The oldest known sledge of the type which has a single runner is about 5,000 years old; the runner in this case is about twelve inches wide by sixteen feet long. These sledges were probably pulled by the hunters themselves; but dogs, or dog and man (both methods of traction are still used by Siberian natives), probably drew the sledges of the later Stone Age, which were fitted with long, rather narrow runners. Stone Age and Bronze Age sledges had one feature in common – the carrying portion of the sledge was raised above snow and slush by sledge-posts set in the runner in two rows, side by side. Samoyed sledges are sometimes made in that style even now.

Siberian peoples – for instance, the Ostyaks and Kamass-Samoyeds, the Soyots and the Tunguses – and the Lapps in Europe have used till recently sledges fashioned from a single tree trunk, usually pulled by man. These long trough sledges resembled a dug-out canoe, and apparently they developed under the stimulus of Scandinavian boat-building into the Lappish boat-sledge, pulled by a reindeer, which has keel, sides and frame-bows and looks like a boat broken in half. Skiing hunters have used a similar sledge,

narrower and lighter. These boat-sledges have been common in some parts of Finland from the Middle Ages until now.

Still more primitive sledges are known from Siberia and Canada. Thus the Tunguses cut out a wooden board for conveying their kills. Both ends of the board are slightly raised so that it runs easily in the snow. More familiar is the primitive Indian toboggan of thin boards ending in a bow curving up and back. Eskimos use the primitive form of two-runner sledge which has no sledge-posts – the superstructure, that is to say, rests directly upon the runners, which are made of drift-wood, or if wood is lacking, of whalebone and also walrus teeth.

Sledges depend to a great degree in their construction and size upon whether they are drawn by dog, reindeer or horse. Thus dog-drawn sledges are long, narrow and close to the ground, on three or four pairs of sledge-posts. The bow acts as a buffer and prevents the sledge from getting stuck among trees and bushes. To draw them at least two dogs are always needed, though four dogs or even ten are required for a heavy load. Dogs have always been used by the people who live on the coast of the White Sea, in their fishing and seal-hunting over the sea ice; by the Syryens on the west side of the Urals, and especially by the Northern Asiatic peoples, such as the Ostyaks, the Voguls, the Gilyaks, the Kamtchadals and the Ainus. The dogs are harnessed so that they follow each other in file, though Eskimos generally set them in a row side by side, so that each dog pulls directly on the sledge with its own strap.

Reindeer sledges in Western Siberia are broad, rather short, high and stable, usually raised on five pairs of sledge-posts which slope slightly backwards. Two to four reindeer are harnessed side by side, each one tugging on its own trace. These reindeer sledges and the method of harnessing are conditioned by plenty of open space, by wide frozen rivers and treeless tundra.

Horse-drawn sledges have been in use since ancient times in the snow zones of Europe. One main type, the western sledge, belongs to Scandinavia, Central Europe and Western Finland. Its runners end in a bow which does not rise very far and to which the side rails of the sledge extend. Sledges of this kind, beautifully carved, have been found in Norway in a rich woman's burial-mound of A.D. 800.

In most of Eastern Europe and in Russian Siberia the depth and abundance of snow make it essential to build horse sledges with runners curving upwards in a high bow. The side rails stretch only as far as the first sledge-post; after which a twisted branch continues to the bow. A singular feature in the harness of these sledges is the collar-tree, a piece of wood in the shape of a capital U upside down, which goes over the horse's neck just above the collar.

In Finland and Sweden work sledges differ as much as English carts, waggons and carriages; so-called double sledges heavily built and joined by rope or cable are used in the woods for timber transport. Sledges have been surmounted by various kinds of coachwork. Long, broad travelling sledges were furnished with a hood. Sledges for journeys to church or pleasure excursions had a high bow, and a coach-box and were charmingly painted. Sledges used by the upper classes, especially in the seventeenth and eighteenth centuries, were carved and gilded. Romantic sleighing parties such as Selma Lagerlof describes in *Gosta Berlings Saga* are now a thing of the past; yet when it came to long journeys, nothing was lonelier than sledge travel over the snow; by day or by night. A Finnish poem runs

> Brightly shines the moon,
> Lightly drives the dead man:
> Death's stallion clatters
> And the sledge of Darkness
> Rustles. There is booming
> In the hills of night.
> The dogs of Darkness bark.
> The moon hides behind the clouds
> And the sentinel of Darkness
> Shuts the gate.

One should not forget, of course, that primitive sledges have been used and still are used in snowless districts. Thus great slabs of stone were transported by sledge in ancient Assyria, and drays or sledges, which preceded wheel vehicles on the farms, are still used for example in outlying hilly parts of the British Isles – in Cornwall, in Wales, in Westmorland where they bring down loads of bracken from the fells, and in Ireland. (See also *Wheel*).

ILLUSTRATION: Page 267.

Hitting from a distance

SLING, BOLAS and **BOOMERANG** are shooting weapons with a very different range of distribution. The sling is almost world wide, the bolas are not known outside the Americas, and the returning boomerang is only found in Australia, though analogous weapons belonged to India, Egypt and probably prehistoric Europe.

In the ancient world, the sling was carried not only for hunting, but also as a weapon of war, and as late as 1842 the Afghan slingers harried the English force withdrawing from Kabul. Apart from the prowess of David, the words of Numbers xx. 16 prove the skill with which the sling was used in Old Testament times, for there were among the people of Benjamin 'seven hundred chosen men left-handed; every one could sling stones at an hair breadth, and not miss.' The sling is still used in the Middle East by small boys for scaring birds from fields and orchards.

In Great Britain slings were a weapon of the Iron Age Celts before the Roman Conquest. Pebble slingstones and baked clay bullets have frequently been excavated; and it has been argued that Iron Age hill-forts were given extra ramparts as an adaptation against slingstones which were effective up to about one hundred yards. Large slingstone hoards were discovered in the excavations of Maiden Castle, the huge Dorset hill-fort of the Belgae, eventually stormed and carried by Vespasian as commander of the Second Legion, probably in A.D. 43.

The champion slingers of classical times were the Balearic islanders; according to Vegetius in his *Epitoma rei militaris* their children were given practice by having to use their slings to knock down their food from poles. The light troops of both Greek and Roman armies were often equipped with slings and oval-shaped leaden bullets, cast in moulds and ornamented with inscriptions like VICTORIA, or DEXAI, 'Take this'. Many have been found on the field of Marathon. The sling continued to be used by the infantry of European armies for casting grenades until the sixteenth century. Slings were also known in Peru, where they have been found in ancient graves; and in Mexico, where the Aztecs used them against the Spanish troops in 1520.

The bolas (plural of Spanish *bola*, ball) are entirely restricted to the New World. They are used in Argentina for entangling the legs of the rhea and guanaco, and consist of one or two heavy balls for whirling round the head, and a lighter oval-shaped grip. The lashings are of plaited sinews, in the older types wrapped round a groove in the stones, but now usually tied to the leather casings of the balls. The newest and most popular type is the *bolas perdidas*, made of metal balls of lead or copper; these have the advantage that they can be easily seen and retrieved by the hunter returning from a chase. The stone bolas are effective up to a hundred paces, but the *bolas perdidas* have a range half as long again, and an expert is said to be able to hit with them a mark as big as a shilling at fifteen paces.

From the large number of grooved stone balls found buried under the Pampas, it is plain that this weapon was used long before the European discovery of the New World; but it must have been much less deadly before the Spaniards brought in the horse, since a mounted marksman, galloping directly behind the animal, can throw with far greater accuracy and force than a hunter on foot, who has usually to aim broadside at the quarry. The bolas, in consequence, have replaced the bow among many tribes of Patagonia, since they got the horse. The Eskimos and the Indians of North-West America use miniature bolas for catching birds. These consist of small pierced ivory weights, usually seven, attached to strings of reindeer sinew.

The returning boomerang is only a form of the throwing-stick, a simple weapon used all over Australia as well as in North America and South Africa, and found (if the interpretation is correct) in neolithic Britain, and in Denmark in mesolithic times between 5000 B.C. and 2500 B.C. The Australian boomerang is not made to any set pattern, and takes its shape from the grain and structure of the wood. Every weapon, in consequence, has its own particular flight, which is to a large extent accidental as far as the maker is concerned, but which the owner appreciates. Some return in a wide circle, others describe a course like a figure-of-eight, and others again hover for a time before falling at the feet of the thrower. On ancient Egyptian sculpture, boomerang-like weapons are shown in use for fowling;

a specimen of these was recovered by excavation, and an exact copy of it was found to return to the thrower. Some South Indian boomerangs apparently also have this property. In India, too, the boomerang was copied in steel, and may thus have been the prototype of the iron war-quoit or *chakkra*, the characteristic weapon of the Sikhs. This was given momentum by being spun on the index finger of the right hand; spares were carried looped over the left forearm or piled on the turban.

A wooden boomerang is used in Abyssinia and near Lake Chad, but appears to be too thick and clumsy to make a return flight. This again may have been copied in metal and inspired the multiple-bladed iron throwing-knives, some shaped like birds' or animals' heads, which are made over a wide region of Central Africa. (See also *Gun, Blow-gun, Bow and Arrow*.)

Cleaner bodies

SOAP, a little surprisingly, was not known to the great civilizations of antiquity and appears to have been invented by the 'barbarians'.

Not that the early history either of soap or of the clean body is altogether clear. Soap is formed by the union of fatty acids with sodium or potassium, and the Egyptians made a mixture of natron (carbonate of soda) and clay, which they may have used for cleansing. If they did, it was not a true soap. One medical papyrus frequently mentions boiling fats with alkaline substances, but gives no name to a resulting product.

The Assyrians possibly boiled castor-oil with an alkali and so produced a soap; but again the evidence is confused. The ancient Hebrews employed for washing both alkalis and a saponaceous plant. There are a good many washing plants (including the Soapwort of English flower-gardens), the use of which may have preceded the invention of soap in many parts of the world, and such plants continue to be used by the Arabs. As for the alkalis, Jeremiah ii. 22 runs, according to the Authorized Version, 'For though thou wash thee with nitre, and take thee much soap, yet thine iniquity is marked before me.' The Hebrew words are *nether* and *borith*: one means washing-soda again (natron, the Greek *nitron*), the other means potash; neither means soap, and it is probable that true soap was unknown in ancient Palestine.

Greeks and Romans cleansed the body by bathing in hot water and scraping themselves with a strigil. But they had no soap. In excavations at Pompeii there was found – or so it appeared – a soap factory. A sample of the product was analysed, and it turned out to be no more than a fuller's earth. Nevertheless the Romans knew about soap at this time, if they did not make it or wash with it. Pliny the Elder, who was killed in the eruption of Vesuvius which destroyed Pompeii, had mentioned soap specifically – and for the first time that we know of – in his *Natural History*: it was made either 'thick or liquid' from tallow and wood ashes, best of all the ash of beech tree and hornbeam; and it was 'an invention of the Gauls for giving a sheen to the hair'. Both kinds were more used by men than women among the Germans.

Pliny called it *sapo*, which gives us our own word. Like butter (q.v.), this *sapo* was a barbarian confection.

Soap had now made its bow to civilization, but had scarcely begun its conquest of the body. For the first definite indication of soap in the bath we have to wait till the century after Pliny's death: the Greek physician Aretaeus of Cappadocia in his treatise on therapy (c. A.D. 160) recommends soap for washing, in the baths; and his words must be quoted, to mark the inauguration of pleasanter bodies among mankind (his context is a list of treatments for elephantiasis):

There are hosts of other medicines used by the Celts, who are now called Gauls, such as those balls of alkaline material with which they wash their clothes – called soap (*sapōn*). Washing the body with these in the bath is a very good thing.

Soap, though, was still something which had its place rather in the materia medica than the normal toilet. Aretaeus had also mentioned its medicinal virtue; and after his time another medical writer, Quintus Serenus, probably of the third century A.D., wrote in his long poem *De medecina praecepta saluberrima*:

If fearful lividness distain your cheeks, or blackened scar, Be sure to rub on them a cleansing soap.

In the early Middle Ages soap was more widely known, made and applied, though still with a medical tinge; thus a recipe for soap survives from Anglo-Saxon leechcraft of the ninth century. Nonetheless, demand increased. Soap from the Mediterranean area, with its ample supply of olive oil, was celebrated through the Middle Ages, still leaving its mark upon the vocabulary of the soap trade. Before the twelfth century soap was being manufactured in Spain, at Alicante, for example, Valencia and Cartagena. Then Marseilles took the lead, and by the fourteenth century Venice was competing seriously with Marseilles. Venice soap was long imported into England. Spain produced fine white soap, especially from Castile – and 'Castile' is still the name for a white soap of the modern English and American soap factories. Spanish and Venetian soaps were sold in tablets, on each of which was a maker's 'soap mark', such as a half-moon, a sun or a chain.

During the Middle Ages soap was mostly for bodies, and not for laundry: clothing smelt, even if bodies, or some of them, were washed, intermittently. Soap, in fact, was a luxury, enjoyed mainly by the rich, the poorer classes using a lye made from wood ashes. The rise of an English soap industry nevertheless indicates a rising graph of ablution. Bristol was a soap-making city by the twelfth century. Coventry and London soaps were well established by the thirteenth century; and the craft has left behind it that surname the meaning of which is not always recognized under the surviving spelling of Soper. By 1700 whale oil was used for soap-making at Glasgow and west coast towns, Liverpool as well as Glasgow depending upon this arctic source of raw materials, while soapers on the east coast imported tallow from Russia.

The Government had long placed a severe tax on soap – in effect a tax on cleanliness and godliness. Between 1712 and 1853 the tax varied from threepence a pound to a penny a pound. Increasing returns, all the same, were an index of newer and cleaner ways. In a hundred years, though the soap tax was nearly halved in that time, the yield nearly trebled, bringing the exchequer more than a million pounds in 1852.

The abolition of the tax in Gladstone's famous budget of 1853 came at a time when public hygiene and sanitation were being pursued by pioneers with Victorian energy and earnestness and fanaticism. Gladstone described the tax in his budget speech as 'an article of taxation which is most injurious both to the comfort and health of the people'. The tax-free wash and the newly-invented death duties were items of the same budget, a double symbol of a new ablutionary which would reach maturity – and the bath, h. and c. – within the next hundred and twenty years.

Cheaper soap also ended or greatly reduced domestic soap-making, which had always continued side by side with the industrial soaperies; housewives and their maids had boiled up crude soaps from ashes and the waste fat of the kitchen.

Those who are curious about the washing plants which preceded soap should try rinsing the hands in a decoction of Soapwort leaves. In the sixteenth century, this plant (*Saponaria officinalis*), which so often clings on in a semi-wild state outside the garden, was also known as Scourwort, Crowsoap and Fuller's Grass (since fullers had used it to soap their cloth), though it does not seem to have been used by that time. The leaves give an appreciable lather, dry and rather sharp, though refreshing, to the hands. (See also *Baths*.)

Refuge in the earth-house

SOUTERRAINS or earth-houses are among the most exciting and least publicized of the ancient structures of France, the British Isles, Denmark, and Iceland.

Associated with houses, fortified farmsteads and hill-forts (q.v.), they are generally underground passages walled and roofed with stone, which appear to have been refuges, a species of primeval vault or safe for goods, women and children, and even for the master of the household in the last resort. In medieval Iceland earth-houses were tunnelled into rock.

A remarkably well-preserved earth-house or 'fogou', to give the Cornish name, at Halligye, a hamlet near Trelowarren in the Lizard peninsula in South Cornwall, opened at one end into the ditch between the ramparts of a hill-fort which is now destroyed. One descends through a hole (a modern entrance) in the back garden of one of the cottages, and finds oneself in a low stone-walled passage, roofed with long clean slabs. The passage extends for nearly sixty feet; it opens into a roomier passage at one end and turns abruptly into a smaller passage at the other end. Not a twinkle of light comes in. In the absolute darkness parts of the fogou are separated by cross-walls, leaving only a small rectangular hole under a stone lintel, through which the intruder has to crawl on his stomach. The passages are unexpectedly dry.

This souterrain, like most of its kind, was built in the pre-Roman Iron Age, though souterrains were used for centuries to come, into the Dark Ages and the time of Viking raids. Thus the *Landnáma-bóc*, the Book of the Settlements and Generations in Iceland, describes how Sword-Leif the Icelander went harrying in Ireland where many souterrains are to be found in the raths, the fortifications which encircled farmsteads. Leif discovered a great earth-house, 'and went in there, and it was dark inside till light shone from a weapon which a man was holding. This man Leif slew, and took the sword and much other riches. After this he was called Sword-Leif.' Sword-Leif, it may be added, carried his Irish booty and his Irish slaves back to Iceland. The following spring he compelled the slaves to draw the plough for want of oxen, and they turned and murdered him.

Earth-houses are found in a band almost from the Mediterranean and then up the west coast of France to the Breton peninsula. They recur in the west of Cornwall, in Ireland, Scotland, Orkney, Shetland, and Jutland in Denmark, and then Iceland. It is claimed that some, *e.g.* in Caithness, Sutherland and Aberdeenshire, attached to hut-circles, are too conspicuous for places of concealment and must have been storehouses. Very large

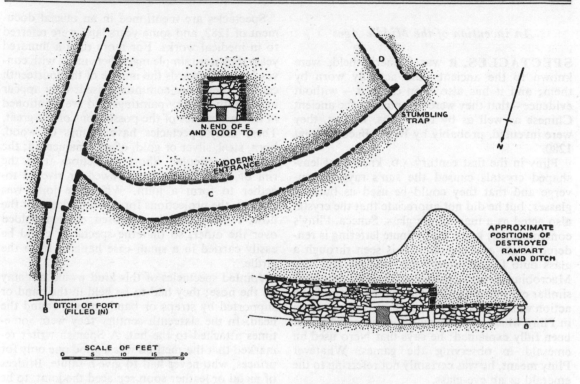

N. END OF E
AND DOOR TO F

STUMBLING
TRAP

MODERN
ENTRANCE

APPROXIMATE
POSITIONS OF
DESTROYED
RAMPART
AND DITCH

DITCH OF FORT
(FILLED IN)

SCALE OF FEET
0   5   10   15   20

Fig. 31. Plan of Souterrain, Halligye.

ones in Angus have roofs above the ground, and according to the same investigator may have been byres for sheep and cattle. However, the entrances to many souterrains would have been well concealed by bracken and scrub, and would not have been quickly discovered in hit-and-run raids. Leif's story also underlines the risk of entering a souterrain. If hit-and-run raiders found the entrance, cracking the safe might be too long a job. Inviolable or no, the souterrain would have given the homesteaders some feeling of security.

A few souterrains may go back to the Bronze Age, but in essence they belonged to the restless, bickering Iron Age of the Celtic migrations and invasions, and they continued to be built as late as the second century A.D., even possibly in the third and fourth centuries; and they were used, as Sword-Leif's exploit makes clear, later still. The rock-tunnels attached to the homesteads of quarrelsome medieval Iceland (and actually called earth-houses) enter in several more tales

told by Ari Thorgilsson, the historian of the *Landnáma-bóc*. Thus Grimr murdered another Icelander: the dead man's widow escaped with her two young children and sent them to a dale out of Grimr's way, where a foster-son of hers kept the boys hidden in the earth-house from mid-winter to harvest time, when the boys went after Grimr, caught him brewing ale in his house, set fire to the house and burnt him to death. Another Icelander, Beorn Hvalmage, or Beorn Whale's Stomach, slew the son of Liotolf. Liotolf and another of his sons trapped Beorn and his seven-year-old boy and killed them both. Revenge followed revenge. Beorn's brothers attacked Liotolf's homestead, Liotolf and Thorstein his son taking refuge in the earth-house. One of the brothers 'found the other outlet, and thus got behind them, and slew them both'. One can hardly doubt that the Iron Age souterrains of Scotland, Ireland and Cornwall had also known many such tragedies.

An invention of the Middle Ages

SPECTACLES, it was formerly held, were known to the ancients and actually worn by them; and it has also been claimed – without evidence – that they were invented by the ancient Chinese as well as by the Arabs. In fact, they were invented, probably by Roger Bacon, about 1280.

Pliny in the first century A.D. knew that lens-shaped crystals caused the sun's rays to converge and that they could be used as burning glasses; but he did not appreciate that the crystal also acted as a magnifying glass. Seneca, Pliny's contemporary, knew that minute lettering is rendered larger and clearer if it is seen through a glass bulb full of water; but both he and also Macrobius (fourth century A.D.), who described similar experiments, thought that the magnifying action was due to the water. There is one passage in Pliny which is somewhat obscure and has not been fully explained: he says that Nero used an emerald in observing the games. Whatever Pliny meant, he was certainly not referring to the emerald as an eye-glass.

In the thirteenth century glass-making revived in the West and some progress was made in optics, in which Roger Bacon was by far the most advanced worker; he wrote a complete description of the passage of light through plano-convex lenses, and certain phrases indicate his acquaintance with the action of a lens employed as a reading glass. Bacon died in 1292, after his heretical views had caused him to be held in confinement at Oxford for fourteen years. In 1305 Giordano da Rivalto preached a sermon in which he referred to the invention of spectacles less than twenty years before. A monument formerly in a church in Florence claimed that spectacles had been invented by the nobleman Salvino degli Armati, who died in 1317. The inscription on the tomb of Alessandro della Spina, who died in 1313, indicates that he also was familiar with spectacles, and that he spread the knowledge of making them. Bacon's method of grinding the lenses was taken to Italy. But possibly no one would acknowledge the source for fear of admitting association with a man of heretical and subversive views.

Spectacles are mentioned in an official document of 1282, and some years later were referred to in medical works. For more than a hundred years they were simple magnifiers made with convex lenses. Towards the middle of the fourteenth century they were commonly used; they appear in fifteenth-century paintings and are mentioned in the inventories of the possessions of the great. These early spectacles have frames of wood, horn, steel, silver or gold, often ornamented; the lenses are circular. Short projections from the rim of either lens were screwed or riveted together to form a joint. When the joint was opened, the projections formed a bridge over the nose. When the joint was closed, one lens folded over the other, so that the spectacles could be easily carried in a small case hanging from the girdle.

Jointed spectacles of this kind would not stay on the nose; they had to be held in the hand or supported by straps or bands passed round the head. In the sixteenth century they were sometimes attached to the hat. A Spanish writer remarked that the method was a good one only for princes, who never had to give a salute. Bridges of metal or leather soon replaced the joint, to be replaced in turn by a short spring bridge which gripped the nose – the first pince-nez.

By the early seventeenth century lenses were ground from three different materials, crown-glass, ordinary glass and the colourless transparent variety of quartz known as rock crystal, which for satisfactory results has to be cut perpendicularly to its optical axis. And by the eve of the fifteenth century concave lenses for the short-sighted were introduced to set beside the convex spectacles which had ruled since Bacon's day.

In the eighteenth century English opticians and spectacle-makers were important, John Dollond (1706–1761), Ramsden, Pierce and the Adamses, father and son, all of them adding to the practical knowledge of optics. Bifocals – in which each lens consisted of two segments of different focal lengths – were in use in England during the last two or three decades of the century, and were much favoured by artists, who had to move their eyes frequently from scene to canvas, and back again. Benjamin Franklin had such combination lenses made for himself, for near sight and the far sight of scenery during his travels.

The problem of the blurred vision due to astigmatism led to definite advances both in optics and spectacle-making. The defect was first recognized in his own eye by the brilliant Thomas Young (1773–1829), responsible also for the Young–Helmholtz theory of colour vision, developing the wave theory of light and deciphering the Rosetta Stone. Young described astigmatism in a communication to the Royal Society in 1801. Sir George Airy the astronomer who in 1817 also found that his own eye was astigmatic, eventually cured the defect by means of cylindrospherical glasses.

Contact glasses, now to the fore, were first used by Kalt of France in 1888 in the treatment of an eye condition. He employed transparent shells, adhering to the cornea under atmospheric pressure. About the same time Fick of Zürich devised small spherical caps separated from the eye by a solution of grape-sugar. The solution caused irritation, and the use of these caps was abandoned.

ILLUSTRATION: Page 126.

Thread for the loom

The SPINDLE is among the fundamental inventions of mankind, since the craft of weaving cloth with the loom, subsequently devised, depends upon spinning – that is to say upon contriving a long, continuous thread out of short natural fibres.

The first threads appear to have been wool and flax; and the spindle is no more than a short stick, bluntly pointed at one end and minutely hooked or notched at the other, and weighted towards the pointed end with a round spindle whorl. Fibres of wool, flax, etc., were twiddled between the fingers and attached to the spindle, which hung down and was made to turn, like a suspended top, the weight acting as a flywheel in miniature. Steadily and evenly the spindle thus twisted the fibres together into a more intimate union while drawing them out at the same time. The

spindle reached the floor and continued to spin there like a top come to ground; the thread so contrived and compacted was wound on to the shaft, the last part was hooked to the notch, more fibres were added, and the twirling, twisting descent began again. Twisting and winding are the fundamentals of the process, the thread keeping its twist when wound on the spindle.

Catullus has left a classic description of spinning in his poem on the marriage of Peleus and Thetis. The spinsters are the Fates, whose spindles, as they work, draw out and twist the thread of destiny. Each in her left hand holds the distaff wound with the wool, ready for spinning:

With their right hand they lightly drew the threads,
And shaped them with stretched fingers, and bent
Their thumb upon the rounded whorl and turned
The hanging spindle; and with their teeth
Continually they plucked and measured off the work
And fluff from the now smooth thread,
Stuck to their dryish lips. Twig-baskets by their feet
Guarded the soft fleece of snowy wool.

This simple, yet not so simple, device goes back to the stone-using phases of human history; and though the wooden sticks have vanished, evidence for spinning always survives in the whorls, which were at first small pottery rings, or else small holed stones.

In some countries the spindle was – and still is – held all the time in the hand; sometimes, as in ancient Egypt, the *whorl* was held between the palms and turned by rolling. In America the Navaho Indian twists the spindle by hand, the spindle lying on the ground beside her. Or the twist may be started by spinning the spindle between hand and thigh. In the Deccan, Indian women spun the finest of cotton threads with a spindle, which rested and turned in a cup on the ground. In some places the spindle took the form of a thin rod, set in a short, thick log.

The spinning-wheel – in essence a flywheel which works the spindle set in a bearing – was not made until late in historic times, in the fifteenth or early sixteenth century. Usually the invention is ascribed to Johann Jürgen, a German wood-carver in Brunswick, about 1533, though the wheel probably came into existence earlier. With the spinning-wheel, the wheel is turned by a crank-and-treadle action, and 'fliers' or horns re-volve about the spindle and form the winding action. Thus the actions of spinning were com-bined and made continuous, twisting and wind-ing occurring simultaneously, while the treadle gave the spinster freedom to alternate and guide the yarn with her hands.

Spinning-wheels and simple spindles have con-tinued in use in the world, in spite of two cen-turies and more of the mechanization of spinning which began in 1738 with the spinning-machine of the Birmingham spinners John Wyatt and Lewis Paul. (See also *Cloth, Silk, Nylon, Rope.*)

ILLUSTRATION: Page 73.

Before the oven

The **SPIT** or broche (a late fourteenth-cen-tury borrowing from the French *broche*) was at first no more than a long iron skewer with a handle at one end to make it easier to turn; it was a medieval adaptation and improvement of the stick of hazel, or other hardwood suitable for skewers, on which meat had been impaled and rotated by hand in front of the fire.

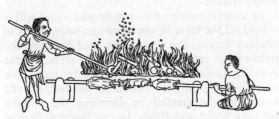

Fig. 32. Spit from Luttrell Psalter, c. 1340.

From about the fifteenth century onwards the long spit was laid on the forked ends of heavy iron fire-dogs, on either side of the fire, and the monotonous task of turning it was given to one of the lowest of the kitchen hands, the turnspit, whose labours were made doubly uncomfortable by the great heat which had to be maintained in the fires summer and winter. Gradually spits were mechanized. The notion of turning them by means of a dog inside a small treadmill is of con-siderable antiquity and may go back a long while before the time of Dr John Caius, who described the dog in his *De Canibus Britannicis* (1570):

There is comprehended under the curs of the coarsest kind a certain dog in kitchen service excellent. For when any meat is to be roasted, they go into a wheel, which they turning about with the weight of their bodies, so diligently look to their business, that no drudge or scul-lion can do the feat more cunningly, whom the popular sort hereupon term turnspits [the name transferred from scullion to dog].

The drum of this treadmill was at least mounted well away from the direct heat of the fire, the power being transmitted by leather thongs or chains, and pulleys.

An alternative method of driving the spit was to wind up a heavy weight on a drum geared through spur and worm-wheel to a driving-wheel. The wooden driving-wheel was connected to the spit by a leather belt and would turn as long as the weight was able to fall. These 'jacks' were known in the late sixteenth century, but were then quite expensive mechanisms. They were made of wrought iron, sometimes with brass components, and cost from ten shillings to thirty shillings each in the seventeenth century.

The most curious method of driving a spit was the smoke-jack which appeared in many great kitchens in the eighteenth century. A fan was en-closed in the chimney and was connected through gearing to the spit. The hot air rising up the chimney rotated the fan, which in turn drove the spit, but only if the fire was burning so fiercely and so wastefully that the rush of hot air and gases up the chimney could provide sufficient power. Count von Rumford (1753–1814), the scientist and inventor, declared that no human invention that had ever come to his knowledge was so absurd as this. Like the dog in the tread-mill, it saved the labour of winding up a weight, and that was about its only advantage. In the nineteenth century other types of jack were sup-planted by the spring-driven jack, which was re-latively easy to wind up.

The irons of the spits themselves were of vari-ous kinds. In 1500 a large roasting iron or broche cost three shillings; and a bird broche sixpence. Bird-spits were often lashed to the main roasting

Continued on p. 371

The Unicorn in Captivity, French tapestry c. 1514.

Portion of a verdure tapestry made at Arras. Fifteenth century.

Magic lantern, from Kircher's *Ars Magna lucis et umbrae*, 1671.

Cooking on a spit. Drawing by D. N. Chodowiecki (1726–1801).

Four-cycle internal-combustion engine c. 1876. (Science Museum, London).

A British hour-glass of the fifteenth century.

Chess: Death checkmating a king. Fifteenth century engraving by an unknown master.
The angel holds an hour-glass.

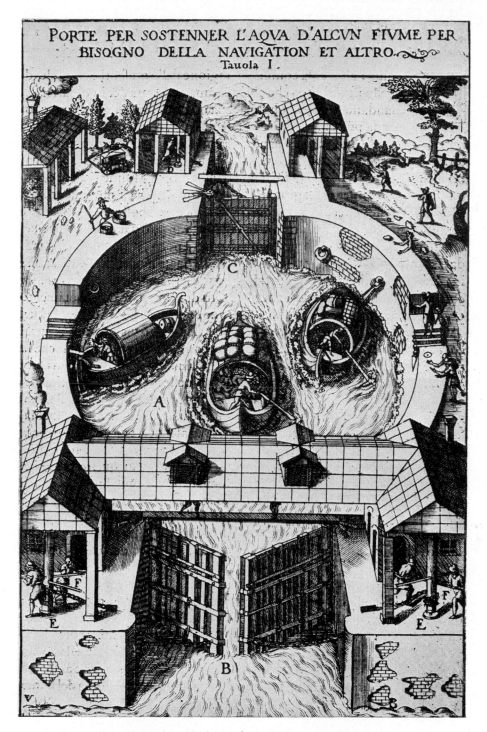

Canals: the hinged lockgates invented by Leonardo da Vinci.

Dice. Achilles and Ajax at play. From a jar painted by Exekias (c. 540–530 B.C.).

Bathing dress in the eighties, from *Sylvia's Home Journal*, 1885.

Women making candles, a nineteenth-century photograph from the National Museum of Wales.

Gallery in neolithic flint mine, Grime's Graves, Norfolk.

Christmas Card of 1848, designed by William Maw Egley.

Harvesting with the scythe. Drawing by Pieter Bruegel (c. 1525–1569.)

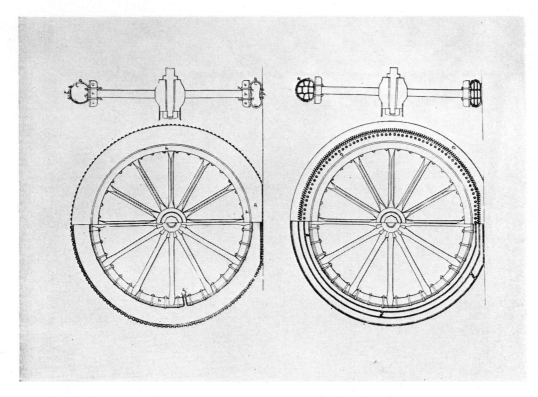

The first pneumatic tyre: diagrams from R. W. Thomson's patent specification, 1845.

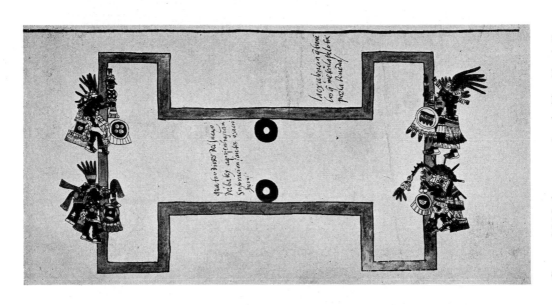

Ceremonial Mexican game played with rubber balls, from the Aztec *Codex Borbonicus*

370

spits, and a whole row of small birds, such as larks, might be threaded on thin wrought-iron skewers, about three feet long. The great iron meat-spit, six or eight feet in length, had a wooden pulley at one end, and was sometimes fitted with sliding barbs, which helped to hold the impaled joints more firmly.

In the basket-spit of the eighteenth century the centre portion was in the form of an ovoid container made of iron bars. Meat could be put in, clamped down by screwing up two of the bars, and cooked without having to be pierced. It was claimed, probably with some justice, that meat was more succulent when cooked in this way. A large dish, usually of tinned iron in later centuries, was set below the joint to catch the dripping, a word which survives from these antiquities of the kitchen, vividly recalling sight and sound. So hot were the fires that the basting spoons needed handles often of three or four feet. It was a matter of skill to maintain a fire hot enough for cooking, yet not fierce enough to burn the meat; and to regulate the fire so that the meal would be ready when called for. However, time measurement was more crude than it is today in most households, and the participants were called for their meal when it was ready, rather than by the clock.

ILLUSTRATION: Page 357.

Water and fire

STEAM-ENGINES in one shape or another go back far beyond the familiar era of Stephenson or James Watt, though it is not possible to say who first made use of steam for any power purpose. As early as the second century B.C. water was boiled in a vessel with a long neck, and the steam which emerged was used as a blast for a fire smelting non-ferrous metals; and somewhere between 62 A.D. and 150 A.D. Heron of Alexandria in his *Pneumatics* describes a form of rotary steam-engine or 'aeolipile', in which two or more radial arms bent at right angles were equidistantly attached around a sphere, pivoted about a diameter. Steam was introduced into the sphere

R

which thereupon escaped from the nozzles of the radial arms turning the whole apparatus.

This was the first steam-engine; and there follows a long gap to the new inventive age of science in the seventeenth century. The *Pneumatics* was now available in translations, and

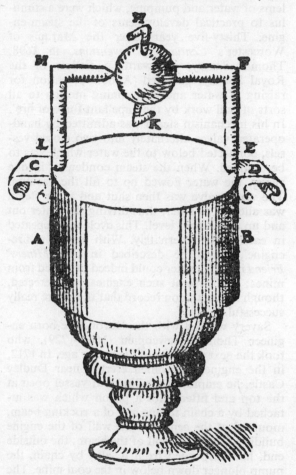

Fig. 33. Heron's Aeolipile.

several minds speculated upon the harnessing of steam. Thus Edward Somerset, Marquis of Worcester (1601–1667) describes in his *Century of Inventions*, which he wrote as a prisoner in the Tower of London and published in 1663, 'an admirable and most forcible way to drive up water by fire'. This is in effect a crude form of displacement engine for raising water, in which steam was admitted to closed vessels containing water; the water was driven out by the pressure, through an upright pipe several feet high. Edward Somerset had built one pumping engine at Raglan Castle before the Civil War, and he built another at Vauxhall after the war.

Deeper mining at this time posed urgent problems of water and pumping, which were a stimulus to practical developments of the steam-engine. Thirty-five years after the Marquis of Worcester's *Century of Inventions*, in 1698, Thomas Savery, afterwards a Fellow of the Royal Society, patented 'A new invention for raising of water and occasioning motion to all sorts of mill work by the impellant force of fire'. In his mechanism steam was admitted by hand-operated valves alternately into two closed vessels, connected below to the water which was to be pumped. When the steam condensed in one vessel, the water flowed up to fill the vacuum. The water-valve was then shut and more steam was allowed to enter, thus driving the water out and up to a higher level. This cycle was repeated in each vessel alternately. With Savery's 'fire-engine', which he described in *The Miners' Friend* in 1702, water could indeed be raised from mines; and several such engines were erected, though it is not upon record that they were really successful.

Savery worked with the Devonshire-born engineer Thomas Newcomen (1663–1729), who took the next step toward the power age. In 1712, in the engine Newcomen erected near Dudley Castle, he employed a cylindrical vessel open at the top and fitted with a piston which was attached by a chain to one end of a rocking beam, mounted at the centre in the wall of the engine building. The other end of the beam, the outside end, had suspended from it, also by chain, the pump plunger down below in the coal mine. The bottom of this open-topped cylinder (which now becomes the engineering term for the chamber in which a piston is driven: it was described in the print of the engine engraved in 1719 as 'a Brass Cylinder 7 Feet 10 Inches high, 21 Inches Diameter, to Rarifie and Condense the Steam') was connected by a valve to the boiler – 'Content near 13 Hogsheads' – which was built directly below. When steam was first admitted into the cylinder, the piston ascended and the pump plunger at the other end of the beam descended.

Steam was shut off and water was allowed into the cylinder, condensing the steam so that the ensuing vacuum caused the piston to descend and the pump plunger to ascend, drawing up its quota of water from the depth of the mine. This engine built by Newcomen was the first saleable and successful steam-engine which the world had seen. Such engines were now an important adjunct to mining.

Press'd by the ponderous air the Piston falls
Resistless, sliding through its iron walls;
Quick moves the balanced beam, of giant-birth,
Wields his large limbs, and nodding shakes the earth.
(*Erasmus Darwin.*)

It fell next to James Watt (1736–1819) to evolve several improvements to Newcomen's pumping engine. Of these the one which mattered most was the invention in 1765 of the separate condenser, in which the steam was condensed for creating the vacuum. Watt also used a cylinder closed at the top, so that steam could be applied to each side of the piston by means of suitable flat or mushroom-shaped valves; and arranged that the steam should be 'cut off' early in the stroke, allowing it to expand to the end. This showed a saving in fuel. When he connected the outer end of the beam by a rigid connecting rod to a crank below, Watt took another decisive step: he made his engine rotative.

Newcomen's engine was thus vastly improved, but if expansive working was to be reasonably efficient, then high steam pressures were essential, and Watt was averse to using more than five pounds per square inch. The Cornishman, Richard Trevithick (1771–1833), who grew up among the tin and copper mines in the west of Cornwall, was more of a visionary. This 'Father of High-pressure Steam' was using sixty pounds per square inch in his engines by 1815. So far the impulse to perfecting the steam-engine continued to be the efficient draining of mines. The engine was stationary; and it was Trevithick who made the first satisfactory *self-moving* steam-engine, which he tested on Christmas Eve, 1801. He followed this up in 1803 with a geared steam-engine to run on cast-iron plate rails, thus introducing to mankind, first the road locomotive, and secondly the railway locomotive.

Another important development at this time was the invention of the short slide valve and the three requisite cylinder ports by Matthew Murray, in 1802. Murray also believed in high-pressure steam, and his form of slide valve is in regular use today. Later in 1812 Murray produced a rack rail locomotive at his Round Foundry in Leeds.

A word needs to be added about the compound engine. Briefly, in such an engine the steam is first expanded down to a particular pressure in the first cylinder and then expanded for another and further stage in the second, and of necessity, larger, cylinder. By this means the maximum amount of work is obtained from the steam. The compound engine was first conceived by Jonathan Hornblower as early as 1781, but since the working pressures were then so low, while compounding depends upon a high pressure, his engine was not very effective. Later, the mine engineer Arthur Woolf used the principle in his first compound engine in 1803, but his design did not become firmly established in a successful form until 1845 when John McNaught of Bury, in Lancashire, made his compound steam-engine.

The development of higher working pressures made possible the co-development of self-moving engines, so much so, in fact, that by 1829 it was left to George Stephenson to demonstrate at the Rainhill Trials that a locomotive with a smooth wheel driving on a smooth rail could travel at twenty-nine miles an hour. After that milestone achievement all ideas of rope haulage on railways were abandoned and the railway locomotive became the established means of mechanical land transport. At the same time steam road-carriages were made and worked by many eminent pioneers, including Walter Hancock, W. H. Church, Goldsworthy Gurney and Alexander Gordon, but to the discredit of the English legislature an Act of Parliament permitted local bye-laws to sanction such extortionate tolls against steam vehicles that they could not run economically.

These bye-laws also restricted the efforts made to carry goods by road, so that development of the heavy haulage engine suffered, and it was not until 1856 that Charles Burrell of Thetford in Norfolk made the first heavy-duty steam road-haulage engine which pulled a test load of fifty tons. In spite of restrictive legislation, traction engines continued to be developed by the various makers into reliable and efficient machines.

For the marine engine we must go back to 1801 (though steamboats without Watt's engine had been devised in America); in that year William Symington ran a small steamboat on a canal in Scotland. In 1805 Richard Trevithick fitted a single-cylinder engine in a barge and propelled it by paddles. Later, Henry Bell was running his famous *Comet*, also a paddle-boat, regularly on the Clyde in 1812. In 1819 the Atlantic was crossed by the *Savannah* using auxiliary steam power as and when necessary. With the rotary engine scarcely anything had been done between the time of Heron's aeolipile and 1884, when Charles Parsons produced the first practical and successful steam turbine. Since then the turbine has been developed enormously for large power units in the power-station and in the largest vessels.

As far as the reciprocating engine is now concerned, modern practice emphasizes the totally enclosed forced-lubrication engine using in some cases a high degree of superheat. Such extremely reliable and efficient engines will run for months without a stop.

ILLUSTRATION: Pages 224 and 225.

A toy before television

The **STEREOSCOPE**, one of the delights of the Victorian age, depends on binocular vision; each of our two eyes observes a slightly dissimilar image, but those two images we fuse mentally into one image which gives the effect of solidity.

Euclid, about 180 B.C., was the first to record the phenomenon of binocular vision. It was noted by numerous later observers, and indeed is evident to anyone who looks at a near object, first with one eye and then with the other. But it was not until 1832 that Sir Charles Wheatstone (1802–1875), the founder of stereoscopy as a science, realized that the appearance of solidity and distance which we see naturally with our two eyes could also be produced artificially be making two drawings from slightly different viewpoints and presenting each to the appropriate eye only, in an instrument of his own invention which he called the *stereoscope* (Greek *stereos*, solid; *skopeo*, I see). In that year stereoscopes of two types were made for him, one with reflecting mirrors, the other with refracting prisms. However, only a brief notice of his observations appeared the following year; Wheatstone at the time was occupied with the electric telegraph, and he deferred the preparation of a paper on the stereoscope until 1838.

He then mentioned to the Royal Society several forms of instrument and described in detail the reflecting stereoscope, in which the two pictures were fixed vertically at each end of a horizontal bar, facing a pair of mirrors midway between them and at right angles to each other. The observer could thus see the reflected pictures simultaneously, each eye seeing only the image intended for it. Drawings of simple geometric figures appeared as solid bodies, but it proved almost impossible to make satisfactory pairs of binocular drawings of more elaborate subjects.

Soon after the publication of the photographic inventions of Fox Talbot and Daguerre, Wheatstone sought to have photographs taken from his instrument; but since it admitted light in all directions, daguerreotypes proved unsuitable because of their shiny metallic surface. Talbot's paper process led to no greater success, since the exposure was too long for taking two consecutive portraits (though it is difficult to understand why photographs were not made of inanimate objects).

In March 1849 Sir David Brewster (1781–1868) described his refracting or lenticular stereoscope to the Royal Society of Edinburgh. It was a modification of the second type of stereoscope suggested by Wheatstone in 1838, in the form of a box in which two small pictures set side by side were viewed through a pair of semi-lenses or prisms which magnified the images. Brewster suggested using photographic pictures, without which his instrument would have remained a scientific toy.

Unable to interest English opticians in producing his stereoscope, Brewster took it to Paris, where a skilful optician, J. Dubosq, began to make stereoscopes at the end of 1850, and in time

for the Great Exhibition at the Crystal Palace in London in 1851, where they were one of the chief attractions after Queen Victoria had publicly shown her interest in stereoscopy. Dubosq was flooded with orders; English opticians began the manufacture of stereoscopes, and within three months nearly a quarter of a million had been sold in London and Paris.

Meanwhile the leading daguerreotypists in London concentrated on taking stereoscopic views of the interior of the Great Exhibition and the objects on view, for what use were the instruments without pictures? They had to use two cameras set up side by side, for a binocular camera as suggested by Brewster in 1849 was not constructed until 1853. If the resulting pictures give somewhat exaggerated depth, it is because the lenses were further apart than the distance between the eyes (which on the average is two and a half inches).

When the wet collodion process was introduced in the early fifties, stereoscopic photography received a tremendous impetus, for the paper positives mounted on cardboard could now be mass-produced and sold at a fraction of the price of the stereoscopic daguerreotypes. By 1858 the London Stereoscopic Company (founded four years earlier) prided themselves on a stock of 100,000 different photographs of famous buildings and places of interest, and they sent their staff photographers as far as the Middle East and America, and added other novelties such as 'ghost' pictures, and sets illustrating 'High Life and Low Life'.

The stereoscope was 'the optical wonder of the age' and did for millions of people what television does today – with the advantage of being cheap enough for the poorest home.

The doctor's chest-examiner

A **STETHOSCOPE** is defined by the *Oxford English Dictionary* as 'an instrument used for examining the chest or other part by auscultation, the sound of the heart, lungs or other internal organs being conveyed by means of it to the ear of the observer.'

In the fourth century B.C. attention was called by Hippocrates, who was regarded as the father of medicine, to a splashing noise which could be heard on shaking a patient who had pus in his chest (empyema). This method was not carried further until 1761, when the Viennese physician Leopold Auenbrugger published his great treatise on percussion. By tapping with a finger of the right hand one of the fingers of the left hand placed in contact with the patient's skin, the physician could now define with considerable accuracy the size of certain organs in the body; he could also deduce the presence of abnormal collections of gas or fluids.

Early in the nineteenth century physicians of the French School began to study the sounds which are themselves produced in the body, as for example the breath-sounds in the lungs and the sound of the heart beating. For this purpose the physician placed his ear on the patient's skin over the organ to be studied. This method was known later as 'immediate auscultation'. It is significant that as late as 1806, Corvisart des Maret, Napoleon's physician and one of the greatest authorities in Europe on diseases of the heart, could talk of hearing the heart beat 'several times' when he listened very close to the chest. For several reasons immediate auscultation was not very satisfactory.

The complementary and more valuable method of 'mediate auscultation' was introduced by the Parisian physician René Théophile Hyacinthe Laënnec (1781–1826) who invented the stethoscope (Greek *stethos*, 'chest'; *skopeo*, 'I see, examine') which is now so familiar a part of the doctor's equipment. Laënnec had used the older method – direct application of the ear to the chest – but was dissatisfied with the results. In 1816, as he tells us, he was consulted by a young woman suffering from heart disease, in whose case the older method could not be used. Laënnec remembered that he had once noticed a group of children playing among felled tree trunks. He had seen one of them scratching the wood at one end of the log and the rest listening at the other end. So he now rolled a quire of paper into a cylinder and applied one end of it to the region of the patient's heart and the other end to his own

ear. He found that he could hear the heart sounds much more clearly than he had ever done before.

Laënnec began to experiment on the construction of stethoscopes, using paper cylinders, wood, cane, glass, and several metals in turn. In the end he adopted the experimental model which is known as Laënnec's stethoscope and which consisted of a cylinder of wood, one and a half inches in diameter and about ten inches in length. A hole about $\frac{1}{4}$ inch in diameter traversed the cylinder throughout its length, and at the lower end opened out into a conical cavity. This cavity could be filled by an accurately fitting plug, which was itself bored to continue the main hole running through the cylinder. For convenience the cylinder was divided into two approximately equal parts, one being shaped to plug into the other. Laënnec published his description of this instrument in 1817, and with it he carried out a most extensive series of observations in many diseases of the heart and lungs. He invented most of the terms for the sounds heard which are still used at the present day. His great work on 'mediate auscultation' – that is, auscultation by the aid of the stethoscope intervening between the ear and the patient's skin – was published in 1819. Diagnosis of diseases of the chest was completely revolutionized.

Laënnec's instrument was soon modified. Lighter stethoscopes were made in the shape of a dumb-bell, shortened to five inches, and in the shape of a trumpet with a bell-shaped chestpiece; some were made to fit in the pocket or inside the doctor's top-hat. In one form of stethoscope the stem was attached to the ear-piece by a short length of stiff rubber tubing – this was the instrument which enabled a character in *Washington Square* (1881) by Henry James to listen to his own heart.

All these stethoscopes were of the 'monaural' type. The 'binaural' or two-eared stethoscope began with an experimental form made in 1829 by a London doctor who used flexible lead pipes. Rubber tubing was developed and in 1855 Dr Cammann of New York described the first binaural stethoscope to be manufactured and marketed. The binaural instrument did not come into general favour in Great Britain until the eighteen-eighties.

Axe, knife, arrowhead

STONE TOOLS have now for a long while been investigated and used to reveal much of the ancient story of mankind.

Two thousand years ago, the Latin poet Lucretius considered that the history of man should be divided into three stages, denoted successively by the use of stone, bronze and iron for tools and weapons. The first he probably guessed at, as we might infer that Adam had stone tools from the fact that Tubal Cain, the 'first metalworker', followed him seven generations later. The Greeks and Romans did not identify the actual stone implements of early man. The ones chipped to shape escaped their notice; the ground and polished stone axes they took for thunderbolts fallen from heaven, a superstition found in every part of the world. These thunderbolts were thought to have curative powers. In 1081 the Byzantine Emperor, Alexius Comnenus, presented the German Emperor Henry III with one mounted in gold. In Burma they were ground up for ophthalmia, in Cornwall boiled for rheumatism. Arrow heads of finely chipped flint were looked upon as weapons thrown by the fairies.

The first man to suspect the true nature of the thunderbolts was a physician of Pope Clement III, who said shortly before 1600 that the stones were the weapons of a primitive people unacquainted with metal. In 1690 a hand-axe of chipped flint found opposite Black St Mary's, near Gray's Inn Lane in London, (and now in the British Museum) was also recognized as human handiwork and described as a 'British' (*i.e.* pre-Roman) weapon. A century afterwards, in a paper in *Archaeologia* in 1800, John Frere declared similar specimens found at Hoxne in Suffolk, to be the tools of a people who 'had not the use of metals'.

The scientific study of stone implements began in the last quarter of the nineteenth century, and went hand in hand with the study of Pleistocene geology, the geology of the last million years of the earth's history. The first broad distinction to be made was between tools shaped by breaking and chipping and those shaped by grinding and polishing. The latter are the hallmark of the Neolithic, or New Stone Age, so often mentioned in this volume, in which the invention of agriculture, weaving, cattle-raising and, it seems, of pottery set man on the path to civilization.

On the other hand stone-chipping, a subordinate technique in the Neolithic period, was the only means known for shaping tools during the preceding Palaeolithic or Old Stone Age. The Neolithic began about 7,000 years ago; the Old Stone Age covers the rest of man's history of about half a million years.

The necessity of using a strong stone of fine grain led early man everywhere to adopt flint, a siliceous concretion formed in chalk, as his principal material. The steel blade of the pocketknife goes back direct to the knife blade of flint. Like glass, flint breaks under a blow with a conchoidal or shell-like fracture, and in a direction more or less predictable. Thus it lends itself better to purposive shaping than coarser stones of granular structure. Glass, of course, is even superior in this respect, but the natural volcanicglass, obsidian, is infinitely rarer than flint. Australian aborigines, who never achieved Neolithic culture and still live the old Palaeolithic life, covet the bottle-glass and telegraph insulators of their white neighbours.

The skill of working flint lies in controlling the fracture and compelling it to follow the lines of the desired implement. Blows from a hard striker – a piece of stone – will remove deep-biting flakes; shallower flakes, thin as an eighth of an inch and less, can be struck off with a piece of wood, once the aim and manner of the blow are mastered. Modern experimenters have rediscovered some of the knacks, but their work does not come up to the best of the Old Stone Age in ease and economy of chipping. Ancient man undoubtedly produced an implement in a number of seconds, discarding a piece as soon as unfavourable features appeared in the flaking or in the grain of the flint. A fine flint tool, the product of the longest craft tradition the world has known, shaped by delicate and unreflecting coordination of eye and muscle, can be a very beautiful object.

If we disregard certain broken pebbles found in South African river-gravels, and some rather dubious flakes of flint found beneath the crag of the East Anglian coast, the earliest flint tool which claims attention is the hand-axe, named Acheulian after a suburb of Amiens. This was an all-purpose tool, more or less pointed with sharp edges and usually a blunt butt; as good for cutting with as to throw at a prey or an enemy. Large flat flakes were removed from the sides to yield a fairly straight edge, further straightened in some cases by pressing off tiny flakes with a hard point (this pressure-flaking is still practised by Eskimos). In France, England, Africa and south-east India the shape of the hand-axe is uniform. In England the older and most numerous specimens come from the gravels of the 100-foot terrace of the Thames (*i.e.* they are found in gravel pits, though less frequently since the advent of mechanical excavators). These hand-axes belong to the warm interval between the second and third phases of the Pleistocene Ice Age and are therefore about 250,000 years old. The same gravels, at Swanscombe, produced the skull of a man who no doubt made some of the tools: except for its greater thickness the skull is little different from that of modern man.

The maker of a hand-axe chipped a piece of flint all round until he reached the desired result. Another technique (possibly the tradition of another race of humanity) made flint knives or weapons from a core, detaching a largish flake already fashioned *in situ*, or requiring little or no trimming. This is the Levalloisian method (so named from a suburb of Paris); and it has not been successfully copied by modern enthusiasts. It required great attention to the mother-core, on which the flake was shaped before being struck off, and from which the ancient expert could strike a series of flakes from a single prepared position.

A smaller flake was the basis of tools found associated with remains of Neanderthal man, an ugly cousin of modern man who failed to survive the last phases of the Ice Age. It was during the final major onset of the ice, when Europe was reduced to arctic conditions for the last time, that races of modern men, indistinguishable from our contemporaries, appeared with a further refinement of the technique of knapping. Long slender flakes were now struck serially with single blows from a cylindrical core, and trimmed by pressure to many shapes of knives, points and burins. These were the tools

used by the astonishing prehistoric cave-painters of central France, and by the Magdalenians whose carvings in bone and antler equal the paintings in exactness and vigour.

In the Neolithic period, when polished stone tools became fashionable, the art of flint-chipping declined in most areas, although in Denmark and North Africa the pressure technique produced some of the most remarkable and beautiful pieces ever made. In temperate Europe the farmer needed to clear trees from his land, and axes of polished flint or other stone were best for this purpose. Occasionally examples occur of a fineness and delicacy of contour exceeding any practical requirements. These are often of greenstone (nephrite) which was exported to considerable distances from its sources in Brittany and Cornwall. Perhaps the stone was venerated as the Chinese venerate jade.

Stone suitable for the manufacture of axes was traded over long distances. The igneous rock of Penmaenmawr, called Craig Lwyd stone, it was discovered in 1919, was worked on a factory site on the mountain side. (The site, after all the centuries, is now mostly destroyed by quarrying.) The roughly chipped products were sent as far as Wiltshire, the final grinding and polishing being left to the customer. Another such factory was discovered in 1947 in Great Langdale in Westmorland. These axes, too, were widely traded, south and north. Elsewhere in Cumberland a Great Langdale axe has been found in its haft of beech-wood.

More dramatic are the mines from which Neolithic men dug nodules of fresh flint for trading to distant parts of south England. The visitor can climb down ladders into two of the shafts at Grime's Graves, the mining area in the Norfolk Breckland. He can enter the galleries which branch in all directions, and see the black flint the miners were after, and the tools of red deer antler which they used.

Within a few miles of these mines an uninterrupted tradition of flint-knapping was maintained until recently in Brandon. Gun-flints were produced mostly for export to Africa. An experienced knapper could make nearly 2,000 gun-flints a day.

ILLUSTRATION: Page 308.

'An invisible eele'

SUBMARINES embody an idea as inevitable
to man as the idea of flying: here was the sea, a
realm of wonders, in which life and movement
were possible to other creatures. In fact or in fantasy man was going to enter that realm, for
more than the brief while allowed to the diver
after pearls, sponge or red coral.

The invention of the submarine is therefore
part of a complex including diving-bell and
diving-dress, both of them old in conception; and
even in practice, older than the first efficient
diving-bell devised by the astronomer Edmund
Halley in 1717 and the first efficient diving-dress
invented in 1819 by Augustus Siebe.

Divers in the Aegean had ways of breathing air
down from the surface, according to the *De
Partibus Animalium* of Aristotle (384–322 B.C.),
Aristotle only mentioning their 'instruments for
respiration', and comparing elephants and their
'lengthened nostril' – ' whenever they have to
traverse the water, elephants lift this up above the
surface and breath through it'; as for diving-
bells, bathysphere and benthoscope, medieval
legend long ago sent Alexander the Great to the
sea-bed in a glass barrel, from which he inspected
Leviathan and all monsters and denizens of the
deep, forestalling Piccard, Beebe and Otis Bar-
ton.

It would be pleasant if one could say that the
submarine had at least begun innocently, as a
mobile form of Alexander's glass barrel or benthoscope. But from the start the submarine was a
war vessel. The Dutch scientist Cornelis Drebbel
(1572–1634) appears to have had destruction in
mind when he devised his submersible rowing-
boat, which he demonstrated in the Thames between Westminster and Greenwich. The boat was
covered in greased hide, and the oars came out
through leather valves or sleeves. Drebbel's demonstration took place about 1620. In 1625 Ben
Jonson's comedy *The Staple of Newes* was acted,
and Jonson had no doubt about the purpose of
the boat:

> *Thom.* They write here one Cornelius-Son
> Hath made the Hollanders an invisible eele
> To swimme the haven at Dunkirke, and sinke all
> The shipping there.

> *Peniboy.* But how is't done?
> *Cymbal.* I'll show you, sir.
> It is an Automa, runnes under water,
> With a snug nose, and has a nimble taile
> Made like an auger, with which taile she wrigles
> Betwixt the coasts of a ship, and sinkes it streight.

This was the proto-submarine, though it seems
to have been little more than a vessel which
could navigate awash.

More than a century passed before the first
genuine and potentially dangerous submarine
appeared. It was built in 1775 at Saybrook, Connecticut, by David Bushnell (c. 1742–1824), in
order to break the British blockade in the American War of Independence. At Yale, Bushnell had
shown that gunpowder could be exploded under
water; and his submarine carried a wooden torpedo or 'magazine' outside on the hull, with a
device for fastening it from inside the submarine
on to the enemy ship. Bushnell's little one-man
vessel was made of sturdy oaken planks. In shape
it looked like a tilted walnut or a wooden top. It
was weighted to float awash, and could be made
to dive by admitting water through a foot-
operated valve in the bottom; in order to surface,
the occupant had to eject the surplus water with
two force-pumps.

This principle is still used to regulate the buoyancy of submarines, the water-ballast tanks
usually being carried outside the main hull and
blown by compressed air. However, whales and
fishes do the job more elegantly: they contract
their bodies by muscular action in order to sink,
and expand them to rise.

Bushnell made a thorough job. His 'submarine
vessel' was driven by two propellers, one vertical,
one horizontal, which were turned by the operator, whose instruments included a depth indicator and a phosphorescent compass. There
was air enough in the vessel to last half an hour.

'Bushnell's turtle', as it was nicknamed, was
tried several times. Manned by Sergeant Esra
Lee in 1776, it reached the British flagship,
Eagle in New York harbour, but Lee failed to
attach the magazine of powder to the *Eagle's* hull.

Bushnell had shown the way; the next steps
were taken by another American, Robert Fulton
(1765–1815), artist and inventor, working with
the French before the end of the French Revolutionary War. Napoleon granted funds for the

Nautilus, which Fulton launched in 1801. In trials it was demonstrated that the *Nautilus* could convey a torpedo, which could be fixed under a ship and exploded.

The French Minister of Marine rejected Fulton's invention as repugnant to the conscience, whereupon Fulton crossed over to the English government, who also rejected his plans; last of all, he tried his own country.

However, Fulton's *Nautilus* had impressed the imagination. In the American Civil War the Confederacy operated a number of submersible iron boats, named 'Davids', which carried a torpedo thrust out ahead on a spar. These were not true submarines, though in 1864 one of them destroyed a Union ship, only to be lost itself in the backwash. The year before the first engine-propelled submarine had been built in France; and in the sixties the writer of science fiction, Jules Verne, went one better, in his prophetic and romantic concept of a second *Nautilus*, the huge submarine which conveyed his wild outlawed cultivated hero Captain Nemo below the oceans of the world, in *Twenty Thousand Leagues Under the Sea* (1870). Unlike the *Nautilus* of Fulton, and unlike the new atomic powered *Nautilus* of the United States Navy, the submarine of Jules Verne and Captain Nemo was in some sense Alexander the Great's legendary benthoscope with an engine added: it was the world's only pleasure submarine, from which giant medusae and rays could be examined through the window. Captain Nemo could solace himself on the organ, in his library, or among his old masters, including Holbein, Velasquez and Leonardo. Verne's *Nautilus* was powered by electricity, which was first employed in fact eleven years later in 1881, in the submarine built by the French engineer Claude Goubet.

In 1905 the Chief Constructor at the Admiralty in London, Sir William White, said that no new principle of submarine design had been discovered or applied since the time of Bushnell; and indeed the tale has been one of refinements – the hydroplanes, or adjustable inclined planes similar to the elevator of an aircraft, for regulating depth, introduced by Fulton, Goubet's batteries for submerged propulsion, and J. P. Holland's use of the gasoline engine for surface propulsion in 1896 (though this was superseded by the Diesel engine which France was the first to adopt for submarines in 1903). The Irish-American J. P. Holland conceived his submarine as a means of destroying the British fleet, and his early work was financed to that end by the Fenian Society of America. Holland's prototype of 1875 was expressly modelled on Robert Whitehead's automobile torpedo, and his later boats may be regarded as progenitors of all modern submarines. English submarine pioneers, it is curious to think, included a Liverpool clergyman the Rev. G. W. Garrett, who tried out his first submarine in the Liverpool docks in 1878.

Nearly a century and a half of experiment, trial, error and building went by before Bushnell's unhappy invention proved itself in the First World War. Disposing of a grand total of 372 U-boats, the German Navy then sank 11,000,000 gross tons of Allied and neutral shipping; in the Second World War 1,098 U-boats sank 14,000,000 gross tons, and American submarines achieved a tremendous destruction of Japanese shipping in the Pacific. Thus the submarine has been exclusively destructive, in aim and deed; it has turned out to be one of the most pernicious inventions of all time.

The surgeon's kit

SURGICAL INSTRUMENTS are known from ancient medical literature, from chance representation, and from examples which survive out of the surprisingly full kit of the Greek and Roman surgeon.

Early forms of the scalpel used for making incisions are depicted on a votive tablet of about 300 B.C. found at Athens on the site of the temple of Aesculapius, the god of medicine. Two of the three instruments on the tablet were 'bellied' scalpels, with a short blade, a straight back and a curved cutting edge, such as were widely employed throughout the Greco-Roman period. Amputation knives, always much larger than the scalpel, and amputation saws, also have a long history before the modern era of operation under anaesthetics. An amputation knife with a steel blade and a bronze handle was recovered from the ruins of Pompeii, which was overwhelmed in A.D. 79. The tenon saw, still the kind used most commonly in amputation, was employed in Greco-Roman practice, though from the Renaissance to about 1750 the bow saw was the usual instrument. Arab surgeons in the Middle Ages had employed both kinds, wielding, too, scalpels, amputation knives, and cauteries (see below).

From Pompeii there also came a Roman trocar and cannula of bronze. These are instruments used in the operation of withdrawing fluid from the peritoneal cavity of a patient with dropsy. The skin and abdominal membranes are pierced with the sharp-pointed trocar. When the trocar is inserted into the body it is contained, except for the projecting point, inside the cannula, which is a hollow tube. As soon as the combined instrument has penetrated to the fluid, the trocar is withdrawn and the fluid escapes through the cannula.

The trocar, as well as surgical saws and scalpels and the magnet for extracting arrow-heads, were among the instruments described by the Indian physician and surgeon Suśruta in the sixth century B.C.

The instruments used in trephining, or removing a circular disc of bone from the cranium, one of the oldest operations of surgery which was carried out in neolithic times both in Britain and continental Europe, were described by Hippocrates (c. 460–c. 370 B.C.), the Greek 'father of medicine', and developed by Roman surgeons. The Roman trephine was a small hollow metal cylinder with a serrated lower border. This was held against the skull and rotated until it cut out a circle in the bone. The difficulty was to keep the trephine in place during the early part of the proceedings, so a central pin was added, which projected slightly below the serrated border. As soon as the trephine began to bite, this pin was removed (in the modern instrument it is withdrawn into the shaft).

The first trephines were rotated between the palms of the hands; surgeons in the sixteenth or seventeenth centuries took to using a brace, similar to the carpenter's brace.

Other ancient instruments include forceps, and the once dreaded cauteries. The surgeons of Homer's *Iliad* extracted arrow-heads with simple forceps in the shape of a flat strip of metal beat into equal lengths. Forceps were known to Suśruta. Ambroise Paré (c. 1510–1590), the French military surgeon, and others, developed long forceps with crossed legs for removing both arrow-heads and bullets. The increasing use of firearms led also in the middle of the sixteenth century to the invention of a bullet extractor. This took the shape of a long stiletto with a screw-point which passed through a tube. The bullet was located with the point of this tube or cannula, pierced with the screw-point of the stiletto and removed.

Cauteries made of iron and shaped like a knife or with bulbous, pointed, or coin-shaped ends, go back to Hippocratic times. The end was heated and applied to arrest bleeding, the appropriate cauteries being employed to remove tumours, for hernia, piles, and conditions of the nose and throat. Sometimes they were applied in cases of sciatica, and even in dislocation of the shoulder. From classical surgery, the cautery descended to the medieval and Renaissance eras. It was used immediately after an amputation. Also the sixteenth century believed that gunshot wounds were all poisoned; to kill the poison most of them were cauterized.

Ambroise Paré dramatically described how as a young surgeon at the siege of a castle near Turin in 1536 he had followed the practice of his seniors and treated wounds by scalding them with oil of elder. His supply of oil gave out, and in the emergency he treated others with simple soothing dressings. Next morning he found to his amazement that these patients had had less pain and had slept more soundly than the men who had been scalded and burned. As a result of Paré's teaching the cauterizing of gunshot wounds slowly died out, though he continued to apply the cautery in certain conditions.

Cauterizing irons were used in the eighteenth century to destroy dead parts of carious bones, to remove cancers and carbuncles, and to deal with epilepsy, sciatica and pain in the teeth; as well as to stop haemorrhage in wounds and amputations. By the second half of the nineteenth century the form of the cautery had not greatly changed, but there were discussions on the best metal for making this ancient and time-honoured and terrifying instrument; some claimed to have shown that a cautery of gold or platinum caused less pain and produced a softer scar. Fortunately for mankind the situation was altered by general anaesthetics, and by galvano-cautery first of all, and then by the diathermy apparatus.

Surprisingly the tourniquet for stopping haemorrhage seems to have been a late development in surgery, employed first by a French surgeon at the siege of Besançon in 1674. He passed a cord loosely round the limb and tightened it by turning a stick. A tourniquet of a pad placed over the vessels tightened by a towel around the limb and a stick was introduced soon afterwards, to be followed in 1718 by the screw-tourniquet of the Paris surgeon Jean Louis Petit; first made of wood, then of metal, this screwed a firm pad directly down on the artery. Petit was the first to employ the name 'tourniquet' for such an instrument. (See also *Anaesthetics, Drugs, Dental Drill*.)

For castles and kings

TAPESTRIES belong especially to the Middle Ages, and were developed in northern Europe to meet a direct need for warmth and comfort. In small houses the thin lath-and-plaster walls made heavy woollen hangings necessary for warmth. Castles could be made more comfortable and habitable by spreading tapestries across the damp, chilly stone of draughty corridors and walls. Tapestry weaving also provided upholstery for beds and hard wooden benches.

True tapestry is made on a loom, on which the warp is stretched, the different coloured wefts being woven in to build up the pattern. Some figured tapestry may have been woven in Gaul in Roman times. Figured tapestry was certainly woven in the Near East, as the dry burial-grounds of Egypt have amply revealed; but such tapestry was mostly worked on a small scale and was used rather for ornamental bands in costume than for wall hangings. In China, silk *K'o-ssu* was evolved from tapestry technique, and was a fabric of extraordinary refinement, with its own long history. The Peruvians also employed a tapestry technique before the Spanish conquest.

European tapestries, however, acquired in the fourteenth century a uniqueness of style and importance. If they were utilitarian they were also hangings of splendour and beauty. Two kinds of loom gave rise to two great schools of weaving. The very finest of medieval tapestries were made on upright looms (high-warp). Fine weaving on horizontal looms did not develop till after 1500 or thereabouts, in Flanders; then, as a quicker process, it rapidly became the general method.

For high-warp weaving Paris, first of all, and then Arras were the principal centres, the word 'arras' being used as a synonym for tapestry in succeeding centuries. The feudal aristocracy ordered rich, costly sets of tapestry for their rooms; enormous hangings worked with historical and mythological scenes and stories for their great halls (in sets of six or more, each piece often measuring fourteen to fifteen feet high by twenty to thirty feet long); and no less splendid ones with religious subjects for their chapels and churches.

Much of the life of the feudal nobles was spent in the field and in travelling. Tapestries accompanied them in their baggage, adorned their tents and pavilions, or were used to form hanging rooms temporarily erected inside a building. Such tapestries were called 'chambers'. Thus an inventory made in 1420 of the possessions of Duke Philip the Hardy of Burgundy (a great patron of tapestry) mentions 'one chamber of high-loom tapestry worked with a little gold, furnished with canopy, head-board and bed cover with a green ground, called the Chamber of the Courts of Loves, where there are several figures of men and women, with scrolls having amorous inscriptions.'

A beautiful set of tapestries of this kind, the 'Lady of the Unicorn', survives at the Cluny Museum in Paris. At Chatsworth, in Derbyshire, the Devonshire Hunting Tapestries are good examples of hall tapestry from the middle of the fifteenth century. At Angers, in France, the Apocalypse tapestries of the fourteenth century show hangings of the kind that were woven for churches and chapels. These were ordered for the Duke of Anjou's chapel about 1375.

Tapestries are frequently mentioned by the chroniclers of the age, since they were so much a part of the medieval scene at royal or ducal courts, at receptions, at banquets, at weddings, carnivals or religious festivals. They were hung on gala occasions from windows and in the streets; and just as they were part of the baggage of a feudal lord, so they accompanied him to battle, and formed part of the rich spoils which a victorious army expected to loot from the enemy camp. The loot from the battlefields of Granson-Morat, where Charles the Bold lost his life in 1476, included several of the finest medieval tapestries, which can still be examined and admired in the museum at Berne.

It was in true medieval vein that the poet Henry Bradshaw, who died in 1513, described a feast given by Ulfer, King of Mercia:

> Clothes of golden and arras were hanged in the hall,
> Depainted with pyctures and hystoryes manyfolde,
> Well wroughte and craftily with precious stones all
> Glyterynge as Phebus, and the beaten golde
> Lyke an earthly paradyse, pleasaunt to beholde

and both Cardinal Wolsey and Henry VIII were sufficiently of the Middle Ages to make enormous collections of tapestries, some of which remain at Hampton Court. The Habsburg collections have also partly survived in Vienna and in Spain. In France many of the best of the royal tapestries were melted down during the Revolution to obtain the metal from the gold and silver thread, but the Louvre, together with the Cluny Museum in Paris still preserve some wonderful late medieval examples. None of these is more beautiful than the set depicting the Hunt of the Unicorn which is now in the Cloisters in New York and which is among the world's major works of art; five tapestries in the set were probably made for Anne of Brittany when she married Louis XII in 1499, two extra tapestries having been added, possibly in 1514, for the marriage of Anne's daughter to Francis I. They are remarkable for design and execution and for their brilliant naturalism – noticeable in the wealth of flowers which, in the final panel at least, form a symbolic

flora in accord with the subject of the whole series.

Tapestry design tended to become more and more formal. The first big change came in 1515, when Raphael was asked to design the great tapestries of the Acts of the Apostles for the Sistine Chapel. He introduced the full Renaissance style into the art of tapestry. The Brussels weavers worked wonders with his empty foregrounds and spaces, the low horizon and wide skies, and the simply folded and undecorated draperies. Yet all these things were really foreign and inimical to tapestry design, which thrives best on crowded scenes and lavish detail. Technical improvements, especially with dyes, made possible a much closer reproduction of painted designs. With the aid of one hundred and fifty colour tones, a tapestry could soon reproduce a picture in a manner which had been impossible in the Middle Ages when the weaver could command only fifteen or twenty tones. In the middle of the eighteenth century the French painter Oudry, artistic head of the Gobelins factory, insisted upon exact reproductions of the painted originals. The results could be superb, but only in the most favourable and expensive circumstances. The ordinary run of tapestries, which then as always were produced on a commercial basis, began to decline rapidly in quality; moreover, in the eighteenth century interior decoration became elaborate and minute in its contrivance, leaving no room for the broadly decorative use of tapestry, which now lost favour.

The modern revival, for which the artist Jean Lurçat (who works at Aubusson) is so greatly responsible, has set great store on a return to medieval methods and simplicity, which is indeed necessary in modern conditions and with the modern distribution of wealth.

ILLUSTRATION: Page 355.

Smoke signals to Morse code

The **TELEGRAPH** is a logical outcome of man's desire to be able to pass messages rapidly over a distance, particularly in emergency. A simple warning could be conveyed by beacon fires or smoke signals. Polybius, in the second century B.C., described a code for sending spelt-out messages by exhibiting combinations of torches at the sides of a screen. Audible telegraphs, such as African tom-toms, have a most indefinite history, but visual methods of telegraphy recurred again in the eleventh century when the Arabs developed the heliograph, and in 1792, when Claude Chappe installed a system of rotating arms at the tops of towers dotted over the landscape in France. The Chappe semaphore spread all over Europe in the next fifty years and has left its mark in many a place called 'telegraph hill'. It was claimed that a simple message, relayed from tower to tower, could be transmitted over the 160 miles between Paris and Lille in about twenty minutes if the weather was clear.

The electric telegraph, independent of the weather, of darkness and of watchmen to relay signals, began with a suggestion made nearly forty years before the Chappe semaphore was built. There had been intriguing experiments such as those of the Abbé Nollet about 1746: he formed a circle, 1,800 yards in length, composed of Carthusian monks joined together by iron wires. When he discharged a battery of Leyden jars into this circle the last monk jumped at the same instant as the first, thus demonstrating that the electric shock was practically simultaneous at each end. An anonymous Scotsman who signed himself 'C.M.' proposed in the *Scots Magazine* of 1753 that similar effects should be used for signalling. It was not, however, until 1838–1839 that the first practical electric telegraph was erected along the line of the Great Western Railway between Paddington, London, and Slough, a distance of $18\frac{1}{2}$ miles. The inventors were Sir Charles Wheatstone and Sir W. F. Cooke, and their apparatus caught the popular imagination in 1845, when the perpetrator of a brutal murder in London fled by train and was arrested at Slough as the result of a telegram. A like stimulus was given to wireless telegraphy some sixty-five years later by the arrest of the murderer Crippen, who had fled by sea.

Cooke and Wheatstone did much to simplify the instruments employed; but in this they were eclipsed by the American artist and inventor Samuel Morse (1791–1872), whose 'sounder' was developed from his embosser of 1853, spelling out the signals by audible dots and dashes in the Morse code. Morse and others were also early in the field of type-printing telegraphs, but here the major credit for early machines must go to the piano keyboard instrument invented in London in 1855 by D. E. Hughes. It was able to print messages on tape without code and was the simple forerunner of the modern teleprinter. In 1874 Thomas Alva Edison, in America, made a remarkable saving in the cost of telegraphic circuits by perfecting the duplex system, in which messages in each direction could be sent simultaneously over a single line. In the multiplex system a large number of messages can be transmitted simultaneously. Other important developments such as the five-unit code for perforating tape which then actuates automatic transmitting apparatus at high speed, are too technical for detailed description. It is worthy of mention that Sir Charles Wheatstone devised a perforated tape apparatus in 1858, and improved it in 1867.

Telegraphs in modern times have been made much more efficient by the provision of thermionic amplifiers or repeaters where necessary. For the first transatlantic cables there was no such refinement, and success depended largely on the extremely delicate 'syphon recorder' invented by Lord Kelvin in 1867. The first Atlantic cable was laid in 1858, but although signals were detected by galvanometer for a few weeks, the cable then broke down, and it was not until 1866 that, in a cable 1,852 nautical miles long, success could be claimed. Another cable had been laid unsuccessfully in 1865, but was later repaired and brought into use. In 1924 a cable, magnetically loaded continuously with a new nickel-iron alloy, provided what was almost the first technical advance other than in detail. Such cables, with modern amplifying devices, make telegraphy over the longest submarine cables both speedy and certain. The telegraph need not fear the rivalry of radio communication which depends on satisfactory atmospheric conditions. Telegraphy has gone from ingenuity to ingenuity, not only have devices been made that receive messages in printed form but the actual handwriting of the sender can be reproduced at the receiving end. (See also *Telephone, Radio, Television.*)

ILLUSTRATION: Page 274.

'Watson, come here. I want you'

The **TELEPHONE,** or the germ of the idea, goes back to the string telephone every child has played with, in which a tightly held string is stretched between two diaphragms. The scientist Robert Hooke in 1667 first demonstrated that the voice could be carried privily over considerable distances in this way.

However, it was Philip Reis of Friedrichsdorf who first showed that sounds could be transmitted and reproduced electrically. He was a musician, and his primitive apparatus of 1860 was thought of more as a means of transmitting violin music, though it seems clear from his notes that he realized it might apply equally to speech. Since his invention had no consequences in practice, there is nothing to detract from the primacy of the achievement of Alexander Graham Bell (1847–1922), who went to the New World as a young man and in 1876 demonstrated his telephonic instrument consisting of a diaphragm actuated by an electro-magnet. Bell spoke the first sentence to be clearly heard at the receiving end, 'Watson, come here. I want you,' to his assistant on March 10th of that year. By one of those curious coincidences which have marked other inventions (such as bakelite), Bell and another inventor, Elisha Gray, applied for telephone patents on the same day.

Bell's telephone used similar apparatus for transmission and reception, and it soon became evident that his transmitter was inefficient. In 1877 Edison patented a carbon transmitter with compressed lamp-black between small platinum discs. It was an improvement, but it was not nearly so effective as the carbon microphones developed by Professor Hughes of London in 1878. It was in January of 1878 that the world's first completely fitted public telephone exchange was opened at New Haven, Connecticut, U.S.A. The first switchboards contained only fifty circuits, operated even in those days by women.

The automatic telephone also originated in the U.S.A. The first automatic exchange opened at La Porte, Indiana, in 1892, three years after A. B. Strowger had taken out his first patent. The story was that Strowger, an undertaker (or mortician) was infuriated by the delays on the female-operated switchboards of the time. He set to work to devise a mechanical alternative and hit upon the idea of step-by-step switching. This was not a very difficult proposition, since at the most there were perhaps one hundred telephones connected to the system in the small town of La Porte. The subscriber's circuit could easily be found by jerking a switch upwards for tens and round for units to the necessary degree. It was when thousands, or even tens of thousands of subscribers were connected to a system that really complex problems were encountered. The answer has been found in a system, still recognizable as Strowger's basic idea, in which a switch first searches for free apparatus when the receiver is lifted. As dialling progresses a number of electric pulses are put into the system. The first two or three sets of pulses are fed into a master switch or 'Director' which translates them into a switching operation selecting the right exchange. At the required exchange the subsequent series of pulses actuate two further switches which go up for thousands and round for hundreds, and up for tens and round for units. If it is free, the one possible outlet after all this searching is the subscriber's number required, and the bell rings. Other switches record the numbers and value of completed calls.

One of the difficulties of telephoning over great distances in the early days was that of amplifying the speech currents when they became too feeble to actuate the receiver intelligibly. This was overcome with the development of the thermionic valve amplifier between 1913 and 1919. It is now not only possible to receive the most distant calls as clearly as local messages, but radio-telephony over the longest distances has made it possible to communicate economically with places that would have been far too expensive to reach if the cost of cable had to be reckoned. Radio links have the disadvantage of uncertainty and it is now considered that the heavy load between Britain and America is enough to justify a highly expensive transatlantic cable with long-life amplifiers sunk to the ocean bed at intervals along the route. The ownership of telephone services varies; in America private companies operate them, in Great Britain the Post Office with the exception of Hull, where telephones are municipally operated. (See also *Telegraph, Radio, Television.*)

Seeing into space

The **TELESCOPE** was discovered by a Dutchman, but which Dutchman and when he did it are not certain. Spectacles had been known since the thirteenth century, and there was in 1600 a flourishing spectacle-lens-making industry in the town of Middelburg in Holland. It seems probable that one of the spectacle-makers of this town, or perhaps even a child playing with the lenses, noticed by chance that if one lens was held a little distance in front of another the weathercock of a neighbouring church viewed through the lenses appeared larger and nearer. The two people with the strongest claims to the discovery are Jan Lippershey and Zacharias Janssen, but the evidence in favour of either is not conclusive and the date can only be given as being within ten years of 1600.

The military implications of the discovery were realized by Prince Maurice of Nassau, the commander of the Dutch forces, who expressed a vain hope that it could be kept from the enemy.

Galileo, in Venice in 1609, heard a vague account of the invention and, working out from first principles what would be the likely arrangement, made a telescope for himself. He kept improving on his first telescope, and during the first half of 1610 he made about a hundred, supplying them to those who were curious to see and use the new invention. Galileo very quickly turned a telescope towards the moon and other heavenly bodies, and he discovered four satellites or moons circulating round the planet Jupiter. He could see many more stars than with the naked eye; the seven stars of the Pleiades were seen to be forty, and he was able to resolve portions of the Milky Way into innumerable minute stars. He immediately published in *Siderius Nuncius*, an account of the new discoveries made with the telescope, including the fact that the sun had spots, which came as a great shock to many who had believed the sun to be perfect.

Another watcher of the skies, Johannes Hevelius of Danzig, learning from Galileo, used a telescope to make a very careful map of the moon, which he published in 1647 in his book entitled *Selenographia, sive lunae descriptio*. Trying to get better results, Hevelius and later Christiaan Huygens used what were called aerial telescopes. They were fantastically long, sometimes as much as two hundred feet, and as it was not practicable to have a telescope tube of this length the lens was supported aloft by a tower or pole.

The earliest telescopes suffered from the defect known as chromatic aberration; images had coloured borders. The celebrated Isaac Newton was aware that the colours were produced when white light was refracted, or bent in its path, at the lens surface, and he believed that no image could be produced by a lens without colour. So in 1668 he designed and made a reflecting telescope which used a concave mirror in place of a lens. Newton's telescope was highly successful, but his view that colour was inseparable from the use of a lens was proved wrong by John Dollond ninety years later, when by combining lenses of two different types of glass he was able to produce an achromatic lens which gave an uncoloured image.

The basic principle of the telescope is that an image is formed by a first lens, usually referred to as the object-glass, or, as in Newton's telescope, by a concave mirror, and this image is magnified by observing it through a relatively powerful second lens, called the eye-piece or eye-lens. A problem in design is to get as much light as possible into the telescope so that high magnification can be used without the complete disappearance of the picture. At the same time distortion of the picture must be reduced to a minimum. The larger the object glass or mirror used in the telescope, the more light it will collect and the greater will be its capacity for viewing faint or distant objects.

Two types of telescope, the terrestrial and the astronomical, each with its own special requirements, have to be considered. Terrestrial telescopes, used for observing objects on the earth's surface either by way of sport or nature-study or for more serious purposes in battle at sea or on the land, have to be light and handy and have to give an erect picture. Mirrors are unsuitable for these, nor can lenses of more than a few inches diameter be used if the telescope is not to become too heavy. Binocular field-glasses and opera-glasses are terrestrial telescopes fixed together in pairs so that both eyes can view at once. Field-glasses are telescopes made short by bending the light back and forth along its own path by means of reflecting prisms.

Astronomical telescopes should usually be fixed in position to keep them steady, and can therefore, in contrast with most terrestrial telescopes, be made heavy and large. Most of them give an inverted picture because it is immaterial which way up a heavenly body appears, and erecting the image causes loss of precious light. An improvement in the light-gathering power of lenses has been made owing to the surprising discovery, during the Second World War, that if a thin film of metal is deposited on the lens surface more light gets through. The process is known as 'blooming' the lens, because the metal film looks like the bloom on the surface of freshly gathered grapes or plums.

Progress in astronomical telescopes has been towards even bigger ones. The mirror in Newton's original reflecting telescope was two inches across. William Herschel (1738–1822), the discoverer of the planet Uranus, made one four feet across, which he used in a telescope forty feet long. In 1842 the Earl of Rosse at Birr Castle in Ireland made a six-foot mirror, which remained the largest in the world for the next seventy-five years, until it was ousted by the hundred-inch mirror at Mount Wilson Observatory in California.

The site for such a large telescope has to be carefully chosen, because all the advantage of the large size is lost if the atmospheric conditions are unsatisfactory. The telescope must not be near a town with its bright lights and smoky atmosphere. The best site is a mountain top, with its clear and rarefied air, in a district with a good climate free from clouds and mist. The British climate is not ideal, nevertheless a hundred-inch telescope is in course of construction for the Royal Observatory at Hurstmonceux in Sussex. The largest telescope so far constructed is the two-hundred-inch Hale telescope on Mount Palomar in California, with which it is possible to probe the outer confines of space and to solve many outstanding riddles of the universe. These huge telescopes are as dependent on engineering as optical techniques. Their problems may be partly by-passed with radio and electronic microscopes. (See also *Microscope*.)

ILLUSTRATION: Pages 130 and 165.

On the screen

TELEVISION is older in its idea than one may suspect. It depends on the sensitivity of selenium to light, from which it produces an electric current; this was discovered by May in 1873. Eight years later Shelford Bidwell had produced a crude but workable system of picture telegraphy. In those days there were no amplifiers and the transmission was necessarily over wires. This mechanical exploration of the picture was known as scanning. In 1926 the first demonstration of true television – by which is meant the transmission of live pictures and their reception without intervening wires – was made by John Logie Baird (1888–1946), using a scanning method devised by Nipkow in 1884. Baird's demonstration was possible only by reason of developments in thermionic amplifiers and light-sensitive photocells since Bidwell's wired attempts in 1881. It was true television, but in quality it left much to be desired. From 1929 to 1935 the British Broadcasting Corporation transmitted experimental programmes on this system, in which the picture was scanned in only thirty lines at the very low frame frequency of twelve-and-a-half pictures per second. This gave an unpleasant flicker.

As early as 1906 von Leiben suggested that the cathode-ray oscillograph, in which a beam of electrons can be controlled by electromagnetic fields in such a way that they leave a trace on a fluorescent screen, should be used for reproducing pictures; variations in picture brightness were to be the main controlling force. On 18 June 1908 *Nature* in London published a remarkable letter from A. A. Campbell-Swinton. He declared that scanning and reception by cathode-ray oscillograph held out the only hope of effective television owing to the complete absence of inertia with the cathode rays, which could thus sweep and be swept at speeds that would be unthinkable in any mechanical device. In the Baird mechanical system a picture three inches by two inches required, for resolution equivalent to that of a newspaper illustration, over a quarter of a million signals per second. In a cathode-ray system a rate many times this value presents no great difficulty.

By 1911 it was realized that the cathode ray

might be so controlled that it would go fast over the dark parts of the scene to be produced and slowly over the light parts, although at the time there was no means of exercising such control. The end of the cathode-ray tube is coated with a fluorescent material that glows for a short time with an intensity proportionate to the time it is under bombardment by the ray. If the ray sweeps over it very fast that part of the screen would therefore hardly glow at all and would look dark, whereas a slow-moving ray would make the screen look bright.

C.F.Jenkins in America and Baird in England made successful transmissions in 1925. The first regular commercial television by cathode-ray means was started in Great Britain in November 1936 although the first commercial exploitation was that of a Broadway act in 1926. The Marconi-E.M.I. system adopted by the B.B.C. in 1936 was based on scanning the picture in 405 lines. Compared with the original Baird system of thirty lines, the result was about sixty times as effective, but Great Britain's pioneering success was hardly an unmixed blessing, since the existence of many thousands of sets pegged the standard to the 405-line picture, which is less finely detailed than it need be. Practical 1000-line systems have been devised.

Baird's mechanical system had severe limitations, but he demonstrated a number of refinements which are just the same, in principle, as those possible to cathode-ray television. Thus, in 1927 he demonstrated 'noctovision' using invisible infra-red rays to activate the photocells. He also experimented with big-screen television, colour television (which is fairly simple in theory, but requires three times the number of signals and triple synchronization in practice) and projections.

Perhaps the most significant new development is the discovery made at the Bell Laboratories in the U.S.A. that light may be 'amplified' even as sound. The potentiality of this for wider screens needs no emphasis. Colour television set productions in the U.S.A. was well advanced by 1956 and European countries were not far behind. Closed-circuit television in colour – whether by wire or tube – is proving strikingly useful in industry and medicine, where students, hygienically out of the way, can watch operations. (See also *Radio*.)

ILLUSTRATION: Page 307.

Ninety-eight point four

THERMOMETERS, invented at the end of the sixteenth or beginning of the seventeenth century, were first of all air thermoscopes, *i.e.* the phenomena observed in them depended on the expansion or contraction of air by heating or cooling.

The principle goes back to Heron of Alexandria (between A.D. 62 and A.D. 150) and to the fountain he describes in his *Pneumatica*, which played when touched by the sun's rays. This toy was essentially a thermoscope or thermometer, though it was not used to measure degrees of heat. The invention of the thermometer has been ascribed to four different men – Galileo, Santorio Sanctorius (1561–1636), professor of medicine at Padua and founder of the instrumental approach to medicine, Robert Fludd (1574–1637), physician and rosicrucian, and the Dutchman, Cornelis Drebbel (1572–1634).

Galileo never claimed the invention, and indeed mentioned the thermoscope only once in his writings. The claim is made for him by several of his friends, especially Sagredo, who himself improved the instrument. Conflicting contemporary authorities give the date of the invention as either 1592 or 1603. Galileo's thermoscope consisted of a glass globe drawn out at one point into a long tube open at the end. The bulb, containing air, was heated by the hands, and the instrument then immersed in a vessel containing water. As the bulb cooled, water was drawn up into the tube. Subsequent heating or cooling produced an alteration in the water level which could be measured.

As for Robert Fludd's claim, in 1617 he described – in his *Utriusque Cosmi ... physica atque technica historia* – an apparatus he used to support his cosmic theory, and which he almost certainly copied from a Bodleian manuscript of the works of Philo of Byzantium. In 1626 Fludd reproduced his own figure, mentioned that the instrument was not easy to make, and described and illustrated another instrument which he said was a modification of the one he had previously described. The new instrument was, in fact, a thermoscope, and Fludd now laid claim to have been its inventor. The evidence either way is not conclusive.

The claims made for Drebbel relate to the 'Dutch thermometer', a U-tube with limbs of unequal length and a bulb at the end of each limb. These thermometers were common in Holland by 1624, and the evidence suggests that the first example may have been constructed by Drebbel at any time between 1598 and 1622. Drebbel was not a learned man, and whatever the date of his first instrument, it is fairly certain that he had not read accounts or seen illustrations of thermoscopes produced in other countries.

The fourth claimant, Sanctorius, was quite probably the original inventor of the thermometer, at some date before 1611; his commentary on Avicenna, published in 1612, contains what is certainly the first description and illustration of the thermometer, or thermoscope. His was also the first thermometer to be used clinically. It should be said that Sanctorius spent much of the latter part of his life in a chair suspended from a steelyard. In this chair he ate, worked and slept, and, using his innumerable observations of changes in weight, he wrote the treatise which established him as the founder of the scientific study of metabolism.

The thermoscope of Sanctorius was similar in design to the one attributed to Galileo. He used several types, some with straight tubes and another with several bends, with which he estimated the heat of the expired air. Sanctorius did not measure the actual temperature of the air, but the change in level it produced during a small, fixed interval of time. It may be mentioned that the word 'thermometer' (*thermomètre*) first occurred in a work by Leurechon published in 1624.

These thermoscopes or air-thermometers suffered from a serious disadvantage: they were markedly affected by the pressure as well as by the temperature of the atmosphere. Robert Boyle, the formulator of the law which states the relationship between the pressure and volume of a gas, made this point very clear. Liquids were not so affected, and the first liquid thermometer appears to have been made by the French physician and chemist Jean Rey, who filled the bulb and part of the stem with water. The end of the stem was not sealed, and evaporation must

have led to conflicting results. Rey also used his instrument for clinical purposes (1632). Further advances were made by members of the famous group of scientists who worked in Florence, the Accademia del Cimento. One of its founders, the Grand Duke Ferdinand II of Tuscany, is said to have substituted coloured alcohol for water, and he sealed the end of the tube. Later on, in the second half of the seventeenth century, the Florentines used mercury.

Several steps led to the fixed scale for thermometers. For example, Sir Isaac Newton used a linseed oil thermometer and constructed a scale

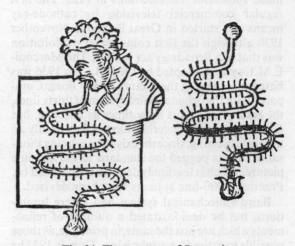

Fig. 34. Thermometer of Sanctorius.

of degrees based on certain temperatures which were apparently fixed. He employed this thermometer in the experiments which led to the formulation of his Law of Cooling. It was difficult at first to come to an agreement on the fixed points suitable for a scale. About 1714 G. D. Fahrenheit (1686–1736) devised his scale based on the three points, zero (what was then considered the lowest temperature attainable), thirty-two degrees (the freezing point of water) and ninety-six degrees (blood heat of the human body). Later he extended his scale to include the boiling point of water (212°). In France R. A. F. de Réaumur (1683–1757) introduced his scale in 1730, with eighty degrees separating the freezing and boiling points of water. What was virtually the centigrade scale reversed (*i.e.* 100 degrees between the freezing and boiling points of water) was introduced in 1742 by Anders Celsius (1701–1744) in Sweden.

Although Sanctorius and Rey had used their thermometers clinically, it was a hundred years before their example was followed and extended. Hippocrates had recommended the physician to use his hand to measure the temperature of the patient's body, and from early times it was appreciated that in a fever the body temperature is raised. But even after the thermometer had been invented it was not realized for a long while that the *degree* of temperature produced by a fever should be measured.

The first systematic clinical use of the thermometer was due to the English doctor George Martine (1702–1741), who considered that most of the temperature observations which had been made were valueless. He found that the figure which had been accepted for the normal temperature of the human body was too low, and he raised it to ninety-seven or ninety-eight degrees.

The nature of animal heat was not understood at this time, Martine, for example, thinking it was caused by the friction of the blood against the walls of the vessels. A step towards understanding was made when George Fordyce, Joseph Banks, Daniel Solander and Charles Blagden subjected themselves to excessive heat in a room heated to a very high temperature, and showed that there was no change in the temperature of the body during this experience. The great scientist and surgeon, John Hunter (1728–1793), had meanwhile been carrying out experiments on animals; these showed that the production of animal heat is a vital process, 'that power which preserves and regulates the internal machine'. Hunter used thermometers of a simple type, but only in observations on the animals. James Currie (1756–1805) – the biographer of the poet Robert Burns – published a work in 1798 in which he advocated the use of cold or hot water for the treatment of fevers and certain other diseases. He used the thermometer as a routine measure – an instrument like John Hunter's, with an adjustable ivory scale attached to the stem. As he was dealing with infectious diseases, though, he had his thermometers made with an angle between the bulb and the main part of the

stem, so that he could stand behind the patient while he made a reading. Currie's thermometer was seven inches long.

In England also John Davy made extensive investigations (1839) on the temperature of different parts of the body, on the temperature of the body under different conditions, and on the temperature in various races.

A thermometer to register the maximum temperature reached in a period of exposure was obviously required. In 1742 James Six had devised the first practical maximum and minimum thermometer, in which the indices were set by a magnet; but this was a method which could not be applied to the clinical thermometer. Professor T. Phillips of Oxford showed an experimental thermometer at the Great Exhibition in 1851 in which the maximum temperature reached was recorded by having a small air bubble in the column of mercury. When the temperature fell, the air bubble retained the short column of mercury above it as an index. The straight, self-registering thermometer, in the pairs sold together as Aitken's thermometers (after the pathologist Sir William Aitken), was of this kind. The other thermometer in each pair was curved, registered no maximum and was read in position, usually in the armpit.

All the men who have been mentioned so far were ploughing lone furrows. The thermometer was not generally used by doctors; 'taking the temperature' was not the routine of nurses, doctors and mothers, and the thermometer was not found in London hospitals, for example, until about 1867. A year later, in 1868, C. R. A. Wunderlich, professor of medicine at Leipzig, published a treatise on medical thermometry which turned the scale. He had used the thermometer for fifteen years, made readings in 25,000 patients, and made several million individual observations, and in his treatise he dealt exhaustively with the variations of temperature in health and in all the common diseases.

Aitken's thermometers were much favoured now, but doctors found them too large. His straight thermometer was nearly a foot long. When the air bubble in this self-registering instrument was shaken down, the bubble sometimes disappeared into the bulb. At last in the eighteen-sixties Sir Thomas Clifford Allbutt

(1836–1925) devised the short clinical thermometer we all know, a little longer and a little stouter. Instead of using an air bubble in the mercury, Allbutt's thermometer has a constriction in the capillary tube just above the bulb by means of which the thread of mercury is broken to register the maximum temperature.

Keeping the coffee warm – or cold

The **THERMOS FLASK**, now familiar in every house, can be traced back to suggestions made in 1850 by the English inventor Lewis Gompertz.

The outer protective casing houses the actual flask, which is double-walled, with a near-vacuum in the annular space between the walls. The design reduces to a minimum the rate at which heat is transferred through the walls by conduction, radiation and convection. The insulating properties of the vacuum, which prevents heat flow by the elimination of convection currents, had been known since the early part of the nineteenth century, but the application of the principle was delayed by the difficulty of making such vessels out of glass.

Gompertz in his *Mechanical Inventions and Suggestions* (1850) included the following 'Suggestions to Produce a Fire-proof Box': 'The box is made of steel, etc., highly polished, as polished metals reflect back the heat as well as the light that are cast upon them, this box is then put into a much larger air-tight case of iron, and has legs of thin wire to prevent its touching the outside case, and all the air is pumped out so as to leave a vacuum between the two boxes, and so that no heat can be conveyed to it by the contact of air, and as the radiant heat is rendered harmless by the polish and the heat of contact is prevented by the vacuum, it seems that the heat is kept out entirely, excepting through the small wire legs.'

Here were the fundamentals of a vacuum ves-

sel, though there is no evidence that Gompertz tried to make his box. Indeed, he was doubtful if it could be made. Forty-two years later, in 1892, Professor (later Sir) James Dewar was carrying out low-temperature research at the Royal Institution in London. His work involved liquefied air, oxygen and other gases, but when he attempted to make optical measurements on these liquefied gases, a rapid ebullition interfered, even when the liquids were stored in simple double-walled containers of glass.

Dewar had to devise a way of isolating the liquefied gases from their warmer surroundings. He found that he could reduce the convective transfer of heat by surrounding the container with a high vacuum. His next step was to reduce the transfer still more by silvering the inner walls of the vessel where they came in contact with the near-vacuum.

Dewar improved his flask still more in 1906, when he made use of charcoal to produce an even greater vacuum. Charcoal absorbs gases; a small quantity was put into the annular space separating the walls of the flask, and while the flask was being evacuated the charcoal was heated to drive off any absorbed gases it might already contain. The flask was now sealed, liquefied gas was poured in, and the charcoal cooled by conduction through the inner walls and then absorbed any traces of air still left in the vacuous space. By this means it was possible to make efficient metal vacuum flasks for the storage of liquefied gas.

The *Collected Papers of Sir James Dewar* (1927) give the story of the development of the vacuum flask, and many of the original Dewar vessels are still to be seen at the Royal Institution. But Dewar had no share in marketing his flasks. The domestic vacuum flask based on Dewar's principles was introduced in Germany about 1904 by Reinhold Bürger, and the prize in a competition for a suitable name for the flask was awarded to the man who submitted 'Thermos' (Greek for 'hot').

In 1907 the patent rights for the British Empire, South America and many other countries were secured by English business men who formed a company to manufacture the flasks; 'Thermos' was registered as a trade name; but has now found its way into the language and the dictionaries. (See also *Refrigerator*.)

The threshing machine

The **THRESHING MACHINE** has to separate the ears of corn from the straw, and the grains from the chaff, or the light husks by which they are covered, as well as from the weed seeds which are inevitable in any field crop. Only the grain, stripped of the husks, is wanted by the miller to make flour.

The manual processes of separation have been worked out over a period of thousands of years. Firstly the crop must be ripe and reasonably dry for fair success. Secondly the ears must be torn from the straw without excessive breaking or bruising of the grain. This has long been done by beating the sheaves of corn with flails; also by treading them with cattle; or by dragging over them a wooden board set with flints, or by beating them over a barrel. Each method is laborious, but if the straw is required undamaged for thatching, it is even more so, the labourer taking a double handful of corn by the butts and beating off the ears on a stone, or an iron-shod board. When one or other of these laborious processes is completed, there remain, after sweeping, a pile of grain and a pile of straw. The grain is still mixed with husks and short, broken straws and weed seeds, so the pile has to be thrown, shovelful by shovelful, into a strong breeze, induced naturally by opening doors opposite each other in a barn, or created by the additional hard labour of turning a four-armed framework hung with sackcloth. The breeze then blows the husks, straw and light weed seeds farther than it can blow the heavy ears. This is the process of winnowing, the piles of fairly clean grain rising close to the shoveller.

The labour and drudgery involved from start to finish in this basic process of food supply were tiresome enough to encourage inventive minds from the seventeenth century onwards. In 1743 there came the nearest approach to a partial solution by the Scotsman, Michael Menzies, who devised an arrangement of flails worked by a water-wheel. The flails wore out too quickly for the machine to be a success. Revolving drums with beater bars to thresh the ears from the straw seemed possible alternatives to flails, but they all bruised the grain too much. In 1786 another Scotsman, Andrew Meikle, eliminated this defect to a large extent by building a machine in which two revolving rollers fed the grain evenly into the drum. Two years later he combined a winnowing fan in a machine that also had oscillating sieves to grade the corn. His patent of 1788 thus anticipated, in primitive form, the machines that became so well known in mid-nineteenth century.

Horses at first supplied the power, followed by steam and the long-funnelled traction engines, and then by the tractor. In 1872 a Cornish farmer who had been settled for forty years in Ontario wrote in a letter home as follows:

… as for threshing we never hear the old English farmer's music of two flails and a cuckoo, as we have no cuckoos in this country, and flails are only used by new settlers in the bush, who have not sufficient crop to make it worth while to hire a threshing machine. These useful machines are now kept by men who travel round the country threshing for the farmers.

The 'old English farmer's music of two flails' changed into the quiet hum of traction engine and threshing machine, celebrated in a sonnet by Tennyson's elder brother, Charles Tennyson Turner (1808–1879), who imagined Virgil enjoying the new farmyard scene –

Flush with the pond the lurid furnace burn'd
At Eve, while smoke and vapour fill'd the yard;
The gloomy winter sky was dimly starr'd,
The fly-wheel with a mellow murmur turn'd;
While, ever rising on its mystic stair
In the dim light, from secret chambers borne,
The straw of harvest, sever'd from the corn,
Climb'd, and fell over in the murky air.
I thought of mind and matter, will and law,
And then of him, who set his stately seal
Of Roman words on all the forms he saw
Of old-world husbandry: *I* could but feel
With what a rich precision *he* would draw
The endless ladder, and the booming wheel!

The threshing machine much reduces the old back-breaking and arm-aching drudgery of the flail, though threshing days remain days of hard, dry and troublesome work, the chaff finding its way through one's clothing. It is giving way to the combine harvester, which is reaper and threshing machine combined in a self-propelled unit, but it still retains an important place in the agricultural economy. The thresher may now have a machine attached to bale the straw, and various other refinements; but in essence it remains unmistakably the descendant of the machine Meikle patented in 1788. (See also *Flail, Reaping Machines.*)

In the can

TINNED FOOD or canned food on the larder shelf we owe to two persons in chief, the Frenchman Nicolas-François Appert (1750–1841), and the ingenious Englishman Bryan Donkin (1768–1855), engineer, manufacturer, and Fellow of the Royal Society, who adopted and improved upon Appert's methods.

Fresh food was particularly required on board ship and by naval authorities; Appert, who had been a distiller and a confectioner, had his own theories of fermentation and decay, and he systematized a method of bottling in the small factory he set up in 1806 at Massy, on the southern outskirts of Paris. There his foods were packed in special wide-mouthed bottles, which were closely corked and sealed, and then sterilized by placing them in a bath of water which was brought up to the boil. He experimented with meat, vegetables, eggs, milk, fruit (including tomatoes), fruit juices and even truffles and mushrooms.

On 2 December 1806 no less than eighteen different foods preserved by Appert were placed in a chest and taken aboard the *Stationnaire* in the roads at Brest, and kept at sea till 13 April 1807. The containers were then opened, and the beef, the fillet of mutton, the fowls, the young partridges, the beans and peas, etc., were all of them good after four months and ten days. The French naval authorities were impressed. Appert was awarded twelve thousand francs (£500) by the Minister of the Interior on condition that he explained his methods in print. So in 1810 his book *L'Art de conserver pendant plusieurs années toutes les substances animales et végétales* was published; in

1811 it was translated and published again in London, with a second edition in 1812.

Appert was aware that his process opened a long prospect: 'he purposes to multiply', it was said in the commendations printed in his book, 'the enjoyments of the Indian, the Mexican and the African, as well as of the Laplander, and to transport into France from remote regions, an infinity of substances which we should desire to receive in their natural state'.

In 1811 he was approached by Bryan Donkin, with two partners, who paid him £1,000, presumably for detailed instruction in his methods. Donkin, however, who had one of the nimblest minds of the age, quickly found that simple boiling in a water-bath was not reliable. The approach of both men was empirical, food preservation having no scientific basis until after Pasteur's studies into bacteriology. Nevertheless, Donkin's experiments in his engineering factory on the Bermondsey marshes led him to raise the temperature of the bath by adding chloride of lime. Sterilization was made more complete.

Donkin realized also that the containers must be changed; glass was too fragile, and was bound to limit the sales of preserved food. For a while he tried 'white jars', as he calls them in his diary in 1812; then he changed to cans of tinned iron. Whether Appert had ever used cans is uncertain; but it seems not, since he expressly wrote in *L'Art de conserver* that he had not ventured 'to make any experiment with a vessel made of any other substance'.

Two British patents are sometimes mentioned to prove that iron cans were devised in 1810. One of them vaguely suggests 'preserving vessels' of 'iron, glass or any other metal', the other does no more than mention 'vessels of glass, pottery, tin or other metals'. The tinplated cans used by Donkin and his partners were heavy and made by hand, filled through a hole in one end, over which a tinned iron disc was soldered. The recommended means of opening them was by hammer and cold chisel. 'Tinned can' or 'tinplate can' was too cumbersome a term, shortened eventually to 'tin can', then by the English to 'tin' and by the Americans to 'can', a word they were already using in the eighteen-sixties.

In 1813 Donkin contrived that samples of his preserved food should be tasted by the British commander-in-chief, then the Duke of York. In June 1813 the three partners received a letter from Kensington Palace:

Gentlemen,

I am commanded by the Duke of Kent to acquaint you that His R.H. having procured introduction of some of your patent beef on the Duke of York's table, where it was tasted by the Queen, the Prince Regent, and several distinguished personages and highly approved. He wishes you to furnish him with some of your printed papers in order that His Majesty and many other individuals may according to their wish expressed have an opportunity of further proving the merits of the things for general adoption.

I am, Gentlemen,
You most obedient servant,
Jon. Parker

Messrs Donkin, Hall and Gamble.

The Navy made purchases. Donkin, Hall and Gamble's tinned foods were quickly on sale in the ports; and on sea voyages their meat was found to be admirable by passengers who could afford it. In the first six months of 1817 they sold nearly £3,000 worth of tinned meat. Very soon their foods began to aid arctic exploration; supplies accompanied Parry, Franklin and Ross, Parry in 1824 taking roast and boiled beef, roast veal, pea soup, carrots in gravy, etc., on his fourth expedition to discover the North-West Passage. In 1937 some of these containers were found, and the food inside was still edible.

Appert's methods were fundamentally those of modern canning. What he called his 'discovery' would be, he wrote, 'of the greatest use in sea voyages, in hospitals and in the home'. Yet 'discovery' was too large a word. A writer in the *Edinburgh Review* in 1814, noticing the translation of *L'Art de conserver*, maintained that home bottling by heat had been practised for years, pointing also to a Thomas Saddington, who had bottled fruit in London in 1807, and incidentally to an advocate named Forsyth who had prepared what we should call 'dehydrated' potatoes. But it was Appert who gave the stimulus to Bryan Donkin, and to the foundation of a world industry. As a Frenchman he might have preferred the delicate flavour of his bottled wares to the curiously altered taste of food from the can.

Canned food was not a gastronomic advance, exactly.

Yet the writer in the *Edinburgh Review* had the wit to recognize that a step had been taken toward the emancipation of women: 'We do not desire to see the time and faculties of our modern fair devoted exclusively to household arts, and the various modes of domestic industry, in which many of their venerable predecessors wore away the greater part of their lives. We rejoice rather in that progress of the arts which has removed even the pretext for such unprofitable drudgery.' Sewing-machines, vacuum-cleaners and refrigerators also combine to alleviate household drudgery.

By 1870 canned food – from the United States especially – was a part of common life. Ruskin as the Galahad of Lady Nature against the machine was writing in his autobiography in the eighteen-eighties of happy countrymen in France who lived off the meat of their own herds 'untainted by American tin' – a misfire, since the tin had been English first of all.

Toothpick, tooth-brush, tooth-paste

TOOTHPICKS long preceded the tooth-brush (which was probably invented by the Chinese) as an essential personal implement. Sir Leonard Woolley discovered at Ur a toilet-set consisting of a pair of tweezers, an ear-scoop and a toothpick which were attached by their ends to a ring. The instruments were of gold, and they were kept in a conical gold case. The approximate date of this toilet-set was 3500 B.C. Later in time, but used by races which were still without written records, are toilet-sets of bronze or silver found at various sites in Italy, France, Germany and Switzerland, in which the individual articles are similarly attached to a ring, or sometimes to a stout fibula (a large safety pin) which was fixed to the outer garment. From the Crimea comes a gold combination instrument; one end, shaped like a tiny dagger, forms the toothpick; the flattened ear-scoop at the other end is separated from the toothpick by a 'handle' in the form of a female figure. The ancient Chinese also had toothpicks; these were in the form of bronze pendants, running to a hook at the lower end. The ancient Hebrews did not use specially manufactured articles for this purpose, but in the Talmud we find references to the *qésem*, which was a simple splinter of wood.

Frequent references to the use of toothpicks occur in the classical Greek and Roman authors. It is probable that the Greeks did not use specially designed toothpicks, but they habitually employed splinters of wood or quills. When possible the wood was from the mastix tree (*Pistacia lentiscus*), which was a native of the island of Chios and gave also a resin used as chewing-gum. From Greece the use of this wood for toothpicks spread to Rome, and from there throughout the classical world. The poet Martial refers several times to toothpicks under the name *dentiscalpia*, and those which were made of mastix wood were called *lentisci*. So great was the demand for the wood that the tree had to be imported to Italy, and large mastix groves were planted on the coast north of Naples. The mastix tree is peculiarly associated with the teeth, and its wood is still used for toothpicks. In Imperial Rome other substances were also used for this purpose. Quills of various kinds were employed. For example, in his famous *Natural History* Pliny says that picking the teeth with the quill of a vulture makes the breath sour, while the use of a porcupine quill makes the teeth firm. In the Roman world toothpicks were also made of metal, and there are references to individual instruments made of silver. During the Later Empire toilet-sets of bronze were frequently used, and included toothpicks. As elsewhere, the set of instruments was suspended from the dress by means of a fibula.

Not much is known about the toothpick in the Middle Ages. The celebrated physician Johannes Arculanus, writing in the second half of the fifteenth century, emphasized the use of a toothpick after every meal to clear particles from between the teeth, but he saw no need to recommend any appliance other than a splinter of wood. But already at that time custom decreed that every well-dressed individual should carry a toilet-set, or at least a toothpick, attached to his person. Some portraits show the toothpick suspended round the neck by a fine chain. A celebrated sixteenth-century necklace of precious stones shows an ornamental toothpick attached to it by a chain. These toothpicks were sometimes straight, but were not infrequently curved. They were sometimes combined with an ear-scoop, but often formed part of a toilet-set, which in the sixteenth and seventeenth centuries were made of gold or silver, and incorporated not only an ear-scoop, but also a knife, fork, spoon and a hunting whistle. Individual toothpicks often took the form of grotesque human figures, or represented various animals. For example, in the figure of a lizard the tail might form the toothpick, while the head, set on an elongated neck, formed the ear-scoop.

In the seventeenth century the individual items of a toilet-set were often hinged together at one end, much as a knife with several blades is today. They included not only a toothpick and ear-scoop, but also tweezers, and sometimes manicure instruments. From this period the toothpick became less and less a decorative object, and the emphasis came to be placed on the case in which the toothpick was carried, either as an individual object or as part of a toilet-set. In the eighteenth and nineteenth centuries these cases were made of gold, silver, ivory or less precious materials, and they were often heavily decorated. The introduction of the steel pen (see *Pen*) made it necessary to find an alternative market for the goose quill, and hence the increasing use to which sharpened quills were put as toothpicks. Both quills and mastix wood toothpicks were cheap, and a number of them could therefore be placed on the table, used and then discarded. Hence, from the artistic angle, emphasis now fell on the container which was placed on the table. The nineteenth century shows numerous examples of figures of men, beasts and birds wrought in silver, into which a supply of toothpicks could be stuck to combine artistically with the whole. But with the increasing use of the tooth-brush in the nineteenth century the toothpick suffered an inevitable decline.

Tooth-brushes may be regarded as of two kinds: the ancient type – the fibre-pencil – in which the fibres were a continuation of the handle, and were indeed formed from it; and the modern type in which the bristles are inserted into the handle at right angles to it. A fairly early example of the fibre-pencil is the *miswâk* of the

Mohammedan world. This was frequently made of roots or twigs of the *arâk*, a wood which is rich in sodium bicarbonate. A portion of the root or branch is stripped of some of its bark at one end, the whole is soaked in water, and the stripped end is beaten until the fibres separate to form a fine brush. The used portion can thus be renewed daily, and the wood contains an aromatic juice which has an astringent effect on the gums. The *miswâk* was used by Mohammed himself as a religious ritual, which is enjoined on all his followers. A similar form of cleansing stick is found throughout Africa and in many other parts of the world. Suśruta, the great Indian physician of the sixth century B.C., gave detailed instructions for preparing fibre-pencils and for cleaning the teeth. 'A man', he wrote, 'should leave his bed early in the morning and brush his teeth. The tooth-brush should be made of a fresh twig of a tree or a plant ... twelve fingers long and like the small finger in girth ... The twig of a plant possessed of any of the four tastes as sweet, bitter, astringent and pungent should alone be collected and used.' The brush was smeared with a tooth-paste compounded with honey and oil and other ingredients. Suśruta explained that cleaning the teeth removed bad smells from the mouth, gave men relish for their food and cheerfulness of mind and inclined them to religion.

Cleansing of the teeth was recommended by the Greek and Roman medical writers, but the means employed consisted of the finger, a piece of cloth or a small sponge, with which various substances were applied to the teeth. The fibre-pencil again reappeared in Europe in the post-Renaissance period. For example, Fauchard, the French writer whose great work on dentistry (1746) is regarded as the foundation of the subject, advised a fibre-pencil made of a portion of the root of marshmallow for cleaning the teeth. The preparation of his fibre-pencil was a very complicated process which involved the use of many substances, including wine or brandy, and took ten days.

The modern tooth-brush is regarded as having been invented by the Chinese, and a seventeenth-century Chinese encyclopaedia gives the date as 1498. The bristles were inserted at right angles to the handle. Since then there has been little change in this important article. This brush was introduced to Europe about the second half of the eighteenth century, and was followed by the decline not only of the fibre-pencil, but also of the toothpick.

From the earliest times mouth-washes, tooth powders and pastes have been used to clean the teeth. The substances employed are too numerous to mention. Honey has always been important. Even as late as 1746 Fauchard gave instructions for making pastes and powders which contained many substances, such as pumice, coral, mother-of-pearl, crab's eyes, dragon's blood, calcined alum and various essential oils. In recent times tooth powders have consisted mainly of precipitated chalk and powdered orris-root, with in some cases charcoal or pumice, and flavouring agents. The paste is made from the powder by the addition of honey or glucose syrup. (See also *Dental Drill*.)

Torch and lantern

The **TORCH** as the small electric illuminator we all carry on dark nights, had its origin both in the lighted sticks carried in many parts of the world and in the directional lantern.

The torch on the whole was a means of travelling illumination out of doors: the chief requirement was that it should burn fiercely and so resist wind and rain. Homer mentions the pine torch which has been used down to modern times (and is still used in the East and in the Pacific), though it drops unwelcome globules of molten resin and exudes sticky carbon specks.

In the South Sea Islands and areas of similar climate elsewhere in the world, torches have been made of resinous material bound up in leaves. The medieval flambeau of the thirteenth and fourteenth centuries was contrived of four tow wicks impregnated with resin, the whole bunch coated with wax. Grooves were scraped out between each pair of wicks to provide channels down which excess wax and resin might flow, instead of becoming wind-borne. In the eighteenth century cotton wicks were usually employed. The links or torches used by link-boys hired to light the way in London till little more than a century ago were twists of rags or strands of rope dipped in pitch, resin or melted candle ends. Wrought-iron link extinguishers survive alongside the doorways of many Regency and Early Victorian houses in London. Before the thirteenth century any readily burning matter was carried outdoors in cressets, small iron baskets flaring at the top of poles; the poles, later known as torch staves, were retained for carrying flambeaux aloft. When stone or earth floors were the rule in the Middle Ages, the torch was even brought indoors. It might drop red hot cinders to the ground, but there was nothing to catch fire. The sticky carbon specks might settle on hangings and clothing, but those who had hangings were usually rich enough to be indifferent, and the care of clothing among people who bathed little and were used to the ragged state of their servitors was not regarded as important. At banquets there would be candles on the table, but torchbearers would stand to illuminate the otherwise gloomy scene outside the limited range of the candle flame. Light in darkness so impressed the human mind before the days of modern illumination that 'torchbearer' is still used metaphorically, though it is now a fossilized image.

The alternative to the torch was the hand lamp or lantern in which the flame, oil or candle, was protected from the elements. The horn lantern, in which the translucent panes are made from thin layers of ox-horn treated by heat, scraping and pressing, is mentioned by Plautus, the Roman dramatist, in the third century B.C. They were essential for the farmer, who needed in his journeys to the byre to keep the naked flame from hay or straw. But, like the more dangerous torch, the horn lantern and its later versions dissipated light in all directions equally. A directional light was required. In the thirteenth century luxurious lanterns were made inset with small ovals of crystals, intended solely as decorations, though the directional rays so caused can hardly have been overlooked. Early in the eighteenth century – which was a long time later – glass bull's-eyes were made to do what the oval crystals had done accidentally. The bull's-eye lantern not only lit the way ahead, but by keeping the light off the lantern-holder it gave him the advantage over anyone he might encounter – with the disadvan-

tage that anything outside its restricted range of illumination might pass unnoticed. The beam also was not very strong; so the primitive torch or link, which would reveal the footpad by its spread of light, did not become obsolete until the spread of efficient street lighting and efficient policing.

The electric dry battery torch, which is so brilliant and so handy, was produced in modest quantities in New York in the closing years of the nineteenth century; in London in 1913–1914 it supplanted altogether the oil lanterns used by policemen. Light by acetylene was to some extent a rival in the early years of the present century. The electric torch could pry into any remote corner so easily that its limited directional beam was much less of a drawback.

ILLUSTRATION: Page 115.

Totem and totem pole

TOTEM POLE is the popular name of the carved wooden house-posts and mortuary columns peculiar to the Haida, Tlingit, Kwakiutl and allied tribes of the coasts of British Columbia and Alaska, and of the islands offshore. The poles are generally carved from a single tree. They usually stand in front of the house, as symbols of the occupant; sometimes, however, they take the form of commemorative columns, set up by the heir after the funeral feast. These commemorative columns are doubtless a survival of the carved mortuary posts. Before the missionaries introduced the custom of burial, they were built to support a box containing the body.

The very tall poles are comparatively modern, and have only been made since traders introduced iron tools. The older poles were shaped with adzes of stone, and rarely consisted of more than two superimposed figures. Captain Cook thus describes the posts which he saw in Nootka Sound in 1778: 'But, amidst all the filth and confusion that are found in the houses, many of them are decorated with images. These are nothing more than the trunks of very large trees, four or five feet high, set up singly, or by pairs, at the upper end of the apartment, with the front carved into a human face; the arms and hands cut out upon the sides, and variously painted; so that the whole is a truly monstrous figure. The general name of these images is *Klumma*.'

The name *totem* was applied to these poles by Europeans: it is originally an Ojibway word (*ot-ote-m*, meaning a man's *ote*, clan-name or clan-animal), and seems to have been introduced into the English language by J. Long, who in 1791 wrote *Voyages and Travels of an Indian Interpreter and Trader*. Under 'totemism' is now included a wide range of beliefs about a mystical affinity or sympathy between humans and some objects or creatures in the world of nature. Among some peoples a man may have an individual totem, but more usually the totem belongs to the clan, the group linked by ties of kinship, within which marriage is not permitted. The relation between the clan and its totem creature is often considered one of common ancestry, and if it is an animal, various prohibitions on killing and eating it normally follow from this belief. (See also *Pictures and Statues*.)

Among the Indians of the north-west coast of America there is no taboo on killing the totem species, although it is not eaten. A man must marry outside his clan, and as descent follows the female line, the wife and children have the same totem, which is different from that of the head of the family. It is not considered that the totem species and the clan share a common descent; the clan, rather, is alleged to have acquired its totem by reason of an adventure of one of its ancestors with some mythic animal. Many of the devices on the totem poles record such traditional episodes.

A normal pattern for a totem pole is to portray the owner's totem crest at the top and that of his wife and children at the bottom, and to fill the intermediate space with figures which recall historical or mythical events connected with these totems.

Thus in Fig. *a*, a Haida column, the surmounting image represents *Hoots*, the brown bear, which is the totem of the head of the household who erected the column. At the bottom is *Tsing*, the beaver, the totem of the wife and children. Above this is the group of the bear and hunter, a common device, which is found on many of these house-posts. The story is that the

hunter *Toivats* on one occasion visited the house of the King of the Bears, who was absent. His wife being at home, he made love to her. When the bear returned, he found his wife in confusion, and accused her of infidelity; which she denied. The bear was still suspicious. One day he fastened a magic thread to his wife's dress; when she went out, he followed it and found her in the arms of the hunter, whom he immediately killed.

Above the effigies of the bear and hunter is *Tetl*, the great raven, having in his beak the new

Fig. 35. Haida house-post and totem pole, Prince of Wales Island.

moon and in his claws the dish containing fresh water, illustrating the common legend of the creation. According to this, Tetl, the benefactor of man, stole from his uncle *Kaunk*, the enemy of man, the new moon, *Kung*, which he had imprisoned in a box. He also got fresh water by a stratagem from the daughter of Kaunk, for he stole from her, unawares, a dish of fresh water, and flew with it out of the smoke-hole of Kaunk's house. Above the raven are four discs, called *skil*, of a kind which often appear on the high ceremonial hats of figures on the totem poles. They indicate achievements which redound to the credit of the owner, such as a victory in war, or the giving of a great ceremonial feast.

The emblems on totem poles do not necessarily follow the traditional pattern; they may be designed to represent some special exploits or intentions of the owner. For example, the column erected in front of the feast house of the famous Kaigani chief Skowl at Kasa-an (Fig. *b*) carries on the top Skowl's totemic crest, the eagle, while below this is a series of three figures, one pointing up to the Europeans' heaven, the next representing an angel, and the third a Russian missionary. Skowl's object here was to commemorate the failure of the missionaries to convert his people, and to ridicule their efforts. The figure at the bottom of the pole, below the spread eagle, is one of the early traders on the coast.

The art of these totem poles is very stylized, and the various creatures can be identified by characteristic symbols. Thus the three birds most commonly shown are distinguished by the shape of the beak; the raven's beak is straight, the eagle's is curved, and the hawk's beak is bent at the tip so as to rest on the mouth or chin. The shark's special feature is his vaulted forehead marked with three crescents, while the beaver is known by his large incisor teeth, and the killer whale by his dorsal fin. Occasionally natural objects are personified, such as the moon, which is shown with a circular face similar to the hawk's.

The Indians of the north-west coast, before their sophistication, were conscious of class distinction and they were addicted to social rivalry to a degree unknown elsewhere in aboriginal America. Except for the slaves, every man was able to improve his position by marriage or by the accumulation and exhibition of wealth. Prestige could be enhanced by giving extravagant feasts, or by openly destroying valuables, such as copper plates, canoes, and even slaves. In this context the significance of the totem pole is clear; it was a convenient and ostentatious way of displaying the owner's pride in his family's history and achievements. In Europe, crest and coat of arms are not dissimilar means of ostentation and distinction.

Although totem poles are only found on the north-west coast of America, very similar wooden posts have been recorded in the Hawaiian and Marquesas Islands, and in Tahiti. In New Zea-

land, too, the carved posts of the Maori, known as *Tikis,* resemble the American totem poles not only in design, but also in purpose and in mode of erection; but they served both as house-posts and as mortuary columns; and like the American totem poles, they were set up by digging a trench under the lower end and hauling up the top with a rope, which passed over a branch or support acting as a pulley. These resemblances are among many pointing to a close ethnic connection between the Indians of north-western America and the present inhabitants of Polynesia.

ILLUSTRATION: Page 77.

The motor horse

The **TRACTOR,** as the machine ox or machine horse of the farm, or rather as many oxen or horses in one, was the inevitable outcome of nineteenth-century mechanization and of the drift of labour from country to town.

The first farm substitute for a mixture of horse power and man power was the fixed steam engine, on large farms which drove machines in the barn or dairy. Steam ploughing was hardly practicable until, in 1858, John Fowler, in England, dragged a multi-furrow plough across the field by means of a steel wire running from an anchor on one side of the field to a drum on a traction engine at the other. The plough, with opposite-facing blades on a counterbalance arm, was then tipped the other way. The traction engine and the anchor were moved forward, and the next set of furrows was cut. Later this process was simplified by using two traction engines, and steam ploughing was commonly done by contractors with heavy machines that might cut up to sixteen furrows at once. The apparatus was too unwieldy, too limited in what it could do and above all too expensive for all but the very largest farms.

The internal-combustion engine gave promise of better things, but generating power enough to keep going was as much as the motor-car could manage in its early days. Nevertheless in 1902, after five years of experiment, Dan Albone built a serviceable motor tractor at Biggleswade, in England, with a two-cylinder internal combustion engine, two speeds, forward and reverse, and a drawbar from which it was claimed that a double furrow plough could be drawn through the earth. The two horizontally opposed cylinders were said to be capable of developing as much as twenty-four horse-power. The machine also had the power take-off which is to be found in all modern tractors – a pulley wheel, that is to say, from which power can be obtained for driving stationary machines such as threshers, wood saws, balers, churns, etc., by means of a belt. With various improvements which left the basic design practically unchanged, hundreds of these tractors were made for home use and for export to many parts of the world. The company which built them continued in existence to 1921, when it succumbed, like so many others, in a period of economic depression.

In later years there were many other rival tractors, some of them machines of almost unbelievable clumsiness; and the next most important step was undoubtedly the entry of Henry Ford into the tractor market. He laid out a huge plant for mass production and before he had started production he received, in 1917, an English order for 5,000 tractors at 700 dollars each. Great Britain was desperate for home-grown food and impossibly short of male labour, with so many taken for the forces and factories. Delivery had to begin in six weeks and be complete three months later. Ford delivered the whole quantity on time.

Since then tractors have improved greatly in design, flexibility and performance. The giant pneumatic tyre or the caterpillar track has replaced the spade-edged wheel for gripping the ground. The hydraulic lift mechanism, of which Harry Ferguson, a Northern Irishman with American associations, has been a notable pioneer, has made control even less exacting manually. The choice of a tractor depends upon the work it will be expected to do, and whether it will work alone or be one of a fleet. The petrol-engined tractor is commonly chosen for an all-purpose machine where there may be long periods of work at very much less than the full load of which the tractor is capable; the diesel-engined machine is frequently preferred for continuous heavy work at or about full load. A horse-drawn plough can turn over about fifteen times the area that a man can dig in a day, but an average tractor can do four times as much as a horse. (See also *Plough, Internal-Combustion Engine.*)

ILLUSTRATION: Page 261.

First trump to last

The **TRUMPET** was, as far as can be told, known to every ancient civilization of the world's history; it appears in countless drawings and carvings from the earliest times, and it is continually described as a vital part of religious and royal ceremony and as a stimulant and a signal on the field of battle. Though for the latter purpose it is now obsolete, the trumpet has never lost its ancient association with pomp and panoply, from the temple processions of Egypt and Assyria to the Coronation fanfares of present-day kings and queens, and Christian tradition tells us that its call will be the last sound heard upon earth.

Essentially the trumpet consists of a cylindrical metal tube, with a cup-like mouthpiece at one end, in which the sound is produced by the vibrations of the player's lips, and a flared bell at the far end. Early trumpets were hardly musical instruments so much as sound instruments with a shrill penetrating tone. Homer in the *Iliad* described the cry of the enraged Achilles as being shrill as a trumpet call, Plutarch compared the blare of Egyptian trumpets to an ass's bray, and everyone knows the effect its clangour was supposed to have had on the walls of Jericho. From early times trumpets were used in pairs, probably for the sake of visual pattern and symmetry and not so as to have two ranges of notes available. Experiments made with the pair of trumpets found in Tutankhamen's tomb show that only one clean note was obtainable from each. All the trumpets of the ancient world had such limitations, though some would probably raise three or four notes. Nonetheless, they were regularly used. Egyptian soldiers and priests are known to have been playing trumpets by 1415 B.C., a type known as a *qarna* appeared in Nebuchadnezzar's band in the first half of the sixth century B.C., a shell trumpet is shown being played by an ape on a relief of the second century B.C. in India; and trumpets are also known to have been important in the religious rites of Tibet, China, Mexico, Peru and New Zealand, to name only a few parts of the world. The Greeks believed that the trumpet had been invented by the Etruscans, who were great bronze workers, and a Greek trumpet dating from the second half of the fifth century B.C. is preserved in Boston. Characteristically the Greeks were the first people to take an interest in the actual performance on the instrument; trumpet-playing contests were an item in the Olympic Games of about 400 B.C.

The Romans, with their over-developed military tastes, made great use of trumpets. The discovery of face-bandages shows that the pressure required to blow the Roman trumpets was considerable, which in turn supports the designation of the tone as *raucus* and *terribilis*. The Romans also introduced the curved *lituus*, the shape of which made it much easier to play: no longer need the player support the weight of the instrument on the ground or at arm's length, or, as in China and Tibet, employ an unfortunate small boy to walk in front bearing the brunt of the weight and din. The trumpet was now readily portable; but the direct ancestor of the trumpet we use is not the *lituus*, but the claro (which gives our word 'clarion'), an Eastern instrument introduced as a result of the Crusades. The claro was a shorter version of the busine, introduced at the same time, which was a straight cylindrical metal instrument giving rise to the trombone. Busine and claro were still coarse in tone (a fourteenth-century writer speaks laconically of 'the ilke orible bosyne') but their possibilities were apparent, and as in the case of other instruments, the use of them was quickly reserved for the court and the nobles.

By new methods the tubing could now be bent in any way, and with the advances in construction and performance the trumpet at last was taken into the orchestra of the seventeenth century. The players of those days attained a great degree of virtuosity, and indeed modern trumpeters can manage only with difficulty the higher passages that Bach wrote as a matter of course.

The invention of the clarinet (which, as its original name, clarionet, 'little clarion', implies, was not dissimilar in the high register) caused the working range of the trumpet to descend from these dizzy altitudes, and players have now lost the power to pitch the highest notes with certainty, gaining in exchange a control over the rest of the instrument that was probably denied to their ancestors.

The tone, too, has gradually softened with the passage of the years, but it has not lost its character; rather an unsuspected sense of romance has been revealed in those bright sounds. The trumpet may on occasion still strike like a sword through the web of orchestral sound, but it is also capable, in the hands of a fine player, of lyricism and a flaring beauty that it has never known before. Composers and players alike recognize that it is still the instrument of pomp and circumstance, but they know too that a gentler touch will bring rewards. The advice of the fifteenth-century Leckingfelde Proverb has at last been found true –

Immoderate wyndes in a Clarion causithe it for to rage;
Soft wynde and moderate makithe the sownde to assuage.
Therfore he whiche in that instrument wolde have swete
    modulacion,
Bustius wyndes must leve and use moderacion.

QWERTYUIOP

TYPEWRITERS had an immediate and obvious effect on social history, the first practical machine of commercial importance having been the Remington No. 1 of 1876. This was the fulfilment of ten years' experimentation by the Wisconsin newspaper editor Christopher Latham Sholes, who was helped at first by the printers Samuel W. Soulé and Carlos Glidden. Patents were taken out in 1868. The business man James Densmore then joined Sholes, and supplied the drive, the criticism and finally the salesmanship that interested the armament and sewing-machine firm of Remington and Sons, of Ilion, New York, in an untried product of the most doubtful value.

The typewriter was now a fact. But it was realized that an arduous course of six months' work would be required to train competent operators; and when the New York City Young Women's Christian Association announced its intention of subjecting young women to such treatment, it was argued that it was far beyond the capacity of female minds and constitutions. The Association persisted; but was sufficiently prudent to choose the first eight typewriting students more for their physical strength than for their looks or mental capacity. All of the eight graduated without breakdown or ill effects, and so, in conditions of society in which work for women was menial or degrading for the most part, here was a new chance for the respectable girl who had to earn a living.

The early typewriters were slow, crude and cumbersome, but it was shortage of trained typists rather than the defects of the typewriter that caused much difficulty to begin with. In the whole of the year 1881 only 1,200 machines were sold by Remington and Sons. The original eight girls from the Y.W.C.A. showed the way. The trickle became a stream and the stream a river in flood as more and more offices, formerly a preserve of men, demanded more and more female secretaries. There were still many conservative and prejudiced employers, and it is on record that one typewritten letter was returned from Kentucky with a marginal note that 'you don't need to print no letters to me, I kin read writen'.

Typewriter history began long before 1876. The engineer Henry Mill (c. 1683–1771) took out an English patent, of which no details survive, in 1714. Towards the end of the eighteenth century machines to emboss letters for the benefit of the blind were made by various inventors, but they all suffered from being undeniably slow in operation. The first American patent was taken out in 1829 by William Austin Burt (1792–1858), surveyor and inventor, who called his machine a 'typographer'. It was a large box with the type swinging on a sector which could be brought to the correct place for the impression of selected letters by pressing an index figure into the appropriately labelled holes. All these 'indexing' machines were very slow.

For any considerable speed it proved to be essential to have a regularly arranged keyboard, operating type-bars by way of levers; and it was this feature that made the work of C. L. Sholes so important. The No. 1 typewriters, made in the Remington factory in 1874 were 'up-strike' machines; that is to say, the type-bars, when the keys were struck, travelled upwards from below towards the underside of the roller around which the paper was passed. The work done was therefore not visible to the operator unless the roller (or platen) was turned to bring the typing into view. This disadvantage was partly overcome in 'down-strike' designs working from front, rear

Fig. 36. Remington No. 1, 1874.

or side, of which one of the best known was the Oliver machine of 1894, in which the types were arranged in two banks at the sides. The forerunner of the modern office typewriter with the type arranged in a semi-circular basket form, striking more or less upwards from the front, and the work completely visible as it is being printed, was the Underwood machine of 1897.

The so-called 'noiseless' typewriters were introduced in 1910, after sixteen years of experiment. They were not successful until, in 1915, a toggle and weight were added to the mechanisms so that the key pressure brought the type nearly up to the platen, after which the overthrow of the weight completed the action. The type-bars in these designs are arranged radially, so that those bars which come from the edges tend to hit the platen obliquely and cause blurring.

Some of the essential features of modern machines are of considerable age. The familiar 'QWERTYUIOP' keyboard arrangement dates back to the Sholes typewriter of 1874. The so-called 'Universal' keyboard was devised, not so much for philological reasons, although these were considered, but so that the most-used letters should be spaced as far apart as possible to avoid the clashing of type-bars. With improved mechanical designs there is no longer any need for such caution, but though more efficient arrangements of the letters have been demonstrated, changing the standard keyboard would mean a worldwide re-training of typists.

Adding capital letters to the lower-case letters on the type-bars, and fitting a shift key for the change from one to the other dates to the Remington No. 2 machine of 1878. This was not at first regarded as much of an improvement on the double keyboard with separate keys for capitals and small letters. In those days typists looked continually at the keys. However, an operator named McGurrin taught himself to play the keyboard of a Remington No. 2 as a touch pianist might play a piano. He had been doing this for ten years when, in 1888, a contest was staged at Cincinnati with the champion of those who believed in looking at the keys. McGurrin won so handsomely that touch-typing has been standard for professionals ever since.

Modern electric typewriters produce work of a very uniform appearance, since variable finger-pressure on the keys does not affect the momentum with which the type hits the paper. The keys simply release a pivoted friction cam mechanism that falls on to a rotating friction roller. The roller gives a uniform kick to each mechanism dropping upon it. This in turn is transmitted to the type-bar, which hits the paper and is then caught up again on the recoil. A movement of the key of one-eighth of an inch is sufficient to set the type-bar mechanism in motion, so that on these electric machines very high speeds can be obtained with very little fatigue to the operator.

ILLUSTRATION: Pages 163 and 217.

U

Parapluie and parasol

UMBRELLAS (through the Italian from the Latin *umbra*, shade) were by origin sunshades, rather than protections against rain. Coming from the East, they were private and perambulant oases of shade. In the East the sun annihilates, shade is a luxury, and rain a blessing.

In China umbrellas have been known from the twelfth century before Christ, and have been an attribute of dignity and high office. All over the East they have been and are associated with royalty. Nimrod rode to war beneath an umbrella; in Siam the total furniture of the royal audience-chamber was three umbrellas, while the monarch of Ava signed himself 'King of the White Elephants and Lord of the Twenty-Four Umbrellas'. Imported to Europe, the sunshade retained its dignity to some extent as a rich ceremonial jewel in Venice and in Papal Rome, but it had also been used in classical Greece and Rome mainly and merely by women, and in Renaissance Italy, for everyday wear, by horsemen. It did not divide into its dual role till the seventeenth and eighteenth centuries. The French distinguish exactly its two functions: *parasol* and *parapluie*. In more recent times the *parasol* has been appropriated by women, but the *parapluie*, anti-rain, may be worn without reserve by either sex.

The sunshade in the eighteenth and nineteenth centuries was ubiquitous: earlier it had been made generally of leather and had to be managed by a sturdy servant, but the introduction of whalebone for the ribs made it light enough to be handled personally by its owner. Silk was the most popular covering, in all colours of the rainbow; being furled and unfurled, and twirled, the parasol blossomed through the summers to Edwardian days – and then, abruptly, became obsolescent, a victim of the First World War, of streamlining, and of the revolutionary dogma that handsome people are slightly sunburnt. It still appears at Ascot, and on the beaches, but it is no longer a normal accessory of feminine dress.

The progress of the umbrella was more complicated. As with the sunshade, weight, to begin with, militated against it, and it was also considered effeminate, 'a screen commonly used by women to keep off rain' (1708). By the mid-eighteenth century it was becoming popular in France, but it had to fight all the way against snobbism: 'An umbrella is a sure sign that one possesses no carriage' (1768). Jonas Hanway (1712–1788), London merchant and philanthropist, was the first Englishman to carry one, about 1750: he caused some uproar, and his example did not catch. The honour of popularizing the umbrella in England is claimed by John Macdonald, or 'Beau Macdonald', a much-travelled gentleman's gentleman, who wore a fine silk umbrella in London in 1778: he, too, aroused the popular fury, particularly from coachmen and chair-men, and his sister refused to be seen with him. He persisted, and in a year or so, the umbrella was a commonplace, spreading more slowly through the countryside. Jonathan Couch of Polperro in Cornwall recorded the astonishment of the natives about 1800 when the financier of the smuggling interests in that Cornish village paraded the streets with a red umbrella sent him as a present from the brandy shippers of Roscoff in Brittany. Patents for improving the umbrella now followed fast: between 1806 and 1826 the frame was reduced from ten pounds in weight to one and a half; metal displaced whalebone, alpaca came in, and then, about 1850 Samuel Fox, inspired by the Great Tubular Bridge at the Menai Straits, conceived the Paragon frame with ribs of U-shaped steel that gave to maximum lightness a maximum strength; and to Fox, some three hundred thousand pounds profit.

The subsequent history of the umbrella has been funereal, staid and black. Its first historian, Sangster, described those who wore it in 1855 – 'Such men', he said 'we feel certain at the first glance, are not addicted to dissipation, nor do they yield to the seductions of the Casino: they are essentially family men ...' Perhaps now dons and undergraduates are the true doyens of the gamp, leaving specimens copiously in railway-racks, lecture-rooms and damply in oak hall-

s

stands; but in its purest form, sharp and slender and dangerous as a sword, the umbrella in Great Britain, at least, or in London, is now the emblem of the City man and all pseudo-City men (*e.g.* members of the peerage, the Brigade of Guards and certain bailiffs), and it is always, when worn by men (except for golf), black. London, at least, might be brighter if men wore coloured umbrellas; the City in a shower could then sprout, like the dark avenues of a forest which smoulder with all the most dangerous fungi.

The umbrella is distributed unevenly, and is probably most frequent in Great Britain, where weather is notoriously unpredictable. It is popular too especially in another group of islands of temperamental inclemency – Japan; but there the umbrella is both parapluie and parasol, made traditionally from bamboo and oiled paper, cheap, light and expendable. In Japan, too, can be traced the most satisfactory and consistent iconography of the umbrella, for the Japanese (with perhaps the Chinese) are the only people who persistently depict rain in their art: in hundreds of their prints the umbrella twirls, or, half-open, echoes the cone of Mount Fuji. In Europe the umbrella has inspired few great pictures, beyond Renoir's, although individual umbrellas have won great affection (a Miss Alice Mercy Cox of Bayswater willed that hers should rest with her in her grave).

Students of the umbrella should, finally, be warned against confusion with the parachute. Any apparent relationship is purely of structure and not of function. General Beurnonville confused the two in 1793, when escaping from a window forty feet up in the fortress of Ollmütz; he used an umbrella as a parachute. He broke both his legs.

ILLUSTRATION: Page 130.

Next to the skin

UNDERCLOTHES now seem a logical intermediary between the sensitive skin and the outer thicker fabric that takes the rough wear; and they owe their existence not a little to the development of hygiene and personal cleanliness: our outer layers may go occasionally to the cleaners, our under layer comes off and goes into the wash every week.

The Egyptians had fine linen, and Egyptian court ladies sometimes wore long transparent garments very similar to the chemise of yesterday or the nightgown of today. But they wore them *over* their usual outfit of jewelled girdle and beaded collar.

When the Greeks ceased to drape themselves in oblongs of woollen cloth held together by brooches or pins, and evolved the sleeved *tunic*, they started on the long path to vest and pants. To the modern eye a Greek in a tunic has the odd appearance of *being in his underclothes*, and in a sense he is. Or rather his single garment *became* underclothes in later periods of culture. If we cease to belt the tunic, it turns into a shirt, and thus shirts, visible or invisible, or else the smock, which is simply the longer feminine version, became *the* foundation garment in Western Europe, except for the desperately poor. We still say 'without a shirt to his back' as an expression of extreme indigence.

Shirts could be of all degrees of fineness and elaboration. The Norman knights wore shirts which were embroidered round the neck and wrists, but were simple in construction. Neckbands did not appear until the fourteenth century and wrist-bands until the fifteenth. Women's smocks fell to the ankles and were full and sometimes pleated. It was the Normans who introduced the word 'chemise'. During the eleventh, twelfth and thirteenth centuries it had long straight sleeves and a round neck. The materials used were linen, hemp and such silk textiles as cendal and samite.

Men, in addition to the shirt, wore braies or breeches. Both terms were used synonymously during the early Middle Ages, but in the second half of the twelfth century braies became definitely an undergarment, and the term breeches was finally applied to the outer garment only. Thirteenth-century braies varied in length from ankle to knee. They usually had wide legs, a full seat and a string at the waist, forming a girdle to which the stockings were attached by cords.

There was little change in essentials until the beginning of the sixteenth century. At that time both men and women wore low necks, so that the top of the chemise or shirt, gathered with a drawstring, was just visible above the outer garments. It was only necessary to draw the string more tightly round the neck to produce a kind of incipient ruff; and the development of the ruff, its increasing size and its final stage as a separate article of clothing, dominate the dress of the Tudor period.

Women's clothes followed the masculine mode. The top of the chemise appeared above the top of the gown in a frilled border, becoming sometimes a high collar, or even a ruff round the throat, together with a low-cut square décolletage. Chemises were usually made of cambric or holland, and only occasionally of silk. They were, however, embroidered with silk or even with gold thread. Elaborate specimens were presented to Queen Elizabeth by those anxious to gain her favour. We hear, for example, of 'a cambric smock, wrought with black silk in the collar and sleeves, the square ruffs wrought with Venice gold and edged with small bone lace of Venice gold'. Men's shirts were almost equally elaborate, for as early as 1533 a sumptuary law laid it down that no man under the rank of a knight should wear 'pleated shirts or shirts garnished with silk, gold or silver'.

Men wore a waistcoat under the doublet. It was made with or without sleeves and was usually quilted or bombasted. Early in the seventeenth century it was called a vest, and, since it was invisible, it can perhaps be classified as underclothes.

It is uncertain when petticoats, as separate undergarments, first began to be worn. A foreign observer, writing in 1585, remarks that 'the women of England wear three cloth gowns or petticoats one over another'. The appearance of wearing many petticoats could, however, be obtained by the use of the farthingale, which in Elizabeth's declining years assumed the proportions of a cartwheel worn round the waist with the outskirt hanging from its rim. Sometimes the same effect was obtained by means of a thick bolster-like bustle. The farthingale went out of fashion about 1617, but various similar devices have reappeared at intervals in the form of hoops, panniers or crinolines.

The corset also has a long history. Its equivalent can be found as early as the fourteenth century in the shaped and stiffened bodices of the period. The typical triangular shape of the Elizabethan bodice was obtained by the use of stiff rods, or busks of bone or wood. But in Elizabethan times and almost until the end of the eighteenth century the corset formed part of the dress. It was only later that it became a separate undergarment.

The date at which women began to wear some sort of drawers is a matter of controversy. Fynes Moryson in his *Itinerary* (1605–1617) remarks that 'the city Virgins and especially Gentlewomen in many places in Italy wear silk or linen breeches under their gowns'. Drawers are thought to have been introduced into France by Catherine de' Medici, but little is known of their use in England. In general they were not worn until the nineteenth century. The free-swinging crinoline of the eighteen-fifties made them essential. It was not until the late seventies that the new practice of combining chemise and drawers in a single garment produced 'combinations'.

The main event in the history of male underclothes in the nineteenth century was the invention of the shirt with detachable collar, detachable cuffs and even a detachable front. This was a boon to poorer respectable classes, since it enabled the appearance of gentility to be preserved without excessive laundry bills. The First World War abolished cuffs and fronts, and brought in the soft collar, detachable or undetachable.

After 1918 women's underclothes ceased to be made almost exclusively of linen. Silk and various synthetic fabrics were substituted and still hold the field. Underclothes, in the nineteen-twenties became extremely scanty and diaphanous. After various attempts to combine two garments in 'cami-knickers' and the like, they seem to have settled down into some form of 'pants and brassiere'. The latter is quite a modern invention. According to some authorities it is simply a tightened form of camisole, invented in 1920 or a little earlier for sportswomen or to enhance the fashionable straight line of the day. Throughout the twenties it served as a 'flattener', but since 1930 has striven to emphasize, and even to enhance, the beauty of the natural bosom. (See also *Cloth, Handbags, Handkerchief, Nightclothes, Nylon, Bathing Costumes*.)

Dust by suction

VACUUM-CLEANERS work on an extremely simple principle, which was demonstrated by one of the inventors of these mechanisms, the Englishman H. C. Booth, when he placed a handkerchief on the back of an upholstered seat in a London restaurant and sucked at it through his mouth. He showed a friend the dirt trapped on the linen surface; and then designed and constructed a machine to perform the same process, patenting in 1901 a cumbersome, piston-operated vacuum pump.

Booth was not the first to think of suction-cleaning, but he was early in the field, and he was ignorant of unsuccessful devices patented before his own. Mounted in horse-drawn vans his vacuum-cleaners, operated by a gasoline engine, were drawn up at the kerbside outside the premises to be cleaned, and hose-pipes from the vacuum chamber were run across the pavement and in by the doors and windows. A cleaning squad then got to work. The revolutionary development ahead was still to mechanize the broom and the carpet-sweeper – to substitute a daily routine of vacuum-cleaning, or more properly suction cleaning, for the cumbersome procedure launched by Booth and others. Household vacuum cleaners originated in America, on the basis of David Kenny's stationary 'apparatus for removing dust' patented in 1903. James M. Spangler patented an electrically-driven suction carpet-sweeper in 1908, the Hoover Company was marketing such machines soon after, using the rotary suction fan and the bag for trapping the dust, which are still basic.

High-speed fans draw the air through as rapidly as possible and discharge it, dust and all, into the bag, which is slightly porous. The air escapes through the innumerable tiny interstices between the threads of the fabric, which are yet so small that the dust is trapped.

Thus the story of household cleansing goes from the broom made from the pliable twigs of the broom plant or heather or the birch tree; from birds' wings and feather mops and other mops, from brushes and from dusters, to the revolving brushes of the carpet-sweeper invented in mid-nineteenth century; and from the creaking carpet-sweeper to the new whirring efficiency of the vacuum-cleaner – a name which the *Oxford Dictionary* records first for 1903.

The honey's sweet, and so are you

VALENTINES are the earliest form of greeting card, first found in printed form in the eighteenth century.

No one knows which St Valentine (of several possible ones) is tied to February 14th as the day of the mating of birds and humans:

> Oft have I heard both youths and virgins say,
> Birds chuse their mates, and couple too, this day;
> But by their flight I never can divine
> When I shall couple with my Valentine.
>
> (Robert Herrick, *Hesperides*, 1648.)

Charles d'Orleans, Lydgate, the Paston Letters, Shakespeare, Chapman, John Gay – all of these witness that the day was devoted to a species of playful human mating, the charm of which was the double doubt as to the choice of partner and the degree of seriousness. When Margery Brews married her 'well-belovyd Valentyn, John Paston, Squyer' (1477) she was neither the first girl nor the last to do so; the heroine of Ophelia's song in *Hamlet* ('And I a maid at your window, to be your Valentine') who paid with her honour for the expression of her preference, may have had her parallels in real life; but many more cherished the innocent sentiment which led to such a bequest as that made in 1535: 'I gyf and bequeth to my Valentyn Agnes Illyon ten shillings.'

Luck, or accident, or anonymity, were essentially part of the notion of a Valentine. Choice of partner might be made on St Valentine's Eve from folded screws of paper containing a name, and by some form of divination; or on St Valentine's morning by the 'accident' of first encounter. The choice might be accompanied by a present, and this might be serious or trivial: a ring such as Pepys records the Duke of York giving to Lady Arabella Stuart in 1667, worth £800; or the grand piano which an embarrassed young lady of Norwich refused to accept in 1872.

By some traditions the present was not to be given immediately, but in the form of a pair of gloves upon Easter Day. And by others the present, though made upon St Valentine's Day itself, must be anonymous, left upon the doorstep with no other message than 'Good morrow, Valentine' or 'St Valentine's Love'. To this tradition belongs the custom of sending an anonymous copy of verses whose sender must be guessed. This custom is the origin of the *Valentine* proper, the message decorated by hand, or engraved, or printed, which is the earliest form of greeting card.

In the eighteenth century youths and maidens who found composition difficult were helped by the publication of *Valentine Writers*. These handbooks, first referred to in 1723, contained stock forms of verse and greeting which could be copied or adapted. The verses looked less bald when tricked out with the charming curves of eighteenth-century penmanship, with true love knots, hearts, doves and Cupids.

By folding paper and using sharp scissors the ingenious made and coloured the most charming cut-out emblems. But already by the mid-eighteenth century the stationers had come to the aid of those who were not skilful or ingenious, by commissioning copperplate engravings to which the sender might add his (or her) own handwritten message or verse. By 1822 Dr Nares could note in his *Glossary* that the sending of Valentines 'makes several additional sorters necessary at the Post Office in London'. Lord Macaulay about 1850 wrote:

> ... On earth the postman toils along,
> Bent double by huge bales of song,
> Where, rich with many a gorgeous dye,
> Blazes all Cupid's heraldry –
> Myrtles and roses, doves and sparrows,
> Love-knots and altars, lamps and arrows.
> What nymph without wild hopes and fears
> The double rap this morning hears!

Unnumbered lasses, young and fair,
From Bethnal Green to Belgrave Square,
With cheeks high flush'd, and hearts loud beating
Await the tender annual greeting.
The loveliest lass of all is mine –
Good morrow to my Valentine!

In Norwich in 1872 no less than 150,000 letters passed through the Post Office on St Valentine's Eve.

The nineteenth-century stationers showed great ingenuity and, at first, exquisite taste, in making new kinds of Valentine. The new processes of reproduction: lithography and aquatint; embossed and lace papers (the first dating from about 1820); acrostic Valentines, silhouette Valentines, daguerreotype Valentines, and mirror Valentines began to proliferate. There were mechanical Valentines with figures that rolled their eyes and put out their tongues, churches whose doors opened to show the wedding inside, Cupids that hovered and Cupids that rowed boats. There were nonsense Valentines with cabbages for heads, insulting Valentines and ribald Valentines. There were cobweb Valentines and cameo Valentines, and pretty Valentines in *theorem-work* which by stencilled watercolours fixed with gum arabic very plausibly imitated Indian Khaligat painting.

By the mid-century, both in England and America, Valentines were being produced by assembly-line technique: rooms full of girls sitting side by side each adding her constituent to the growing fantasy, sticking, perforating, embossing, clipping, painting, and blowing on the metallic powders for fancy borders (a bonus was given for this last task, to buy milk against lung trouble).

By 1880 the vogue began to blow itself out; Christmas cards and picture postcards burgeoned; and this folk-custom that had become an industry shrank into triviality. It could live so long as it still represented a personal offering, half earnest, half jest, in a community that was still social enough for gossip to count. It shrivelled in cities where no one knew his next-door neighbours, and where the 'New Woman' was going out on her bicycle in her bloomers and asking for the vote.

Yet, like so many other customs over which prophets have mourned, it has been a long time dying; one can still go into the stationer's and buy a Valentine. (See also *Christmas Card*.)

Violin, viola, cello and double bass

The **VIOLIN** family, consisting of the violin, viola, cello and double bass, emerged in its modern form almost abruptly towards the end of the sixteenth century. Instruments played with a bow had been known for many hundreds of years, but lovely as many of them were in sound (and appearance), none of them compares in beauty, strength and range of sound with the modern instruments. This family is the backbone of the orchestra, and in its various members some of the greatest executive musicians of all time – Spohr, Paganini, Sarasate, Joachim, Ysaÿe, Kreisler, and Casals, to name a very few – have found the perfect medium for their art.

The earliest history of the family is obscure, and the lineage extremely hard to trace clearly. Kathleen Schlesinger, a painstaking and erudite scholar, has drawn a thread right down from the Egyptian kithara, through the Greek and Roman kithara, the Spanish vihuela, the famous and wonderful viol family, and so, by means of many other minor links, to the violins of Italy. The remoter ancestors of the violin were plucked. The branch which was to bear such rich fruit in sixteenth-century Cremona although of the same family is separated from the others by the use of the bow; these became lutes, lyres, guitars and even the humble banjos and ukuleles.

Stringed instruments played with a bow were unknown to the Assyrians, the Hebrews and Egyptians (the translation of a Hebrew word as 'bow' is probably a mistake for 'plectrum'). It is thought, however, that further east a bowed instrument existed in about 3000 B.C.: the Hindus claim great antiquity for their *ravanastra*, and even claim to have invented the bow, and there are indications of the existence of a kind of violin in various parts of Asia at a very early date. Its development was slow, for the primitive state of the bow was such that any plucked instrument would give a stronger and cleaner sound than the best bowed instrument. With the beautifully tensed bows of today we are apt to forget how scratchy primitive ones must have been, awkwardly stretched and unresined as they were.

When bowed instruments arrived from the East is unknown: the earliest illustration dates from the ninth century A.D., and shows a blind musician with a harp and a curious spade-shaped instrument accompanied by a bow some ten feet long. From this time onwards various fiddle-like instruments are seen in manuscripts, drawings and carvings, primitive in construction and doubtless unsatisfactory in performance, but wearing something of the aspect of the true violin to come. In the tenth century there appeared the *vielle*, or *fiedel*, which was pear-shaped and was played on the shoulder (later, in the larger versions, on the knee). The oldest representations in England are painted on the roof of Peterborough Cathedral: these date from the twelfth century, and the resemblance to the violin lies not only in the general shape but extends to the *f*-shaped sound-holes. The violin's immediate ancestors of the period were the *rebec*, the *crwth* of Wales and its very close relative the *fidla* of Norway, and the *fithele* of the Middle English period. All these instruments, however, were driven into extinction or at best restricted to a folk use by the advent of the viols in the fifteenth century.

The viols were of two main kinds, *viola da braccio* and *viola da gamba* – that is, played on the arm or held on the knees. The family differed from the violins in having generally flat backs, C-shaped sound-holes, sloping shoulders, broad, thin necks, fingerboards marked with frets for the notes, and on an average six strings. By now the bow had become more serviceable (in Rousseau's phrase it was 'the soul of the viol'); according to modern standards the slack horsehair and the convex bowstick are crude, but they were purposely made in this way so as to allow the playing of chords over several strings. The viols were, and still are, of great beauty, but they are limited in range, and so restrained in tone that it was inevitable they should be outmoded owing to the ever-increasing demands of composers. So the violin family was born; it has never been ousted from its supreme position and is never likely to be, even though the viols still have their enthusiasts, and the music written for them sounds right only on them.

It is generally believed that it was Gasparo da Salo, an excellent maker of viols working in Brescia, who first produced instruments of the true violin type about 1580. His instruments were stronger in every way than the viols – sometimes to the point of crudity – but they gave for the first time in the long history of evolution, experiment and error the true singing tone of the violin. Other Brescian masters learned their trade in his workshop, while in nearby Cremona was born Andrea Amati, now renowned as the first really great violin-maker. A man of noble birth, and with no record of apprenticeship to the craft, he produced instruments of such beauty of tone, such elegance and quality, that his example was directly responsible for the great makers of Cremona who followed: Stradivari, Guarneri, the Ruggieri, and Bergonzi were all pupils in his workshop; with their respective families and other great makers of Cremona – Seraphin, Guadagnini, Gagliano – they reached a peak of style and artistry that has never been equalled. Much of their success has been attributed to a closely-guarded formula for varnish, now lost beyond recall; whether the particular excellence of Cremonese violins depended on this or on some intangible quality we cannot now tell. The instruments were recognized as exceptional at the time of their creation, and were in demand, but they have improved with playing and matured with age. Many of the finest Amatis and Stradivaris are even now at their prime, others are tired and old, and will never recover their former warmth.

Violin, viola, cello and double bass are a truer family than any other instrumental group, for their similarity of tone joins them in perfect consort, and their individual characteristics add variety without spoiling the blend. The violin is the brilliant member of the family, gay, passionate, cool and sparkling, with a nimbleness of voice and a soaring song that are unrivalled by any other instrument; the viola is melancholy, with a brown, husky whisper that can swell to a great richness; the double bass is ponderously masculine, though even those gruff tones can be sweetened; while the cello sings its tunes with infinite variety. Whether as solo instruments, in the string quartet (two violins, viola, cello) or in the orchestra, this is a group with a sympathy that would be the envy of any human family, the highest development of a line of aristocrats. It is a far cry from this honoured position of today to the surly ordinance of 1685 whereby 'if any person or persons, commonly called fiddlers, or minstrels, shall at any time ... be taken playing, fiddling, or making music in any wine, alehouse, or tavern, or shall be proffering themselves, or desiring, or entreating any person or persons to hear them play ... they shall be adjudged rogues, vagabonds, and sturdy beggars'.

ILLUSTRATION: Page 259.

Most necessary

The **WATER-CLOSET** in a primitive form belongs to the ancient civilizations.

In ancient Mesopotamia in the Akkadian palace excavated at Tell Agmar and in the ancient cities (2500 B.C.–1500 B.C.) of the Indus Valley the simplest domestic privy was very neatly devised. Thus at Mohenjo-daro seat-closets of about 2000 B.C. have been found in some of the dwelling-houses, on ground floor or first floor. Built of brick, they were connected by a sloping conduit to the street drain or to a pottery vase outside. Egyptian closets at Tel-el-Amarna of about 1350 B.C. were not dissimilar, consisting of a stone slab pierced with a keyhole shaped opening above a pottery receptacle which could be removed.

Closets built over a conduit of running water were known to the inhabitants of Knossos in Crete c. 1400 B.C., and inherited by the Greeks and Romans of the classical period. Thus the ruins at Thamugadi (Timgad), the town which

Trajan founded in North Africa in A.D. 100, include the dignified marble seats of a public latrine raised over a water runnel. Latrines on this plan survived in the East. Thus Agra in the Middle Ages had marble latrines above flowing water scented with attar of roses. Houses at Pompeii, which was destroyed in A.D. 79, often had niche-like closets supplied with water. These opened off the kitchen.

Methods in medieval Europe were less systematic. London in the fourteenth and fifteenth centuries had at least twelve public latrines, of which there is record, and probably more. Some were built over the Thames. London Bridge had its several public 'necessary houses'. Privies were common, and were frequently built over streams, including Walbrook and the Fleet River. The *necessarium* of monasteries may occasionally have been built over a runnel or conduit of water, as by the Benedictines of Furness Abbey. Castle latrines were sometimes kept clean by the running water of a moat, though castle garderobes also emptied direct into the moat, corbelled draughtily out from the walls; or they might overhang in this way crag or precipice.

However, in medieval times and for long after most European latrines or privies were placed over large pits, straddled by wooden seats, which might rot and break with unhappy consequences. The privies of the Middle Ages often resembled the small plank huts still to be found behind farmhouses and country cottages.

Not until the Elizabethan era was the notion advanced of an odourless closet with a controlled supply of water. In 1596 the courtier Sir John Harington, who had a passion for cleanliness and hygiene in advance of his time, published his *Metamorphosis of Ajax* (a punning title – 'the metamorphosis of a jakes', *i.e.* a privy), full of elaborate classical references and conceits.

To keepe your houses sweet, clense privie vaultes;
To keep your soules as sweet, mend privie faults

he wrote; but he also described in detail the first valve water-closet.

Instead of the modern pan, Harington had a bowl which could be filled with water from a cistern to a covering deodorizing depth of two feet, and which could be emptied when necessary through an underlying valve into the cesspit. The main point of Harington's invention was that it attempted to seal off the cesspit and the cesspit stench which had so long scarified mankind – except for the brief moment of emptying. 'Plan-plots of a privy in perfection' in his book instruct the workman; and Harington had such a 'privy in perfection' in his own house at Kelston in Somerset.

This invention was stillborn; but by the middle years of the eighteenth century crude water-closets were in common use (the *Oxford English Dictionary* traces the word 'water-closet' back to 1755). These early W.C.s suffered by the odours and gases which still rose up from the soil pipe and the cesspit, and in 1775 there came a great advance when Alexander Cumming (1733–1814), mathematician, mechanic, Fellow of the Royal Society and watchmaker of Bond Street, patented his 'Watercloset upon a New Construction'. His solution was ingeniously simple and it has been in use ever since: the soil pipe immediately below the pan was bent into a syphon; or as Cumming put it in his specification, 'the pipe which carried off the soil and water is recurved about twelve or eighteen inches below the pan or bason, so as constantly to retain a quantity of water to cut off all communication of smell from below'.

Improvements and patents followed thick and fast. Joseph Bramah, for instance, patented a two-valve water-closet in 1778, which had the advantage of discharging its content by one valve and admitting fresh water by the other valve, simultaneously. It is curious to see that the water valve was specially placed 'to prevent the bad effects of the frost which hath always been a complaint of water-closets'. Thomas Rowntree describing his water-closet of 1789, spoke of the reservoir holding water 'which may be hot, cold, or medicated'. Between 1775 and 1866 nearly 300 patents were taken out relating to water closets, earth-closets, and urinals, the inventors working towards the simpler trouble-proof closets of our own day, not easily fouled or blocked.

The climax came in 1870, when John Randall Mann, of East Cowes in the Isle of Wight, patented Mann's Syphonic Improvement for Water-closets, odour-free (as a *sine qua non*), self-emptying and self-cleansing. Only three years before medical officers of health in London had been mostly in favour of mechanical earth-closets, using dry earth.

Before the water-closet could triumph completely it was also necessary to deliver a controlled quantity of water to the pan automatically, with a sufficient momentum, and without an extravagant call on the water supply. The problem was finally solved by another benefactor to mankind, Rogers Field (1831–1900). After long experiments, this sanitary engineer (who was named after his great-uncle, the poet Samuel Rogers) perfected his Syphon Automatic Flushing Tank. Such two-gallon tanks were long known as 'water-waste preventers'; their introduction met the complaints of water companies which were an obstacle at first to the spread of the W.C.

Water-closet and bath now advanced together, ultimately joining forces in the bathroom. The dull mustard-coloured seatless stoneware pans of the early closets gave way to pans below comfortable seats, to pans of white porcelain opulently decorated with blue flowers – irises, for instance, growing up from the syphon – and pans at last which are severely white and hygienic. At the standard sixteen inches doctors now consider lavatory seats to be far too high, and many more are dropping to the recommended height of twelve to thirteen inches.

The water-closet divides the human race. Eastern closets are made which conform to the primeval squatting posture, having instead of a seat two porcelain foot-rests. (See also *Bath, Soap*.)

'Clack, clack, clack vrom hour to hour'

WATER-MILLS date at any rate to the first century B.C., when, according to Strabo, Mithradates, King of Pontus, near the southern shore of the Black Sea, possessed a wonderful novelty named a *'hydraletes'* a 'water-grinder'.

Earlier devices were the saddle quern and the pestle and mortar, then revolving mills drawn by donkeys, which seem first to have appeared in the Mediterranean World about the fifth century

B.C., and which were soon followed by portable hand-mills or rotary querns. The donkey-mills supplied flour on a large commercial scale to town-dwellers, the rotary querns, which rapidly gained popularity, were characteristic of the peasant culture of the Roman Empire. In the same century as Mithradates and his water-grinder, a Greek epigram attributed to Antipater of Thessalonica describes such a machine, and congratulates the slave-girls of being free at last of the drudgery of the quern:

> Work no more, girls who laboured at the mill:
> Sleep, and let the birds sing to the rosy dawn. Ceres
> Has bidden the water nymphs to do your work.
> Obeying her, they rush upon the whirling spokes,
> Compel the axle round, and so the heavy mill.

Probably this earliest water-mill was a peasant adaptation of the rotary quern, not at first a rival in commerce to the established donkey-mills. Probably also it belonged to the primitive type of water-mill, which has a horizontal wheel at the lower end of a vertical shaft, turning the upper millstone direct, without gearing. This 'vertical mill' has a wide past or present distribution, from China on the east across central Asia and eastern and southern Europe to Ireland, the Hebrides, the Shetlands, the Faeroes and Scandinavia. A recent discovery in Denmark suggests that this simple type may have been known there during the Roman Iron Age, and according to legend it was introduced into Ireland in the third century A.D. As a rule several of these little mills, each housed in a small hut, are placed at intervals across a single stream, and they are used in common by the local farmers – an element of peasant, as opposed to urban, culture.

Late in the first century B.C. the Roman engineer Vitruvius described a modification of this mill, which includes the essential features of the modern water-mill – that is to say, a vertical mill-wheel set on a horizontal shaft, geared to drive the vertical spindle attached to the upper stone. Nothing more is heard of this improved device until after the official adoption of Christianity in the fourth century, when this 'Vitruvian' water-mill ousted the old mills worked by animal or slave labour and became the standard mill of the urban civilization of the later Empire. Owing to its gearing and since it could be driven by a really large water-wheel, this mill was well fitted for the commercial production of flour. At first the wheel was undershot, i.e., it was turned by a swift-flowing current without any dam or mill-pond, but the overshot wheel was in use in Athens, below the Parthenon, by the fifth century A.D.

When Rome was besieged by the Goths in A.D. 536, the besiegers tried to starve the city by cutting off the water supplying the mills, which then stood on the Janiculum Hill. Thereupon the Romans transferred some of the mills to boats moored on the Tiber, so that the mill-wheels were still turned by the swift current of the river. Possibly the defeated Goths may have been so impressed by these water-mills that they took the idea home with them and constructed similar mills on the German rivers. At any rate the early distribution of the Vitruvian mill was mainly northwards throughout Germany and eastern and northern France, from which it reached Anglo-Saxon Britain by the eighth century, passing on to North America in the seventeenth century. Thus in Europe an area of Vitruvian mills was surrounded by an area of the more primitive 'vertical mills'. Domesday Book records the existence of 5,624 such Vitruvian mills in England in 1086. Milling became one of the recognized callings of the countryside, and the miller a stock character of country life, and the mill the best known of machines in the pre-industrial age. Chaucer has the miller to the life in the *Reeve's Tale*, and the rhythmical clatter of the country mill, or rather of the revolving upper millstone sounding above the quietness of the wooden gearing, is best preserved in the refrain to a poem by William Barnes (1801–1886), the Dorset poet:

> While clack, clack, clack vrom hour to hour
> Wi' whirlen stwone, and streamen flour
> Did goo the mill by cloty Stour.

(a *clote* is a water-lily). The water-wheel had many adaptations – for example, raising the beams which thumped and fulled the cloth in fulling-mills, or raising the stamps which crushed ores in the mining areas.

In commercial milling a great forward step was taken in America in the seventeen-eighties when Oliver Evans (1755–1819) invented and developed his automatic mill, near Wilmington. In the eighteen-thirties, Swiss engineers, notably Jakob Sulzberger, built the first successful mills in which the stones going back nearly 2,000 years were replaced by the rollers of modern milling practice. Even now, though, the old green-wheeled and dusty Vitruvian mills have not altogether disappeared from the European countryside. (See also *Querns, Windmills*.)

ILLUSTRATION: Page 272.

***

Pennyweights, ounces, pounds

WEIGHTS and measures, which were the progenitors of those employed in Europe until the metric system was introduced in the nineteenth century, were evolved gradually from about 5000 B.C. or 4000 B.C. onwards by the ancient civilizations of the Middle East. About 3000 B.C., long before there was any international trade, the Chinese also invented a well coordinated system, based mainly on red millet seed. Their standards had no evolutionary effect outside China.

Balances and weights were used first of all not, as one might think, in commerce, but for weighing gold dust. Weighing as a commercial act began about 2500 B.C. in the great cities of the Indus Valley, Harappa and Mohenjo-daro, and in the Sumerian cities of Mesopotamia – *e.g.* Ur of the Chaldees. In Egypt all the early evidence points to commerce by barter: the first signs of the balance in ordinary trade come as late as 1350 B.C. Pictorial evidence of weighing in Egypt goes back another thousand years to the Fifth Dynasty (c. 2500 B.C.), and shows the balance only in the hands of the jeweller and goldsmith, or for weighing the gold ingots of one of the temple treasuries; actual evidence goes back further still, since limestone weights and a small primitive balance beam have been found in predynastic graves in Egypt at Naqada.

These are the oldest weights at present known. Sir Flinders Petrie, who collected many thousands of ancient weights, dated these Naqada specimens to 7000 B.C.–5000 B.C., though 4000

B.C. is more probable; he found that they belong to what was later known as the 'Beqa' standard, which has the longest history of any weight standard and has been associated through all the centuries with the weighing of gold.

All weights until about 1450 B.C. were of stone, generally polished; which is fortunate, since they do not deteriorate; they keep their evidence, whereas the ancient bronze weights suffer by corrosion.

The Beqa standard began about 4000 B.C. with the Beqa shekel of about 200 grains, and it gradually split between 3000 B.C. and 700 B.C. into three important sub-standards of 192 grains, 206 grains and 211 grains. Only small units were required in the earliest times, since a general system of barter meant that weighing was pointless except for the precious metals. These at the time included copper as well as gold, followed later by silver and lead. The larger units came later, and were generally known as minas. They were evolved by multiplication of basic shekels, of which there were eight principal standards, varying from 120 to 218 grains in use among the ancient civilizations of the Middle East. These were the origin of all the standards of weight later employed in Europe.

Of the three Beqa shekels the most important and longest lived was the 192-grain unit; this was the standard of the mines in Nubia (the Sudan), from which the Egyptians derived such quantities of gold, and originally it appears to have been based on the weight of 256 selected wheat grains. It was handed down through Greek and Arab times with only a rearrangement of subdivisions and multiples.

About 675 B.C. the island state of Aegina produced the first European silver coinage. The weight of this was based on the lower Beqa standard, the 192-grain standard of the Nubian gold mines. The Beqa shekel was the Aegina stater, which was divided into two drachmae and into twelve obols of sixteen grains each. This coinage acquired an international fame for uniformity of type, weight and purity that endured for centuries after it had ceased to be minted; and it transmitted its weight standard wherever it passed in trade.

In the seventh century A.D. the Arabian empire came into being, and stormily expanded till it stretched from northern India through Persia, the Middle East and North Africa into Spain. The Arabs settled down under the enlightened Caliphs of the Abbasid Dynasty (A.D. 750–1258) to the study of Greek science. For gold bullion (but not for their coinage) they adopted the Aegina–Beqa standard of weight; and built up a new system based on the quarter of the Aegina stater, *i.e.* 48 grains, which became the Arabic gold dirhem, subdivided in 16 kirat.

The system was:

$$1 \text{ kirat} = \begin{cases} 3 \text{ hebbeh (barley corns)} \\ 4 \text{ khambeh (wheat grains)} \end{cases}$$

$$16 \text{ kirat} = 1 \text{ dirhem} = 48 \text{ grains}$$
$$10 \text{ dirhem} = 1 \text{ wukiyeh (oz)} = 480 \text{ grains}$$
$$12 \text{ wukiyeh} = 1 \text{ ratl (lb)} = 5{,}760 \text{ grains}$$

Thus under the Arabs the ancient Beqa shekel returned as a gold standard once more. The Arabic gold system passed to Europe by trade in the medieval period under the general name of Troy Weight. In the fifteenth century Troy Weight was adopted in England, and at the pure Arabic standard; the only difference was that the 48-grain dirhem was divided into two English 'pennyweights' of 24 grains each, with 20 penny-weights to the ounce.

As the basis of their silver coinage the Arabs adopted one of the ancient shekels known as the 'Khoirine'. This had begun about 2000 B.C. as a silver shekel in Egypt at a weight of 172 grains; it spread to Babylonia and Persia and became the Persian silver standard under Darius the Great (521–485 B.C.) at a slightly increased weight, the silver 'siglos' coinage weighing half a Khoirine shekel, 86·5 grains. When the Arabs adopted the Khoirine in the seventh century A.D. they increased it to a standard of 176 grains, the quarter of which, 44 grains, was the weight of the earlier Arabic silver dirhem coinage. Under the Abbasid dynasty (A.D. 750) the silver dirhem reached and maintained a weight of 45 grains. The Arabic silver ounce was 10 dirhems (450 grains) and the silver ratl or pound was 12 ounces (5,400 grains), the system being exactly similar to that of the gold dirhem.

Late in the eighth century A.D. the Harun-al-Rashid, who was Caliph from A.D. 768 to 809, sent an ambassador to Charlemagne, king of the Franks and Emperor of the Holy Roman Empire, which then included all France, bearing amongst other gifts, specimens of the Arabic coinage, weights and measures. Visiting the court of Charlemagne about the same time, Offa, king of Mercia, then the leading power in England and the most able of all the Anglo-Saxon kings before Alfred, decided to adopt for his coinage the standard of the Arabic silver dirhem of 45 grains. In A.D. 791, Offa instituted the first English silver 'penny-sterling' of 22·5 grains, exactly half the contemporary Arabic silver dirhem. Then the 'pennyweight' was literally the weight of the silver penny, and 20 pennyweights went to the ounce of 450 grains, and 12 ounces to the silver pound of 5,400 grains, exactly the same as the Arabic silver ratl.

This pound weight became known in England as the Moneyers' Pound, and later under the Norman kings (who made no alteration in the Saxon weights and measures) it became the 'Tower Pound', and remained the English standard for silver coinage until finally abolished by Henry VIII in 1527, in favour of English Troy weight based on the Arabic gold dirhem of 48 grains.

Meanwhile, however, the Tower Pound flourished in England and gave rise to a Merchants' Pound, as described in a royal ordinance of Henry III, the Assise of Bread and Ale of 1266, which defined the Tower Pound system for coinage and commercial weight for the first time (the original is in Latin):

By the law of the whole Kingdom of England the measure of our Lord the King was composed in the following way; the English penny which is called a ster-lyng, round and uncut, ought to weight 32 grains of wheat taken from the middle of the ear. And the ounce ought to weigh 20 pennies. And 12 ounces make the London Pound, that is to say 20 shillings sterlyng.

And 8 pounds make the gallon of wine, and 8 gallons of wine make the London Bushel; and 8 bushels make the London Quarter; and 12½ pounds make the London Stone.

And let it be known that the pound of pennies and of spices and confections as well as of apothecaries' goods, consists of 20 shillings; the true pound of all other things is of 25 shillings.

The true Ounce consists of 20 pennies, and the pound contains 12 ounces. In all other things the pound contains 15 ounces. The true Ounce here also is 20 pennies in weight.

The silver penny sterling from ample evidence of the actual coinage weighed 22·5 grains, *i.e.* Offa's standard and the Arabic silver half-dirhem. The ordinance therefore established:

The ounce = (20 × 22·5) grains = 450 grains
The pound = (12 × 450) grains = 5,400 grains
(coinage pound)
The pound = (15 × 450) grains = 6,750 grains
(Merchants' Pound, or Libra Mercatoria).

The 'shilling' mentioned in the ordinance was only a term of account. It did not exist then as an actual coin. 'Apothecaries' goods' are mentioned for the first time in an English statute of the Realm as being weighed by the same weight as the coinage.

The 15-ounce Merchants' Pound of 6,750 grains appears at first sight to be an anomaly, but actually it was the same as the commercial pound of many South German cities included in the Holy Roman Empire at this period, with which England had profitable trade relations.

In the fourteenth and fifteenth centuries, with the expansion of English home industries, particularly the wool trade, England was the meeting place of two great traffic lanes of rival international trade. From the North, the Baltic and North Sea route, controlled by the Hanseatic League, traded to the east coast ports of Hull, Boston and Lynn (King's Lynn). From the South, the Mediterranean trade controlled by Venice and Genoa passed up the coasts of France and Spain to our south coast ports and up the Thames to London. This southern trade favoured coinage and bullion weight systems based on the Arabic gold dirhem of 48 grains, just as the Hanseatic northern trade favoured the Arabic silver system of the 45 grain dirhem.

English merchants, faced by much intolerance from the Germans of the Hanseatic League which refused to allow them reciprocal trading facilities in the German markets, turned their attention more and more to the Mediterranean trade. This naturally opened the way to an alteration in the English bullion weight system – the gradual change-over from the Tower Pound or silver standard used by the Hanseatic cities to the Troy Pound or gold standard, favoured by the Italians.

The Troy Pound is first mentioned in English Statutes of the Realm in 1414, in a statute dealing with the price and composition of English goldsmiths' work of silver-gilt, weighed by the 'pound of Troy'. A statute of 1423 dealing with the coinage and the scarcity of 'White Money' within the realm, regulating the price of bar and plate silver at thirty shillings the Pound of Troy of the same alloy as the 'sterling coinage'.

In these two statutes the Troy Pound is 'permissive' only, but it is quite evident that among English goldsmiths and silversmiths, the Troy system was already well established. Imports of the precious metals came almost exclusively from the Mediterranean trade route which used that system.

The English Mint system was still that of the Tower Pound of 5,400 grains (12 ounces of 450 grains), but exchange between the two systems was simple: 15 Troy ounces of 480 grains = 16 Tower ounces of 450 grains, both being equal to 7,200 grains, or the Tower Pound = 11¼ Troy ounces. The Troy system was exactly the same as the Arabic gold system, except that the dirhem of 48 grains was represented by two pennyweights of 24 grains, the system being:

24 grains = 1 pennyweight (dwt)
20 dwt = 1 ounce (oz) = 480 grains
12 oz = 1 pound (lb Tr. or Pd. Tr.)
= 5,760 grains.

In 1497 Henry VII instituted Troy weight as the legal bullion standard, clearly defined on a statutory basis, the provisions of which were written in English for the first time. The Troy pound, ounce and pennyweight were established for silver, gold and bread principally, and for spices and 'electuaries', *i.e.* apothecaries' goods. At the same time a Merchants' Pound of 16 Troy ounces was established for all other goods except wool, for which the avoirdupois pound of Edward III of 6,992 grains was maintained.

Henry VII also defined capacity measure both for grain and liquids as containing 100 Troy ounces of wheat at threshing dryness for the Winchester gallon, with the pint (⅛ gallon) containing 12½ Troy ounces. Copies of all Henry's weights and measures, duly certified and stamped with the royal cypher, were sent to some forty-three of the principal cities and towns of England.

In 1527 Henry VIII finally abolished the Tower Pound, ordering the Mint to use only the Troy pound.

In 1588, under Elizabeth I, the Citizens' Jury that produced the third and final series of Avoirdupois Standards, also produced a set of Exchequer Troy Standards of great accuracy, based upon the existing standards kept by the Goldsmiths' Company. These Exchequer Standards of 1588 (now preserved at the Science Museum in London) are a series of thirteen bronze 'cup-shape' weights, made to fit one inside the other exactly. They range from $\frac{1}{8}$ oz to 256 Tr. oz in binary progression, totalling 512 Tr. Oz. = $42\frac{2}{3}$ Tr. Pd. These were the Primary Reference Standards of the Realm for Troy weight from 1588 to 1824, *i.e.* for 236 years. So well were they kept that when re-weighed in 1873 by the Warden of the Standards Department of the Board of Trade, none of the weights up to 8 oz (3,840 grains) was deficient by more than 1·09 grains; from 16 oz to 128 oz the worst deficiency was 5·04 grains on the weight of 64 oz (30,720 grains). On the largest weight, 256 oz (122,800 grains), the deficiency was 53·58 grains, but this one, as the container for all the rest of the set, naturally took most of the wear.

In 1758 the Carysfort Commission on Weights and Measures prepared three new Troy Pound standards of bronze, one of which was legalized in 1824 as the Imperial Troy Pound of 5,760 grains, but was destroyed by the great House of Commons fire in 1834. One of its fellows made at the same time, and inscribed 'lb T 1758', is also in the Science Museum. In 1855, when new Imperial Standards were legalized, the Troy Pound lost its premier position to the Avoirdupois Pound (7,000 Troy grains), but remained the standard for bullion. Finally, in 1878, the Troy Pound was abolished to do away with the anomaly of two different pound standards, but the Troy ounce, pennyweight and grain were retained for bullion and coinage. Thus we still weigh as the Egyptians weighed their Nubian gold. But the Metric System will eventually prevail. (See also *Coins.*)

ILLUSTRATION: Page 264.

Waters of life

WELLS developed, no doubt, from small scrapes or soak-holes such as are made by Australian aborigines.

A second stage would be to clear such a hole and protect it by a rough setting of stones. A drop in the level of this protected soak-hole could lead to a third stage – that of deepening the shallow pit, which might need to be lined to prevent it caving in. The pit would now become a true well, shafted with a hollow tree-trunk or even walled with shorn timber.

True wells, vertically excavated to a considerable depth, solidly walled or framed, developed only with the rise of cities in the Near East, when populations became too large for the natural water supply, or were compelled to live too many streets away for fetching and carrying the water of a spring. Thus there were wells in the ancient cities of Harappa and Mohenjo-daro in the valley of the Indus (2500 B.C.–1500 B.C.). The wells there are like our own domestic wells, circular, walled carefully with brick and surrounded by a brick coping; and often deep, since additions had to be made to the well-shafts as the occupation level of each city rose during a thousand years. The wells opened sometimes into the houses, as in older farmhouses and other dwellings in Europe. Many of these shafts are now bare and emergent like factory chimneys.

Mohenjo-daro had wells and drains. So had Greek cities of the Mycenaean civilization, c. 1600 B.C. In the palace of the Mycenaean city of Phylakopi, excavated on the volcanic island of Melos in the Cyclades, a well had been sunk in the courtyard, shafted not with brick or stone, but with short lengths of earthenware piping of a large diameter – as if the hollow tree trunk had been imitated in clay.

Well-digging spread to the Etruscans and to the Romans, and later into the Roman provinces, reaching Britain, where a good many Roman wells have been excavated. Frequently the Romans lined, or framed, their wells with timber instead of stone (a common method also in the United States as settlement moved westward); and since drawing up water by hand out of a well is not at all easy, the bucket catching the sides, jumping about and spilling, the Romans developed winches and the overhung iron wheels, which are still common throughout Italy.

The Romans distinguished 'spring', *fons*, from 'well', *puteus*. Our word 'well' comes from the Old English *wiella*, meaning not an artificial water-shaft, but that which 'wells up', a natural spring, the sense preserved in 'holy well', 'Tunbridge Wells', of 'well-head' for the source of a stream. The Roman well had presumably been forgotten. Wells were commonly dug again in the Middle Ages, in castles and in cities. Elsewhere people would often depend lazily enough upon the natural unaugmented supply – even where it was apt to fail in dry weather; or they would fashion one of those crude dip-wells fed by a minute trickle, which are still common in the English countryside, though frowned upon by the sanitary official. The Celtic monks who lived on the sea-rock of Skellig Michael, in the Atlantic, in the Dark Ages and Early Middle Ages had no well among their beehive huts, only two dip-wells, which store the faintest trickle of water. In the Isles of Scilly as late as the eighteenth century islanders were content to drink water from off their thatch or out of brackish pools, or to row to other islands for fresh water in casks, rather than go to the trouble of well-digging – a tricky, dangerous craft which has left behind it the simile 'as cold as a well-digger's knee' (the English surname 'Weller' does not come from digging wells: the word meant a metal-founder).

The ancient city wells held their reputation, on the whole, till early in the nineteenth century, though they had long been supplemented with supplies brought in by pipe (particularly bored sections of elm-tree, a device the Romans had used) and by conduit. Nineteenth-century inhabitants of the City of London thought the chilly sparkling water of their wells preferable to piped water – little knowing that the sparkle was due to the gases of gross contamination. To meet the increasing thirst for water in recent times caused by growing population, industry and agriculture, new sources had to be found by deeper borings. Artesian wells, first developed in Artois in the twelfth century, go down to several thousand feet; in Australia some wells go down for more than a mile. (See also *Bath*.)

Wheel behind wheel

The **WHEEL** and wheeled vehicles – the wheel and the use of the horse in traction – developed in the Near East.

It was only when the first urban civilization grew up that the wheel became necessary to man. He then had goods and foodstuffs to transport to concentrations in the cities. The wheel could no doubt have been invented by some palaeolithic hunter, but inventions are only taken up or taken into everyday life when circumstances call for them, as they called for them some five thousand years ago in the flat lands of the Middle East.

For many thousands of years palaeolithic and mesolithic man had lived by hunting; he had wandered in search of game, in smallish bands, like the Australian aboriginal today. Even the first neolithic farmers or cultivators produced only food enough for their own needs; their life in self-sufficient villages, unearthed at Jarmo, in Iraq, at Jericho, and elsewhere, dating back to about 5000 B.C., involved no transport requirements for which simple wheel-less vehicles such as the sledge (q.v.), the travois, or the slide-car, were not enough. These have their own long history, and are still in use today in peripheral environments, and environments too difficult for the wheel.

By the fourth millennium B.C. the rich soil of Mesopotamia and Egypt yielded sufficient grain to feed men engaged in professions and crafts other than farming – priests, tool-makers, gem-cutters, traders and others could give their services in exchange for the food grown by the agriculturalists. The fertility of the soil in these river areas – to which the valley of the Indus should be added – caused the 'Urban Revolution'; the rise of cities, the development of writing, law-making, and organized religion.

In Egypt foodstuffs could travel by water, by the artery of the Nile along which the cities grew up in a narrow strip. In Mesopotamia, city-states, such as Ur of the Chaldees, were dotted all over the fertile land between the Tigris and the Euphrates, a much wider extent; and in Mesopotamia wheeled vehicles were in use before 3000 B.C.

Evidence for the wheel in the ancient world is luckily of several kinds, not confined solely to actual examples. This is fortunate, since wood survives only in special circumstances of great dryness or extreme dampness; and farmers leave their worn-out vehicles to rot; they do not transport them to dry sand or tip them into a bog for the benefit of future generations. With the coming of writing, everyday objects were used as picture signs, and early records furnish their evidence; scenes are engraved on rock, are painted on tombs and on temples. In early Greece signet rings have given information about

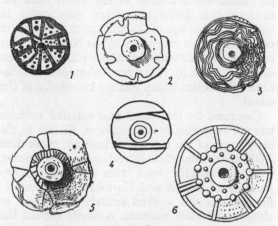

Fig. 37. Early model wheels from Susa 2–6 and Tepe Djori 1.

the type of wheel in vogue. Models of houses, ploughs, carts, have been found everywhere in the ancient world, possibly toys, possibly cult-objects representing full-sized counterparts. Religious beliefs have added their quota of information, since in parts of Europe, the use of the wheel led to the 'sun-disc' and the ritual cauldron mounted on a wheeled chassis, and the hearse, which can claim to be one of the earliest type of vehicle. Drawings of these survive.

The evidence shows a surprising diversity in the forms of cart or waggon in the Near East and in ancient, prehistoric Europe. The form of wheel is another matter: it strongly suggests that this root invention was diffused from a centre in the Near East – that the imported or acquired wheel was added under the local variety of wheel-less vehicle.

Clay tablets from the ancient city of Erech in Mesopotamia itself exhibit a sign representing a sledge. This is shown as a square surmounted by a triangle (the body of the sledge), placed on runners with a marked upward curve in front. Another sign shows the earliest representation of a wheeled vehicle in the world; and this portrays the whole sledge of the other sign, upward-curving runners and all, *with wheels underneath*. The sequence and the process must have been repeated elsewhere, in regions where skilled woodworkers, continuing to make the chassis in the form they were accustomed to, learned to add and to make the wheel from observation of 'foreign' carts.

The circumstances of the invention of the wheel are lost in antiquity, though conjecture has been busy. A convenient theory postulates the development of wheel and axle from tree-trunks employed as rollers to transport heavy objects, such as huge stone statues. If the centre were gradually shaved away for convenience, the result would be two solid wooden wheels at the extremities of an axle made in one piece with them. However, this raises two problems for the archaeologist: he must expect to find that the earliest wheels were cut from solid wood, in one piece. He must also find drawings and models (if not actual examples) showing that the axle moved with the wheels, before being attached to the bottom of the vehicle, leaving the wheels to revolve on their own.

The archaeological evidence does not uniformly concur with this theory. One early chariot model does show a detached axle, turning with the wheels; but in the ancient graves at Ur unmistakable copper bolts were discovered, with which the axle of a waggon had been firmly attached to the waggon base. The theory is even less well supported when it comes to the construction of early wheels. All of the earliest known wheels are built up: not one has that solid end-of-a-log form essential to the theory. The first wheels are made of three pieces of wood which are held together by transverse struts.

This built-up wheel was adopted in Europe, but not until after European peoples had already adopted the later form of wheel with spokes, which had come into use in the Near East about 2000 B.C. The Egyptian Pharaohs are pictured in light war chariots with slender four-spoked wheels. Mycenean princes in Greece, about 1500 B.C., are shown in similar vehicles. After another 500 years had gone by the wheel appeared in northern Italy and in central and northern Europe. The 'new' invention did not arrive in Britain until the Iron Age began there, about 500 B.C.

Corroboration is provided by the circumstances in which wheeled vehicles have been recovered. At first wheeled vehicles are restricted to kings and chiefs (it was the rich who had the first motor cars). In the Near East the earliest wheels are found in the rich burials of kings and queens, with whom their retainers sacrificed themselves. In Europe, where a number of graves are grouped together, it is only those with rich grave-goods, indicating royal or chieftain's burials, which are provided with wheeled hearses. In the Marne region, from which the earliest Iron Age invaders of Britain came, the chiefs were buried in their chariots in deep pits, which were deepened to take the wheels. Similar burials have been uncovered in Britain, although here, for practical considerations, only symbolic parts of the chariot were abandoned to the dead. These were the famous chariots which confronted Caesar when he raided Britain in 55 B.C. – and it should be noted that there is no archaeological evidence for the presence of scythes on the axle.

Oxen were the first traction beasts, harnessed to the first vehicles as they had been to the plough. Horses were used to draw the lighter, speedier chariot, which was the first horse-drawn vehicle. When the possibilities of the horse were realized, the harness was not modified all at once; the horse was simply substituted for the heavier beast, the yoke being then transferred from the plough, with the central shaft which ran between the pair of animals. The horses were attached to the yoke by a band round the neck. While suitable for the ox, this band pressed against the windpipe of the horse as it strained forward, making it impossible to get the best out of this animal until the subsequent invention of the horse-collar.

The origin of the metal tyre may also be traced back to the Near East. The iron bands around the wheels of the Celtic chariot were shrunk on to the felloe as the wheelwright still shrinks on his tyres today. This was an improvement on the first metal tyres, used in Elam before 2000 B.C., which were in segments, clamped over the rim of the wheel. However, the need to protect the wooden edge of the wheel from wear had been realized from the time when the wheel was first used. The earliest models and vase paintings of wheeled vehicles show a curious 'cogged' rim to each wheel. This has been explained by wheels of 5,000 years ago, which have been found with copper nails thickly driven into the felloe all the way round the circumference.

After the iron tyres of the Iron Age, there was no fundamental change in the wheel until the modern era. Pneumatic tyres then came in with the rubber age of the nineteenth century – in other words, an invention of the Near East was combined at last with the rubber which had been developed first by those pre-Columbian civilizations of America which had no knowledge of the wheel.

Conquest by the wheel and wheeled vehicles has not been steady and uniform. As late as the early years of the nineteenth century, more than 2,000 years after their introduction into Britain, wheeled vehicles were rare in the country parishes of Devon and Cornwall, for example; the farmers still worked entirely with drays or sledges and pack animals. Animals carried the dung to the fields, fetched seaweed from the beaches and lime from the kiln, and brought in the harvest of hay or corn piled high and shakily on their backs.

It may also be remarked that boats were a more highly elaborated vehicle of travel and transport at a much earlier period. Nature provided more or less level water. In the hilly countries man had to build his roadways, before he could give up some of his uncomfortable but convenient dependence upon waterways.

The wheel's importance as something to roll on must not make us forget its other uses. The turbine wheel, the water-wheel and paddle wheel, the high-speed grinding wheel, the gramophone disc, so obviously better than any phonographic cylinder, are only a few examples of the wheel's true function, that of the lever; for a wheel is 'a lever all the way round'. (See also *Pneumatic Tyres, Sledges, Boats, Motor-Car, Coaches, Roads, Potter's Wheel.*)

Hair on the head

WIGS (wig is short for 'periwig', from the French *perruque*) perform now two duties; in both they disguise, but for different ends: actors and spies wear them to change their own identity, but bald men and women wear them to supplement their failing hair.

More often than not it is fashionable to own some hair; those who are bald do not look as others do, and such people have always been open to public ridicule. On the other hand, when it is fashionable to have hair and much of it, then it is splendid to have even more than anyone else: hence arose a third duty of the wig, as panache to proclaim the splendour and social status of its owner.

Wigs were known in Assyria and in ancient Egypt, in Palestine and in Greece. In Tacitus' day, and later, German tribes made large profits on blonde hair exported to Rome, while the Church Fathers spoke harshly of those who wore false hair; but the true efflorescence of the wig began only in the seventeenth century. At the court of Louis XIII it was fashionable for the nobility to wear the hair long: unfortunately the noblest of them all, the King, began prematurely to lose his hair. He supplemented it to begin with; but eventually he took to a wig proper, and the court by courtesy had to follow suit. For men, the European wig had arrived, and during two centuries it was almost a convenience to be bald – if you were not, you had to crop your hair to accommodate the wig. Women rarely went to such lengths, though Barnaby Rich in James I's reign had complained of their 'lousy commodity of periwigs ... monstrous mop-poles of hair': in fact, women generally supplemented rather than replaced.

In England the male wig became *de rigueur* only about 1663. By 1700 it had attained its full growth, falling well below and about the shoulders, rising high from the forehead in two peaks; and so it bloomed on through the reign of Queen Anne. Through the reigns of the three Georges the wig waxed and waned; the 'natural', or full-bottomed wig, was cultured into a myriad hybrids: 'the pigeon's wing, the comet, the cauli-flower, the royal bird, the staircase, the she-dragon, the rose, the cut bob, the long bob, the spinage seed ...' Lady Mary Wortley Montagu's son arrived from Paris in 1751 with an iron wig, spun of the finest wire. Occasionally one of these types would fossilize as an accessory of ceremonial costume: so the Speaker of the House of Commons still wears a full-bottomed wig, and wigs are proper to English judges, barristers and the Lord Chancellor.

This variety was not a symptom of health: the wig was failing – in 1765 the wig-makers, in a petition to George III, deplored their decline, 'occasioned by the present mode of men in all stations wearing their own hair'. They were countered by a mock petition on behalf of the Body-Carpenters, urging his Majesty to wear a wooden leg. An uneasy period followed: men dressed their hair to look like a wig even if they did not wear one, and in the 1770s the macaronis launched their toupets to heights yet undreamed of (in caricatures their hairdressers work on ladders); but before long undergraduates, to the fury of the authorities, were wearing their own hair unashamed, cropped and unpowdered, braving the nickname of 'Apollo'. When Archbishop Sumner, in 1858, put on his wig to marry the Princess Royal, it was but a gesture of quaint old-fashioned conservatism.

Now, though the wig of disguise remains, the wig of ostentation has vanished. Its vogue consorted oddly with the Age of Reason which it graced: all the great men of Reason wore it – Locke, Newton, Pope, Lord Burlington and Gibbon, even Lessing and Voltaire and Dr Johnson: its emphasis is certainly on the head, but the common sense of cutting off one's own hair in order to wear someone else's is arguable.

Yet the wig had its virtues; even the painter Hogarth admitted that 'the full-bottomed wig, like the lion's mane, hath something noble in it, and adds not only dignity but sagacity to the countenance'. It offered variety: you could wear your own hair as a wig (like Pepys), but other sources were used – wives, German blondes, the poor, and, often, the dead (but not at plague time); you could be dark or you could be fair to choice. Priests could even have their wigs tonsured. Pepys argued for the cleanliness of the wig as against that of his own hair, but birds and mice were alleged to nest in later, more complicated, forms.

Wigs were expensive, cumbrous, inflammable, and too vulnerable to *lèse-majesté* (a French actress once did some skilful angling with hooks and lines before the play began; when the curtain rose, the wigs of the orchestra soared with it). It seems unlikely that they will return under modern conditions of society, but, should men start to wear their hair long again, anything might happen.

ILLUSTRATION: Page 127.

Power from the wind

WINDMILLS were developed much later than the water-mill; they are first mentioned by the Arab geographer Al-Mas'ūdī in his *Meadows of Gold and Mines of Precious Stones*, an encyclopaedic work he compiled in the tenth century. He mentions windmills in Seistan in north-west Persia, which were horizontal windmills, with sails mounted on a vertical shaft and turning in a horizontal plane. Seistan, which is a wheat and barley district, still has such mills, modifications of which are also to be found on one part of the Chinese coast.

Probably the windmill was invented by Arabs. Certainly in Europe there is no proof of its existence before the twelfth century, two hundred years after Al-Mas'ūdī's time. One was at work in Normandy about 1180. In England Bury St Edmunds had a windmill by 1191. These corn mills were of the familiar type with sails turning in a vertical plane. The earliest were 'post-mills', in which a wooden box-like body contains all the machinery and carries the sails, and is mounted on a suitably braced vertical wooden post. This post sockets into a horizontal beam on the level of the second floor of the mill, and the whole body can be turned round on top of the post, so that the sails can be faced square into the wind.

The post-mill developed into the tower-mill (though the two types continued side by side), in which all the machinery was placed in a fixed tower of masonry or wood with a movable roof or cap carrying the sails; thus only the cap had to be turned on top of the tower when the direction of the wind changed. The first known illustration of a tower-mill occurs in a French manuscript of 1420.

These early windmills were turned into the wind by means of a long tailpole, extending to the ground from the bottom floor in the case of a post-mill or from the cap in the case of a tower-mill. In 1745 Edmund Lee patented the fantail, which does this work automatically by wind power. A small 'windmill' is fixed to the rear of the mill with its vanes at right angles to the mill-sails proper. When the sails face square into the wind, the vanes of the fantail present an edge to it and do not turn; when the wind veers, it turns the vanes, and these, being connected by gearing either to wheels at the base of the ladder in post-mills, or in tower-mills to a geared rack at the top of the tower, turn until the sails face square into the wind once more.

Older sails were simply wooden frames spread with cloth. In 1772 the millwright Andrew Meikle, the pioneer of the threshing-machine (q.v.), invented the shuttered sail, putting hinged shutters like those of a venetian blind into the frame and controlling them by a spring to each sail. His invention was improved upon in 1807 by Sir William Cubitt, who operated all the shutters in all the sails simultaneously by remote control, by weights on a chain which varied according to the power required in the mill.

In England windmills, whether for grinding or the secondary purpose of drainage, are obsolete or obsolescent. Windmilling technique is more difficult than water-milling technique, and the windmill is more expensive to maintain and less easy to adapt to other purposes. So the wooden post-mills fall apart, and the tower-mills stand derelict and shorn of their sails. A hill-top will have no more trace of its old mill than the sheer name of 'Windmill Hill' or the stone footings of the tower, raised higher into the wind, perhaps on a round barrow of the Bronze Age.

In the Netherlands the sombre wheels turn against the endless sky still as on the canvas of some seventeenth-century master. There the windmill is indispensable; and there in 1923 windmill sails underwent a new modification when aerofoils were fitted with success to the leading edges.

Elsewhere, too, from Greece and the Isles of Greece to the almost waterless Canary Isles, windmills of a Mediterranean type hold their own. (See *Water-mills, Querns.*)

ILLUSTRATION: Page 322.

Wreaths for the quick and the dead

WREATHS and garlands have, everywhere and since time immemorial, been decorations in religious ceremonies, occasions of festivals, banquets and dances. They are usually an expression of joyful feeling (as such they are mentioned in the Apocrypha, in *The Wisdom of Solomon* 'Let us crown ourselves with rosebuds'). At a sacrifice in ancient Greece the temple, the altar, the worshippers, the animal victims and the baskets containing the offerings were decorated with flowers. The Greek magician, when practising divinatory rites, wreathed himself, and the gods always appeared wearing a wreath, perhaps a sign of the aura supposed to surround their heads, which in Christian times became the halo.

The Greek kings, victors in athletic games and warfare, were honoured with a laurel wreath. 'A crown of grass and flowers, plucked on the spot, was given to the Roman general who conquered a city. A crown of oak leaves with acorns was bestowed upon the soldier who in battle saved the life of a Roman citizen.' (*Encyclopaedia Britannica*, 1953 ed.). Wreaths of ivy were worn at banquets, and it has been suggested that the ivy was chosen because its dark clustered berries resemble grapes.

The bridegroom in ancient Greece presented the bride with her wreath, mostly of myrtle, and at their wedding both wore wreaths supposed to bestow good fortune. In Germany, before bridal crowns came into fashion, the bride used to wear her hair loose, decorated with ribbons, a headband or a wreath. Opera lovers will remember the chorus in Weber's *Freischütz*: 'Wir winden dir den Jungfernkranz'. The eighteenth-century 'Maidens' Garlands', similar to the 'Virgin's

crown' have been preserved in some Shropshire churches. Each of them hangs from a rod with a heart, and some of these bear dates and initials. The garlands are made of a wooden frame, about a foot in diameter; they are adorned with paper flowers, streamers and pairs of gloves cut out of white paper.

The origin of the ancient custom of presenting the dead with flowers or wreaths of leaves and evergreens has not yet been satisfactorily explained. A moving description of the custom of dressing the graves with flowers can be found in the *Diary* of the Rev. Francis Kilvert. On Easter Eve, 1870, baskets full of flowers were taken to the graveyard, and women and children with knives cut holes in the turf of the green mounds. 'More and more people kept coming into the churchyard as they finished their day's work. The sun went down in glory behind the dingle, but still the work of love went on through the twilight and into the dusk until the moon rose full and splendid. The figures continued to move about among the graves in the calm clear moonlight and warm air of the balmy evening ... The flowers most used were primroses, daffodils, currant, [word illegible] laurel and box.'

City gates, boundary stones, houses, ships, and even animals were sometimes decorated with wreaths and garlands. To procure a happy fate, the ancient Greeks used to attach a wreath to the door of the house when a child was born. If it was a boy, the wreath was of olive branches; if a girl, it was of woollen threads. The birth of a boy was obviously more welcome. The young man of Greece would put garlands at the door of his love. In Germany (a common sight of the reconstruction after the bombing of the Second World War) a wreath or a young pine tree, decorated with red ribbons, is attached to the roof-tree of a newly-built house, or factory even, when the framework of the roof has been completed. Then the owner, the builder and his workmen, will forgather, drinks are handed round and a toast is proposed to the happiness of the future inhabitants. This informal celebration is the survival of an old blessing ceremony.

Animals were, and still are, decked with wreaths, garlands and even crowns. In Bavaria the *Almabtrieb, i.e.* the driving home of the cattle from alpine pastures, usually takes place about

16 October and seems to be a kind of thank-offering, for only if all has gone well during the summer will the animals be thus decorated. Fifty years ago these decorations were far more elaborate, but even the paper wreaths, crowns and garlands of recent years give the cows a festive look, as they follow the 'farmer's pride' (*Glockenkuh*), the cow with a large bell fastened to its neck.

An appeal to the vegetation-spirit which is believed to reside in the flowers of the wreaths and garlands becomes evident in some seasonal festivals, especially those held during the spring (see *Maypole*). Sir James Frazer, in *The Golden Bough*, has dealt extensively with the King and Queen of May, or Whitsuntide, and also with Jack-in-the-Green, the May Day mummer, who was covered from head to foot with leaves and garlands. Rather surprising are representations of Jack-in-the-Green in some English cathedrals and churches, for instance, at Ely, Canterbury, Norwich, Exeter, Hereford, Worcester, Southwell Minster, etc., carved on roof bosses, corbels, etc., showing the face wreathed in leaves of oak or hawthorn.

Every Whit Monday, at the small town of Bampton, in Oxfordshire, the Morris dancers dance from morning till night in the streets and in the gardens, to the accompaniment of either a fiddle or an accordion. Minor changes are to be noticed from year to year. Lately small girls, nicely dressed up, have walked about carrying garlands and dolls, a custom which had lapsed for some time. This is certainly a reminiscence of the May King and Queen. On Ascension Day the five wells at Tissington, in Derbyshire, are dressed with flowers. Their original stone frontage is on this day hidden by a wooden arch, covered with plaster of paris; while it is still wet, flowers without leaves are stuck into it to form religious symbols, and short texts from the Bible. Robert Chambers, in *The Book of Days* (1862–1864), became quite lyrical about this custom, which he recognized to be of great antiquity: 'It is scarcely possible to describe the vivid colouring of these wreaths and garlands, and the devices of every hue'. He called it one of the most beautiful of all the English customs.

At the Harvest Home (the celebration at the end of the harvest) a wreath or crown, sometimes made of the last ears of corn, and decorated with flowers, tinsel and coloured ribbons, used to be presented to the English farmer for a small consideration in money. The verses which were then recited allude to the harvest wreath's power of averting evil and bringing prosperity. On Lammas Day, at the Harvest Thanksgiving, some of the smaller churches in Oxfordshire are still delightfully decorated with whole sheaves of corn.

The 'Ale Garland', of ivy, stuck on small beer-barrel hoops, to betoken good-will at Christmas time, has lately been revived by an Oxford inn.

Sometimes wreaths were worn to dispel headaches. They were also put into beehives to make a new swarm stay, a custom reported from Switzerland. But these customs may arise simply from the cooling influence and the refreshing smell of the flowers. (See also *Coffins*.)

ILLUSTRATION: Page 34.

Z

The Tower of Babel

The **ZIGGURAT** was an artificial mountain supporting a temple.

Ruins of about a score of such structures are known. The oldest ziggurat discovered is at Warka, in Iraq, the biblical Erech. This goes back to the fourth millennium B.C., and is an irregularly shaped mound, originally forty feet high and covering an area of about 420,000 square feet. The best-preserved ziggurat stands at Ur of the Chaldees, and was built about 2000 B.C. It is now about 190 feet high, and it has an oblong ground plan of 150 by 130 feet. Of all ziggurats, the most famous is the Tower of Babel (or Babylon), square in ground plan, like all the later ziggurats, and described more fully by Herodotus than by the Old Testament. In 1899 excavations were started at Babylon, and ever since there has been controversy about the nature and appearance of its ziggurat. The Greek descriptions cannot easily be harmonized with the information contained in ancient clay tablets, and the excavations were less informative than had been expected. Only the ground plan was discovered, a square with sides of about 275 feet. The building itself was a low and formless heap of brickwork, left apparently when Alexander the Great's attempt at reconstruction was interrupted by his sudden death in 323 B.C.

All the various sources have been taken into account in the construction of the model which illustrates this article. The ziggurat rose in seven stages, which were painted, according to Herodotus in different colours. The temple on the top was blue (fragments of blue glazed bricks found on the site of Babel suggest that it was built of this glittering material). A triple stairway gave access to the lowest stages, and a spiral ramp led to the top. Around the ziggurat was an open court, and the main temple of the god who was worshipped on the site, stood at the foot, either built up against the ziggurat, or, as at Babylon, in a separate enclosure nearby.

The body of the ziggurat was built of sun-dried bricks strengthened at intervals with layers of rush matting. For the plain of the Tigris and Euphrates lacked stone and wood, and supplied only mud in unlimited quantities as a building material. But unbaked bricks weather badly and our aerial photograph of the ziggurat of Djokha Zembil, near Susa, illustrates the sad condition in which these massive structures survive. It also shows the enclosure wall surrounding the sacred precincts. Even in their present ruined state the ziggurats are most impressive, for their huge man-made bulk dominates the featureless plain for miles around.

The word ziggurat derives from an ancient Babylonian verb meaning 'to be high'; it is therefore descriptive rather than explanatory. But recently the designation of the temple on top of the ziggurat has been discovered. This is a word best translated as 'place of passage'. The same word is used in the ordinary temples for the ante-room leading into the Holy of Holies, where the god was supposed to dwell. But the temple on the top of the ziggurat would not seem to lead to anything beyond itself. It was evidently viewed as a 'place of passage' for the god, who was thought to 'land' there and pass on when he came down to dwell among his people in the temple at the foot of the ziggurat, and likewise to pass through it again on his return to the heavens. It is significant that several ziggurats are called 'Mountain, bond between heaven and earth', although that name has also a deeper meaning, as we shall see.

Herodotus was told a detailed story about the use made of the temple on the top of the ziggurat of Babylon:

... inside the temple stands a great bed covered with fine bed-clothes, with a golden table by its side. There is no statue of any kind set up in the place, nor is the chamber occupied of nights by anyone but a single native woman who, as the Chaldeans, the priests of this god, affirm, is chosen for himself by the deity out of all the women of the land. They also declare – but I for my part do not credit it – that the god comes down in person into this chamber, and sleeps upon the couch.

(Rawlinson's translation.)

There is a great deal of Babylonian evidence for the celebration of a divine marriage which symbolized and was thought to ensure the fruitfulness of nature, and hence the prosperity of man. Herodotus alone tells us that it was consummated on top of the 'mountain', the ziggurat, but there is some corroboration for this report. For in Babylonia 'mountain' was a concept as heavily charged with religious meaning as 'cross' is in our world and as 'west' was in Ancient Egypt. The 'mountain' stood for 'the earth'. In it were concentrated the mysterious vital forces which revive the seemingly dead vegetation in spring and autumn, and fill the parched river-beds with water after the deadly summer. The sun, too, reappears daily on the mountains of the east, and the rain clouds gather upon the mountains before they discharge their blessing over the plain. The Great Mother, source of all life, is called Ninharsag, Lady of the Mountain. Thus the mountain is essentially the mysterious sphere of action of the divine powers. When, therefore, the Babylonians, with an immense expenditure of wealth and labour, erected the ziggurats of their temples, they created the conditions under which communication with the divine, upon which their well-being depended, became possible.

ILLUSTRATION: Page 314.

ZIPPERS, ZIPS or ZIP-FASTENERS are an ingeniously developed version of the old hooks and eyes of male and female dress. The ziggurat builders of Mesopotamia (see the last entry) had their buttons, and their metal pins derived from bone pins and natural thorns; Bronze Age Europe had its *fibulae* or safety-pins. At the other end of the time scale, the zipper comes from applying the complex, exact techniques of our machine age to the simplest everyday requirements.

Hooks and eyes in the seventeenth century fastened men's breeches to their doublets, and were common also on women's clothing; as 'hooks and crochettes' (*i.e.* little hooks), they go back at least to the early sixteenth or late fifteenth centuries – convenient, but upon a close-fitting garment the wearer joined them each to each only with awkwardness and irritation and an expense of time and spirit. Matters were not improved by Victorian dress; and it may be said that the zipper emerged out of stays and tight corsets.

American Patent Office records of the eighteen-fifties and German patents from 1868 show that inventors looked forward to fastening the divisions in a dress in some mechanical way, without the labour of uniting hooks to eyes, one by one, or the labour of sewing them one by one along the dress divisions. In Chicago in the nineties Whitcomb L. Judson invented a way of closing and unclosing hooks and eyes with a sliding clasp. He exhibited his device in 1893 at the Colombian Exposition at Chicago; and was now backed with resolution by Colonel Lewis Walker.

With Walker's Universal Fastener Company, Judson improved these first 'separable fasteners', eventually (about 1905) constructing a machine to make them. They were marketed under the punning trade name of 'C-Curity' – a name too ambitious for fasteners which were not at all c-cure – at this stage. To improve matters, Walker engaged a Swedish engineer Gideon Sundback; to the first advances he is said to have replied, 'I make dynamos. Who wants to fool with hooks and eyes?'

By 1913 Sundback had produced his 'Hookless 2', the fastener in its modern form, with identical units or members upon either side, along tapes. This was a highly successful fastener which could not unlock when twisted, though its action needed improving; and its success with the world had still to be assured.

The use of the fasteners on clothing was still uppermost in the mind. A British patent filed by Sundback in 1915 describes 'Improvements in Separable Fasteners for articles of dress and for other purposes'.

Careful examination of a zipper of this time or the present day will confirm its relationship to the old serried hooks and eyes, and reveal, too, the ingenuity of Sundback's ideas. 'Two flexible stringers are locked and unlocked by a sliding cam device mounted on both members' – which is to say that 'hooks' and 'eyes', fixed at precise regular intervals on tapes which are sewn to the dress, can be locked and unlocked. Each unit on the tape, each blunt 'hook' is, in fact, both hook *and* eye, a hook backed with an eye, or socket. Each unit on one stringer is both 'hook' and socket or eye for each of its two appropriate units on the other stringer.

The slide brings the stringers and their units together, hook to socket, and locks them, when pulled in one direction; pull the slide the other way, and a central triangular wedge in its wide end divorces and opens what the metal convergence towards the narrow end had put together and joined so firmly.

For a while up to the First World War fasteners were manufactured also in Paris under the Sundback patents, but without any notable success; and they went slowly in America, adopted here and there as a novelty. Sundback, to quote his English patent again, made successful efforts 'to decrease the weight and bulk, to increase the flexibility, and security of locking'. The turn came at last when America entered the war. Separable fasteners were taken up by the U.S. Navy on flying-suits and by the U.S. Army on belts and pockets, and in aeroplane fabric; but the world still did not realize what it was being offered – something which would soon be thought indispensable, soon be applied to a thousand-and-one uses.

After the First World War, in 1919, a Birmingham factory began to make English fasteners by purchase of the extra-U.S. rights; but sales came slowly. The fastener wanted a name; and it was in the twenties, in America, that it became known, echoically, as the 'zipper', which expresses so neatly the slickness, sound and movement of the device. There are different stories of how the name began; it has been ascribed to an American firm who added the fastener to galoshes in 1921, and then in 1923 called these galoshes 'zippers'. In 1925 an advertisement in *Scribner's Magazine* inserted by the pioneer firm declared 'No fastening is so quick, secure, or popular as the "zipper" '.

English 'Lightnings' were shown at the British Empire Exhibition at Wembley in 1925. On the stand a sample 'Lightning' was opened and shut by visitors more than three million times.

'Lightning' might do for a trade designation, but it did not fit the tongue; and 'zip' in various forms soon crossed the Atlantic, the *Daily Express* on 6 September 1927, writing of a tango suède costume 'complete from the zip fastening to the little hat', which was 'attracting many admirers'. Later in 1927 the *Daily Express* wrote of sports suits with 'zip-fasteners'; in 1928 the same paper mentioned 'zipper fasteners' and of bootees fastened with 'zippers'. The Turks use the word 'zipli', and by 1944 'zip-fastener', word and object, was familiar enough in English to be applied by a poet to the Spleenwort fern

> On quarry walls the spleenwort spreads
> Its green zipfasteners and black threads
> (Norman Nicholson, in *Five Rivers*.)

(See also *Buttons, Safety-pin*.)

INDEX

ACKNOWLEDGEMENTS

Acknowledgements and thanks for the right to reproduce illustrations listed in the contents page are also due to the persons and institutions shown below. The following abbreviations have been used: – P.P.L. *Picture Post Library;* C.O.I. *Central Office of Information;* W.H.M.M. *Wellcome Historical Medical Museum;* M.C. *Mansell Collection, London.*

BLACK AND WHITE PLATES. *Page* 19 W.H.M.M. 24 and 25 By courtesy of the Director of the Science Museum, South Kensington. 28 Crown copyright. From an exhibit in the Science Museum, South Kensington. 34 Conzett & Huber, Zurich. 67 By courtesy of the Director of the Science Museum, South Kensington. 74 Crown copyright. From an exhibit in the Science Museum, South Kensington. 32, 68 and 69 H.Gernsheim, London. 80 By courtesy of the Director of the Science Museum, South Kensington. 120 and 115 Roger Viollet, Paris. 126 W.H.M.M. 130 Crown copyright. From an exhibit in the Science Museum, South Kensington. 164 By courtesy of the Director of the Science Museum, South Kensington. 165 Crown copyright. From an exhibit in the Science Museum, South Kensington. 173 C.O.I. 216 From the Bryant and May collection in the Science Museum, South Kensington. 163 and 217 Crown copyright. From an exhibit in the Science Museum, South Kensington. 224 By courtesy of the Director of the Science Museum, South Kensington. 225 and 261 Crown copyright. From an exhibit in the Science Museum, South Kensington. 178 P.P.L. 262 and 263 R.B.Fleming, London. 264 By courtesy of the Director of the Science Museum, South Kensington. 268 and 269 W.H.M.M. 270 Roger Viollet, Paris. 271 Crown copyright. From an exhibit in the Science Museum, South Kensington. 19 W.H.M.M. 308 R.B.Fleming, London. 310 C.O.I. 312 By courtesy of the Director of the Science Museum, South Kensington. 316 and 318 Crown copyright. From an exhibit in the Science Museum, South Kensington. 67 Roger Viollet, Paris. 259 M.C. 356 H.Gernsheim, London. 357 P.P.L. 358 Crown copyright. From an exhibit in the Science Museum, South Kensington. 359 W.H.M.M. 274 Crown copyright. From an exhibit in the Science Museum, South Kensington. 259 W.B.Fagg. 361 By courtesy of the Director of the Science Museum, South Kensington. 364 M.C. 307 Crown copyright. From an exhibit in the Science Museum, South Kensington.

For permission to include copyright material we are indebted to the following: P. 235 *Collected Poems 1925–1948 of Louis MacNeice* (Faber & Faber Ltd). P. 345 *The Kalevala* translated by W.F.Kirby (J.M.Dent & Sons Ltd). P. 151 The line drawing is taken from *The Finger Print System at Scotland Yard* by F.R.Cherrill. By permission of H.M. Stationery Office.